Welcome to

SRA Real Math

Take your students farther than they've ever imagined.

Discover the Difference of Real Math

Discover *Real Math* to help meet today's standards

Let quality mathematics research support the daily challenges you face.

Great teachers need great tools to meet the demands of education today. Just as each teacher takes a different approach to teaching, each student has individual ways of understanding. *Real Math* offers you meaningful instruction specifically designed to reach each student.

Real Math's true-to-life applications, standards-based curriculum, and extensive teacher resources will help you open your students' eyes to all math has to offer. They learn essential math skills while understanding the important role of math in daily life.

The nuts and bolts.
Understanding is at the heart of every *Real Math* lesson. Success in basic computational skills is only the beginning. The difference with *Real Math* is that it elevates basic learning to a new level of engagement and application by connecting thinking and reasoning to learning.

Why settle for merely "Adequate" Yearly Progress?
More than ever before, teachers are accountable for the performance of their students. Your focus as a teacher is being directed toward meeting mandated goals like Adequate Yearly Progress (AYP) or student performance on mandated tests.

Real Math offers you **differentiated instruction** designed to help you make AYP and meet standards by offering **research-based, standards-based**, quality education for all students, including English language learners, high-achieving students, and those in need of intervention.

The test of time.
Incorporating over 30 years of research with the latest mathematical findings, *Real Math* helps you build and reinforce learning with proven lessons. *Real Math* is an all-inclusive tool for engaging your students while building their math competency.

Take five.
Just as Reading First has identified key elements for teaching children to read, the mathematics research community* has identified five key proficiencies that students need to achieve in math. Those strands are: understanding, computing, applying, reasoning, and engaging.

> *Real Math* is the first program to fully integrate all five strands of mathematical proficiency throughout every lesson.

"The program has been very beneficial for teachers and students. Teachers have a variety of tools to help struggling students as well as those children doing an outstanding job who need enrichment. The teacher manual is so user-friendly that our teachers can pick it up on a daily basis and implement a successful lesson with ease."

–Kim Leitzke
Math Teacher Leader
Barton Elementary School
NCLB Blue Ribbon Award 2003
Milwaukee, WI

Use actual working tools to demonstrate mathematical thinking as it is applied outside of the classroom.

* Kilpatrick, J., Swafford, J. and Findell, B. eds. *Adding It Up: Helping Children Learn Mathematics.* Washington, D.C.: National Research Council/National Academy Press, 2001.

Kilpatrick, Jeremy, Martin, W. Gary, and Schifter, Deborah, eds. *A Research Companion to Principles and Standards for School Mathematics.* Reston, VA: National Council of Teachers of Mathematics, Inc. 2003.

Real Math is the first program to fully integrate all five strands of mathematical proficiency as defined by today's research*.

The five key proficiencies that students need to achieve in math are:

1 Understanding
Comprehending mathematical concepts, operations, and relations—knowing what mathematical symbols, diagrams, and procedures mean

2 Computing
Carrying out mathematical procedures, such as adding, subtracting, multiplying, and dividing numbers flexibly, accurately, efficiently, and appropriately

3 Applying
Being able to formulate problems mathematically and devise strategies for solving them using concepts and procedures appropriately

4 Reasoning
Using logic to explain and justify a solution to a problem or to extend from something known to something not yet known

5 Engaging
Seeing mathematics as sensible, useful, and doable

By incorporating all five strands, *Real Math* frees you from the daily challenge of gathering materials to meet state standards, allowing you to pursue your passion for doing what you love most—teaching.

T03

Discover meaningful, true-to-life instruction

Reach each student with explicit instruction and conceptual development.

Engaging lessons that appeal to your students' personal interests go a long way toward maintaining their attention. Revisiting concepts in different contexts over time ensures understanding by making math personal. This personal understanding and appreciation of mathematical concepts helps you develop greater thinking and mastery in each student.

A dual approach.
Real Math's explicit lessons combine **skill-building** and **problem-solving instruction** that includes unique lesson ideas, the latest technology, and engaging games.

Thinking Stories, which are narratives interspersed with questions for students to answer, require students to consider problems in novel ways. As an integral part of *Real Math* lessons, games provide skill practice and stimulate critical thinking as students formulate strategies and solve true-to-life problems.

Everything you need.
Real Math's all-inclusive program gives you everything you need to face the diverse challenges of your classroom. The wealth of teacher resources includes easy-to-use lesson plans, teaching tips, activity ideas, reteaching strategies, practice sessions, professional development, technology, and assessment opportunities at every level.

Show students how math adds adventure in and out of the classroom.

Five-a-day.

All five math proficiencies are integrated and interwoven into every lesson so your students develop a full understanding of mathematics with every turn of the page. *Real Math* concepts are carefully developed using research-supported strategies, including features like *Teaching for Understanding* that emphasize concept development to build comprehension of mathematical concepts, operations, and relations.

Boost thinking power.

Some other math programs show a quick increase in test scores as students develop computational skills, then see scores drop off as students fail to develop critical thinking skills. However, every lesson in *Real Math* features questions and problems that require thinking, not just calculating. As you help students build math comprehension, they will excel on standardized tests, which require constructed responses and problem-solving skills.

Real Math doesn't just help you teach why math is important, but shows students how it can be applied in their after-school activities.

SRA Real Math
Discover the Difference

Discover a versatile way to teach

All-inclusive, flexible lessons offer guided instruction, practice, and assessment for every task.

Step-by-step guide.
Explicit instruction walks you through the details of each *Real Math* lesson, offering everything you need to perform each task. Because *Real Math* is flexible to fit your teaching style, it reduces time spent planning so you can focus on what's most important: teaching.

Easy teaching. Easy learning.
Multiple opportunities for students to understand each exercise make preparing to meet state standards part of every lesson.

Game on.
Real Math activities, such as games and technology projects, ensure that students use key skills to absorb essential ideas and information.

Teaching Lesson 1.8

Mental Math 5
 Ask students to respond to exercises such as the following.

a. Six plus how many equals 13? 7
b. Eighteen minus how many equals 9? 9
c. What number minus 5 equals 8? 13
d. Four plus how many equals 12? 8
e. What number minus 7 equals 3? 10
f. Eleven minus how many equals 5? 6

1 Develop 20

Tell Students In Today's Lesson They Will
find the perimeters of rectangles and squares.

Guided Discussion UNDERSTANDING Whole Group
Define perimeter as the length of the path around the boundary of a figure.
- Draw a square on the board and label each side 10 cm.
- Have students find the perimeter by adding the lengths of the sides of the square.

Next draw a rectangle and label its sides 10 cm and 15 cm.
Have students find its perimeter by adding the lengths of the sides together. Then ask the students questions such as the following:

■ **What are some realistic examples of situations that might require finding the perimeter?** Possible answers: determining the jogging distance around a field; building a fence around a garden; making a frame for a picture

Skill Building ENGAGING Small Group
- Have students work in small groups or with partners to find the perimeter, of various items in the classroom, such as a rectangular table or desk tops.
- Ask students to explain how they found the perimeters, and compare the groups' results.
- Some students may be curious about finding the perimeter of curved objects. Although this concept is not formally addressed at the fourth-grade level, students might enjoy using yarn or string to find the length around the outside of round objects, such as tires, plates, and CDs.

2 Assign Student Pages 25

Pages 30–31 UNDERSTANDING
Have students complete pages 30–31 on their own.
Before students do the problems on student page 30, remind them that *cm* is the symbol for centimeter(s). Also encourage them to make diagrams to help them solve the word problems on page 31.
Problems 11–12 If the dimensions are whole numbers of centimeters, rectangles with a perimeter of 20 cm can have the following dimensions: 1×9, 2×8, 3×7, 4×6, and 5×5. Rectangles with a perimeter of 10 cm can be 1×4 or 2×3. Congruent rectangles (such as 1×9 and 9×1) are counted only once. If numbers other than whole numbers are allowed, for example, $1\frac{1}{2} \times 8\frac{1}{2}$ cm, there are an infinite number of such rectangles. As an extension to this problem, you can have students find the area of each rectangle by counting the squares. Ask them to find the rectangle that has the greatest area. The 5×5 rectangle has an area of 25 square centimeters.

Monitoring Student Progress

If . . . students have difficulty reading and understanding the word problems,	Then . . . have the students work in small groups with at least one good reader per group.

As Students Finish

Game Roll a 15 Game or Roll 20 to 5 Game (introduced in Lesson 1.7)

e Games Roll a 15 Game or Roll 20 to 5 Game

Leave a lasting impression.
Practice through games, realistic problem solving, interactive projects, and writing activities assures student engagement and piques interest.

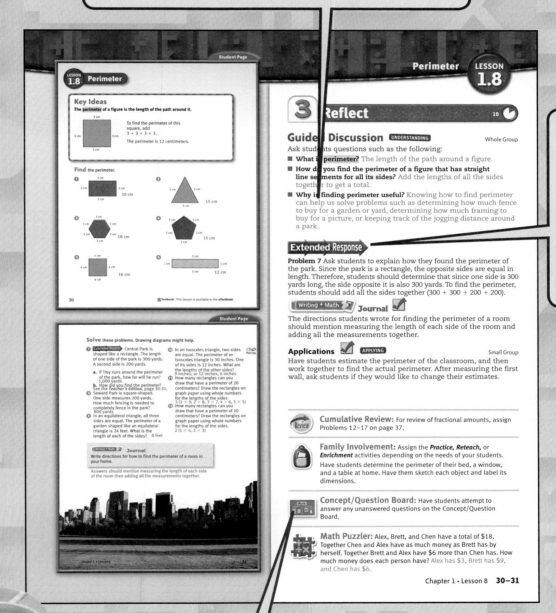

Make it personal.
Encouraging students to explain their thinking personalizes math and helps them internalize and apply concepts.

Teach them to think for themselves.
Real Math helps you promote realistic thinking and problem-solving skills. Your students learn to ask relevant questions while you help them learn to find answers by conducting their own research.

Fun materials maintain student interest and help reinforce computational thinking skills.

SRA Real Math
Discover the Difference

Discover the value of ongoing assessment

Use resources and strategies to differentiate instruction for each student.

Making progress.
Look for specific ongoing assessment and progress monitoring strategies in each lesson for a complete evaluation of student understanding. This ongoing assessment offers you strategic solutions for every learning situation and helps you make certain that your students fully grasp content. With enrich, practice, and reteach materials, you'll ensure no student is left behind.

Vital extras.
Valuable tools, such as the *English Learner Support Guide,* Extended Response, Guided Discussion, Writing + Math Journal prompts, projects, and **WebQuests,** provide opportunities for students to demonstrate understanding in real contexts, not just on tests.

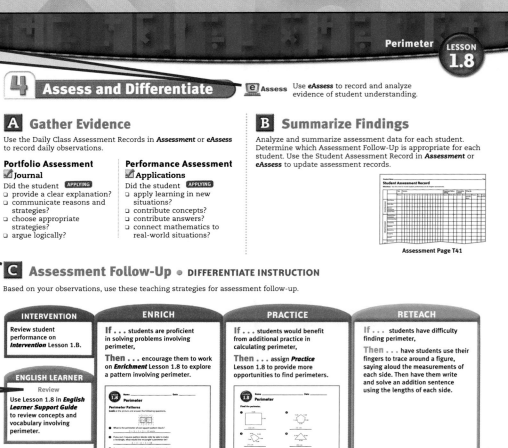

Discover how technology can take your lessons beyond the everyday

Prepare students for a lifetime of learning with interactive instruction.

Keeping up with technology.

Technology resources for teachers and students enrich instruction and expand learning. *Real Math* helps you build skills by offering the latest in technology to help take your classroom to the next level. *Real Math* features useful materials such as the following:

- **ePlanner** online lesson planning helps make your job easier by organizing daily, weekly, and monthly lesson plans and homework detail, linking to all technology components.

- **ePresentation** enables you to present each lesson electronically through an interactive presentation. It also provides lesson summaries and electronic lessons that can be accessed from home.

- **eAssess** online assessment tools allow you to create assessments that students can take online and view reports based on math topics, standards, and differentiated instruction.

- **eMathTools** are math technology resources including number lines and multiplication tables, geometric exploration tools, and probability simulations.

- **eGames** offer electronic versions of games from each grade level.

- **Building Blocks** activities are engaging, research-based computer activities that develop math understanding.

- **eTextbook** gives students access from home with an electronic version of the *Student Edition*.

For additional resources, visit SRARealMath.com.

Online Professional Development

Build confidence and expertise in delivering *Real Math* lessons using Online Professional Development. This series of six online courses includes video excerpts and demonstrates how *Real Math* lessons implement each of the following:

- Teaching Computational Fluency

- Teaching for Understanding

- Teaching Applications of Mathematics

- Teaching Mathematical Reasoning and Problem Solving

- Engaging Children in Mathematics

- Mathematics Classroom Management

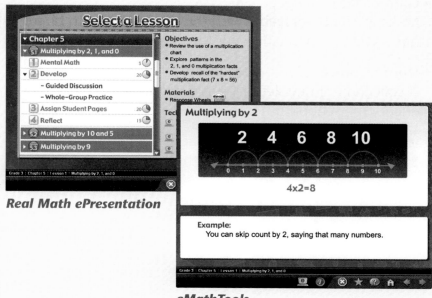

Real Math ePresentation

eMathTools

SRA Real Math
Discover the Difference

Discover the confidence of comprehensive teacher support

Extensive resources include empowering materials for you and your students.

TEACHER MATERIALS prepare you with great tools and resources.

- **Teacher's Edition,** Grades PreK–6
  A wealth of background information and strategies helps you provide quality instruction.

- **Manipulative Kits,** Grades PreK–6
  These complete Manipulative Kits support concept development and are available in individual, module, and teacher manipulative packages.

- **Assessment,** Grades K–6
  A variety of assessment options helps you evaluate student proficiency and inform instruction.

- **Game Mat Package,** Grades K–6
  Make learning enjoyable with these exciting math board games and manipulatives for the classroom.

- **Home Connection,** Grades PreK–6
  A collection of newsletters, surveys, and activities encourage school-to-home communications.

- **Home Connection Game Package,** Grades K–6
  Support learning at home with this math games kit.

STUDENT MATERIALS are unique and engaging, giving you a fresh approach to teaching mathematics.

- **Big Books,** Grade PreK
  These counting books include math concepts specifically chosen for preschoolers.

- **Student Edition,** Grades K–6
  Research-based lessons offer development and practice for all concepts.

- **Across the Curriculum Math Connections,** Grades K–6
  Engaging cross-curricular projects and **WebQuests** help develop mathematical proficiency.

- **Student Assessment Booklet,** Grades K–6
  This convenient assessment tool helps keep students on track.

- **Exercise Book,** Grades 3–6
  Build math skills using these exercises from the hardbound student books to help students record their answers and show their work.

Materials that offer hands-on learning go a long way in engaging conceptual thinking skills and problem solving.

With materials to DIFFERENTIATE INSTRUCTION, you meet the needs of all your students.

- **Intervention Support Guide,** Grades K–6
  Bring all students up-to-speed with alternative approaches, more intense instruction, and additional practice of prerequisite skills for every chapter.

- **English Learner Support Guide,** Grades K–6
  Take advantage of strategies for previewing and reviewing lesson concepts and vocabulary.

- **Enrichment Support Guide,** Grades K–6
  This guide includes activities for every lesson designed to expand lesson concepts.

- **Practice Workbook,** Grades K–6
  This workbook version offers extra practice for your convenience.

- **Practice Blackline Masters,** Grades K–6
  Reproducible pages offer extra practice for every lesson.

- **Reteach Support Guide,** Grades 1–6
  Use this tool to offer alternative strategies for presenting lesson concepts.

Professional development from SRA/McGraw-Hill provides you with an unparalleled level of support, resources, and partnership.

Real Math is based on a strong, standards-based philosophy of instruction. A key to successful implementation of the program within your school or district is to have an understanding of its background and how to apply its research-based principles in your classroom. You'll find that professional development opportunities for *Real Math* are hands-on, giving you the chance to gain valuable experience with each component of the program.

Because each school is different, your SRA/McGraw-Hill sales representative will customize a professional development plan to fit your needs. Here are some resources your school or district may utilize:

- On-site training upon implementation

- Weekend seminars and regional training

- Summer institutes

- Online professional development

- Workbooks and guides

- Classroom demonstrations

- After-school workshops with teachers and administrators

- Orientation sessions for the community, parents, and parent groups

- Mentor teachers and coaches

- Resources online at **SRAonline.com**

Discover the experience *Real Math* authors bring to every lesson

Steve Willoughby is Professor Emeritus at both New York University and the University of Arizona. He has taught all grades from first through twelfth. He has been a professor of both education and of mathematics at the University of Wisconsin and at New York University (where he also was the Head of the Division of Mathematics, Science, and Statistics Education), and a Professor of Mathematics at the University of Arizona. Dr. Willoughby served as President of NCTM from 1982 to 1984. Dr. Willoughby has published more than 200 books and articles on mathematics and mathematics education and is the principal author of *Real Math*. In 1995, he received the Lifetime Achievement Medal for Leadership in Mathematics Education from the Mathematics Education Trust.

Carl Bereiter is a Professor Emeritus of Educational Psychology and Special Advisor on Learning Technology at the Ontario Institute for Studies of the University of Toronto. He has published widely on a variety of topics in instruction, cognitive psychology, and educational policy. Honors include a Guggenheim Fellowship, fellowships at the Center for Advanced Study in the Behavioral Sciences, and election to the U.S. National Academy of Education.

Peter Hilton is Distinguished Professor of Mathematics Emeritus of the State University of New York, Binghamton, and Distinguished Professor of Mathematics at the University of Central Florida, Orlando. He is the author of eighteen books and over 500 research articles. His areas of special interest are algebraic topology, homological algebra, and group theory. Professor Hilton has served as Chairman of the United States Commission on Mathematical Instruction and Secretary/Treasurer of the International Commission on Mathematical Instruction.

Joseph H. Rubinstein is a Professor of Education at Coker College in Hartsville, South Carolina, where he teaches prospective teachers how to teach mathematics and science. He was chairperson of the education department at Coker for fifteen years. He received B.A., M.S., and Ph.D. degrees in biology from New York University. He served as Director of the Open Court Publishing Company's Mathematics and Science Curriculum Development Center for its first seven years, where he coauthored and directed a nationwide field-testing program for *Real Math*.

Douglas H. Clements, Professor of Early Childhood, Mathematics, and Computer Education at the University at Buffalo, State University of New York, has conducted research and published widely on the learning and teaching of geometry, computer applications in mathematics education, the early development of mathematical ideas, and the effects of social interactions on learning. Along with Julie

Sarama, Dr. Clements has directed several research projects funded by the National Science Foundation and the U.S. Department of Education's Institute of Educational Sciences, one of which resulted in much of the mathematics software and activities included in *Real Math*.

Joan Moss is an Associate Professor of Mathematics Education at the University of Toronto. She has more than twenty years experience as a classroom teacher, scholar, and researcher. Her extensive research has included studies of the development of children's understanding of rational numbers and the development of early algebraic reasoning. Dr. Moss has been widely published with research articles and chapters for the National Council of Teachers of Mathematics as well as the National Academy of Science. She is a member of the National Council of Teachers of Mathematics, American Educational Research Association, the North American Chapter of the Psychology of Mathematics Education, and the Canadian Mathematics Education Study Group.

Jean Pedersen is Professor of Mathematics and Computer Science at Santa Clara University, California. Along with Peter Hilton, she has published six books and over ninety research articles in mathematics. Her research interests include polyhedral geometry, combinatorics, and the teaching of mathematics, especially geometry, to precollege students.

Julie Sarama is an Associate Professor of Mathematics Education at the University at Buffalo, State University of New York. She conducts research on the implementation and effects of software and curricula in mathematics classrooms, young children's development of mathematical concepts and competencies, implementation and scale-up of educational reform, and professional development. Dr. Sarama has taught secondary mathematics and computer science, gifted math at the middle school level, preschool and kindergarten mathematics enrichment classes, and mathematics methods and content courses for elementary to secondary teachers.

Contributing Authors

Hortensia Soto-Johnson is Assistant Professor of Mathematics, University of Northern Colorado. B.S. Chadron State College (Mathematics); MS in Mathematics, University of Arizona; Ph.D. in Educational Mathematics, University of Northern Colorado.

Erica Walker is Assistant Professor of Mathematics and Education, Teachers College, Columbia University. B.S. cum laude, Birmingham-Southern College (Mathematics, Spanish minor); M.Ed., Wake Forest University (Mathematics Education); Ed.M., Ed.D., Harvard University (Administration, Planning, and Social Policy).

Real Math

Teacher's Edition

Grade 3 • Volume 2

Stephen S. Willoughby

Carl Bereiter

Peter Hilton

Joseph H. Rubinstein

Joan Moss

Jean Pedersen

Columbus, OH

The McGraw-Hill Companies

Authors

Stephen S. Willoughby
Professor Emeritus of Mathematics
University of Arizona
Tucson, AZ

Carl Bereiter
Professor Emeritus
Centre for Applied Cognitive Science
Ontario Institute for Studies in Education
University of Toronto, Canada

Peter Hilton
Distinguished Professor of
Mathematics Emeritus
State University of New York
Binghamton, NY

Joseph H. Rubinstein
Professor of Education
Coker College
Hartsville, SC

Joan Moss
Associate Professor, Department of Human
Development and Applied Psychology
Ontario Institute for Studies in Education
University of Toronto, Canada

Jean Pedersen
Professor, Department of
Mathematics and Computer Science
Santa Clara University, Santa Clara, CA

PreKindergarten and Building Blocks Authors

Douglas H. Clements
Professor of Early Childhood and Mathematics Education
University at Buffalo
State University of New York, NY

Julie Sarama
Associate Professor of Mathematics Education
University at Buffalo
State University of New York, NY

Contributing Authors

Hortensia Soto-Johnson
Assistant Professor of Mathematics
University of Northern Colorado, CO

Erika Walker
Assistant Professor of Mathematics and Education
Teachers College, Columbia University, NY

Research Consultants

Jeremy Kilpatrick
Regents Professor of Mathematics Education
University of Georgia, GA

Alfinio Flores
Professor of Mathematics Education
Arizona State University, AZ

Gilbert J. Cuevas
Professor of Mathematics Education
University of Miami, Coral Gables, FL

Contributing Writers

Holly MacLean, Ed.D., Supervisor Principal, Treasure Valley
Mathematics and Science Center, Boise, ID
Edward Manfre, Mathematics Education Consultant, Albuquerque, NM
Elizabeth Jimenez, English Language Learner Consultant, Pomona, CA

Kim L. Pettig, Ed.D., Instructional Challenge Coordinator
Pittsford Central School District, Pittsford, NY
Rosemary Tolliver, M.Ed., Gifted Coordinator/Curriculum Director, Columbus, OH

National Advisory Board

Justin Anderson, Teacher, Robey Elementary School, Indianapolis, IN
David S. Bradley, Administrator, Granite, UT
Donna M. Bradley, Head of the Lower School, St. Marks Episcopal
Palm Beach Gardens, FL
Grace Dublin, Teacher, Laurelhurst Elementary, Seattle, WA
Leisha W. Fordham, Teacher, Bolton Academy, Atlanta, GA

Ebony Frierson, Teacher, Eastminister Day School, Columbia, SC
Flavia Gunter, Teacher, Morningside Elementary School, Atlanta, GA
Audrey Marie Jacobs, Teacher, Lewis & Clark Elementary, St. Louis, MO
Florencetine Jasmin, Elementary Math Curriculum Specialist, Baltimore, MD
Kim Leitzke, Teacher, Clara Barton Elementary School, Milwaukee, WI
Nick Restivo, Principal, Long Beach High School, Long Island, NY

SRAonline.com

SRA

Send all inquiries to:
SRA/McGraw-Hill
4400 Easton Commons
Columbus, OH 43219

ISBN 0-07-603715-0

3 4 5 6 7 8 9 WEB 12 11 10 09 08 07

The McGraw-Hill Companies

Number Concepts

CHAPTER 1

Exploring 💡 Problem Solving **Theme: Teamwork—Doing Things Together**

CHAPTER 2

Multidigit Addition and Subtraction

Exploring  **Problem Solving** Theme: Tree Houses

Measuring and Graphing

CHAPTER 3

Exploring 💡 **Problem Solving** Theme: Urban Gardens

CHAPTER 4

Multiplication Concepts

Exploring  Theme: Dogs

Multiplication and Division Facts

CHAPTER 5

Exploring 💡 Problem Solving Theme: Arts and Crafts

Exploring 💡 **Problem Solving** Theme: Playgrounds—Real and Imaginary

Multidigit Multiplication and Division

CHAPTER 7

Exploring 💡Problem Solving **Theme: Banks and Money Machines**

Exploring 💡 Problem Solving Theme: Advertising

Measurement

Exploring 💡 Problem Solving **Theme: Camping (Including Campfire Stories)**

CHAPTER 10

Decimals

Exploring  Problem Solving Theme: Totem Poles and Other Monuments

Geometry

CHAPTER 11

Exploring 💡 Problem Solving **Theme: Homes**

CHAPTER 12

Data Analysis and Probability

Exploring  Problem Solving Theme: Farms

Getting Started

This section provides an overview of classroom management issues and explanations of the **Real Math** *program elements and how to use them.*

Real Math is a comprehensive program designed to achieve these goals:

Teach basic skills with understanding so students can use them fluently to solve real problems and help understand the real world

•

Teach students to think mathematically so they can reason, understand, and apply mathematics meaningfully in order to identify, solve, and communicate about real problems

•

Teach students to reason so that they have sufficient confidence and understanding to reconstruct or even construct mathematical methods that they have forgotten or never learned

•

Engage students in mathematics so they enjoy math, see it as understandable and useful, and willingly use it to help them understand their environment

Real Math is a program that acknowledges the critical role teachers play in math education. The program is designed to provide thorough background, teaching strategies, and resources to support teacher delivery of a coherent mathematics curriculum that will develop student understanding and enjoyment of mathematics.

The following pages are designed to help you get started with **Real Math.**

A variety of program materials are designed to help teachers provide a quality mathematics curriculum. The first step in getting started is to familiarize yourself with the program resources.

Core Materials

Teacher's Edition

The **Teacher's Edition** is the heart of the **Real Math** curriculum. It provides background for teachers and complete lesson plans with explicit suggestions on how to develop math concepts. It explains when and how to use the program resources.

Student Edition

The **Student Edition** includes developmental activities, practice exercises, games to help develop higher-order thinking skills and practice traditional basic skills, as well as problem-solving explorations, and cumulative reviews.

Essential Materials

The key materials beyond the textbook that students must have to complete the program activities are **Number Cubes** and **Number Strips** at Grades K–2, and **Response Wheels, Equivalence Cards,** and **Number Cubes** at Grades 3–6. The materials are in the **Individual Manipulative Kits** or the **Essential Materials Module**.

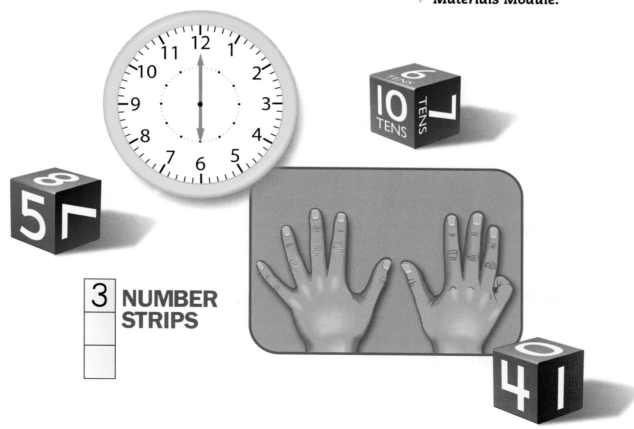

In addition to these core components of the program, the following materials provide specific resources to facilitate instruction.

Component	Grades	Purpose
Practice Blackline Masters	K–6	Extra practice for every lesson
Practice Workbook	K–6	Workbook version of extra practice for teacher convenience
Enrichment Support Guide	K–6	Activities for every lesson designed to expand lesson concepts
Reteach Support Guide	K–6	Alternative strategies for presenting lesson concepts
Intervention Support Guide	K–6	Instruction and practice of prerequisite skills for every chapter to bring all students up to speed
English Learner Support Guide	K–6	Strategies for previewing and reviewing lesson concepts and vocabulary for students learning English
Assessment	K–6	Variety of assessment options to evaluate student proficiency and inform instruction
Student Assessment Booklet	K–6	Assessment booklets for teacher convenience
Home Connection	PreK–6	Newsletters, surveys, and activities to encourage home and school communications
Across the Curriculum Math Connections	K–6	Cross-curricular projects and **WebQuests** that develop math proficiency and provide interesting math applications
Exercise Book	3–6	A duplication of the **Student Edition** exercises in a workbook format
Big Book	PreK	Counting book specifically chosen for preschoolers
Game Mat Kit	K–6	Contains 15 copies of each of the Game Mats at each grade level and enough playing pieces, **Number Cubes,** and play money for an entire class; includes a **Guide for Using the Game Mats** and a set of color transparencies of the basic version of each game
Home Connection Game Kit	K–6	Math games kit for home use that includes the game mats and cube games
Manipulative Kits	PreK–6	Available in Topic Modules or Individual Kits to support concept development; available in convenient packaging options
Professional Development • Online/CD • Books		Six professional development courses that offer school districts complete staff development in math education
Calculator Package		Calculators available for classroom convenience

Real Math Technology Resources

Math resources designed to facilitate instruction and record keeping and to expand student learning

For Teachers		For Students	
e Planner	A tool to help teachers plan daily lessons, plot year-long goals, view program components, and assign homework	**Building Blocks**	**Activities** (PreK–6) Engaging research-based activities designed to reinforce levels of mathematical development in different strands of mathematics
e Presentation	An online presentation tool to enable teachers to present each lesson electronically and links to *eGames, eMathTools,* and *eTextbook* for easy demonstration purposes	**e Textbook**	An electronic version of the **Student Edition** that students can access from home
e Assess	An assessment tool to grade, track, and report electronic versions of assessments • View reports of assessments taken online • Create assessments from a database of items correlated to standards • Enter scores from paper assessments	**e Games**	(K–6) Electronic versions of twelve games from each grade level of **Real Math;** competitive games that involve luck, skill, and strategy to help practice skills and develop mathematical thinking
	Professional Development A series of six online courses that teach different aspects of mathematics	**e MathTools**	Electronic math tools to help students solve problems and explore math concepts

Chapter Organization

The first few pages of each chapter help you understand the chapter focus and see how concepts are developed.

Chapter Overview

- **Teaching for Understanding** provides the big ideas of the chapter.

- **Skills Trace** shows where concepts were previously introduced and how they will be followed up.

- **Prerequisite Skills** help determine if students are ready for the chapter.

- **Games** and **Problem Solving** provide an overview of key chapter experiences.

- **Math Background** provides mathematical and pedagogical information relevant to the chapter.

- **What Research Says** offers insights into children's learning and research-based teaching strategies.

- **Planning Guide** includes objectives that explain how the key concepts are developed lesson by lesson and which resources can be used in each lesson.

- **Technology Resources** list resources that are available to help with planning or to support instruction.

Chapter Introduction

Each Chapter Introduction introduces concepts and provides ways to assess prior knowledge.

- **Pretest** helps evaluate what students know and do not know about the chapter concepts in order to determine what to reteach, emphasize, or skip.

- **Access Prior Knowledge** offers preliminary discussion about chapter concepts to determine what students know.

- **Exploring Problem Solving** introduces the chapter theme and concepts by exploring the ways in which students solve real-world problems.

- **Concept/Question Board** establishes connections and applications of the chapter concepts to students' thinking and lives outside the classroom.

- **Assess and Differentiate** uses assessments to summarize and analyze evidence of student understanding and to plan for differentiating instruction.

- **Project Overview** outlines two projects that students can work on during the course of the chapter that apply chapter concepts across the curriculum.

Lessons

Lessons provide overview, ideas for differentiating instruction, complete lesson plans, teaching strategies, and assessments that inform instruction.

Exploring Problem Solving

These lessons introduce, compare, and use problem-solving strategies and appear in the beginning, middle, and end of each chapter.

Cumulative Review

Cumulative Review exercises provide practice for standardized-test formats in the middle and end of the chapter and allow you to evaluate if students are retaining previously developed concepts and skills.

Individual Oral Assessment

These individual assessment interviews in the middle of each chapter provide an opportunity to individually evaluate student understanding.

Thinking Stories (K–3) and Exploring Problem Solving

These activities at the end of each chapter offer applications of lesson concepts and development of students' mathematical thinking and problem-solving abilities.

Chapter Wrap-Up

The Chapter Wrap-up provides ways to review chapter concepts and assess student understanding.

- **Key Ideas Review** refreshes student knowledge of the key concepts.

- **Chapter Review** provides a review of chapter concepts.

- **Practice Test** is in the same format as the Chapter Test and gives students a chance for self-assessment before taking the Chapter Test.

Once you understand how a chapter is organized, survey the resources in each lesson.

Lesson Planning

The first page of each lesson helps teachers prepare to teach each lesson.

- **Context of the Lesson** explains how the lesson is developed in the context of the chapter and includes information about how concepts were previously developed, as well as specific information about expectations of student performance.

- **Planning for Learning: Differentiate Instruction** provides ideas for planning how to adapt the lesson depending on assessments of student understanding.

- **Lesson Planner** includes Objectives, Materials lists, and Looking Ahead tips to prepare for upcoming lessons.

Lesson Plans

Every lesson throughout *Real Math* is structured in the same way.

Mental Math

- **Mental Math** is a five-minute warm-up at the beginning of each lesson that provides cumulative review.

Develop

- **Develop** is the heart of the lesson instruction. Here are suggestions for how to introduce lesson concepts, ideas for Guided Discussion, Skill Building, and Strategy Building activities to develop student understanding.

Assign Student Pages

- **Assign Student Pages** explains when to have students complete the lesson pages and ideas for what they can do when they finish.

Reflect

- **Reflect** is a vital part of the lesson that offers ways to help students summarize, reflect, and expand on their understanding of the lesson concepts.

Assess and Differentiate

- **Assess and Differentiate** uses informal and formal assessments to summarize and analyze evidence of student understanding and plan for differentiating instruction.

*In **Real Math** there are activities that will occur again and again. Establishing rules or routines for these activities with students will facilitate instruction.*

Mental Math

Mental Math exercises provide cumulative review and computation practice for students and provide opportunities to assess students' skills quickly. Mental Math is an essential component of *Real Math* because it helps students review skills they have already learned that are prerequisite skills for upcoming lessons.

Most Mental Math exercises are done in the following four steps, which include the **Find, Hide,** and **Show** routine. The pace should be lively enough to keep things moving, yet not so fast that students do not have time to think.

Step 1

Present a problem orally, by writing it on the board, or by using *ePresentation.*

Step 2

Students **find** the answer and arrange their *Response Wheels, Number Cubes,* or other response device to display it.

Step 3

Students **hide** the answer while you provide enough time for most students to find the answer.

Step 4

Students **show** the answer to you, while you show and say the answer to the class.

This four-step process allows students to participate in a nonthreatening way. You can tell instantly whether all students are participating and whether they have the right answer. If a student gets a wrong answer, only that student and you know it. You can make note of students who are struggling and give them extra help later on.

Tips

- Occasionally add a "peek-to-be-sure" step to the Find, Hide, and Show procedure. Some students will have found an answer and hidden it while waiting for others in the class to do the same. This is the time to give the "Peek" command, which asks the students who have found answers to check them. This keeps them involved during the few seconds of waiting for the "Show" command.

- Use judgment to decide when to give the "Show" command. You do not have to wait for every student to find and hide an answer. But you should wait long enough so that students who are making progress toward a solution have time to finish. Remember, too, that students who cannot answer in time will know they are having difficulty, and you will also know they are having difficulty. The rest of the class need not know. Prolonged waiting only calls attention to the slower students. Furthermore, after you say "Show," a few more seconds will pass while you are checking answers, and during this time students still have time to find and show their responses.

- Encourage students. Because response exercises are active exchanges between you and the students, use these opportunities to let them know you are pleased with their efforts and that you have confidence in them.

- If it is difficult for you to see all the response-card answers when students are at their seats, have them sit on the floor closer to you. Or you might walk around the room, but do this quickly so you do not slow the lively pace of the exercise.

Guided Discussion

"Teachers must make judgments about when to tell, when to question, and when to correct. They must decide when to guide with prompting and when to let students grapple with a mathematical issue.... The point of classroom discourse is to develop students' understanding of key ideas. But it also provides opportunities to emphasize and model mathematical reasoning and problem solving and to enhance students' disposition toward mathematics."

—Kilpatrick, J., Swafford, J. and Findell, B. eds. *Adding It Up: Helping Children Learn Mathematics.* Washington, D.C.: National Research Council/National Academy Press, 2001, p. 346.

Guided Discussion is expected in almost all **Real Math** lessons. In Guided Discussion students speak the language of mathematics, communicate mathematically, explain their thinking, and demonstrate understanding.

Routines or rules for Guided Discussion established at the beginning of the year can make discussions more productive and promote listening and speaking skills.

1. Pay attention to others. Give full attention to the person who is speaking. This includes looking at the speaker and nodding to show that you understand.

2. Wait for speakers to answer and complete their thoughts. Sometimes teachers and other students get impatient and move on, ask someone else, or give the answer before someone has a chance to think and speak. Giving students time to answer is a vital part of teaching for understanding.

3. Listen. Let yourself finish listening before you begin to speak. You cannot listen if you are busy thinking about what you want to say next.

4. Respect speakers by taking turns and making sure that everyone gets a chance to speak and that no one dominates the conversation.

5. Build on others' ideas by making connections, drawing analogies, or expanding on the idea.

6. Ask questions. Asking questions of another speaker shows that you were listening. Ask if you are not sure you understand what the speaker has said, or ask for clarification or explanation. It is a good idea to repeat in your own words what the speaker said so you can be sure your understanding is correct.

RESEARCH IN ACTION

"One of the most striking aspects of Japanese classrooms, especially at the first-grade level, was the amount of verbal explanation that occurred during mathematics class. We were able to identify segments that contained explanations by either the teacher, a student, or both the teacher and a student.... Nearly 50 percent of all Japanese first-grade segments contained verbal explanations, compared with only about 20 percent of the American segments....Whereas the American teachers were more likely to stress participation in nonverbal activities or the asking of short-answer questions to lead students into a new topic, Japanese teachers would give, and ask students to give, lengthy verbal explanations of mathematical concepts and algorithms."

—Stigler, James W. *"The Use of Verbal Explanation in Japanese and American Classrooms,"* Arithmetic Teacher, October 1988.

Questions to Ask

Questions help teachers learn about student thinking and consider instructional implications of that knowledge. Teachers should be prepared for unexpected answers and probe further with questions to understand student thought processes. Sometimes the unexpected answer demonstrates true insight.

Not all questions are the same. Questions have different purposes.

- **Engaging Questions** invite students into a discussion, keep them engaged in conversation, and invite them to share their work. Engaging questions are typically open-ended and encourage different ways of responding.

- **Exploring Questions** ask students to provide explanations, make analogies, or identify problems and solutions.

- **Synthesizing Questions** ask students to identify patterns, make generalizations or rules, or argue, prove, or demonstrate their assumptions.

- **Clarifying Questions** help students explain their thinking or help you understand their thinking.

- **Refocusing Questions** help students get back on track or move away from a dead-end strategy.

See Appendix A for more information about Guided Discussion.

Games

Games are a vital part of **Real Math.** They have been written specifically for the program to support the concepts and skills being taught. Students enjoying the friendly competition may not even realize how much math they are learning and practicing.

Purposes of Games

- Games provide practice to reinforce new skills and review previously covered topics.

- Most **Real Math** games place students in an environment in which they are expected to recognize situations that can be analyzed by mathematical thought, to formulate their own problems, to solve those problems, to use their solutions to improve their game-playing strategies, and to communicate with other players about their strategies.

- Games give students a chance to work out important mathematical ideas and problem-solving strategies.

- Games give you an opportunity to informally monitor student progress by watching students as they play.

- Games allow students of all ability levels to compete fairly. Winning games requires a mix of chance, skills, and thinking strategies.

Types of Games

Game Mats are found in the **Game Mat Kit** and are reproduced in Appendix D. The **Game Mat Kit** contains fifteen copies of each of the different **Game Mats** in a grade level, which should accommodate a class of thirty because most games are played by two or more players. The package also contains enough playing pieces, **Number Cubes,** and play money for an entire class, along with a **Guide for Using the Game Mats** and a set of color transparencies of the basic version of each game. Reduced-size copies of the **Game Mats** can also be found in the back of this **Teacher's Edition.**

Many of the **Game Mats** have both a basic and a harder version for differentiating instruction.

Cube and Other Games

Directions for **Cube Games** that require only **Number Cubes** are in the **Teacher's Edition** or **Student Edition** of appropriate lessons. Directions for all **Cube Games** are reproduced in the **Home Connection Support Guide** and in the **Home Connection Game Kit.**

Many of the **Cube Games** have variations that extend the mathematics or provide applications for new thinking strategies. Variations can be learned quickly, making the **Cube Games** even more practical and useful in the classroom.

eGames are electronic versions of some of the **Game Mats** and **Cube Games.**

Building Blocks electronic activities and games are referenced in appropriate lessons. These activities provide additional opportunities for practice and exploration.

Routines for Introducing Games

1. Familiarize yourself with the rules of each game by playing it before showing students how to play it.

2. Demonstrate, do not just tell, how a game is played. Overhead projector versions of the **Game Mats** are provided for demonstrating games in front of the class. The **ePresentation** or **eGames** can be displayed for the class to see how to play those games.

3. Let students who already know the game rules (perhaps from a previous grade) help students who are new to the games.

4. Do not teach strategies to students. Rather, encourage students to develop their own game-playing strategies and discuss their strategies in small groups or as a class.

Tips for Using Games

- Stress enjoyment and learning rather than competition. Emphasize sportsmanship, fair play, and taking turns.

- Change the composition of the game-playing groups from day to day. Students can learn different things by playing with different partners. From time to time, use groups of both similar and mixed ability levels.

- Assign a referee to each group. The referee makes sure that rules are followed, reminds players when it is their turn, keeps track of the score, and in some games acts as banker. Referees are especially helpful in the lower grades.

- Encourage students to play games during their free time in school and at home. Make the games easily accessible, perhaps in a math center.

See Appendix A for more information about **Real Math** Games.

Thinking Stories and Exploring Problem Solving

"Problem solving is a complex endeavor that requires critical thinking and therefore, on a logical basis, more development than most other types of lessons."

—Grouws, Douglas A. and Thomas L. Good. "Issues in Problem-Solving Instruction," *Arithmetic Teacher*, April 1989.

Real Math includes problems solving in every lesson. **Real Math** Exploring Problem Solving lessons and Thinking Stories are designed to provide further opportunities to explore and discuss problem-solving strategies and alternative approaches to solving problems.

What are Thinking Stories?

Thinking Stories are an essential component of **Real Math** Grades K–3 that help develop students' problem-solving skills. The stories describe people using mathematics and logic in correct and incorrect ways. The stories are designed to be read to students. Interspersed throughout the stories are questions that ask students to solve problems, make predictions, and analyze the characters' thinking. The same Thinking Story characters appear in all grade levels, so they "grow" with the students. Each character has peculiar thinking patterns that students come to know. For example, Mr. Muddle takes things too literally, Ferdie jumps to conclusions, Ms. Eng does not provide enough information, and Mr. Breezy provides too much information.

use zone

Routines for Thinking Stories

1. Read each story aloud.

2. Stop for each question, and discuss possible answers after you ask it. Some questions have brief answers and should be handled quickly. Others call for deeper thinking or have a range of possible answers and will require several minutes of discussion. Encourage and discuss answers.

Problem Solving

Wait for students to respond. A minute or two of silence while students think is a good idea.

3. If your students enjoy a particular story, consider reading it again another day.

What are Exploring Problem Solving Lessons?

The Exploring Problem Solving lessons at the beginning, middle, and end of each chapter in Grades K–6 also promote development of reasoning and problem-solving abilities. These lessons provide real problems that can be solved in a variety of ways. The lessons model different problem-solving strategies and provide opportunities for students to solve rich problems and discuss their problem-solving strategies. In Grades 4–6, Exploring Problem Solving includes nonfiction articles from which interesting problems are derived and explored.

Routines for Exploring Problem Solving

1. Read the lessons with students.

2. Discuss the problems and any sample solutions so that everyone understands what the problem is asking.

3. Allow students to solve problems on their own or in small groups. Showing students how to do a problem robs them of valuable thinking and their investment and confidence in their own solutions.

4. Facilitate a discussion of alternative problem solutions, and have students discuss advantages, limitations, unique features, and generalizable features of different solutions.

See Appendix A for more information about Thinking Stories and Exploring Problem Solving.

Assign Student Pages, As Students Finish, and Reflect

In almost every lesson, teachers will assign student pages to complete during class. Students will finish at different times and should know what they can do to use their extra time productively until the Reflect part of the lesson. Students should not feel penalized for finishing early and should do something that is mathematically rewarding.

Assign Student Pages

Assign Student Pages Routines

Student book exercises in **Real Math** are primarily nonmechanical. Student book pages help students learn to think about the problems. For example, addition and subtraction problems are mixed earlier than in traditional programs so students learn to pay attention to what a problem says, rather than to add unthinkingly whenever they see two numbers. This early mixing of problems also helps establish the relationship between addition and subtraction.

Because student book exercises are nonmechanical, they sometimes require your active participation.

1. Make sure students know what pages to work on and any special requirements of those pages.

2. Tell students whether they should work independently or in small groups as they complete the pages.

3. Tell students how long they have to work on the student pages before you plan to begin the Reflect part of the lesson.

4. Tell students what their options are if they finish early. Suggested options are listed under the Assign Student Pages heading in each lesson. These include

   a. suggested **eMathTools** to use.

   b. **Game Mats**, **Cube Games**, **eGames**, and **Building Blocks** activities to play.

   c. Writing+Math Journal suggestions.

5. As students work on the student pages, circulate around the room to monitor their progress. Use the Monitoring Student Progress suggestions for ideas on what to look for. Comment positively on student work, and stop to ask exploring, synthesizing, clarifying, or refocusing questions.

6. You may also use this time to work with English learners or students who need intervention.

7. You may want to complete the Informal Assessment checklists on the last page of each lesson.

8. Since games are an important and integral part of the program that provide necessary practice in traditional basic skills as well as higher-order thinking skills, when games are included in a lesson, be sure to stop work on student pages early enough to leave enough time to play the game.

Reflect

Reflect Routines

1. At the designated time, have students stop their activity and direct their attention to reflecting on the lesson.

2. Use the suggested questions in Reflect, or ask students to consider these ideas:

   a. Think about related matters that go beyond the scope of the lesson

   b. Summarize ideas about the lesson concepts

   c. Compare how the lesson concept or skill is similar to or different from other skills

   d. Identify ways to apply the lesson in other curricular areas, other strands of mathematics, or in the world outside of school

   e. Discuss solutions to Extended Response questions

Assess and Differentiate

Assessment Follow-Up: Differentiate Instruction

Based on your informal assessments and observations, choose from the following to differentiate for homework:

   a. Complete the student pages

   b. Family Involvement suggestions, such as playing a **Real Math** game

   c. Enrichment ideas

   d. Practice

   e. Reteach

Differentiate Instruction

"Classrooms grounded in best-practice education, and modified to be responsive to student differences, benefit virtually all students. Differentiation addresses the needs of struggling and advanced learners. It addresses the needs of students for whom English is a second language and students who have strong learning style preferences. It addresses gender differences and cultural differences."

—Tomlinson, Carol Ann, *The Differentiated Classroom: Responding to the Needs of All Learners.* 1999, p.24

Instruction can be differentiated in three key ways:

- **Content** is what the teacher wants students to learn and the materials or mechanisms through which that is accomplished. Differentiating the content may be teaching prerequisite concepts to students who need intervention, or by asking questions that cause students to think beyond concepts covered in the lesson.

- **Process** is how or which activities the students do to ensure they use key skills to make sense of the content. Differentiating the process may include alternating the pace of the lesson.

- **Product** is how the student demonstrates what he or she has come to know. Differentiating the product may include assigning Enrichment, Practice, or Reteach activities to complete.

Real Math provides a wealth of support for differentiating instruction, but teachers must make decisions based on their assessments of student understanding and performance.

Routines for Differentiating Instruction

1. Plan for differentiation

a. To prepare for a lesson, scan the suggestions in Planning for All Learners for differentiating instruction on the first page of each lesson. Be prepared to differentiate the content or process depending on your estimation of student understanding.

b. English Learner strategies **differentiate the process** for introducing the lesson by previewing key concepts and vocabulary.

c. Intervention lessons **differentiate content** for those students who have not yet mastered prerequisite skills.

d. Enrich strategies **differentiate the process** if students already understand the content.

e. Practice strategies **differentiate the process** if students need practice.

f. Reteach strategies **differentiate the process** if students are not understanding lesson material.

2. Monitor student progress
As students participate in Mental Math, Guided Discussion, Skill Building, Strategy Building, Games, and other lesson activities, be alert to signs of understanding and misunderstanding. The Informal Assessment Checklists include rubrics to help gather evidence about students' math proficiency.

3. Follow-Up
Summarize your formal assessments and informal observations, and consider how to differentiate student products in the lesson follow-up assignments. Program resources include

a. **Enrichment** activities for students who have a secure understanding.

b. **Practice** activities for students who have adequate understanding.

c. **Reteach** activities for student who have an emerging understanding.

4. Adjust tomorrow's lesson
Based on student understanding and performance, consider how the next lesson should be adjusted for different learners.

"Differentiating instruction does not mean just having students do different things. When a teacher lacks clarity about what a student should know, understand, and be able to do as a result of a lesson, the learning tasks she creates may or may not be engaging and we can almost be certain the tasks won't help students understand essential ideas or principles. A fuzzy sense of the essentials results in fuzzy activities, which in turn results in fuzzy student understanding. That's a barrier to high-quality teaching and learning."

—Tomlinson, Carol Ann, *The Differentiated Classroom: Responding to the Needs of All Learners.* 1999, p. 4

See Appendix A for more information about Differentiating Instruction.

Using Technology

Technology Resources for Teachers

Real Math includes several pieces of integrated technology for teachers designed to increase efficiency and effectiveness of instruction and assessment.

Suggested Procedures for Using Technology

e Planner

- **Yearly Planning** Use the **ePlanner** before school begins to plan out the mathematics course for the year. Plot out school events, holidays, and testing periods, and then organize lessons to ensure that key topics are addressed.

- **Weekly Planning** Use the **ePlanner** to adjust daily lesson plans and pacing based on your assessment of student understanding.

e Assess

- **Daily Records** Use **eAssess** to record daily formal and informal assessments.

- **Report Cards** Use **eAssess** to print student and class reports to determine grades.

- **Parent-Teacher Conferences** Use **eAssess** to print student reports to discuss with parents.

e Presentation

- **Planning** Use **ePresentation** to preview lesson concepts and activities before class.

- **Presentation** Use **ePresentation** to present multimedia lessons to students. **ePresentation** includes the complete lesson, including Guided Discussion questions, **eGame** demonstrations, and **eMathTools.**

Technology Resources for Students

Real Math provides engaging technology resources to enrich, apply, and extend learning.

e Games are electronic versions of appropriate cube and mat games to extend practice and skill- and strategy-building activities in engaging contexts.

e MathTools are electronic tools that students can use to solve problems, test solutions, explore concepts, or demonstrate understanding.

Building Blocks activities are designed to reinforce key concepts and develop mathematics understanding.

e Textbook is the complete **Student Edition** in electronic format.

Routines for Using Technology

1. Determine rules for computer use, and communicate them to students. Rules should include

   a. sharing available computers. Some teachers have a computer sign-up chart for each computer. Some teachers have the students track this themselves.

   b. computer time. You might limit the amount of time students can be at the computer or allow students to work in pairs. Some teachers have students work until they complete an activity. Others allow students to continue on with additional activities.

2. Familiarize students with your rules for proper use of computers, including how to turn computers on, load programs, and shut down the computers. Some teachers manage computers themselves; others have an aide or student in charge of computer management.

3. Using the suggestions for As Students Finish under **Assign Student Pages** in each lesson, make sure the computers are on, the programs are loaded, and that students know how to access the software.

4. Make sure students know what to do once they complete the computer activity.

See Appendix A for more information about using **Real Math** Technology.

Managing Materials

Managing Materials

Real Math provides a wealth of resources. Establishing procedures for use of materials will simplify management issues and allow students to spend more time developing mathematical understanding.

Books

Teacher's Edition and **Support Guides** should be at your fingertips.

Student Editions may be kept at student desks or on a shelf in the classroom.

Response Wheels*

Each student in Grades 3–6 gets one **Response Wheel.** Because they are used daily, **Response Wheels** should be kept in students' desks, notebooks, or mathematics books. They should be stored in such a way that they are not likely to become bent or lost. You may wish to number or otherwise identify each card so that each student can be responsible for his or her card.

Number Cubes*

Each student in Grades 1 and 2 gets four **Number Cubes.** Because they are used frequently, it may be best to have the students keep the cubes in their desks, perhaps with their play money (see next column). In Grades 3–6, students have two cubes that are used to generate random numbers.

> * **Response Wheels** and **Number Cubes** are packaged in the **Essential Materials Module** and as part of the **Individual Student Manipulative Kit,** for your convenience.

Game Mat Kits

The **Game Mat Kit** includes fifteen copies of each **Game Mat** and game kit playing pieces packaged in individual bags. There is storage space for the **Game Mat** and the playing pieces in the **Game Mat Kit** box. Students will benefit from a demonstration of how you want to have students put pieces back in bags and return them and the **Game Mats** to the kit.

Manipulatives

Real Math manipulatives come in three configurations.

- **Individual Manipulative Kits** These kits include **Number Cubes,** money, clock faces, rulers, interlocking cubes, counters, pattern blocks, tape measures, and spinners. A kit appropriate for Grades K–2 and another kit for 3–6 are available. These kits can be stored at student desks or in a designated tub or shelf in the classroom.

- **Manipulative Modules** Manipulatives are also available in modules for specific topics: Counting, Base-Ten, Fractions, Geometry, Measurement, Money, and Time. These kits contain enough materials for class use.

- **Teacher Manipulative Kit** This kit provides presentation-style manipulatives and overhead-projector manipulatives for demonstration purposes.

See Appendix A for more information about Materials.

It is important to keep parents informed about what their children are doing in mathematics so they can support students' mathematical understanding and development at home.

Family Involvement

Family members can play a critical role in students' success in mathematics if they understand how to help. For example, the games, Thinking Stories, and other activities in **Real Math** may be unfamiliar to parents. Parents need to be assured that these are important activities designed to develop a solid understanding of mathematical concepts and provide essential practice with arithmetic skills.

Real Math has several elements built into the program that can enable family-school communications.

Home Connection

This book includes ready-made Parent and Student Surveys, Newsletters, and Games that teachers can use to communicate with student families. Newsletters are available for every chapter.

Home Connection Game Kit

This kit includes all the **Game Mats** and **Cube Games** for a grade level, packaged in a game box along with the pieces needed to play the games. Families can purchase the kit, or you can establish a "lending game library."

Assessment Resources

Assessment includes several resources to communicate with families.

- **Student Assessment Record** is a convenient form to record all student assessments on a daily or weekly basis. These forms are handy to use at parent-teacher conferences.

- **Parent-Teacher Conference Checklist** provides a helpful way to organize thoughts about students in preparation for parent-teacher conferences.

Parent Aides

Often parents are willing to volunteer to help out in the classroom. There are many ways they can help.

- Computer Management—Make sure computers are on and loaded with appropriate software. Be available to troubleshoot and answer questions while students use the computers.

- Intervention Aide—Use the **Intervention Support Guide** to work with students to build prerequisite skills.

- English Learner Aide—Use the **English Learner Support Guide** to work with English Learners to preview and review lesson concepts.

- Manipulatives Manager—Make sure manipulatives are available for student use, when appropriate.

Family Participation

There are many ways that families can assist students in learning math.

Playing Games

Playing games with students is an enjoyable way to help them practice their math skills. **Home Connection** contains reproducible directions for each of the **Cube Games.** Reproductions of the **Game Mats** are in the back of this **Teacher's Edition.** The **Home Connection Game Kit** is also available.

Practicing Basic Facts

Home Connection contains reproducible flash cards for basic facts and directions for games using the cards. Make sure parents and helpers understand how best to use flash cards.

- Never ridicule students for incorrect answers.

- Stop practice when the student becomes disinterested.

Using Math in Everyday Life

Encourage parents to show students how they use mathematics throughout the day and to ask for students' help. For example, families can estimate the total cost of a shopping trip, measure ingredients and adjust recipes for new quantities when cooking, and estimate when to leave on a trip to arrive by a certain time.

The lessons are designed to be taught at a lively pace. Students should move quickly from activity to activity. In this way, they will remain alert and interested in what they are learning.

Pacing

Here are some tips for proper pacing:

- Be prepared. Materials must be ready, and you must be ready. Sections in the lesson plans titled Looking Ahead and Materials will help you prepare the items you will need in time for when they are needed. Also, read the lesson plan in advance or preview the **ePresentation** so you will not lose time figuring out what to do while the lesson is in progress.

- Use the time estimates. To help you manage time, lesson plans suggest a number of minutes for each activity. These times cannot be precise for every teacher and for every lesson. Some activities will take you more time and some will take less. Even so, the suggested times will help you to plan in advance how you will carry out each activity.

- Watch the clock. Use it as an ally. The clock can tell you when you have concentrated on an activity too long, even before students show signs of restlessness. It can tell you when you have lapsed into too much talking or when you are shifting too slowly from one activity to another.

Using Lessons over Two Days

Most lessons can be completed in one day (about 45–60 minutes of class time). However, you may find that you occasionally need to spend an extra day on some lessons. Refer to the Lesson Plans chart at the beginning of each unit for pacing suggestions. When you decide to take two days for a lesson, try dividing it as follows:

Day 1
- Review skills that students will need for the lesson.
- Do all suggested Teach activities, but not the **Student Edition** pages.

Day 2
- Review and/or adapt the Mental Math exercises from the previous day.
- Provide additional teaching and practice on related skills.

- Allow plenty of time for students to work on the **Student Edition** pages.
- Devote time to a related **Cube Game** or **Game Mat.**
- Extend the Reflect discussion.

Adjusting Instruction for Longer or Shorter Math Sessions

Most teachers have about 45–60 minutes each day to devote to mathematics. If your schedule varies greatly from that consider the following tips for adjusting instruction.

If you have more than 60 minutes for math...
- Lengthen Guided Discussion and game times by five minutes each (more when new games are introduced).
- Repeat whole-group activities when you feel that students will remain interested.
- Use the **Reteach, Practice,** and **Enrichment Masters** and the **Cross-Curricular Connections** provided throughout the **Teacher's Edition.**

If you have fewer than 45 minutes for math...
- Do not eliminate the Games or Thinking Stories. These help develop mathematical intelligence and are essential portions of the curriculum.
- Do the Thinking Story and Exploring Problem Solving activities outside the regular mathematics period (e.g., first thing in the morning, right after lunch, or at read-aloud time).
- Play games that reinforce previous lessons outside the regular class period, such as every Friday, perhaps.
- Conduct Mental Math on basic facts outside the regular mathematics period.
- Reduce time spent on a few lesson components by a minute or two.
- Have students spend more time working on student pages outside of class.

Real Math is rich in opportunities and resources to conduct comprehensive assessments that inform instruction. The **Real Math** Assessments are designed to evaluate all math proficiencies.

Goals of Assessment

1. To improve instruction by informing teachers about the effectiveness of their lessons
2. To promote growth of students by identifying where they need additional instruction and support
3. To recognize accomplishments

Phases of Assessment

Planning As you develop lesson plans, you can consider how you might assess the instruction, determining how you will tell if students have grasped the material.

Gather Evidence Throughout the instructional phase, you can informally and formally gather evidence of student understanding. The Informal Assessment Checklists and Student Assessment Records are provided to help you record data.

Summarize Findings Taking time to reflect on the assessments to summarize findings and make plans for follow-up is a critical part of any lesson.

Use Results Use the results of your findings to differentiate instruction or to adjust or confirm future lessons.

Real Math is rich in opportunities to monitor student progress to accomplish these goals.

Informal Daily Assessment

Informal Daily Assessments evaluate students' math proficiencies in computational fluency, reasoning, understanding, applying, and engaging. Mental Math exercises, Games, Thinking Stories, and **Student Edition** pages can be used for day-to-day observation and assessment of how well each student is learning skills and grasping concepts. Because of their special nature, these activities are an effective and convenient means of monitoring students. Games, for example, allow you to watch students practice particular skills under conditions more natural to them than most classroom activities. Mental Math exercises allow you to provide adequate work and time to see individual responses, give immediate feedback, and involve the entire class.

Simple rubrics enable teachers to record and track their observations. These can later be recorded by hand in the Student Assessment Record or in **eAssess** to help provide a more complete view of student proficiency.

Formal Assessments

The **Student Edition** and **Assessment** provide formal assessments for each chapter. Included are Pretests, Speed Tests, Daily Quizzes, Practice Tests, and Chapter Tests to evaluate students' understanding of chapter concepts. Cumulative Review, Key Ideas Review, and Chapter Review are available to prepare students for formal assessments.

Mastery Checkpoints provide periodic progress checks.

Individual Oral Assessment

Oral Assessment, which is in the middle of the chapter, provides an opportunity for teachers to interview students and get a first-hand assessment of student reasoning and understanding.

Individual Portfolio Assessment

Journals and Chapter Projects can be used for Portfolio Assessment.

See Appendix A for more information about Assessment.

Assessment

The Mastery Checkpoints are key Grade 3 skills for which students are expected to demonstrate mastery. **Assessment** contains a blackline master for each Mastery Checkpoint.

Grade 3 includes key skills that are important for students' future progress. To help monitor progress for each student, corresponding Mastery Checkpoints appear throughout the Grade 3 **Teacher's Edition.** Each Mastery Checkpoint appears in the lesson where most students are expected to have achieved proficiency. The table to the right provides a list of the Grade 3 skills and corresponding lessons that include the Mastery Checkpoints.

Do not delay the progress of the entire class while waiting for all students to demonstrate success with a particular skill. More teaching and practice on that skill are always given in a later lesson, usually the following lesson. At that time, you can focus on students who need extra help.

Mastery Checkpoints

The Mastery Checkpoint Chart in **Assessment** provides a convenient way to keep track of your students' progress.

- Fill in the names of all the students in the class.

- When a Mastery Checkpoint is encountered in the **Teacher's Edition,** follow the suggestions for observing each student. Then record students' progress, as follows:

Place an **R** in the appropriate column beside the name of each student who demonstrates success on the skill in question.

Pencil in a *P* in the appropriate column for each student who grasps the concept but still needs further practice to sharpen his or her skill. Assign extra practice to these students.

Pencil in a *T* for each student who has not yet grasped the idea and needs further teaching. Give extra teaching to these students.

Change *T*s (needs teaching) to *P*s (needs practice) and *P*s to *R*s (just needs refreshing) as students demonstrate success on the skill.

Grade 3 Checkpoints		
Number	**Lesson**	**Topic**
1	1.2	Addition and Subtraction Facts
2	1.4	Inequalities and Equalities
3	1.7	Numbers to 10,000
4	2.4	Two-Digit Addition and Subtraction
5	2.5	Addition and Subtraction Applications
6	2.8	Three-Digit Addition and Subtraction
7	2.9	Approximating Sums and Differences
8	2.10	Column Addition
9	2.11	Four-Digit Addition and Subtraction
10	3.1	Telling Time to the Nearest Minute
11	5.6	Multiplication Facts
12	5.9	Division Facts
13	6.5	Inverse Operations
14	7.1	Multiplication by 10, 100, and 1,000
15	7.4	Multiplying by a One-Digit Number
16	7.9	Arithmetic Applications
17	8.3	Simple Fractions
18	9.4	Measuring Length and Weight
19	10.2	Familiarity with Money (Coins and Bills)
20	10.5	Understanding Decimal Numbers
21	10.7	Addition and Subtraction of Decimal Numbers
22	10.8	Converting Metric Units of Length
23	12.7	Interpreting Line Graphs

See Appendix A for more about Assessment.

Lessons

Multidigit Multiplication and Division

Teaching for Understanding

This chapter develops students' previous knowledge of multiplication and division. Students will become familiar with multiplication and division for greater numbers. Students will also learn to apply their knowledge in practical situations.

Prerequisite Skills and Concepts

- Multiplication Facts • Place Value to 1,000 • Multidigit Addition and Subtraction

Multidigit Multiplication and Division Skills Trace

Before Grade 3	Grade 3	After Grade 3
Grades K–2 Informally introduced to multiplication and division	**Chapter 5** formally introduced multiplication and division facts. **This chapter** formally introduces multiplication and division algorithms.	Introduces strategies for multiplication and division before introducing algebra

Problem solving is in every lesson. This chapter includes the following:

CHAPTER INTRODUCTION focuses on breaking up numbers to make it easier to find a total (pp. 248I–249C).

EXPLORING PROBLEM SOLVING The first lesson explores the Make a Table and Write an Equation strategies (pp. 260–261, 261A). The second lesson explores how the arrangement of objects may or may not affect how many can fit in a box (pp. 278–278A).

THINKING STORY In "Clever Consuela" students help a character develop strategies for a computer program (pp. 288–291).

Shopping Game (Lesson 7.1), **Roll a Problem Game** (Lessons 7.2), **Cube 100** (Lessons 7.6)

Math Background

Multidigit Multiplication and Division

Multiplication and Division Algorithms

- With the multiplication and division algorithms introduced in this chapter, as with other mathematical procedures in *Real Math*, a goal of the program is for students to believe they could have worked it out for themselves and that in the future if they forget the procedure, they can figure it out again by themselves.

- The algorithms developed in this chapter are not the only possible ways to do multiplication and division, but they are ones that students have been successful with during decades of field tests.

- As with the algorithms for addition and subtraction taught in earlier grades, one advantage to understanding the multiplication and division algorithms is that the same steps work for numbers with any number of digits.

- The multiplication algorithm is introduced in the context of a practical area problem that can be solved by previously introduced techniques. Students find a more efficient way of solving the problem by breaking the area up into sections, and so develop an algorithm for 2-digit by 1-digit multiplication in which the sections in the diagram correspond to the partial products in the algorithm.

Multiplying by Powers of 10

- Numbers that can be written as 10 with an exponent (such as $100 = 10^2$ and $1,000 = 10^3$) are called powers of 10. One way to multiply by a power of 10 is to count the number of zeros in the power of ten and write that many zeros after the other factor.

- This rule works because writing a zero to the right of a number (or numeral) moves each digit of the number one place to the left. In our numeration system, this makes each digit of the number ten times greater (and so makes the number ten times greater). For example, 70 is 7 tens, or 10 times 7; 2,430 is 243 tens, or 10 times 243. Students should recognize that there is a connection between this rule and the fact that our number system is based on ten.

- Because the order of factors does not affect the product, the rule works, for example, for both 3×100 and 100×3.

Checking Division

- The inverse relationship between multiplication and division (as with addition and subtraction) is an important mathematical idea that, among other things, allows us to do various computations without knowing the usual algorithm or facts. For example, to divide 132 by 11, we can simply search for a number that can be multiplied by 11 to get 132.

- This also provides an important way to check to see if a computation has been done correctly. With multiple choice tests, often estimation and checking by multiplication will eliminate the need to do a division problem.

Approximation

- In this chapter, as is true throughout *Real Math*, lessons focus on using approximation when exact answers are difficult or unnecessary to find.

  Students are also encouraged to think of the order of magnitude of an answer both before and after doing a problem in which they are seeking a precise answer. This will help students detect unreasonable answers in their work and that of others, and will be useful in evaluating answers from calculators and computers to make sure answers make sense.

- Checking answers to see that they make sense is easier than the precise checks that are commonly used (such as checking a division answer using multiplication). It is also more useful and more likely to be used, since precise checks often are more difficult than redoing the problem. Of course, exact checks should be taught and used, but only as one of many useful ways to check an answer.

- Students should begin developing not only the habit of checking answers, but also the judgment to decide which kind of check is appropriate in a given situation.

CHAPTER 7 Overview

What Research Says
About Multiplication and Division

How Children Learn Multiplication and Division

"Step-by-step procedures for adding, subtracting, multiplying, or dividing numbers are called *algorithms*... Learning to use algorithms for computation with multidigit numbers is an important part of developing proficiency with numbers. Algorithms are procedures that can be executed in the same way to solve a variety of problems arising from different situations and involving different numbers."

"Understanding and fluency are related. ...instructional programs that emphasize understanding algorithms before using them have been shown to lead to increases in both conceptual and procedural knowledge. So there is some evidence that understanding is the basis for developing procedural fluency."

Kilpatrick, J., J. Swafford, and B.Findell, eds. *Adding It Up: Helping Children Learn Mathematics.* Washington, D.C.: National Research Council/ National Academy Press, 2001, pp. 196–198.

"The multiplication and division algorithms are complex embedded methods that are not easy to understand or carry out. They demand high levels of skill in multiplying a multidigit number by a single-digit number within complex embedded formats in which multiplying and adding alternate."

Fuson, Karen F. "Developing Mathematical Power in Whole Number Operations" in Kilpatrick, Jeremy, W. Gary Martin and Deborah Schifter, eds. *A Research Companion to Principles and Standards for School Mathematics.* Reston, VA: National Council of Teachers of Mathematics, Inc. 2003, p. 85.

Research-Based Teaching Techniques

"In grade 3, students should focus on the meanings of, and relationship between, multiplication and division. It is important that students understand what each number in a multiplication or division expression represents. For example, in multiplication, unlike addition, the factors in the problem can refer to different units. If students are solving the problem 29×4 to find out how many legs there are on 29 cats, 29 is the number of cats (or number of groups), 4 is the number of legs on each cat (or number of items in each group), and 116 is the total number of legs on all the cats. Modeling multiplication problems with pictures, diagrams, or concrete materials helps students learn what the factors and their product represent in various contexts."

National Council of Teachers of Mathematics. *Principles and Standards for School Mathematics.* Reston, VA: NCTM, 2000.

RESEARCH IN ACTION

Inverse Operations Chapter 7 will reinforce the inverse relationship between multiplication and division.

Estimation In Chapter 7 students will gain experience in making estimates in order to determine the reasonableness of the answers that they arrive at in performing multiplication and division procedures.

Algorithm Chapter 7 provides further development of the sequences of rules and procedures that become the common algorithms for the operations of multiplication and division.

Vocabulary

remainder (Lesson 7.5) what is left after you cannot divide a number any further

English Learner

Cognates

For English learners, a quick way to acquire new English vocabulary is to build on what is known in the primary language.

English	Spanish
multiply	multiplicar
repeated addition	adición repetida
product	producto
dimensions	dimensiones
digit	dígito
to group	agrupar
equally	igualmente
division	división
to divide	dividir
to estimate	estimar
correct	correcto
total	total
mathematical	matemático

Access Vocabulary

English learners may understand words in different contexts or not understand idioms. Review chapter vocabulary for this concern. For example:

multiply mentally	do the multiplication in your mind instead of with paper, pencil, or calculator

Chapter Planner

Lessons	Objectives	NCTM Standards	State Standards
7.1 Multiplying by 10, 100, and 1,000	To explore patterns when multiplying by 10, 100, and 1,000	Number and Operations, Algebra	
7.2 Multiplying Two-Digit Numbers by One-Digit Numbers	To develop familiarity with multiplying a two-digit number by a one-digit number	Number and Operations, Connections	
7.3 Multiplying Three-Digit Numbers by One-Digit Numbers	To explore algorithms for multiplying a three-digit number by a one-digit number	Number and Operations, Connections	
7.4 Applications of Multiplication	To enhance students' understanding of multiplying three-digit numbers by one-digit numbers using practical applications	Problem Solving, Connections	
7.5 Division with Remainders	To develop familiarity with remainders in division	Number and Operations, Connections	
7.6 Reasonable Answers to Division Problems	To clarify concept of division by showing that the same division problem can have several different answers in a practical situation	Number and Operations, Problem Solving	
7.7 Dividing Two-Digit Numbers by One-Digit Numbers	To explore algorithms for dividing a two-digit number by a one-digit number	Number and Operations, Connections	
7.8 Dividing Three-Digit Numbers by One-Digit Numbers	To explore algorithms for dividing a three-digit number by a one-digit number	Number and Operations, Connections	
7.9 Problem-Solving Applications	To clarify concepts of arithmetical operations by using practical situations in which students decide which operation to use	Number and Operations, Problem Solving, Connections	

Vocabulary	Manipulatives and Materials	Games to reinforce skills and concepts
	• Response Wheels • Craft sticks or other base-ten materials (about 25 bunches of 10) • Shopping Game Mat	Shopping Game
	• Response Wheels • Number Cube (one 0–5)	Roll a Problem (Multiplication) Game
	• Response Wheels • Number Cubes (0–5 and 5–10)	Roll a Problem (Multiplication) Game
	• Response Wheels • Yearly calendar (optional)	Roll a Problem (Multiplication) Game
remainder	• Response Wheels • Package of counting sticks (100 count)	Roll a Problem (Multiplication) Game
	• Response Wheels • Number Cubes (0–5 and 5–10) • Strategy Building activity from Develop section (in worksheet format)	Cube 100
	• Response Wheels • Play money ($10 bills and $1 bills)	Cube 100
	• Response Wheels • Play money	Cube 100
	• Response Wheels • Counters	Harder Shopping Game

Additional Resources

Differentiated Instruction

Intervention Support Guide Provides instruction for the following prerequisite skills:

- 7.A Multiplication Facts
- 7.B Place Value to 1,000
- 7.C Multidigit Addition and Subtraction

Enrichment Support Guide Extends lesson concepts

Practice Reinforces lesson skills and concepts

Reteach Support Guide Provides alternate instruction for lesson concepts

English Learner Support Guide Previews and reviews lesson concepts and vocabulary for English learners

Technology

The following electronic resources are available:

ⓔ **Planner** Lessons 7.1–7.9

ⓔ **Presentation** Lessons 7.1–7.9

ⓔ **Textbook** Lessons 7.1–7.9

ⓔ **Assess** Lessons 7.1–7.9

ⓔ **MathTools** *Calculator* Lesson 7.1

ⓔ **Games** *Cube 100* Lessons 7.6, 7.7, and 7.8

Building Blocks *Function Machine 3* Lesson 7.1; *Field Trip* Lesson 7.4; *Function Machine 4* Lesson 7.6; *Number Tools: Multiplication Word Problems* Lesson 7.8; *Number Tools: Multidigit Multiplication and Missing Factor Problems* Lesson 7.9

Assessment

Informal Assessment rubrics at the end of each lesson provide daily evaluation of student math proficiency.

Chapter Planner, continued

Problem Solving	When to Use	Objectives	NCTM Standards	Skills Covered
Chapter Introduction pp. 248I–249C 15–30 minutes	Use after the Chapter 7 Pretest.	To introduce chapter concepts in a problem-solving setting	Number and Operations	Multiplying and dividing simple numbers
Exploring Problem Solving pp. 260–261, 261A 30–45 minutes	Use anytime during the chapter.	To explore methods of solving nonroutine problems	Number and Operations, Connections	Multiplying and dividing two- and three-digit numbers
Exploring Problem Solving pp. 278–278A 45–60 minutes	Use anytime after the first Exploring Problem Solving.	To explore methods of solving nonroutine problems	Number and Operations, Connections, Problem Solving	Multiplying and dividing multidigit numbers
Thinking Story—Clever Consuela pp. 288–289, 290–291	Use anytime during the chapter.	To develop logical reasoning while integrating reading skills with mathematics	Algebra	Patterns, Functions, Variables

Review	When to Use	Objectives	NCTM Standards	Skills Covered
Cumulative Review p. 262–263 15–30 minutes	Use anytime after Lesson 7.4.	To review concepts and skills taught in Lessons 7.1–7.4	Number and Operations	Multiplying by 10 and 5; Measuring and graphing; Multiplication, area, and approximate measure; Variables and arrow notation
Cumulative Review p. 279–280 15–30 minutes	Use anytime after Lesson 7.9.	To review concepts and skills taught in Lessons 7.1–7.9	Number and Operations, Connections, Problem Solving	Rounding; missing factors; division and multiplication functions; writing multiplication sentences
Chapter 7 Review pp. 282A, 282–283 30–45 minutes	Use after Lesson 7.9.	To review concepts and skills taught earlier in the chapter	Number and Operations, Connections	Multiplying and dividing multidigit numbers

Assessment	When to Use	Objectives	NCTM Standards	Skills Covered
Informal Assessment Rubrics pp. 251A–277A 5 minutes per student	Use at the end of each lesson.	To provide daily evaluation of math proficiency	Number and Operations, Connections, Problem Solving	Computing, Understanding, Reasoning, Applying, Engaging
Pretest (*Assessment* pp. 94–95) 15–30 minutes	Use prior to Chapter 7.	To provide assessment of prerequisite and chapter topics	Number and Operations	Multiplying and dividing
Individual Oral Assessment p. 263A 5 minutes per student	Begin use after Lesson 7.4.	To provide alternate means of assessing students' progress	Number and Operations, Problem Solving, Algebra	Multiplying and dividing two- and three-digit numbers
Mastery Checkpoint (*Assessment* pp. T66–T69) 5 minutes per student	Use after Lessons 7.1, 7.4, and 7.9.	To provide assessment of mastery of key skills	Number and Operations, Connections, Problem Solving	Multiplying and dividing multidigit numbers
Chapter 7 Practice Test pp. 284–285, 286–287 30–45 minutes	Use after or in place of the Chapter 7 Review.	To provide assessment or additional practice of the lesson concepts	Number and Operations, Connections, Problem Solving	Multiplying and dividing multidigit numbers
Chapter 7 Test (*Assessment* pp. 101–104) 30–45 minutes	Use after or in place of the Chapter 7 Review.	To provide assessment of the chapter concepts	Number and Operations, Connections, Problem Solving	Multiplying and dividing multidigit numbers

Technology Resources and Support

Visit SRAonline.com for online versions of the **Real Math** eSuite.

Technology for Teachers

e **Presentation**	**Lessons 7.1–7.9** Use the **ePresentation** to interactively present chapter content.
e **Planner**	Use the Chapter and Lesson Planners to outline activities and time frames for Chapter 7.
e **Assess**	Students can take the following assessments in **eAssess:** • Chapter Pretest • Mastery Checkpoint **Lessons 7.1, 7.4 and 7.9** • Chapter Test Teachers can record results and print reports for all assessments in this chapter.
e **MathTools**	*Calculator* **Lesson 7.1**

Technology for Students

e **Textbook**	An electronic, interactive version of the **Student Edition** is available for all lessons in Chapter 7.
e **MathTools**	*Calculator* **Lesson 7.1**
e **Games**	*Cube 100* **Lessons 7.6, 7.7, and 7.8**
TECH KNOWLEDGE	**TechKnowledge** Level 2 provides lessons that specifically teach the Unit 10 Internet applications that students can use in this chapter's projects.
Building Blocks	*Function Machine 3* **Lesson 7.1;** *Field Trip* **Lesson 7.4;** *Function Machine 4* **Lesson 7.6;** *Number Tools: Multiplication Word Problems* **Lesson 7.8;** *Number Tools: Multidigit Multiplication and Missing Factor Problems* **Lesson 7.9**

Multidigit Multiplication and Division

1 Introduce Chapter 7   5

Chapter Objectives

Explain to students that in this chapter they will build on what they already know about multiplication and division. They will

- multiply multidigit numbers.
- divide multidigit numbers.

Pretest COMPUTING

Administer the Pretest on **Assessment** pages 94 and 95. The Pretest covers the following prerequisite skills and topics from the chapter:

- Function machines (Problems 1–3)
- Multiplication (Problems 4–6)
- Inverse functions (Problems 7–9)
- Multiplication patterns of 10, 100, 1,000 (Problems 10–12)
- Multiplying multidigit numbers by one-digit numbers (Problems 13–15)
- Division (Problems 16–18)
- Applying multiplication and division (Problems 19–22)

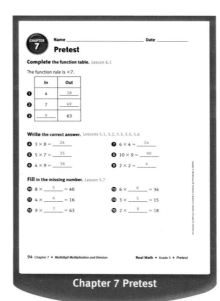

Chapter 7 Pretest

Access Prior Knowledge UNDERSTANDING

Remind students of the problem they solved on page 26 where they decided how much space 1,000,000 pennies would take up. Have them talk about stacking pennies as a way to keep track of how much money they have.

2 Explore Problem Solving   30

Tell Students In Today's Lesson They Will

figure out if stacks of pennies make more than $1.

Materials

None

Using Student Pages

Have students look at the illustration on page 249. Read the problem together. Then guide them through Questions 1–3.

Have students work on their own or with a partner on Questions 4 and 5. Circulate around the room, and offer support as needed. If students seem to be unable to make progress, support them with questions such as the following:

- **If you know how many pennies are below the line and how many are above it, how can you find the total?** add those two numbers
- **How can counting by 10s help you count all the pennies below the dotted line?** There are 10 in each stack, so you can count by 10s as you count each stack.
- **How many pennies are above the line in each stack?** 7
- **How many stacks are there?** 6
- **What can you do next to help you find the total number of pennies?**

Answer to Problem 5

Students might visualize adding 2 to every stack to make 25 or subtracting 3 from every stack to make 20.

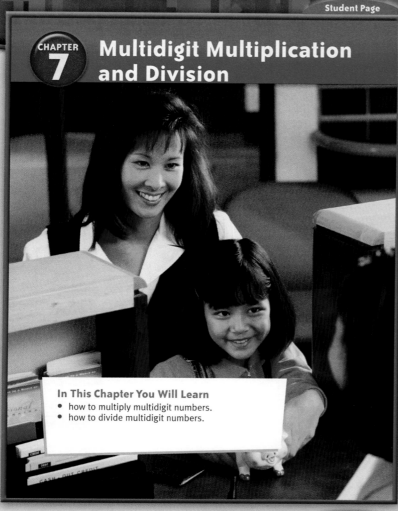

CHAPTER 7
Multidigit Multiplication and Division

In This Chapter You Will Learn
- how to multiply multidigit numbers.
- how to divide multidigit numbers.

Concept/Question Board APPLYING

Questions

Have students think of and write three questions they have about multidigit multiplication and division and how they can be used. Then have them select one question to post on the Question side of the Board.

Concepts

As students work through the chapter, have them collect examples of how multidigit multiplication and division are used in everyday situations. For each example, have them write a problem that relates to the item(s). Have them display their examples on the Concept side of the Board. Suggest the following:

- sport banquets
- cell phone bills

Answers

Throughout the chapter, have students post answers to the questions and solutions to the problems on the Board.

Problem Solving

Roger is going to take his pennies to the bank. He piled them into equal stacks. He has 6 stacks that are all the same height. He wants to know if he has enough pennies to make $1.

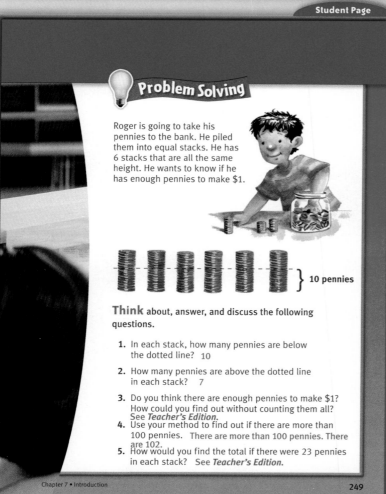

} 10 pennies

Think about, answer, and discuss the following questions.

1. In each stack, how many pennies are below the dotted line? 10

2. How many pennies are above the dotted line in each stack? 7

3. Do you think there are enough pennies to make $1? How could you find out without counting them all? See *Teacher's Edition*.

4. Use your method to find out if there are more than 100 pennies.   There are more than 100 pennies. There are 102.

5. How would you find the total if there were 23 pennies in each stack? See *Teacher's Edition*.

**Reflect** 10

**Knowledge Age Skills**

Problem Formulation, Planning, and Strategizing Have groups present their answers and their strategies for solving Questions 4 and 5. In discussion, bring out the following points:

- Numbers over 10 can be thought of in groups of tens and groups of ones—as 10 plus some more, 20 plus some more, 30 plus some more, and so on.
- Thinking about numbers in parts can help make it easier to find a total.
- Some problems do not ask you to find an exact number, but you may need to do an exact calculation in order to answer the question. In this problem, the total is so close to $1 that many students will find the exact total. Others may approximate, figuring that 60 and 42 is more than 100.

Sample Solutions Strategies

Students might use one or more of the following strategies to solve the problem.

Write Equations

Students might use words, numbers, and symbols to represent the problem.

Total number of pennies = total below the line + total above the line

Total number of pennies = 6×10 + 6×7

Use a Physical Model

Students might use counters to regroup the six groups of 7s into groups of 10 until they have four more 10s, at which point they will know they have more than 100 in all.

Use Number Sense

Students might visualize adding 3 to every stack to make 20, or 2 tens. They might reason as follows: six groups of 2 tens is 12 tens, or 120. But I have to take back the 6 groups of 3 that I added. $120 - 18 = 102$.

Home Connection

At this time, you may want to send home the letter on pages 26–29 of *Home Connection.* This letter describes what students will be learning and what activities they can do at home to support their work in school.

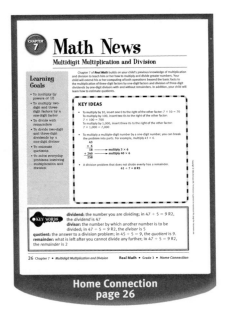

Home Connection page 26

Assess and Differentiate **Assess** Use *eAssess* to record and analyze evidence of student understanding.

Gather Evidence

Use the Daily Class Assessment Records in **Assessment** or *eAssess* to record Informal and Formal Assessments.

Informal Assessment
☑ **Access Prior Knowledge**
Did the student `UNDERSTANDING`
- ❑ make important observations?
- ❑ extend or generalize learning?
- ❑ provide insightful answers?
- ❑ pose insightful questions?

Informal Assessment
☑ **Concept/Question Board**
Did the student `APPLYING`
- ❑ apply learning in new situations?
- ❑ contribute concepts?
- ❑ contribute answers?
- ❑ connect mathematics to real-world situations?

Formal Assessment
☑ **Pretest** `COMPUTING`
Review student answers in each problem set.
- ❑ Function machines (Problems 1–3)
- ❑ Multiplication (Problems 4–6)
- ❑ Inverse functions (Problems 7–9)
- ❑ Multiplication patterns of 10, 100, 1,000 (Problems 10–12)
- ❑ Multiplying multidigit numbers by one-digit numbers (Problems 13–15)
- ❑ Division (Problems 16–18)
- ❑ Applying multiplication and division (Problems 19–22)

Summarize Findings

Analyze and summarize assessment data for each student. Determine which Assessment Follow-Up is appropriate for each student. Use the Student Assessment Record in **Assessment** or *eAssess* to update assessment records.

C Assessment Follow-Up ● DIFFERENTIATE INSTRUCTION

Based on your observations of each student, use these teaching strategies for a general approach to the chapter. Look for specific Differentiate Instruction and Monitoring Student Progress strategies in each lesson that relate specifically to the lesson content.

ENRICH	PRACTICE	RETEACH	INTERVENTION	ENGLISH LEARNER
If . . . students demonstrate **secure understanding** of chapter concepts, **Then . . .** move quickly through the chapter, or use *Enrichment* Lessons 7.1–7.9 as assessment follow-up to extend and apply understanding.	**If . . .** students grasp chapter concepts with **competent understanding,** **Then . . .** use *Practice* Lessons 7.1–7.9 as lesson follow-up to develop fluency.	**If . . .** students have prerequisite understanding but demonstrate **emerging understanding** of chapter concepts, **Then . . .** use *Reteach* Lessons 7.1, 7.2, 7.4, and 7.5 to reteach lesson concepts.	**If . . .** students are not competent with prerequisite skills, **Then . . .** use *Intervention* Lessons 7.A–7.C before each lesson to develop fluency with prerequisite skills.	Use *English Learner Support Guide* Lessons 7.1–7.9 for strategies to preteach lesson vocabulary and concepts.

Math Across the Curriculum

Preview the chapter projects with students. Assign projects to extend and enrich concepts in this chapter.

Create a Monetary System

SOCIAL STUDIES WebQuest

4 weeks

MATH OBJECTIVE
To reinforce studies of multiplication by multiplying numbers by 10, 100, and 1,000 to create a monetary system

SOCIAL STUDIES OBJECTIVE
To reinforce studies of economics by researching currency

TECHNOLOGY OBJECTIVE
To use a spreadsheet program to organize and calculate data

Have students use technology to research other countries' monetary systems and show the currency.

For this project, students use the Internet to investigate the following information:

- names and denominations of currencies
- what the currencies in other countries look like

For specific step-by-step instructions for this project, see *Across the Curriculum Math Connections* pages 72–77.

KA ➤ Knowledge Age Skills

High-Level Responsibility Students are responsible for creating an entire monetary system.

Creative Work with Ideas Students create a meaningful design for a new currency.

TECH KNOWLEDGE *TechKnowledge* Level 3 provides lessons that specifically teach the Unit 10 Internet and Unit 7 Spreadsheet applications that students can use in this project.

Research Coin Minting

SCIENCE

2–3 weeks

MATH OBJECTIVE
To reinforce studies of multiplication by applying multiplication to research on coin minting

SCIENCE OBJECTIVE
To reinforce studies of physical change by learning about coin minting

TECHNOLOGY OBJECTIVE
To use the Internet to research coin minting

Have students use mathematics to research coin minting. To broaden the science concept, have students write about types of physical changes and properties of matter you are currently studying.

As part of the project, students should consider the following issues:

- the United States' coin minting process
- applying multiplication to coin minting
- United States coin and world coin history
- writing a creative research report

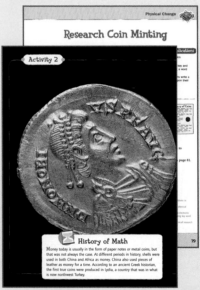

For specific step-by-step instructions for this project, see *Across the Curriculum Math Connections* pages 78–82.

KA ➤ Knowledge Age Skills

Creative Work with Ideas Students write reports that present and use research in creative ways.

Effective Communication Students write reports that effectively communicate research information.

Lesson Planner

OBJECTIVES
To explore patterns when multiplying a number by 10, 100, and 1,000

NCTM STANDARDS
Number and Operations
- Understanding meanings of operations and how they relate to one another
- Computing fluently and making reasonable estimates

Algebra
Understanding patterns, relations, and functions

MATERIALS
- *Response Wheels
- Craft sticks or other base-ten materials (about 25 bunches of 10)
- Shopping Game Mat

TECHNOLOGY
- **Presentation** Lesson 7.1
- **Building Blocks** Function Machine 3 (from Lesson 6.6)
- **MathTools** Calculator

TEST PREP
Cumulative Review
Mental Math reviews skip counting by 10, 100, and 1,000 (Lesson 4.2).

Extended Response
Problems 14 and 17

Writing + Math
Journal

Multiplying by 10, 100, and 1,000

Context of the Lesson This is the first of four lessons on multidigit multiplication. In this lesson students will explore patterns for multiplying by powers of ten with whole numbers *only*. In Grade 4 these same methods are used in the development of multidigit multiplication algorithm.

See page 248B for Math Background for teachers for this lesson.

Planning for Learning ● DIFFERENTIATE INSTRUCTION

INTERVENTION
If . . . students lack the prerequisite skill of place value to 1,000,

Then . . . teach *Intervention* Lesson 7.B.

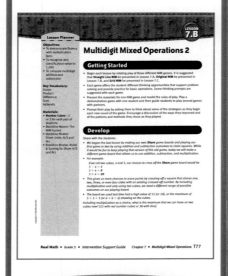

Intervention Lesson 7.B

ENGLISH LEARNER
Preview

If . . . students need language support,

Then . . . use Lesson 7.1 in *English Learner Support Guide* to preview lesson concepts and vocabulary.

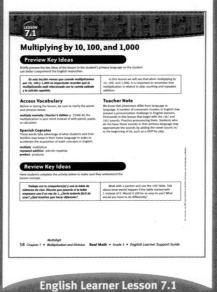

English Learner Lesson 7.1

ENRICH
If . . . students are proficient in the lesson concepts,

Then . . . emphasize the student pages.

PRACTICE
If . . . students would benefit from additional practice,

Then . . . extend Skill Building before assigning the student pages.

RETEACH
If . . . students are having difficulty understanding multiplying by 10, 100, and 1,000,

Then . . . extend Guided Discussion before assigning the student pages.

Access Vocabulary
multiply mentally do the multiplication in your mind instead of with pencil, paper, or calculator

Spanish Cognates
multiply multiplicar
repeated addition adición repetida
product producto

---

*Manipulative Kit Item

Mental Math 5

  RESPONSE WHEEL Review counting by 10s, 100s, and 1,000s, using examples such as the following:

a. 10, 20, 30   40
b. 600, 500, 400   300
c. 40, 50, 60, 70   80
d. 600, 700, 800, 900   1,000
e. 300, 400, 500, 600   700
f. 1,000; 2,000; 3,000; 4,000   5,000
g. 30, 40, 50, 60   70
h. 6,000; 7,000; 8,000; 9,000   10,000

1 Develop 30

Tell Students In Today's Lesson They Will
explore patterns when multiplying by 10, 100, and 1,000.

Guided Discussion UNDERSTANDING
Whole Group

Have ready about 25 bunches of 10 craft sticks or whatever materials you are using. Hold up a bunch of 10 sticks.

■ **How many craft sticks do you think are in this bunch?** Accept any reasonable answer, but most students should guess 10.

Count out the sticks to demonstrate that you do indeed have 10. Then tell students there are 10 sticks in *each* small bunch you have. Count out 5 bunches while students are listening and watching.

■ **How many craft sticks do I have now?** 50

If necessary, discuss the fact that there are several ways to indicate the number 50 orally; for example, *fifty, five tens, five times ten.*

Write on the board $5 \times 10 = ?$ Review with students that 5×10 is the same as 5 tens or 50.

Do the same with several other examples, such as the following:

- 9 bunches of 10 90
- 20 bunches of 10 200
- 10 bunches of 10 100
- 23 bunches of 10 230

Be sure to write each problem on the board (i.e., $23 \times 10 = 230$) *before* students count by 10s to confirm the answer. Write each problem under the previous problem so students may begin to see the pattern of writing a 0 to the right of each number being multiplied by 10. If there are discrepancies or questions about the product, demonstrate counting by 10s on the **eMathTool: Calculator.** Ask questions such as the following:

■ **What pattern do you see?** writing a 0 to the right of each number being multiplied by 10 or they are multiples of 10

■ **How many craft sticks are in 10 bunches of 23 sticks?** 230

When someone gives the correct answer, write out the problem $10 \times 23 = 230.$

■ **Explain how you know this is correct.** According to the Commutative Law of Multiplication, order does not affect the product; $10 \times 23 = 23 \times 10.$

Follow a procedure similar to that used previously, but use hundreds and thousands instead of tens, and omit the concrete objects. Then write the numbers on the board as you lead students in unison counting by hundreds up to ten hundred. Explain that ten hundred and one thousand are the same numbers.

Give four or five word problems that require multiplication by 100 and 1,000. Use examples such as the following:

- I have 5 boxes of nails. Each box contains 100 nails. How many nails do I have altogether? 500
- How many nails would I have if each box contained 1,000 nails? 5,000
- I have six $100 bills. How many dollars is that worth? $600
- I have one hundred $5 bills. How many dollars is that worth? $500

Skill Building APPLYING
Whole Group

 RESPONSE WHEEL Give problems involving multiplication by multiples of 10, such as the following:

a. 7×10 70
b. 16×10 160
c. 10×80 800
d. 3×100 300
e. 18×100 1,800
f. $1,000 \times 60$ 60,000
g. 123×10 1,230
h. 10×284 2,840
i. 100×100 10,000
j. $1 \times 1,000$ 1,000

2 Assign Student Pages 20

Pages 250–251 APPLYING

Have students complete the exercises on pages 250 and 251 independently.

Monitoring Student Progress

If . . . students have difficulty multiplying by powers of 10,	Then . . . have students use skip counting or repeated addition to help them to see the relationship between skip counting and multiplication.

As Students Finish

 Building Blocks *Function Machine 3* (Introduced in Lesson 6.6)

Game **Shopping Game** (Introduced in Lesson 6.1)

LESSON 7.1 Multiplying by 10, 100, and 1,000

Key Ideas
When multiplying by 10, 100, or 1,000, it is important to remember that multiplication is related to skip counting and repeated addition.

$5 \times 10 = ?$

5 tens = 50

$5 \times 10 = 50$

1 8 tens = ◼ 80
   $8 \times 10 = $ ◼ 80

2 7 tens = ◼ 70
   $7 \times 10 = $ ◼ 70

3 4 hundreds = ◼ 400
   $4 \times 100 = $ ◼ 400

4 9 thousands = ◼ 9,000
   $9 \times 1,000 = $ ◼ 9,000

5 10 thousands = ◼ 10,000
   $10 \times 1,000 = $ ◼ 10,000

250 🔲 Textbook This lesson is available in the *eTextbook.*

Use your knowledge of base ten to do these exercises mentally.

6 $20 \times 10 = $ ◼ 200
7 $16 \times 1,000 = $ ◼ 16,000
8 $100 \times 21 = $ ◼ 2,100
9 $1,000 \times 19 = $ ◼ 19,000
10 $100 \times 93 = $ ◼ 9,300
11 $1,000 \times 63 = $ ◼ 63,000
12 $92 \times 100 = $ ◼ 9,200
13 $65 \times 1,000 = $ ◼ 65,000

14 Mr. Baccari, the park ranger, has 3,500 yards of fencing. The park has 4 sides. Each side is 1,000 yards long. Does Mr. Baccari have enough fencing to surround the park? no

15 Extended Response Sharla has thirteen $10 bills. Does she have enough money to buy the skates? Explain.

16 Estefan and Miguel collected soda pop tabs. On Monday and Tuesday they collected 123 soda pop tabs. On Wednesday and Thursday they collected 184 soda pop tabs. How many soda pop tabs did they collect in those 4 days? 307

17 Extended Response There are 7 boxes of balloons. Each box has 100 balloons. There are 629 children. Can each child have a balloon? Explain. yes; See *Teacher's Edition* for possible answers.

18 Northview School is 30 years old. Do they have enough classrooms for 400 students? not enough information

19 yes; 13 × 10 = $130, which is greater than $109.

 Writing + Math 📝 Journal
Explain how you would find the product of 40×6.

See *Teacher's Edition* for possible answers.

---

3 Reflect   5 🕐

Guided Discussion UNDERSTANDING   Whole Group

Ask students for ideas on how they might find the answer to $1,040 \div 10$. Encourage discussion for all reasonable answers. Possible answers might be as follows:

- $10 \times 100 = 1,000$, which is close but not enough.
- $10 \times 200 = 2,000$, which is too much.
- $10 \times 150 = 1,500$, which is too much but closer.
- $10 \times 110 = 1,100$, which is still too much but even closer.
- $10 \times 105 = 1,050$, which is still too much but very close.
- $10 \times 104 = 1,040$, which is the answer.

  $1,040 \div 10 = 104$

If time permits, have students solve other exercises such as the following:

a. $470 \div 10 = 47$ **b.** $4,500 \div 10 = 450$

c. $630 \div 10 = 63$ **d.** $8,700 \div 100 = 87$

Extended Response

Problem 17 $7 \times 100 = 700$, which is greater than 629.

 Journal ✔️ REASONING

The most common method is repeated addition, such as $40 + 40 + 40 + 40 + 40 + 40$. Students may be able to conclude that 4 tens $\times$ 6 = 240.

 Use Mastery Checkpoint 14 found in **Assessment** to evaluate student mastery of multiplication by 10, 100, and 1,000. By this time students should be able to correctly answer eighty percent of the Mastery Checkpoint items.

 Curriculum Connection: Students may be interested in researching the history of the U.S. bills that are powers of 10. For example, the $10 bill, the $20 bill, the $100 bill, and so on.

 Cumulative Review: For cumulative review of previously learned skills, see page 262–263.

Family Involvement: Assign the **Practice, Reteach,** or **Enrichment** activities depending on the needs of your students.
Encourage students to play the **Shopping Game** with a friend or a relative.

 Concept/Question Board: Have students look for additional examples using multidigit multiplication and division and post them on the Concept/Question Board.

 Math Puzzler: Which has more days, the first 6 months of a regular year or the last 6 months? How many more days? last 6 months; 3 more days

Assess and Differentiate

 Assess Use **eAssess** to record and analyze evidence of student understanding.

A Gather Evidence

Use the Daily Class Assessment Records in **Assessment** or **eAssess** to record daily observations.

Formal Assessment
☑ **Mastery Checkpoint**

Did the student
- ❑ use correct procedures?
- ❑ respond with at least 80% accuracy?

Assessment Page T66

B Summarize Findings

Analyze and summarize assessment data for each student. Determine which Assessment Follow-Up is appropriate for each student. Use the Student Assessment Record in **Assessment** or **eAssess** to update assessment records.

Assessment Page T41

C Assessment Follow-Up ● DIFFERENTIATE INSTRUCTION

Based on your observations, use these teaching strategies for assessment follow-up.

INTERVENTION

Review student performance on **Intervention** Lesson 7.B to see if students have mastered prerequisite skills for this lesson.

ENGLISH LEARNER

Review

Use Lesson 7.1 in **English Learner Support Guide** to review lesson concepts and vocabulary.

ENRICH

If . . . students are proficient in the lesson concepts,

Then . . . encourage them to work on chapter projects or **Enrichment** Lesson 7.1.

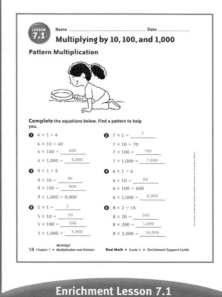

Enrichment Lesson 7.1

PRACTICE

If . . . students would benefit from additional practice,

Then . . . assign **Practice** Lesson 7.1.

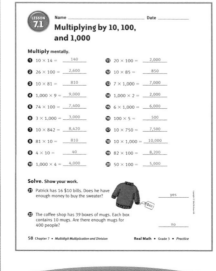

Practice Lesson 7.1

RETEACH

If . . . students are having difficulty understanding multiplying by 10, 100, and 1,000,

Then . . . reteach the concept using **Reteach** Lesson 7.1.

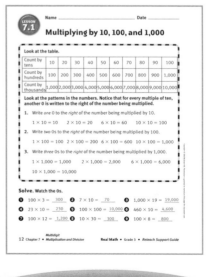

Reteach Lesson 7.1

Lesson Planner

OBJECTIVES
To begin to develop students' understanding of how to multiply a two-digit number by a one-digit number

NCTM STANDARDS
Number and Operations
Understanding meanings of operations and how they relate to one another

Connections
Recognizing and using connections among mathematical ideas

MATERIALS
- *Response Wheels
- *Number Cube: one 0–5

TECHNOLOGY
 Presentation Lesson 7.2

TEST PREP
Cumulative Review
Mental Math reviews multiplying by powers of 10 (Lesson 7.1).

Extended Response
Problems 13 and 16

Multiplying Two-Digit Numbers by One-Digit Numbers

Context of the Lesson This is the second of four lessons on multidigit multiplication. In this lesson students will begin to develop their understanding of multiplication of two-digit numbers by a single-digit number by using an area model and finding the partial areas. In Lesson 7.3 students will apply this method to multiplication of three-digit numbers by single-digit numbers.

See page 248B for Math Background for teachers for this lesson.

Planning for Learning ● DIFFERENTIATE INSTRUCTION

INTERVENTION

If . . . students lack the prerequisite skill of multiplication facts,

Then . . . teach *Intervention* Lesson 7.A.

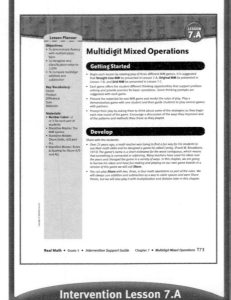

Intervention Lesson 7.A

ENGLISH LEARNER

Preview

If . . . students need language support,

Then . . . use Lesson 7.2 in *English Learner Support Guide* to preview lesson concepts and vocabulary.

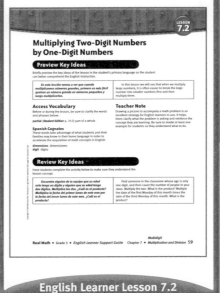

English Learner Lesson 7.2

ENRICH

If . . . students are proficient in the lesson concepts,

Then . . . emphasize the **Roll a Problem Game (Multiplication).**

PRACTICE

If . . . students would benefit from additional practice,

Then . . . extend Guided Discussion before assigning the student pages.

RETEACH

If . . . students are having difficulty understanding multiplying a two-digit number by a one-digit number,

Then . . . extend Guided Discussion before assigning the student pages.

Review Vocabulary
Review from Lesson 4.7: **area**

Spanish Cognates
dimensions dimensiones
digit dígito

*Manipulative Kit Item

Mental Math 5

  RESPONSE WHEEL Use examples such as the following to review multiplying by powers of ten.

a. $10 \times 5 = 50$ **b.** $6 \times 10 = 60$

c. $134 \times 10 = 1,340$ **d.** $10 \times 20 = 200$

e. $10 \times 12 = 120$ **f.** $1,000 \times 26 = 26,000$

g. $38 \times 10 = 380$ **h.** $26 \times 100 = 2,600$

1 Develop 25

Tell Students In Today's Lesson They Will

learn how to multiply a two-digit number by a one-digit number.

Guided Discussion UNDERSTANDING
Whole Group

1. Tell the class this story:

A group of children in Tidytown spent Saturday mornings cleaning the town parks. One morning, after the children had picked up all the papers, bottles, cans, and other litter from one section of Polly Park, they decided to plant grass on it. They measured that section of the park and found that it was 8 meters wide and 19 meters long. (Write dimensions on the board.)

The children went to Tony's Lawn and Garden Shop and found that 1 bag of the right type of grass seed would cover about 30 square meters. (Write this information on the board.)

- **How many bags of grass seed do they need to cover that section of the park?**

2. Let students suggest ways of finding the answer to the question. They should realize that they need to find the area of the section, which means computing 8×19.

- Some students may suggest adding 19 eight times to get the answer.

- Some students may suggest that the children in the story simply buy a bag of grass seed, spread it, and buy another bag when the first one is used up, and so on. However, this is not the most efficient method.

- A student may suggest multiplying 19×8, but the class doesn't yet know how to do this except by repeated addition.

3. Whether or not a student suggests it, draw on the board an outline of the park section, divide it into two parts, and label the dimensions. Be sure that before performing any calculations, you have students estimate the answer first. In this instance, the estimated answer is between 80 (10×8) and 160 (20×8).

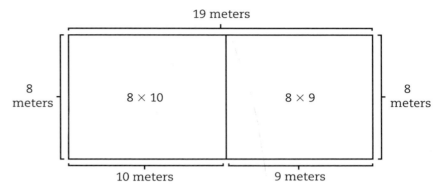

Ask questions such as the following:

- **Can anyone tell how many square meters are in the left-hand part?** 80 square meters, $8 \times 10 = 80$
- **How many square meters are in the right-hand part?** 72 square meters, $8 \times 9 = 72$
- **How many square meters are there altogether?** 152 square meters, $80 + 72 = 152$

4. Finish solving the problem of how many bags of seed the children in the story must buy. The section of the park is 152 square meters. We know that 1 bag provides enough seed to cover about 30 square meters. Ask questions such as the following:

- **How many square meters will 2 bags cover?** 60 square meters
- **How many square meters will 3 bags cover?** 90 square meters

Continue with this line of questioning until students find that 5 bags of seed will cover 150 square meters. If the children buy 5 bags of seed and spread the seed a little thinner than recommended, they'll cover the 152 square meters. If they buy 6 bags, they'll certainly have enough seed, and they can either spread 6 bags quite thickly or have almost a full bag of seed left over for another part of the park.

Strategy Building REASONING
Whole Group

Roll a Problem Game (Multiplication)

Do three or four rounds of a whole-class subtraction version of the **Roll a Problem Game (Multiplication).** Students may recognize this game as being similar to the **Roll a Problem Game** from Chapters 2 and 3. The rules for the multiplication version of the game are given on student page 255. As in the **Roll a Problem Game** from Chapter 3, the goal is to determine the winner *without* finding the product, although it is perfectly acceptable to determine the precise product if there are uncertainties about who is the winner. *Variations for Playing* include using a 5–10 **Number Cube** and/or trying to get the smallest product.

2 Assign Student Pages 20

Pages 252–253 APPLYING

Have students complete the exercises on pages 252 and 253 independently. Students may use partial products if they are still not sure how to break down the factors.

RESEARCH IN ACTION

"Proficiency with multidigit computation is more heavily influenced by instruction than single-digit computation is. Many features of multidigit procedures are not part of children's everyday experience and need to be learned in the classroom…. Children can and do devise or invent algorithms for carrying out multidigit computations. Opportunities to construct their own procedures provide students with opportunities to make connections between the strands of proficiency. Procedural fluency is built directly on their understanding."

Kilpatrick, J., J. Swafford, and B. Findell, eds. *Adding It Up: Helping Children Learn Mathematics.* Washington, D.C.: National Research Council/National Academy Press, 2001, p. 197.

LESSON 7.2 Multiplying Two-Digit Numbers by One-Digit Numbers

Key Ideas

To help understand how to multiply two-digit numbers, we can use an area model and break the whole area into partial areas. For example:

Ms. Chaccupa wants to carpet her hallway. Her hallway is a rectangle that is 27 feet long and 6 feet wide. How much carpeting will Ms. Chaccupa need for her hallway?

She knows that the answer is the product of 6 × 27, but she doesn't know how to do the multiplication.

Here is what she does:

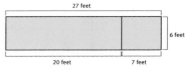

Ms. Chaccupa realizes that when she divides the hallway into sections, she has numbers she can multiply in her head.

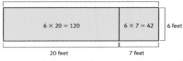

Ms. Chaccupa adds the partial area together to get the whole area.

$$120 + 42 = 162$$

Ms. Chaccupa needs 162 square feet of carpet.

📖 **Textbook** This lesson is available in the *eTextbook*.

If you want to know the area of a rectangle that is 27 units long and 6 units wide, you would multiply 6 × 27.

$$6 × 27 = ?$$

Ann's Work

Step 1 6 × 20 = 120   27
                            × 6
                            120

120 is a partial product.

Step 2 6 × 7 = 42   27
                            × 6
                            120
                             42

42 is a partial product.

Step 3 120 + 42 = 162   27
                            × 6
                            120
                           + 42
                            162

Martin's Work

Step 1 6 × 7 = 42   27
                            × 6
                             42

42 is a partial product.

Step 2 6 × 20 = 120   27
                            × 6
                             42
                            120

120 is a partial product.

Step 3 120 + 42 = 162   27
                            × 6
                             42
                           + 120
                            162

Adding the partial products gives us the whole product.

Multiply. You may draw pictures to help.

❶ 83 × 5 415	❷ 11 × 4 44	❸ 30 × 8 240
❹ 47 × 5 235	❺ 38 × 5 190	❻ 30 × 9 270
❼ 26 × 1 26	❽ 29 × 7 203	❾ 58 × 9 522

Teaching Lesson 7.2

Assign Student Pages, continued

Pages 254–255 APPLYING

Have students complete pages 254–255 independently.

> **Monitoring Student Progress**
>
> **If . . .** students have difficulty understanding the partial product algorithm,
>
> **Then . . .** provide individual or small group assistance emphasizing the parallelism between the partial areas of a rectangle and the partial products of the algorithms.

As Students Finish

Game Roll a Problem Game (Multiplication)

LESSON 7.2 · Multiplying Two-Digit Numbers by One-Digit Numbers

Solve.

10 If Donna gets $6 a week, how much money will she receive in a year (52 weeks)? $312

11 How much will Donna receive in 2 years? $624

Students from Los Amigos School are going on a field trip. Altogether, 350 people are going. Each bus can seat 45 people.

12 How many people can 7 buses seat?   315 people

13 **Extended Response** How many buses should the school use? Why?   8; Seven buses won't seat everyone.

14 If the school rents 8 buses, how many extra seats will there be?   10

15 It costs $52 to rent 1 bus for a day. How much will it cost to rent 8 buses for a day? $416

16 **Extended Response** Suppose that each person going on the trip pays $2. Will that be enough to pay for 8 buses for one day each? How much is left after paying for the buses? Explain.   Yes; $284; 2 × 350 = 700   700 − 416 = 284

254

Textbook This lesson is available in the *eTextbook*.

Game

Roll a Problem Game (Multiplication)

Players: Two or more

Materials: One 0–5 *Number Cube*

Object: To get the greatest product

Math Focus: Multiplying two-digit numbers by one-digit numbers, place value, and mathematical reasoning

HOW TO PLAY

1 Use blanks to outline a multiplication problem on your paper like this:

$$\frac{\times \quad \_\,\_}{\quad \_\,\_}$$

2 The first player rolls the cube three times.

3 Each time the cube is rolled, all players write that number in one of the blanks in their outline. Once a number has been written in a blank, it cannot be moved.

4 The player with the greatest product wins the round.

Variations:

- Use a 5–10 *Number Cube.* If you roll a 10, roll again.

- **Object:** To get the smallest product

Chapter 7 • Lesson 2   255

③ Reflect
10

Guided Discussion ✓ APPLYING
Whole Group

Use the following multiplication arrangement, as in the **Roll a Problem Game (Multiplication)**:

$$\underline{}\ \underline{}$$
$$\times\ \underline{}$$

■ **If the teacher rolls a 3, 4, and 5, what is the greatest and least product possible? Explain how you got your answer.** 215; 135

It is very common for students to multiply left to right. There is nothing wrong with this. Left to right multiplication aids in estimating and approximating. While progressing with the algorithm later in the chapter, students may find that right to left is easier.

 Cumulative Review: For cumulative review of previously learned skills, see page 262–263.

 Family Involvement: Assign the **Practice, Reteach,** or **Enrichment** activities depending on the needs of your students. Encourage students to play the **Roll a Problem Game** with a friend or a relative.

 Concept/Question Board: Have students look for additional examples using multidigit multiplication and division, and post them on the Concept/Question Board.

 Math Puzzler: Naomi has the same number of nickels and dimes. She has 60¢ altogether. How many of each type of coin does she have? 4 nickels and 4 dimes

4 Assess and Differentiate

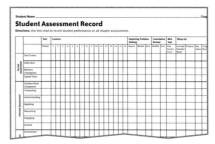 **Assess** Use *eAssess* to record and analyze evidence of student understanding.

A Gather Evidence

Use the Daily Class Assessment Records in **Assessment** or **eAssess** to record daily observations.

Informal Assessment
✓ **Mental Math**

Did the student **COMPUTING**
- ❏ respond accurately?
- ❏ respond quickly?
- ❏ respond with confidence?
- ❏ self-correct?

Informal Assessment
✓ **Guided Discussion**

Did the student **APPLYING**
- ❏ apply learning in new situations?
- ❏ contribute concepts?
- ❏ contribute answers?
- ❏ connect mathematics to real-world situations?

B Summarize Findings

Analyze and summarize assessment data for each student. Determine which Assessment Follow-Up is appropriate for each student. Use the Student Assessment Record in **Assessment** or **eAssess** to update assessment records.

Assessment Page T41

C Assessment Follow-Up ● DIFFERENTIATE INSTRUCTION

Based on your observations, use these teaching strategies for assessment follow-up.

INTERVENTION	ENRICH	PRACTICE	RETEACH
Review student performance on *Intervention* Lesson 7.A to see if students have mastered prerequisite skills for this lesson.	**If . . .** students are proficient in the lesson concepts, **Then . . .** encourage them to work on chapter projects or *Enrichment* Lesson 7.2.	**If . . .** students would benefit from additional practice, **Then . . .** assign *Practice* Lesson 7.2.	**If . . .** students are having difficulty understanding multiplying two-digit numbers by one-digit numbers, **Then . . .** reteach the concept using *Reteach* Lesson 7.2.

ENGLISH LEARNER

Review

Use Lesson 7.2 in *English Learner Support Guide* to review lesson concepts and vocabulary.

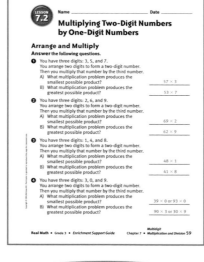

Enrichment Lesson 7.2

Practice Lesson 7.2

Reteach Lesson 7.2

Lesson Planner

OBJECTIVES
- To reinforce students' understanding of multiplying a two-digit number by a one-digit number
- To begin to develop understanding of how to multiply a three-digit number by a one-digit number
- To introduce a shorter algorithm for multiplying two- or three-digit numbers by one-digit numbers

NCTM STANDARDS

Number and Operations

Understanding meanings of operations and how they relate to one another

Connections

Understanding how mathematical ideas interconnect and build on one another to produce a coherent whole

MATERIALS
- *Response Wheels
- *Number Cubes (0–5 and 5–10)

TECHNOLOGY
Presentation Lesson 7.3

TEST PREP

Cumulative Review
- Mental Math reviews multiplication and missing factors (Chapter 5).
- Problem 8 reviews addition (Lesson 1.2)
- Problem 10 reviews writing money amounts (Grade 2, Lesson 1.5).
- Problems 11 and 12 review basic addition (Lessons 1.2 and 2.7).

Multiplying Three-Digit Numbers by One-Digit Numbers

Context of the Lesson This is the third of four lessons on multidigit multiplication. In Lesson 7.2 students found the sum of the partial products to multiply two-digit numbers by one-digit numbers. Students will review this method and apply it to multiplying three-digit numbers by one-digit numbers. Students will also be introduced to a shorter algorithm for multiplying three-digit numbers by one-digit numbers.

See page 248B for Math Background for teachers for this lesson.

Planning for Learning ● DIFFERENTIATE INSTRUCTION

INTERVENTION

If . . . students lack the prerequisite skill of multiplication facts,

Then . . . teach *Intervention* Lesson 7.A.

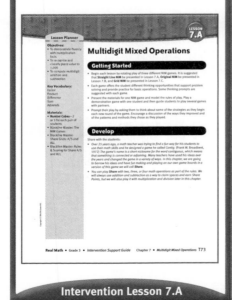

Intervention Lesson 7.A

ENGLISH LEARNER

Preview

If . . . students need language support,

Then . . . use Lesson 7.3 in *English Learner Support Guide* to preview lesson concepts and vocabulary.

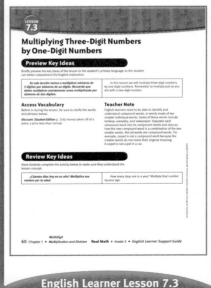

English Learner Lesson 7.3

ENRICH

If . . . students are proficient in the lesson concepts,

Then . . . emphasize the **Roll a Problem Game.**

PRACTICE

If . . . students would benefit from additional practice,

Then . . . extend Strategy Building before assigning the student pages.

RETEACH

If . . . students are having difficulty understanding multiplying a three-digit number by a one-digit number,

Then . . . extend Guided Discussion before assigning the student pages.

Mental Math ⑤

   Practice multiplication facts with exercises such as the following.

a. $5 \times 8 = 40$ **b.** $9 \times 3 = 27$
c. $9 \times 4 = 36$ **d.** $10 \times 4 = 40$
e. $10 \times 10 = 100$ **f.** $6 \times 5 = 30$

1 Develop 25

Tell Students In Today's Lesson They Will
learn how to multiply three-digit numbers by one-digit numbers.

Guided Discussion UNDERSTANDING   Whole Group

1. Write the following problem on the board:

$$6 \times 342$$

Ask students if they have any suggestions about how to do this multiplication. Before beginning, remind students that it is always a good idea to approximate the answer before calculating. In this case the answer should be between 1,800 (6×300) and 2,400 (6×400).

One suggestion for getting an exact product should be to draw a rectangle 6 units high and 342 units long and to divide it as follows:

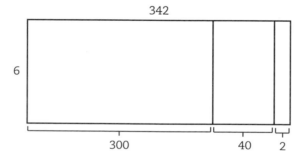

342

6

300   40   2

Students should then be able to find that the partial areas of the larger rectangles are 1,800, 240, and 12 square units. The area of the entire rectangle is therefore $1,800 + 240 + 12$, or 2,052 square units. $6 \times 342 = 2,052$

2. Show students that they can solve this type of problem by finding the partial products and calculating the sum.

Emphasize the relationship between the partial areas and the partial products. We add the partial areas to get the whole area, just as we add the partial products to get the whole product.

3. Give a few more exercises such as the following:

$4 \times 429 = 1,716$ $6 \times 306 = 1,836$ $7 \times 525 = 3,675$

Encourage students to determine the answers without drawing pictures. However, you should do at least one or two of these problems with pictures.

Strategy Building UNDERSTANDING   Whole Group

If students have shown interest and have been doing the last few lessons without difficulty, you may choose to introduce the standard shorter algorithm at this time. There are, however, two important conditions:

1. Do not insist that students use the shorter algorithm.

2. Do not have students write the numbers they are remembering ("carrying") above the next number to be multiplied. The practice of writing carried numbers often confuses students when they get to multiplication problems involving two multidigit numbers. They often forget which superscript applied to which part of the operation. Try to have students simply remember the carried numbers. If they have difficulty doing this, suggest they keep track of a carried number on the fingers of their nonwriting hands.

Skill and Strategy Building REASONING   Whole Group

Roll a Problem Game (Multiplication)

Do three or four rounds of a whole-class version of the **Roll a Problem Game (Multiplication)** but make one factor three digits instead of two digits. As in the **Roll a Problem Game (Multiplication)** from Lesson 7.2, the goal is to determine the winner without necessarily finding the exact product.

2 Assign Student Pages 20

Pages 256–257 ✓ APPLYING

Have students complete the exercises on pages 256 and 257 independently. Encourage shortcuts such as omitting zeros and multiplying mentally when it is appropriate. Remind students to approximate the answer before calculating the exact answer.

Monitoring Student Progress

If . . . students have difficulty with the partial product algorithm,

Then . . . provide individual or small group tutoring in which you draw area models alongside the written exercises. As you work the exercises, emphasize the relationship between the partial areas and the partial products.

As Students Finish

 Game   Roll a Problem Game (Multiplication)

Key Ideas

Multiplying a three-digit number by a one-digit number is done almost exactly like multiplying by a two-digit number.

Ms. Chaccupa wants to carpet her hallway. Her hallway is a rectangle 27 feet long and 6 feet wide. In Lesson 7.2 when Ms. Chaccupa added all of the parts together, she found out the area of her hallway was 162 square feet.

She called the carpet store and found a sale on the carpet she wants. If she buys more than 100 square feet of carpet, she can purchase the carpet at $5 per square foot. She needs 162 square feet, so she is eligible for the discount. How much money will she spend on carpet for her hallway?

Step 1:

$$\begin{array}{r} 162 \\ \times\ \ 5 \\ \hline 500 \end{array}$$

$100 \times 5 = 500$
500 is a partial product.

Step 2:

$$\begin{array}{r} 162 \\ \times\ \ 5 \\ \hline 500 \\ 300 \end{array}$$

$60 \times 5 = 300$
300 is a partial product.

Step 3:

$$\begin{array}{r} 162 \\ \times\ \ 5 \\ \hline 500 \\ 300 \\ 10 \end{array}$$

$2 \times 5 = 10$
10 is a partial product.

Step 4:

$$\begin{array}{r} 162 \\ \times\ \ 5 \\ \hline 500 \\ 300 \\ +\ 10 \\ \hline 810 \end{array}$$

$500 + 300 + 10 = 810$
Add the partial products to get the product.

Ms. Chaccupa's carpet will cost $810.

📖 **Textbook** This lesson is available in the *eTextbook*.

Multiply. You may draw pictures to help.

①
$$\begin{array}{r} 247 \\ \times\ \ 3 \\ \hline 741 \end{array}$$

②
$$\begin{array}{r} 248 \\ \times\ \ 3 \\ \hline 744 \end{array}$$

③
$$\begin{array}{r} 732 \\ \times\ \ 0 \\ \hline 0 \end{array}$$

④ $108 \times 7 = \blacksquare$ 756 **⑤** $111 \times 7 = \blacksquare$ 777 **⑥** $909 \times 9 = \blacksquare$ 8,181

Solve. Be sure to label your answers correctly.

⑦ There are 365 days in a year. How many days are in 2 years if neither year is a leap year?   730

⑧ Mr. Ruiz manages a clothing store. Yesterday he ordered 4 cartons of shirts. Each carton has 250 shirts. How many shirts did he order?   1,000

⑨ The distance around the city race track is 250 meters. Mark ran 4 laps around the track. How far did he run?   1,000 meters or 1 kilometer

⑩ The distance around the country race track is 500 meters. Sarah ran 4 laps around the track. How far did she run?   2,000 meters or 2 kilometers

 ⑪ Yesterday Amanda collected 876 pennies. How much money did she collect? $8.76

 ⑫ When José was 6, he collected 282 soda pop tabs for a local charity. Now that he is 5 years older, he plans on collecting over 1,000. What is José's age now?   11

 ⑬ There were 611 students at Ridgeview South Elementary. In one week 5 students enrolled. How many students now attend Ridgeview South Elementary?   616

 Reflect 10

Guided Discussion **REASONING**   Whole Group

Use the following **Roll a Problem Game (Multiplication)** set up:

$$\begin{array}{r} \_\_\_\ \_\_\_\ \_\_\_ \\ \times \qquad \_\_\_ \\ \hline \end{array}$$

■ **Suppose the teacher rolled a 5, a 4, a 3, and a 2. What is the greatest product? What is the least product?** 2,160; 690
■ **What is 4 × 532?** 2,128

 Cumulative Connection: Students may be interested in reading biographies about Olympic track-and-field medalists such as Jackie Joyner-Kersee, Jesse Owens, Michael Johnson, Carl Lewis, Marion Jones, and so on.

 Cumulative Review: For cumulative review of previously learned skills, see page 262–263.

 Family Involvement: Assign the *Practice, Reteach,* or *Enrichment* activities depending on the needs of your students.

Encourage students to play the **Roll a Problem Game (Multiplication)** with a friend or a relative.

 Concept/Question Board: Have students look for additional examples using multidigit multiplication and division and post them on the Concept/Question Board.

 Math Puzzler: I am thinking of two numbers. Their difference is 2. Their product is 15. What are the two numbers? 3 and 5

Assess and Differentiate

 Assess Use *eAssess* to record and analyze evidence of student understanding.

A Gather Evidence

Use the Daily Class Assessment Records in *Assessment* or *eAssess* to record daily observations.

Informal Assessment
✓ **Student Pages**

Did the student [APPLYING]
- apply learning in new situations?
- contribute concepts?
- contribute answers?
- connect mathematics to real-world situations?

Informal Assessment
✓ **Guided Discussion**

Did the student [REASONING]
- provide a clear explanation?
- communicate reasons and strategies?
- choose appropriate strategies?
- argue logically?

B Summarize Findings

Analyze and summarize assessment data for each student. Determine which Assessment Follow-Up is appropriate for each student. Use the Student Assessment Record in *Assessment* or *eAssess* to update assessment records.

Assessment Page T41

C Assessment Follow-Up • DIFFERENTIATE INSTRUCTION

Based on your observations, use these teaching strategies for assessment follow-up.

INTERVENTION
Review student performance on *Intervention* Lesson 7.A to see if students have mastered prerequisite skills for this lesson.

ENGLISH LEARNER
Review

Use Lesson 7.3 in *English Learner Support Guide* to review lesson concepts and vocabulary.

ENRICH
If . . . students are proficient in the lesson concepts,

Then . . . encourage them to work on chapter projects or *Enrichment* Lesson 7.3.

Enrichment Lesson 7.3

PRACTICE
If . . . students would benefit from additional practice,

Then . . . assign *Practice* Lesson 7.3.

Practice Lesson 7.3

RETEACH
If . . . students are having difficulty understanding how to multiply a three-digit number by a one-digit number,

Then . . . have them use play money ($100, $10, and $1 bills). Use the problem 358 × 6 as an example. Have students lay out 3 hundreds, 5 tens, and 8 ones in a row, then repeat this layout five more times. Ask how many ones (6 × 8, or 48), tens (6 × 5, or 30), and hundreds (6 × 3, or 18), there are. Have students write these numbers in standard form (48 ones = 48, 30 tens = 300; 18 hundreds = 1,800) and add them. Have students solve several similar problems using this method.

Lesson Planner

OBJECTIVES
- To provide further practice with multiplying two- and three-digit numbers by one-digit numbers
- To provide students with experience solving word problems

NCTM STANDARDS
Problem Solving
Applying and adapting a variety of appropriate strategies to solve problems

Connections
Recognizing and applying mathematics in contexts outside of mathematics

Problem Solving
Solving problems that arise in mathematics and in other contexts

MATERIALS
- *Response Wheels
- Yearly calendar (optional)

TECHNOLOGY
e Presentation Lesson 7.4
Building Blocks Field Trip

TEST PREP
Cumulative Review
Mental Math reviews multiplying by powers of 10 (Lesson 7.1).

Multistep Problems
Problems 11–12

Extended Response
Problem 10

Writing + Math
Journal

Applications of Multiplication

Context of the Lesson This is the fourth of four lessons on multidigit multiplication. Students will continue to practice two- and three-digit multiplication through the experience of solving practical, real-world word problems.

See page 248B for Math Background for teachers for this lesson.

Planning for Learning ● DIFFERENTIATE INSTRUCTION

INTERVENTION
If . . . students lack the prerequisite skill of multiplication facts,

Then . . . teach *Intervention* Lesson 7.A.

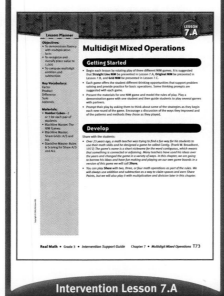

Intervention Lesson 7.A

ENGLISH LEARNER
Preview

If . . . students need language support,

Then . . . use Lesson 7.4 in *English Learner Support Guide* to preview lesson concepts and vocabulary.

English Learner Lesson 7.4

ENRICH
If . . . students are proficient in the lesson concepts,

Then . . . emphasize the Journal activity.

PRACTICE
If . . . students would benefit from additional practice,

Then . . . extend Strategy Building before assigning the student pages.

RETEACH
If . . . students are having difficulty understanding applications of multiplication,

Then . . . extend Strategy Building before assigning the student pages.

Spanish Cognates
to group agrupar
equally igualmente

Mental Math 5

  Use examples such as the following that involve multiplying by powers of 10.

a. $100 \times 4 = 400$

b. $17 \times 100 = 1{,}700$

c. $100 \times 12 = 1{,}200$

d. $21 \times 100 = 2{,}100$

e. $61 \times 100 = 6{,}100$

f. $10 \times 100 = 1{,}000$

g. $1{,}000 \times 12 = 12{,}000$

h. $21 \times 1{,}000 = 21{,}000$

i. $61 \times 1{,}000 = 61{,}000$

j. $100 \times 100 = 10{,}000$

1 Develop 25

Tell Students In Today's Lesson They Will

solve problems, some of which require multiplying two- and three-digit numbers.

Guided Discussion UNDERSTANDING Whole Group

Write a multidigit multiplication exercise on the board and ask students if they can think of a problem the exercise will solve. For example:

$$5 \times 340$$

Possible student suggestions include:

1. Juniper earns $340 in one week. How much does she earn in 5 weeks?

2. Mr. Dee has 5 tables. Each table is 340 centimeters long. If he places them end-to-end, how long will the combined tables be?

3. One bag of apples weighs about 340 grams. About how much will 5 bags of apples weigh?

Skill Building APPLYING Small Group

Divide the class into groups of two or three. Present word problems such as the following, one at a time to the groups. Remind students to approximate first, *before* solving. Discuss their solutions. Use examples such as the following:

- If there are 365 days in 1 year, how many days are there in 3 years (with no leap years)? 1,095 days
- Mr. Rivera earns $131 a day. How much money will he earn in a week if a workweek is 5 days long? $655
- How much will he earn in 8 weeks of work? $5,240
- If Dwayne eats 3 meals each day, and there are 365 days in 1 year, how many meals does Dwayne eat in 1 year? 1,095 meals
- A jug of cider costs 109 cents, and a bushel of apples costs $4. How much will 4 jugs of cider cost? 436 cents or $4.36

2 Assign Student Pages 20

Pages 258–259 APPLYING

Have students complete the exercises on pages 258 and 259 independently.

As Students Finish

 Building Blocks Field Trip

Game Roll a Problem Game (Multiplication)

LESSON 7.4 Applications of Multiplication

Key Ideas

If there are several equal sets of objects, we can find how many there are altogether by multiplying.

A bag of lemons has 12 lemons in it. If Janelle bought 6 bags, how many lemons does she have?

$$12 \times 6 = ?$$

$$\begin{array}{r} 12 \\ \times\ 6 \\ \hline 60 \\ +\ 12 \\ \hline 72 \end{array}$$

$12 \times 6 = 72$

Janelle has 72 lemons.

Solve.

❶ Latisha needs 125 large binder clips. She bought 8 packs with 15 binder clips in each box. Will she have enough binder clips? Why or why not?
no; $15 \times 8 = 120$, which is not enough clips

❷ Ms. Chen earns $325 each week. How much money does she earn in 4 weeks? $1,300

❸ Phyllis and Michele were collecting clothing for a clothing drive. Phyllis collected 19 sweatshirts, and Michele collected 8 pairs of jeans. How many articles of clothing did the girls collect altogether?   27

❹ The Nuts and Bolts Factory can make 534 bolts in 1 hour. How many bolts are made in 8 hours?   4,272 bolts

❺ The Brown Cow Dairy Company produces about 450 gallons of milk each day. About how much milk does it produce in 7 days?   3,150 gallons

❻ There are 356 children at Hidden Hollow Camp. The kitchen staff prepares breakfast, lunch, and dinner for each child. How many meals are prepared for the children every day?   1,068 meals

258   Textbook This lesson is available in the *eTextbook*.

Adam wanted to know about how many hours he spent doing certain things each year. He made some estimates and wrote them in a table.

❼ Write the missing amounts.

Adam's Activity	Hours Each Day	Number of Days Each Year	Hours Each Year
Sleeping	8	365	2,920
Eating	2	365	730
Reading at home	2	250	500
Being in school	5	180	900
Watching television	1	175	175

❽ Does Adam spend more time eating or reading each year?   eating

❾ Does Adam spend more time sleeping than he spends doing the other activities shown in the table?   yes

❿ **Extended Response** About how many hours do you spend reading each year? Explain how you got your answer.
See Reflect in *Teacher's Edition*.

Multistep Most years have 365 days. Leap years have 366 days. Leap years come every 4 years. In a leap year, February has 29 days instead of 28 days.

⓫ Alonzo is exactly 3 years old. One of those years was a leap year. How many days old is Alonzo?
1,096

⓬ Ruth is exactly 6 years old. She has lived through 1 leap year. How many days old is Ruth?
2,191

Writing + Math Journal

Calculate about how many days old you are. The years 2000, 2004, 2008, and 2012 are leap years. Explain how you got your answer.

---

③ Reflect   10

Guided Discussion ENGAGING   Whole Group

 Problems 11–12: Students must account for the extra day in leap years.

Call attention to Problems 11 and 12 and allow students to explain how they got their answers. Ask the following question:

■ **If Ruth is twice as old as Alonzo, why hasn't she lived twice the number of days?**

Through discussion, help students see that $(6 \times 365) + 1$ is not twice $(3 \times 365) + 1$. This may be difficult for some students to fully understand. It is not necessary to provide remediation at this time.

Extended Response

Problem 10: Students can estimate how many hours they spend reading each day, then calculate the total for the year.

Writing + Math Journal

To calculate, students multiply their age in years by 365 and add 1 for each leap year they were alive. Then add in the number of days since their last birthday.

 Use Mastery Checkpoint 15 found in *Assessment* to evaluate student mastery of multiplying by one-digit numbers. By this time students should be able to correctly answer eighty percent of the Mastery Checkpoint items.

SOCIAL STUDIES **Curriculum Connection:** Students may want to research the various calendars that have been created and used, both ancient and modern.

Review **Cumulative Review:** For cumulative review of previously learned skills, see page 262–263.

 Family Involvement: Assign the *Practice, Reteach,* or *Enrichment* activities depending on the needs of your students.

Encourage students to calculate in days and weeks the age of other adults and students, with a friend or a relative.

 Concept/Question Board: Have students look for additional examples using multidigit multiplication and division and post them on the Concept/Question Board.

 Math Puzzler: Angelique bought 2 pencils for 55¢. How much should she give the clerk in order to receive 2 quarters in change?
$1.05

4 Assess and Differentiate

e Assess Use *eAssess* to record and analyze evidence of student understanding.

A Gather Evidence

Use the Daily Class Assessment Records in *Assessment* or *eAssess* to record daily observations.

Formal Assessment
☑ **Mastery Checkpoint**

Did the student
- ☐ use correct procedures?
- ☐ respond with at least 80% accuracy?

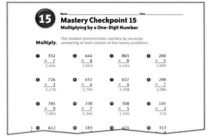

Assessment Page T67

B Summarize Findings

Analyze and summarize assessment data for each student. Determine which Assessment Follow-Up is appropriate for each student. Use the Student Assessment Record in *Assessment* or *eAssess* to update assessment records.

Assessment Page T41

C Assessment Follow-Up ● DIFFERENTIATE INSTRUCTION

Based on your observations, use these teaching strategies for assessment follow-up.

INTERVENTION

Review student performance on *Intervention* Lesson 7.A to see if students have mastered prerequisite skills for this lesson.

ENGLISH LEARNER

Review

Use Lesson 7.1 in *English Learner Support Guide* to review lesson concepts and vocabulary.

ENRICH

If . . . students are proficient in the lesson concepts,

Then . . . encourage them to work on chapter projects or *Enrichment* Lesson 7.4.

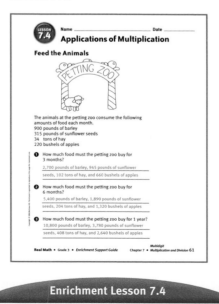

Enrichment Lesson 7.4

PRACTICE

If . . . students would benefit from additional practice,

Then . . . assign *Practice* Lesson 7.4.

Practice Lesson 7.4

RETEACH

If . . . students are having difficulty understanding when to use multiplication,

Then . . . reteach the concept using *Reteach* Lesson 7.4.

Reteach Lesson 7.4

Exploring Problem Solving

Objectives
- To explore the Make a Table and Write an Equation strategies
- To provide practice computing with multidigit numbers
- To explore solving and presenting solutions to nonroutine problems

Materials
None

Context of the Lesson This lesson provides an additional opportunity for students to share and compare methods used to solve real-world, nonroutine problems. The theme of money and banking was introduced in the Chapter Introduction and will be visited again in the second problem-solving lesson.

1 Develop 5

Tell Students In Today's Lesson They Will
- read a problem about saving money to buy a special gift.
- look at how two students are solving the problem in two different ways.
- solve the problem themselves and share how they did it.

Guided Discussion
Ask students to talk about times they have saved for some expensive item. Have them talk about how they saved their money and how long it took them.

2 Exploring Problem Solving 30

Using Student Pages
Have students read the problem on page 260. To be sure they understand the problem, ask questions such as the following:
- **What do the children in the problem want to do?** buy a grill for their parents' anniversary
- **How much does the grill cost?** $247
- **How much money do the children already have?** $43
- **How will they get the rest of the money?** by saving $24 every week
- **What is the problem asking?** how many weeks they will have to save in order to buy the grill if they save $24 per week

---

Exploring Problem Solving

Vera and her brothers want to buy a special present for their parents' anniversary. They have $43 so far. If they save $24 each week, how long will it be before they can buy the grill?

Miriam is making a table to solve the problem.

Now	1 Week	2 weeks	3 weeks	4 weeks
$43	$67	$91		

❶ Why did Miriam write $43 in the first column of her table?
That is how much the children already have.
❷ Why did she write $67 in the second column?
That is how much they will have after they save $24 the first week.
❸ What do you think Miriam will do next?
continue to add $24 each week
❹ Do you think Miriam's strategy will work? Explain.
Yes, she can continue to add $24 a week until she has at least $247.
❺ What happens if Miriam keeps adding $24 but doesn't get $247 exactly?
As soon as the total reaches or passes $247, the children will have enough money. They do not need the exact amount.

ⓔ **Textbook** This lesson is available in the *eTextbook*.

Neil is writing an equation to solve the problem.

❻ What will Neil find out by using his equation?
how much money the children need to save
❼ How will he use his equation to find that out? by subtracting $43 from $247, or by adding numbers to $43 until he gets to $247
❽ After he finds out how much the children need to save, what do you think Neil will try to figure out next?
how long it will take them to save that amount
❾ What equation could Neil write to help him figure that out?
Possible answer: number of weeks × $24 = amount they need to save
❿ Do you think Neil's strategy will work? Explain.
⓫ Work with your group to solve the problem. Use any strategy you like. The children will have to save for nine weeks before they have enough money to buy the grill.

❿ Yes, if he computes correctly, he can first find out how much they need to save and then how many weeks it will take them to save that amount.

Tell students they are going to have a chance to solve the problem, but first they will look at how two students are trying to solve it.

Analyzing Sample Solution 1

Guide students through Miriam's solution by going over Problems 1–5. In discussion, bring out the following points:

- Using a table is a useful way to organize your thinking and keep track of the changing amounts in a problem.
- When trying to figure out how long it will take to reach a goal, you need to consider what you start with.

Analyzing Sample Solution 2

Guide students through Neil's strategy by going over Problems 6–10. In discussion, bring out the following points:

- Using words and symbols can help you understand and keep track of how parts of a problem are related.
- When you write equations to solve a problem, make sure they model the problem accurately. Neil's equation is useful because in order to buy the grill, the children have to have enough money to pay for it. If the amount they save is added to the amount they already have, the sum is the amount they need to save in order to have the cost of the grill.
- After writing equations, check to see that they make sense before spending a lot of time doing computation.

Have students work in groups on Problem 11. As students work on the problem, circulate around the room to observe their progress and provide support as needed. Be sure to compliment students when they persist in the face of difficulty. If students get stuck, you might ask guiding questions such as these:

- **What is the problem asking?**
- **What information do you know?**
- **After they save for a week, how much will they have?**
- **How can you keep track of how much they will have each week?**

Sample Solutions Strategies

Students might use one or more of the following strategies instead of or in conjunction with the strategies presented on the student pages.

Guess, Check, and Revise

After finding the amount they need to save ($204), students might multiply 24 by different numbers until they get an answer that is 204 or more.

Use Number Sense

Students might realize that 10×24 is 240 and that $240 + 43$ would be 283. From there, if they subtracted 24, they would have enough to buy the grill. If they subtracted 24 again, they would not have enough to buy the grill.

Use a Physical Model

Students might act out the problem with play money or other countable objects, for example, keeping track of how many times they have deposited $24 in a "bank" until they have enough money to buy the grill.

Extension

Pose this problem to students:

If the children want to buy the grill in just 5 weeks, how much money will they need to save each week? $41

 **Reflect** 10

 Knowledge Age Skills

Effective Communication Have groups present their solutions, especially groups that used methods that are different from either of the methods presented in the lesson. After each presentation, ask questions such as the following:

- **How is this method different from the ones we have already seen?**
- **How does this method compare to the methods used by Miriam or Neil?**
- **What did you like about the method or the way it was presented?**

In discussion, bring out this point:

When you work on a problem, it is important to think about what the numbers mean—how they fit with what is going on in the story. If the children keep adding $24 each week, they will not get $247 exactly. If they stop after 8 weeks, they will have only $235, which is not enough to buy the grill. They need to save for another week, even though they will have more than the cost of the grill.

Assess 5

When evaluating student work, focus not only on the correctness of the answer but also on whether the student thought rationally about the problem. Questions to consider include the following:

- Did the student understand the problem and the Sample Solutions Strategies?
- Was the student able to explain his or her strategy?
- Was the student able to work efficiently with the numbers?
- Did the student check to see that the answer was reasonable?

CHAPTER 7 Review

Cumulative Review

Review

Assign Pages 262–263

Use the Cumulative Review as a review of concepts and skills that students have previously learned.

Here are different ways that you can assign these problems to your students as they work through the chapter:

- With some of the lessons in the chapter, assign a set of cumulative review problems to be completed as practice or for homework.
  Lesson 7.1—Problems 1–2
  Lesson 7.2—Problems 3–6
  Lesson 7.3—Problems 7–10
  Lesson 7.4—Problems 11–16
- At any point during the chapter, assign part or all of the cumulative review problems to be completed as practice or for homework.

Cumulative Review

Problems 1–2 review multiplying by 10 and 5, Lesson 5.2.

Problems 3–6 review reading bar graphs, Lesson 3.3.

Problems 7–10 review multiplication and finding area, Lesson 4.7.

Problems 11–16 review arrow notation and function machines, Lesson 6.5.

Monitoring Student Progress

If . . . students miss more than one problem in a section,

Then . . . refer to the indicated lesson for remediation suggestions.

Cumulative Review

Multiplying by 10 and 5 Lesson 5.2

Fill in the tables. Look for patterns.

❶ Copy and fill in this table by skip counting. 50; 55; 60; 70; 75

| 35 | 40 | 45 | ▢ | ▢ | ▢ | 65 | ▢ | ▢ | 80 |

❷ Copy and fill in this table by skip counting. 130; 140; 170; 180; 190

| 110 | 120 | ▢ | ▢ | 150 | 160 | ▢ | ▢ | ▢ | 200 |

Measuring and Graphing Lesson 3.3

Use the graph to answer the questions. Each cashier at the store had a different amount in his or her cash register at the end of the day. The bar graph shows the amounts in each cashier's drawer.

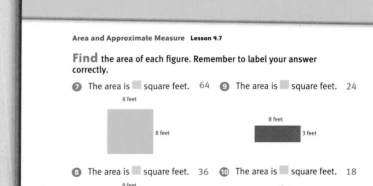

❸ How many cashiers had more than $300 in their register at the end of the day? How many had more than 400? 3;2

❹ How much money was in Lin's drawer? $288

❺ Who had the least amount of money in his or her drawer at the end of the day? María

❻ How much money was there altogether? $1,782

📖 Textbook This lesson is available in the *eTextbook.*

Area and Approximate Measure Lesson 4.7

Find the area of each figure. Remember to label your answer correctly.

❼ The area is ▢ square feet. 64
8 feet

8 feet

❾ The area is ▢ square feet. 24
8 feet
3 feet

❽ The area is ▢ square feet. 36
9 feet
4 feet

❿ The area is ▢ square feet. 18
6 feet
3 feet

Variables and Arrow Notation Lesson 6.5

Solve these problems.

$x \longleftarrow (+10) \longrightarrow y$ $y \longleftarrow (-5) \longrightarrow x$

⓫ If $x = 8$, what is y? $y = 18$
⓬ If $y = 25$, what is x? $x = 15$
⓭ If $x = 36$, what is y? $y = 46$

⓮ If $x = 88$, what is y? $y = 83$
⓯ If $x = 101$, what is y? $y = 96$
⓰ If $x = 72$, what is y? $y = 67$

Individual Oral Assessment

Purpose of the Test

The Individual Oral Assessment is designed to measure students' growing knowledge of chapter concepts. It is administered individually to each student, and it requires oral responses from each student. The test takes about five minutes to complete. See *Assessment* for detailed instructions for administering and interpreting the test, and record students' answers on the Student Assessment Recording Sheet.

Assessment Page T33

Directions

Read each question to the student, and record his or her oral response. If the student answers correctly, go to the next question. Stop when the student misses two questions at the same level. Students may use paper and pencil to solve the starred items.

Materials

None

Questions

Level 1: Prerequisite

1. What is 10 + 10 + 10 + 10 + 10? 50
2. What is 12 × 12? 144
3. What is 100 × 4? 400
4. What is 10 ÷ 2? 5

Level 2: Basic

5. What is 10 × 70? 700
6. What is 20 × 5? 100
7. You want to multiply 56 × 7. What easier multiplication problem can you solve first? Possible answers: Multiply 50 × 7 or 6 × 7.
8. What is 25 ÷ 5? 5

Level 3: At Level

9. What is 1,000 × 7? 7,000
10. What is 11 × 6? 66
*11. What is 372 × 6? 2,232
*12. Melinda has 47 trading cards. She puts them into equal-sized groups of 5. How many will be left over? 2

Level 4: Challenge Application

*13. During their 3-month summer vacation, Steve collected 132 cans of food each month for the food bank. How much food did he give to the food bank? 396 cans
*14. Jasmine bought 25 pounds of birdseed each month for 6 months. How much birdseed did she buy altogether? 150 pounds
*15. If Jasmine bought 12 pounds of birdseed a month for the rest of the year, how much did she buy for those 6 months? 72
*16. How much birdseed did Jasmine buy in a year? 222 pounds

Level 5: Content Beyond Mid-Chapter

*17. There were 402 people signed up for the race. Half of the runners were women. How many women were running in the race? 201 women
*18. Mr. Kretzler and Ms. Mann's classes are going to the museum on a field trip. There are 23 students in Mr. Kretzler's class and 21 students in Ms. Mann's class. The cost for the museum is $3 per student. How much will it cost for the two classes to go to the museum? $132
*19. Flo's Flower Shop received a delivery of 154 roses. Flo will make bouquets of 6 roses. How many bouquets will she have? How many roses will she have left over? 25 with 4 left over
*20. Anthony has 4 friends over at his house. The 5 of them are going to play a card game. There are 52 cards in a deck. Each boy gets the same number of cards. How many cards are left over? 2

OBJECTIVES
- To show students the meaning of remainders in division problems
- To give practice in doing division exercises involving remainders
- To solve word problems, some of which include division with remainders

NCTM STANDARDS

Number and Operations
Understanding meanings of operations and how they relate to one another

Connections
Understanding how mathematical ideas interconnect and build on one another to produce a coherent whole

MATERIALS
- *Response Wheels
- Package of counting craft sticks (100 count)

TECHNOLOGY
ⓔ **Presentation** Lesson 7.5

TEST PREP

Cumulative Review
- Mental Math reviews missing factors and multiplication facts (Chapter 5).
- Problems 3, 7, and 13 review basic division facts (Lesson 5.7).

Extended Response
Problem 14

Looking Ahead
Skill-Building activities from Lesson 7.6 Develop should be prepared in worksheet form.

Division with Remainders

Context of the Lesson This is the first of four lessons on multidigit division. In this lesson students will be introduced to the concept of remainders in division problems with single-digit divisors.

See page 248B for Math Background for teachers for this lesson.

Planning for Learning ● DIFFERENTIATE INSTRUCTION

INTERVENTION

If . . . students lack the prerequisite skill of multiplication facts,

Then . . . teach *Intervention* Lesson 7.A.

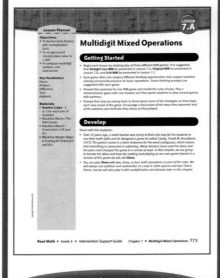

Intervention Lesson 7.A

ENGLISH LEARNER

Preview

If . . . students need language support,

Then . . . use Lesson 7.5 in *English Learner Support Guide* to preview lesson concepts and vocabulary.

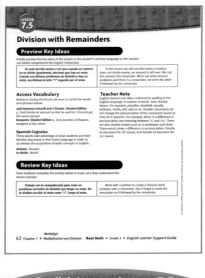

English Learner Lesson 7.5

ENRICH

If . . . students are proficient in the lesson concepts,

Then . . . emphasize the student pages.

PRACTICE

If . . . students would benefit from additional practice,

Then . . . extend Guided Discussion before assigning the student pages.

RETEACH

If . . . students are having difficulty understanding division with remainders,

Then . . . extend Mental Math before assigning the student pages.

Vocabulary
remainder \ri mān´dər\ *n.*
what is left after you cannot divide a number any further

Spanish Cognates
division división
to divide dividir

---

*Manipulative Kit Item

Mental Math 10

  Practice multiplication facts using examples such as the following.

a. $10 \times 4 = 40$ **b.** $7 \times 7 = 49$
c. $6 \times 8 = 48$ **d.** $9 \times 5 = 45$
e. $10 \times 10 = 100$ **f.** $10 \times 8 = 80$

1 Develop 25

Tell Students In Today's Lesson They Will

practice division with remainders.

Guided Discussion UNDERSTANDING

Whole Group

Have 4 students come to the front of the class. Tell the class you have 25 craft sticks to divide equally among these 4 students. (Make sure the class understands that each person is to get the same number of sticks and as many sticks as possible.) Ask questions such as the following:

- **How many craft sticks should each person get?** 6
- **Will there be any left over?** yes

Distribute the sticks to each person, and show that each person does indeed get 6 sticks and there is 1 left over.

Ask how this could have been predicted. Somebody should be able to give an explanation such as this one: Because 4×6 is 24, and 24 is 1 less than 25, each of the 4 people could get 6 sticks and there would be 1 left over. Next, show how to write the answer:

$$25 \div 4 = 6R1$$

Further explain that sometimes students will see division written as $4\overline{)25}$ with $6\ R1$ above.

As you write this, explain that the quotient (6) is written where students have been writing it (above the ones digit of the dividend). Also explain that R1 means there is 1 stick left over, or remaining (that is, a remainder of 1).

Do a few more exercises (including ones that do not have a remainder), such as the following examples:

- $5\overline{)27}$ 5 R2
- $35 \div 8 = 4$ R3
- $9\overline{)53}$ 5 R8
- $42 \div 6 = 7$

When discussing this last example, you might point out that having no remainder is the same as having a remainder of 0 (which we indicate by not writing a remainder with the answer). You might point out, too, that when we are dealing with division with remainders, division is not simply the inverse (or opposite) of multiplication. The only time division is an inverse is when there is no remainder in the quotient, such as in the last example.

2 Assign Student Pages 20

Pages 264–265 APPLYING

Have students complete the exercises on pages 264 and 265 independently. Make sure students are writing the leftover amounts as remainders. Not all problems will have remainders.

Monitoring Student Progress

If . . . students have difficulty with division exercises involving remainders,

Then . . . have students use concrete objects to model the division. The leftover amounts are the remainders.

As Students Finish

Game Roll a Problem Game (Multiplication)

LESSON 7.5 Division with Remainders

Key Ideas

When a number does not divide exactly, we say the leftover amount is the remainder.

Rafael has a dozen muffins to share among 3 friends and himself. How many muffins will each person get?

$12 \div 4 = n$

Rafael passed the muffins out one at a time. When he was finished passing them out, he saw that each person got 3 muffins. $12 \div 4 = 3$

$13 \div 4 = n$

Next Saturday Rafael opened his box of muffins to find there were 13 muffins. When he finished passing them out to his 3 friends and himself, Rafael discovered each person again had 3 muffins but there was one muffin left over. $13 \div 4$ is 3 R1

This answer can be read *3 with a remainder of 1.*

Divide. Use craft sticks or other manipulatives to divide. The first one has been done for you.

1 $7 \div 4$ is 1 R3

2 $8 \div 3$ is 2 R2   **3** $20 \div 5$ is ☐   4   **4** $20 \div 6$ is ☐   3 R2

5 $24 \div 5$ is ☐   4 R4   **6** $30 \div 8$ is 3 R6   **7** $54 \div 9$ is ☐   6

8 $56 \div 9$ is ☐   6 R2   **9** $50 \div 7$ is ☐   7 R1   **10** $10 \div 4$ is ☐   2 R2

264   Textbook This lesson is available in the *eTextbook.*

Answer the questions.

11 Joanne and her 2 friends want to share 20 baseball cards equally.

How many baseball cards should each of the 3 children get? How many baseball cards will be left over?   6 cards; 2 cards

12 Mrs. Sarton has 11 balloons to divide equally among 4 children.

How many balloons should each child get? How many balloons will be left over?   2 balloons; 3 balloons

13 Arnaldo has 40 shells to divide equally among 5 friends.

How many shells should each child get? How many shells will be left over?   8 shells; 0 shells

14 **Extended Response** Mr. Bailey, a zookeeper, has 40 bananas for Koko the ape. Koko eats 5 bananas each day.

How many days will the bananas last? How much does Koko weigh?   8 days; can't tell

15 At the flower shop, Mr. Kane is putting 17 roses into bouquets of 6 flowers each.

How many bouquets can he make? How many roses will be left over?   2 bouquets; 5 roses

---

3 Reflect   5

Guided Discussion ✓ REASONING   Whole Group

How would you find the answer to $1,001 \div 13$?

Encourage students to discuss their methods. Examples of possible answers include:

- $20 \times 13 = 260$, which is not enough.
- $100 \times 13 = 1,300$, which is too much.
- $80 \times 13 = 1,040$, which is too much but closer.
- $70 \times 13 = 910$, which is not enough.
- $75 \times 13 = 975$, which is still not enough.
- $78 \times 13 = 1,014$, which is just barely too much.
- $77 \times 13 = 1,001$, which solves the exercise.

$1,001 \div 13 = 77$

Curriculum Connection: Students may be interested in botany and how different breeds and colors of various flowers are created.

Cumulative Review: For cumulative review of previously learned skills, see page 279–280.

Family Involvement: Assign the *Practice, Reteach,* or *Enrichment* activities depending on the needs of your students.

Encourage students to play the **Roll a Problem Game** or **Roll a Problem Game,** altered with a friend or a relative.

Concept/Question Board: Have students look for additional examples using multidigit multiplication and division and post them on the Concept/Question Board.

Math Puzzler: Ravi has 3 more books than David. David has 5 fewer books than Margaret. Margaret has 10 books. How many books do the 3 friends have altogether? 23

Assess and Differentiate

eAssess Use **eAssess** to record and analyze evidence of student understanding.

Gather Evidence

Use the Daily Class Assessment Records in **Assessment** or **eAssess** to record daily observations.

Informal Assessment
☑ **Student Pages**

Did the student **APPLYING**
- ❏ apply learning in new situations?
- ❏ contribute concepts?
- ❏ contribute answers?
- ❏ connect mathematics to real-world situations?

Informal Assessment
☑ **Guided Discussion**

Did the student **REASONING**
- ❏ provide a clear explanation?
- ❏ communicate reasons and strategies?
- ❏ choose appropriate strategies?
- ❏ argue logically?

B Summarize Findings

Analyze and summarize assessment data for each student. Determine which Assessment Follow-Up is appropriate for each student. Use the Student Assessment Record in **Assessment** or **eAssess** to update assessment records.

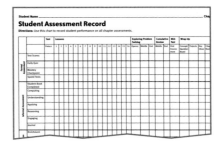

Assessment Page T41

C Assessment Follow-Up • DIFFERENTIATE INSTRUCTION

Based on your observations, use these teaching strategies for assessment follow-up.

INTERVENTION
Review student performance on **Intervention** Lesson 7.A to see if students have mastered prerequisite skills for this lesson.

ENGLISH LEARNER
Review

Use Lesson 7.5 in **English Learner Support Guide** to review lesson concepts and vocabulary.

ENRICH
If . . . students are proficient in the lesson concepts,

Then . . . encourage them to work on chapter projects or **Enrichment** Lesson 7.5.

Enrichment Lesson 7.5

PRACTICE
If . . . students would benefit from additional practice,

Then . . . assign **Practice** Lesson 7.5.

Practice Lesson 7.5

RETEACH
If . . . students are having difficulty understanding division with remainders,

Then . . . reteach the concept using **Reteach** Lesson 7.5.

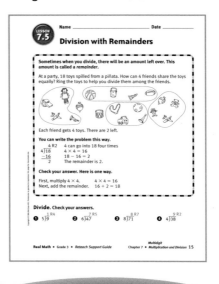

Reteach Lesson 7.5

OBJECTIVES
- To introduce the skill of detecting obviously wrong answers—answers that are contrary to reason
- To provide practice with division exercises and problems, some of which have remainders
- To show that the same division problem can have several different answers in a practical situation

NCTM STANDARDS
Number and Operations
Understanding meanings of operations and how they relate to one another

Problem Solving
Solving problems that arise in mathematics and in other contexts

MATERIALS
- *Response Wheels
- **Skill-Building** activity from Develop section (in worksheet format)
- *Number Cubes (0–5 and 5–10)

TECHNOLOGY
- e Presentation Lesson 7.6
- e Games Cube 100
- Building Blocks Function Machine 4

TEST PREP
Cumulative Review
- Mental Math reviews multiplication and missing factors (Chapter 5).
- Problem 12 reviews regrouping for subtraction (Lesson 2.3).

Extended Response
Problems 4–9

Writing + Math
Journal

Reasonable Answers to Division Problems

Context of the Lesson This is the second of four lessons on multidigit division. In this lesson students will practice finding reasonable and logical answers to division problems they may or may not know how to compute. This skill will be used throughout **Real Math**.
See page 248B for Math Background for teachers for this lesson.

Planning for Learning ● DIFFERENTIATE INSTRUCTION

INTERVENTION
If . . . students lack the prerequisite skill of place value to 1,000,

Then . . . teach *Intervention* Lesson 7.B.

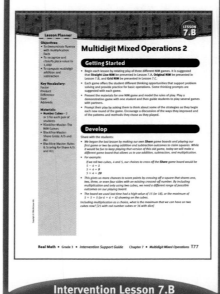

Intervention Lesson 7.B

ENGLISH LEARNER
Preview

If . . . students need language support,

Then . . . use Lesson 7.6 in *English Learner Support Guide* to preview lesson concepts and vocabulary.

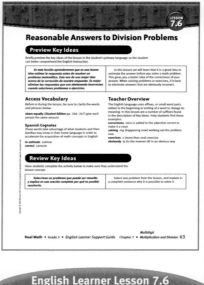

English Learner Lesson 7.6

ENRICH
If . . . students are proficient in the lesson concepts,

Then . . . emphasize the **Cube 100 Game.**

PRACTICE
If . . . students would benefit from additional practice,

Then . . . extend Skill Building before assigning the student pages.

RETEACH
If . . . students are having difficulty understanding reasonable answers to division problems,

Then . . . extend Guided Discussion before assigning the student pages.

Spanish Cognates
to estimate estimar
correct correcto

Mental Math

  Practice multiplication facts. Use examples such as the following:

a. $7 \times 7 = 49$ **b.** $2 \times 8 = 16$
c. $6 \times 8 = 48$ **d.** $0 \times 100 = 0$
e. $10 \times 4 = 40$ **f.** $3 \times 9 = 27$

1 Develop 25

Tell Students In Today's Lesson They Will
learn to use division in different applications

Skill and Strategy Building REASONING Whole Group

Cube 100 Game

Have one or two volunteers play a round of **Cube 100 Game.** The rules for the game are given on student page 269. Remind students that after any roll, instead of adding that number, they may multiply it by the sum of the previous numbers, but it ends their turn. The goal is to be the player closest to but not greater than 100 without going over.

Guided Discussion UNDERSTANDING Whole Group

Ask, *What is 25 divided by 4?* as you write $25 \div 4$ on the board. The most likely answer is 6 with a remainder of 1. Then ask questions such as the following. Discuss each question with the class. Each apparently involves dividing 25 by 4, but the questions have different answers in the real world.

- **One day 4 children earned $25. They decided to divide it equally. How much did each child get?** Although they have not studied decimals yet this year, students should have enough experience with money from their everyday lives and previous grades to know that each child would get $6.25; or $6\frac{1}{4}$ dollars.
- **A class of 25 students has been divided equally into 4 groups. How many students are in each group?** This is impossible. You cannot have $6\frac{1}{4}$ students in a group.

- **At lunch 4 students wish to share 25 cookies equally. How many cookies did each child get?** If they can divide the one remaining cookie into 4 equal pieces, they could each get $6\frac{1}{4}$ cookies.
- **A Ferris wheel seat can fit 4 people. There are 25 people who want to ride the Ferris wheel. How many seats will they need?** They need 7 seats, because 24 people would fill 6 of the seats.
- **I have 25 yards of material. Each suit requires 4 yards. How many suits can I make?** I can make only 6 suits. I will have 1 yard of material left over.

From these problems, students should see that the question *What is 25 divided by 4?* has many possible answers, depending on the situation it is intended to model.

Skill Building APPLYING Whole Group

Write the following problems on the board to help as students find the exact answers. Remind students they will not need to find the exact answers, just eliminate the two obviously wrong answers.

1. $400 \div 10$
   a. 4,000
   b. 40
   c. 1
2. $801 \div 80$
   a. 10 R1
   b. 10 R100
   c. 1 R1,000
3. $784 \div 5$
   a. 1,560 R4
   b. 156 R4
   c. 1 R564
4. $74 \div 4$
   a. 1,800 R2
   b. 180 R2
   c. 18 R2

2 Assign Student Pages 20 🌙

Pages 266–267 APPLYING

Have students complete the exercises on pages 266 and 267 independently. Remind students to be logical in their answers. There cannot be half people, partial animals, sections of tiny items, and so on.

Monitoring Student Progress

If . . . students have difficulty with the word problems,

Then . . . work individually or in small groups helping students to understand the physical situations, acting out the problems and using manipulatives as a model.

RESEARCH IN ACTION

"Estimating before solving a problem can facilitate number sense and place-value understanding by encouraging students to use number and notational properties to generate an approximate result. Estimating is also a practical skill. It can guide students' use of calculators, especially in identifying implausible answers, and is a valuable part of the mathematics used in everyday life."

Kilpatrick, J., J. Swafford, and B. Findell, eds. *Adding It Up: Helping Children Learn Mathematics*. Washington, D.C.: National Research Council/National Academy Press, 2001, p. 215.

LESSON 7.6 Reasonable Answers to Division Problems

Key Ideas

It is often useful in real life to approximate the answer to a math problem. It is helpful, when answering multiple choice questions, to eliminate answers that are obviously incorrect. You should assume, unless told otherwise, that exactly one answer is correct.

Look at this exercise:

Choose the correct answer.

$345 \div 3 = n$

a. $n = 15$

b. $n = 115$

c. $n = 1{,}150$

Even though you may not know how to divide this large number, you do know that $3 \times 15 = 45$, so choice *a* is too small. You also know that $3 \times 1{,}150$ is greater than 3,000, so choice *c* is too great. This leaves choice *b* as the correct answer.

Is each of the following possible? If yes, give the answer. If no, explain why not.

❶ The lunch cost $15. Abigail and Dan each paid half.
   $7.50 each
❷ There are 15 softball players. They are on 2 teams. Each team has the same number of players.
   This is impossible because you cannot have $7\frac{1}{2}$ players.
❸ Joe and Heika have 15 cookies. They share them equally.
   If they can divide the one cookie equally, then they each ate $7\frac{1}{2}$ cookies.

266   ☐ **Textbook** This lesson is available in the *eTextbook*.

Extended Response Solve each problem. Then explain your answer.

❹ Each motorcycle can hold 2 people, and 15 people want to ride. How many motorcycles are needed?

❺ Paulette had 15 marbles. She gave Peter and Nicholas each an equal number of marbles. What is the most marbles Paulette could have given Peter?

❻ Anna and Laura wanted to share equally 15 ounces of orange juice. How many ounces should each get?

❼ Ben and Helena are both 15 years old. They each have $2. If they share their money, how much will each have? $2

❽ David and Gay want to share $15 equally. What is each person's share?

❾ Steve and Joe paid $15 for a book. They want to share it equally. How can they do that?

❿ Each car can carry 7 people, and 55 people must be taken to the airport in a car. How many cars are needed?
   It will take 8 cars because 7 cars will hold only 49 people.

See Reflect in *Teacher's Edition* for possible explanations for Problems 4–9.

Chapter 7 • Lesson 6   267

Chapter 7 • Lesson 6 **266–267**

Assign Student Pages, continued

Pages 268–269

Have students complete student pages 268–269 independently.

Monitoring Student Progress

If . . . students have difficulty detecting obviously wrong answers and are inconsistent doing the calculations,

Then . . . work individually with students, presenting problems of the type on student page 268, but gradually reducing the time the student has to answer.

As Students Finish

Stop students with at least 10 minutes to play the **Cube 100** game.

 Game   Cube 100 Game

 Games   *Cube 100 Game*

 **Building Blocks**   Function Machine 4

LESSON 7.6 • Reasonable Answers to Division Problems

In each problem two of the answers are clearly incorrect, and one is correct. Choose the correct answer.

⑪ 250 ÷ 5
   a. 5,000
   (b.) 50
   c. 5

⑫ 21 ÷ 6
   a. 30 R3
   (b.) 3 R3
   c. 3 R3,000

⑬ 100 ÷ 10
   a. 1
   (b.) 10
   c. 100

⑭ 501 ÷ 5
   (a.) 100 R1
   b. 10 R100
   c. 1 R1,000

⑮ 200 ÷ 2
   a. 10,000
   (b.) 100
   c. 1

⑯ 681 ÷ 10
   a. 680 R10
   (b.) 68 R1
   c. 6,000 R81

⑰ 550 ÷ 10
   a. 55,000
   b. 5,500
   (c.) 55

⑱ 999 ÷ 9
   a. 1
   b. 11
   (c.) 111

Writing + Math ✏️ Journal

Look at the picture, and then answer the question.

What is wrong with the total?

It doesn't make sense to add the numbers because they are not counting the same thing.

Welcome to Cuckoo Corners
Founded	1831
Population	7,049
Altitude	1,100 meters
Total	9,980

268   **ⓔTextbook** This lesson is available in the *eTextbook*.

Game 🎮

Multiplication and Strategies Practice

Cube 100 Game

Players: Two or more

Materials: *Number Cubes:* two 0–5, two 5–10

Object: To get the greatest score that is less or equal to 100.

Math Focus: Adding; multiplying one- and two-digit numbers by one-digit numbers; place value; and probability.

HOW TO PLAY

❶ Roll the *Number Cubes* one at a time, adding the numbers as you roll.

❷ After any roll, instead of adding that number you may multiply it by the sum of the previous numbers. Then your turn is over.

❸ The player with the score closest to, but not greater than, 100 wins the round.

Sample Game

Wendy rolled **6**, and then **3**.

She added: 6 + 3 = 9.

Then she rolled **9**.

She multiplied: 9 × 9 = 81.

She stopped after three rolls.

Wendy's score was 81.

Todd rolled **5**, and then **5**.

He added: 5 + 5 = 10.

Then he rolled **6**.

He added again: 10 + 6 = 16.

He rolled **6** again.

He multiplied: 16 × 6 = 96.

Todd's score was 96.

Todd won the round.

ⓔGames This game is available as an *eGame*.   269

3 Reflect   10

Guided Discussion   APPLYING   Whole Group

Present exercises in which students are asked to detect correct answers by eliminating wrong answers, without actually doing the computation. Allow students to discuss the solutions. Be alert to students who give acceptable explanations but which are different from those given here. Use examples such as the following:

- $375 + 462 = n$

  A. 275

  B. 837

  C. 1,213

  Discussion: *C* is obviously wrong because $5 + 2 = 7$. *A* is obviously wrong because 275 is less than one of the addends. *B* must be the correct answer.

- $376 \div 2 = n$

  A. 405

  B. 207

  C. 188

  Discussion: *A* is obviously wrong because the quotient must be less than 376. *B* is obviously wrong because the quotient must be less than half of 400. *C* must be the correct answer.

- $470 \times 3 = n$

  A. 1,410

  B. 141

  C. 14,100

  Discussion: *B* is obviously wrong because the product must be more than 470. *C* is obviously wrong because $3 \times 500 = 1,500$. The answer must be A because it is less than 1,500.

Extended Response

Problem 4 The answer is 8 because 14 people can use 7 motorcycles and the fifteenth person also needs a motorcycle.

Problem 5 The answer is 7 because $15 \div 2 = 7\ 1/2$ and you can't give away half a marble.

Problem 6 The answer is 7 1/2 or between 7 and 8 ounces because no matter how much orange juice there is, it can be shared equally.

Problem 8 Many students, relying on their everyday experiences, will give the correct answer of 7 1/2 dollars or $7.50. Some may answer more than $7 but less than $8.

Problem 9 Many answers are possible. They might each have it every other day. Steve could read it first and give it to Joe when finished. They might sell the book when they are finished reading it and share the money received. They might donate the book to their school when both have finished reading it. If Joe wanted to keep the book in his library when both have finished reading it, then Joe can pay Steve half of what they agree the book is worth.

 **Journal**

The numbers in this problem represent unrelated items and cannot be added together.

 Curriculum Connection: Students may be interested in the history of softball, such as when and where it began, how the rules have changed, and so on.

 Cumulative Review: For cumulative review of previously learned skills, see page 279–280.

 Family Involvement: Assign the *Practice, Reteach,* or *Enrichment* activities depending on the needs of your students.

Encourage students to play the **Cube 100 Game** with a friend or a relative.

 Concept/Question Board: Encourage students to continue to post questions, answers, and examples on the Concept/Question Board.

 Math Puzzler: Patty and Becky collected dimes. For every 10 dimes that Patty has, Becky has 12. They have 44 dimes altogether. How much money does each girl have? Patty: 20 dimes or $2.00; Becky: 24 dimes or $2.40

Assess and Differentiate

 e Assess Use *eAssess* to record and analyze
evidence of student understanding.

A Gather Evidence

Use the Daily Class Assessment Records in **Assessment** or **eAssess**
to record daily observations.

Informal Assessment

☑ **Mental Math**

Did the student **COMPUTING**
- ❏ respond accurately?
- ❏ respond quickly?
- ❏ respond with confidence?
- ❏ self-correct?

Performance Assessment

☑ **Skill and Strategy
Building**

Did the student **REASONING**
- ❏ provide a clear explanation?
- ❏ communicate reasons and
  strategies?
- ❏ choose appropriate
  strategies?
- ❏ argue logically?

B Summarize Findings

Analyze and summarize assessment data for each student.
Determine which Assessment Follow-Up is appropriate for each
student. Use the Student Assessment Record in **Assessment** or
eAssess to update assessment records.

Assessment Page T41

C Assessment Follow-Up ● DIFFERENTIATE INSTRUCTION

Based on your observations, use these teaching strategies for assessment follow-up.

INTERVENTION	ENRICH	PRACTICE	RETEACH
Review student performance on **Intervention** Lesson 7.B to see if students have mastered prerequisite skills for this lesson.	**If . . .** students are proficient in the lesson concepts, **Then . . .** encourage them to work on chapter projects or **Enrichment** Lesson 7.6.	**If . . .** students would benefit from additional practice, **Then . . .** assign **Practice** Lesson 7.6.	**If . . .** students are having difficulty understanding reasonable answers to division problems, **Then . . .** have them act out the problem. Ask them if the answer makes sense. How could they change the problem so that the answer would make sense?

ENGLISH LEARNER

Review

Use Lesson 7.6 in **English
Learner Support Guide**
to review lesson concepts
and vocabulary.

Enrichment Lesson 7.6

Practice Lesson 7.6

Lesson Planner

OBJECTIVES
- To help students discover how to divide a two-digit number by a one-digit number (with whole-number answers)
- To develop the standard algorithm for dividing a two-digit number by a one-digit number

NCTM STANDARDS

Number and Operations
Understanding meanings of operations and how they relate to one another

Connections
Recognizing and using connections among mathematical ideas

MATERIALS
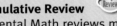
- *Response Wheels
- Play money ($10 bills and $1 bills)

TECHNOLOGY
- e Presentation Lesson 7.7
- e Games Cube 100

TEST PREP

Cumulative Review

- Mental Math reviews multiplication and division facts (Chapter 5).
- Problem 10 reviews adding two-digit numbers (Lesson 2.2).

Writing + Math
Journal

Dividing Two-Digit Numbers by One-Digit Numbers

Context of the Lesson This is the third of four lessons on multidigit division. In this lesson students will use play money to explore and develop a basic algorithm for dividing a two-digit number by a single-digit number with whole-number answers. This procedure will be applied to dividing three-digit numbers by single-digit numbers in Lesson 7.8.

See page 248B for Math Background for teachers for this lesson.

Planning for Learning ● DIFFERENTIATE INSTRUCTION

INTERVENTION

If . . . students lack the prerequisite skill of multiplication facts,

Then . . . teach *Intervention* Lesson 7.A.

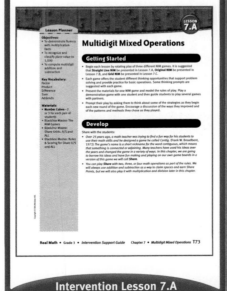

Intervention Lesson 7.A

ENGLISH LEARNER

Preview

If . . . students need language support,

Then . . . use Lesson 7.7 in *English Learner Support Guide* to preview lesson concepts and vocabulary.

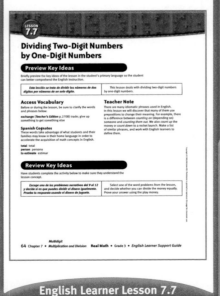

English Learner Lesson 7.7

ENRICH

If . . . students are proficient in the lesson concepts,

Then . . . emphasize the student pages.

PRACTICE

If . . . students would benefit from additional practice,

Then . . . extend Strategy Building before assigning the student pages.

RETEACH

If . . . students are having difficulty understanding dividing two-digit numbers by one-digit numbers,

Then . . . extend Guided Discussion before assigning the student pages.

Vocabulary
Review from Lesson 1.1:
estimate

Spanish Cognates
total total
person persona
to estimate estimar

*Manipulative Kit Item

Mental Math

  Practice multiplication and division facts. Use examples such as the following:

a. 40 ÷ 5 8
b. 9 × n = 0 n = 0
c. 7 × 7 49
d. n × 3 = 9 n = 3
e. 54 ÷ 9 6
f. 6 × 9 54
g. 40 ÷ 8 5
h. n × 5 = 40 n = 8
i. 3 × 9 27
j. 27 ÷ 3 9
k. 49 ÷ 7 7
l. 5 × 8 40

1 Develop

Tell Students In Today's Lesson They Will
explore dividing two-digit numbers by one-digit numbers.

Guided Discussion   UNDERSTANDING Whole Group

Divide the class into groups of three. Have a "bank" at your desk with only $10 bills and $1 bills.

Using only $1 bills and $10 bills (no $5, $20, or $50 bills), give each group seven $10 bills and two $1 bills. Instruct the groups to divide this amount evenly among the members in the group. Students will most likely each take two $10 bills and then state they can't divide the remaining $10 bills fairly. Have students discuss solutions. They may decide to change each $10 bill for ten $1 bills. They can then each have four $1 bills so that each person has $24 (2 tens and 4 ones).

After all the groups have finished, go through the procedures with the class, explaining what they did while you keep a record such as the following:

	3 people	7 tens and 2 ones
Each person gets 2 tens		

		2 tens
		7 tens and 2 ones
3 people *use*	6 tens	
	1 ten	2 ones

Change the tens to ones

		2 tens
		7 tens and 2 ones
3 people *use*	6 tens	
		12 ones

Each person gets 4 ones

		2 tens
		7 tens and 2 ones
3 people *use*	6 tens	
		12 ones
3 people *use*		12 ones
		0

If we draw lines to separate the people, the money to be divided, and the amount each person gets (still putting the tens in the tens column and the ones in the ones column) we get a record that looks like this:

$$\begin{array}{r} 24 \\ 3\overline{)72} \\ 6 \\ \hline 12 \\ 12 \\ \hline 0 \end{array}$$

Strategy Building UNDERSTANDING Small Group

Divide the class into groups of three students each. You may want to assign one or two students as observers or bankers for one or two of the groups. Remember to keep the bank stocked with only $10 bills and $1 bills. Give each group eight $10 bills and seven $1 bills. Have students use the record-keeping method to find what amount of money each member of the group would receive if the money is divided evenly.

Repeat with similar questions so students see that all they really need is the record of what they would have done if they had used play money.

2 Assign Student Pages 25

Pages 270–271 APPLYING

Small Group

Have students work through the example on pages 270 and 271 independently or in pairs. Remind students to estimate the answer before solving.

RESEARCH IN ACTION

"Students acquire proficiency with multidigit algorithms by moving through a progression of experiences. Although there is relatively little research on students' learning of multiplication and division algorithms, it is likely that their learning trajectories are similar to the ones documented for addition and subtraction....The many kinds of errors students make when multidigit methods are not connected to place-value meanings are well documented."

Kilpatrick, J., J. Swafford, and B. Findell, eds. *Adding It Up: Helping Children Learn Mathematics.* Washington, D.C.: National Research Council/National Academy Press, 2001, p. 213.

LESSON 7.7 Dividing Two-Digit Numbers by One-Digit Numbers

Key Ideas

Using play money, we can find a way to divide one number by another.

Felipe's family wanted to divide $96 equally among the 4 members. How much money should each person get?

First, Felipe decided that $96 was close to $100, so each person would get *about* $25. He knew that 25 × 4 = 100.

Then he began dividing the money.

Step 1: Felipe starts by giving each person a $10 bill. He is able to do this 2 times altogether.

Felipe	Sister	Mom	Dad
$10	$10	$10	$10
$10	$10	$10	$10

Step 2: He has one $10 bill and six $1 bills left. He asks his dad to exchange the $10 bill for ten $1 bills. Counting the $1 bills, Felipe discovers he now has sixteen $1 bills.

Step 3: He gives each person a $1 bill. He is able to do this 4 times until he runs out of money.

Felipe	Sister	Mom	Dad
$1	$1	$1	$1
$1	$1	$1	$1
$1	$1	$1	$1
$1	$1	$1	$1

Step 4: They count their money and find they have $24 each.

Textbook This lesson is available in the *eTextbook*.

Here is the record Felipe kept when passing out the money.

Step 1: When he divided the $10 bills, each person got two $10 bills. Altogether it was eight $10 bills, which left Felipe with one $10 bill.

$$
\begin{array}{r}
2? \\
4\overline{)9\text{ tens }6\text{ ones}} \\
\underline{8\text{ tens}} \\
1\text{ ten}
\end{array}
$$

Step 2: Before exchanging money, he had one $10 bill and six $1 bills. He exchanged the $10 bill for 10 $1 bills. Altogether it was $16.

$$
\begin{array}{r}
2? \\
4\overline{)9\text{ tens }6\text{ ones}} \\
\underline{8\text{ tens}} \\
1\text{ ten }6\text{ ones} = 16\text{ ones}
\end{array}
$$

Step 3: Felipe gave four $1 bills to each member of his family. This used all 16 ones and left him with no money.

$$
\begin{array}{r}
24 \\
4\overline{)9\text{ tens }6\text{ ones}} \\
\underline{8\text{ tens}} \\
16\text{ ones} \\
\underline{16\text{ ones}} \\
0
\end{array}
$$

Step 4: They counted their money. They each had $24.

An abbreviated record of Felipe's division looks like this:

$$
\begin{array}{r}
24 \\
4\overline{)96} \\
\underline{8} \\
16 \\
\underline{16} \\
0
\end{array}
$$

Teaching Lesson 7.7

Assign Student Pages, continued

Pages 272–273

Have students complete pages 272 and 273 independently. Remind students to estimate the problem before solving.

Monitoring Student Progress

If . . . students have difficulty with the division algorithm,

Then . . . have students use play money and make the necessary exchanges while they keep written records.

As Students Finish

 Game Cube 100 Game

 Games *Cube 100 Game*

LESSON 7.7 • Dividing Two-Digit Numbers by One-Digit Numbers

Divide. Keep records like Felipe's records to show your answer.

1. $57 \div 3 =$ ▪ 19
2. $36 \div 2 =$ ▪ 18
3. $85 \div 5 =$ ▪ 17
4. $84 \div 4 =$ ▪ 21
5. $64 \div 4 =$ ▪ 16
6. $81 \div 3 =$ ▪ 27
7. $96 \div 6 =$ ▪ 16
8. $95 \div 5 =$ ▪ 19

272   📖 **Textbook** This lesson is available in the *eTextbook*.

Solve. Be sure to label your answer correctly.

9. If 4 students divided $76 equally, how much money did each student get? $19

10. In Ms. Hopkins's class, there are 17 girls and 16 boys. How many students are in Ms. Hopkins's class?   33 students

11. There are 6 boys who want to divide 78 trading cards equally among them. How many cards should each boy get?   13 cards

12. The 5 girls want to divide 65 stickers equally among themselves. How many stickers should each girl get?   13 stickers

Writing + Math Journal

The 5 girls want to divide 66 stickers equally among themselves. Is it possible? Why or why not?

Chapter 7 • Lesson 7   273

---

3 Reflect
5

Guided Discussion REASONING
Whole Group

Ask students if they can think of a way to divide $745 equally among 5 people.

A possible answer would be:

Each person takes $100. Exchange the remaining $200 for 20 tens. From the 24 tens, each person takes 4 tens, leaving 4 tens. Exchange the 4 tens for $1 bills. Each person then takes nine $1 bills. The record would look like this:

$$
\begin{array}{r}
1\ 4\ 9 \\
5\overline{)7\ 4\ 5} \\
\underline{5} \\
2\ 4 \\
\underline{2\ 0} \\
4\ 5 \\
\underline{4\ 5} \\
0
\end{array}
$$

In Lesson 7.8 this will be done carefully and thoroughly, but you may be able to go through the development quickly if students seem to understand this process.

 **Journal**

One sticker will be left over, so it is not possible to divide 66 stickers equally by 5.

 Curriculum Connection: Students may be interested in the currencies used in other countries in the world, such as Mexico, Canada, England, and so on.

 Cumulative Review: For cumulative review of previously learned skills, see page 279–280.

 Family Involvement: Assign the *Practice, Reteach,* or *Enrichment* activities depending on the needs of your students. Encourage students to play the **Cube 100 Game** with a friend or a relative.

 Concept/Question Board: Encourage students to continue to post questions, answers, and examples on the Concept/Question Board.

 Math Puzzler: I am thinking of two numbers. Their difference is 3. Their sum is 13. What are the two numbers?
5 and 8

4 Assess and Differentiate

 Assess Use **eAssess** to record and analyze evidence of student understanding.

A Gather Evidence

Use the Daily Class Assessment Records in **Assessment** or **eAssess** to record daily observations.

Informal Assessment
☑ **Guided Discussion**

Did the student **UNDERSTANDING**

- ❑ make important observations?
- ❑ extend or generalize learning?
- ❑ provide insightful answers?
- ❑ pose insightful questions?

Informal Assessment
☑ **Guided Discussion**

Did the student **REASONING**

- ❑ provide a clear explanation?
- ❑ communicate reasons and strategies?
- ❑ choose appropriate strategies?
- ❑ argue logically?

B Summarize Findings

Analyze and summarize assessment data for each student. Determine which Assessment Follow-Up is appropriate for each student. Use the Student Assessment Record in **Assessment** or **eAssess** to update assessment records.

Assessment Page T41

C Assessment Follow-Up • DIFFERENTIATE INSTRUCTION

Based on your observations, use these teaching strategies for assessment follow-up.

INTERVENTION

Review student performance on **Intervention** Lesson 7.A to see if students have mastered prerequisite skills for this lesson.

ENGLISH LEARNER

Review

Use Lesson 7.7 in **English Learner Support Guide** to review lesson concepts and vocabulary.

ENRICH

If . . . students are proficient in the lesson concepts,

Then . . . encourage them to work on chapter projects or **Enrichment** Lesson 7.7.

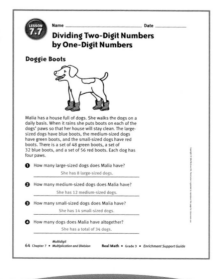

Enrichment Lesson 7.7

PRACTICE

If . . . students would benefit from additional practice,

Then . . . assign **Practice** Lesson 7.7.

Practice Lesson 7.7

RETEACH

If . . . students struggle with comparing exchanging money with dividing,

Then . . . have them think about when they subtract and have to rewrite the number. This is the same concept. Encourage students to model the problems using **Number Cubes**.

Lesson Planner

OBJECTIVES

- To help students discover how to divide a three-digit number by a one-digit number (with whole-number answers)
- To develop the standard algorithm for dividing a three-digit number by a one-digit number

NCTM STANDARDS

Number and Operations
Understanding meanings of operations and how they relate to one another

Connections
Recognizing and using connections among mathematical ideas

MATERIALS

- *Response Wheels
- Play money, $1, $10, and $100 bills

TECHNOLOGY

ⓔ **Presentation** Lesson 7.8
ⓔ **Games** Cube 100
Building Blocks Word Problems 6

TEST PREP

Cumulative Review (Review)

- Mental Math reviews multiplication facts (Chapter 5).
- Problems 5 and 6 review multiplying two-digit numbers by one-digit numbers (Lesson 7.2).
- Problem 7 reviews multiplying three-digit numbers by one-digit numbers (Lesson 7.3).

Dividing Three-Digit Numbers by One-Digit Numbers

Context of the Lesson This is the fourth of four lessons on multidigit division. In this lesson students will further develop the division algorithm from Lesson 7.7. Again the answers will be whole numbers only. Students will use this algorithm in Grade 4 to divide by one- and two-digit divisors.

See page 248B for Math Background for teachers for this lesson.

Planning for Learning ● DIFFERENTIATE INSTRUCTION

INTERVENTION

If . . . students lack the prerequisite skill of multidigit addition and subtraction,

Then . . . teach *Intervention* Lesson 7.C.

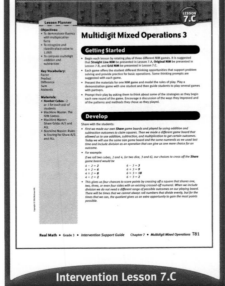

Intervention Lesson 7.C

ENGLISH LEARNER

Preview

If . . . students need language support,

Then . . . use Lesson 7.8 in *English Learner Support Guide* to preview lesson concepts and vocabulary.

English Learner Lesson 7.8

ENRICH

If . . . students are proficient in the lesson concepts,

Then . . . emphasize the student pages.

PRACTICE

If . . . students would benefit from additional practice,

Then . . . extend Guided Discussion before assigning the student pages.

RETEACH

If . . . students are having difficulty understanding dividing three-digit numbers by one-digit numbers,

Then . . . extend Guided Discussion before assigning the student pages.

Spanish Cognates
to contribute contribuir
baseball béisbol

*Manipulative Kit Item

Mental Math 5

  Practice multiplication facts. Use examples such as the following:

a. $3 \times 5 = 15$

b. $7 \times 7 = 49$

c. $8 \times 7 = 56$

d. $6 \times 8 = 48$

e. $9 \times 9 = 81$

f. $7 \times 5 = 35$

g. $4 \times 7 = 28$

h. $7 \times 6 = 42$

i. $4 \times 8 = 32$

j. $8 \times 8 = 64$

k. $6 \times 9 = 54$

l. $8 \times 9 = 72$

1 Develop 25

Tell Students In Today's Lesson They Will

explore how to divide three-digit numbers by one-digit numbers.

Guided Discussion UNDERSTANDING Small Group

Divide your class into groups of seven. (If you have unequal groups, assign watchers; or if there are students who are comfortable with exchanging money, have them be bankers. Have only $1, $10, and $100 bills available in your bank.)

Repeat the process from Lesson 7.7 to calculate 336 ÷ 7. Give students three $100 bills, three $10 bills, and six $1 bills. Either while they are dividing the money or after they have finished, have them keep a record of what happened. For this problem, the record might look like the example below.

7   336

Ask questions such as the following:

■ **Can each person take a $100 bill?** no

■ **What do we need to do?** Change the 3 hundreds to 30 tens.

■ **How many tens do we have now?** 33

■ **How many tens can each person take?** 4

Write the 4 in the tens column above the original amount of money:

$$\begin{array}{r} 4 \\ 7\ 336 \end{array}$$

■ **How many tens does that use?** 28

■ **How many tens are left to be distributed?** 5

Write the 28 and the difference:

$$\begin{array}{r} 4 \\ 7\quad 336 \\ \underline{28} \\ 5 \end{array}$$

■ **What are you going to do with the 5 tens?** change them for 50 ones

■ **How many ones will you have altogether?** 56

Write the new total.

■ **How many ones will each person get?** 8

Write the 8 above the original 6 in the ones columns.

■ **How many ones does that use?** 56

Write the 56 below the bottom 56 in the problem:

■ **How many ones are left?** Subtract 56 from 56, resulting in 0.

Write the difference.

You may now want to draw lines between the number of people, the original $336, and the answer ($48) to get a pattern that looks like the standard algorithm.

$$\begin{array}{r} 48 \\ 7\overline{)336} \\ \underline{28} \\ 56 \\ \underline{56} \\ 0 \end{array}$$

Do two or three more problems such as the following with the groups, keeping records as you go.

$392 \div 7 = 56$ $8\overline{)232}$ 29 $230 \div 5 = 46$ $6\overline{)426}$ 71

2 Assign Student Pages 20

Pages 274–275 APPLYING

Have students complete the exercises on pages 274 and 275 independently. They will need to keep records of their work to show understanding.

As Students Finish

 Building Blocks *Word Problems 6*

 Game Cube 100 Game

e Games *Cube 100 Game*

LESSON 7.8 Dividing Three-Digit Numbers by One-Digit Numbers

Key Ideas

Dividing a three-digit number by a one-digit number is like dividing a two-digit number by a one-digit number.

Alfred and his 5 friends broke Mr. McGinty's window with a baseball while playing next door. The cost to replace the window is $474. How much will each person contribute if Alfred and his friends are going to split the cost of the replacement window equally?

Alfred knew that $474 was a bit less than $600, so first he estimated that each person was going to contribute a bit less than $100, because $6 \times 100 = 600$.

Then he began to find the actual cost with play money.

6)4 hundreds 7 tens 4 ones

Alfred noticed there are not enough $100 bills to divide equally. He decides to exchange all four $100 bills for forty $10 bills. He now has forty-seven $10 bills.

6)47 tens 4 ones

When he divides the $10 bills one at a time into piles, each group gets seven $10 bills. He records this amount.

$$
\begin{array}{r}
7 \text{ tens} \\
6)\overline{47 \text{ tens} 4 \text{ ones}} \\
-\ 42 \text{ tens} \\
\hline
5 \text{ tens } 4 \text{ ones} \rightarrow 54 \text{ ones}
\end{array}
$$

Alfred is left with 5 tens and 4 ones. He exchanges the tens for fifty $1 bills. He now has fifty-four $1 bills.

274   📖 **Textbook** This lesson is available in the *eTextbook*.

Alfred distributes the $1 bills and each pile gets 9 altogether.

$$
\begin{array}{r}
7 \text{ tens } \underline{9 \text{ ones}} \\
6)\overline{47 \text{ tens } 4 \text{ ones}} \\
\underline{42 \text{ tens}} \\
54 \text{ ones} \\
\underline{54 \text{ ones}} \\
0
\end{array}
$$

He has divided all the money. Each person will contribute $79.

Divide. Keep records like Alfred's to show your answer.

❶ $125 \div 5 = \blacksquare$ 25   ❷ $324 \div 6 = \blacksquare$ 54   ❸ $314 \div 2 = \blacksquare$ 157

Solve. Use play money or other manipulatives if you wish. Be sure to label your answer correctly.

❹ Gretchen, Hank, Isaac, Judith, Kevin, Liam, Maggie, and Nell have 584 smelly stickers that they wish to divide equally among themselves. How many stickers will each person get?   73 stickers

❺ There are 3 feet in a yard. How many yards are there in 852 feet?   284 yards

❻ How many feet are in 300 yards?   900 feet

❼ How many feet are in 280 yards?   840 feet

❽ How many yards are in 282 feet?   94 yards

---

3 Reflect   10 ⏱

Guided Discussion   **UNDERSTANDING**   Whole Group

Ask students how they can check to see that they got the correct answer when they divided (for example, 336 by 7). They could multiply 7 times 48 to see if they get 336. Multiplication and division (with no remainders) are inverse operations, division answers can be checked using multiplication. Another possible answer is to approximate 70 ÷ 7 (10) and 700 ÷ 7 (100). Therefore, the answer should be between 10 and 100; 48 is indeed a reasonable answer.

Cumulative Review: For cumulative review of previously learned skills, see page 279–280.

Family Involvement: Assign the *Practice, Reteach,* or *Enrichment* activities depending on the needs of your students.

Encourage students to play the **Roll a Problem Game (Multiplication)** with a friend or a relative.

Concept/Question Board: Have students attempt to answer any unanswered questions on the Concept/Question Board.

Math Puzzler: Josephine bought 2 pears and 1 apple for $1.15. Ersheka bought 3 pears and spent $1.20. Quincy bought 1 apple and 1 mango for $0.85. How much does a mango cost? 50¢

4 Assess and Differentiate

 Assess Use *eAssess* to record and analyze evidence of student understanding.

A Gather Evidence

Use the Daily Class Assessment Records in *Assessment* or *eAssess* to record daily observations.

Informal Assessment
☑ **Guided Discussion**

Did the student **UNDERSTANDING**
- ❏ make important observations?
- ❏ extend or generalize learning?
- ❏ provide insightful answers?
- ❏ pose insightful questions?

Informal Assessment
☑ **Student Pages**

Did the student **APPLYING**
- ❏ apply learning in new situations?
- ❏ contribute concepts?
- ❏ contribute answers?
- ❏ connect mathematics to real-world situations?

B Summarize Findings

Analyze and summarize assessment data for each student. Determine which Assessment Follow-Up is appropriate for each student. Use the Student Assessment Record in *Assessment* or *eAssess* to update assessment records.

Assessment Page T41

C Assessment Follow-Up ● DIFFERENTIATE INSTRUCTION

Based on your observations, use these teaching strategies for assessment follow-up.

INTERVENTION

Review student performance on *Intervention* Lesson 7.C to see if students have mastered prerequisite skills for this lesson.

ENGLISH LEARNER

Review

Use Lesson 7.8 in *English Learner Support Guide* to review lesson concepts and vocabulary.

ENRICH

If . . . students are proficient in the lesson concepts,

Then . . . encourage them to work on chapter projects or *Enrichment* Lesson 7.8.

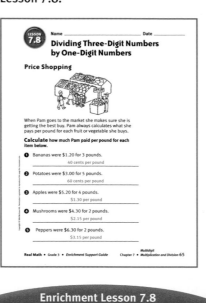

Enrichment Lesson 7.8

PRACTICE

If . . . students would benefit from additional practice,

Then . . . assign *Practice* Lesson 7.8.

Practice Lesson 7.8

RETEACH

If . . . students are having difficulty understanding dividing three-digit numbers by one-digit numbers,

Then . . . have them use play money to demonstrate the steps in a problem such as 515 ÷ 5. 103

OBJECTIVES
To give practice in solving simple word problems

NCTM STANDARDS

Number and Operations
Understanding meanings of operations and how they relate to one another

Problem Solving
Solving problems that arise in mathematics and in other contexts

Connections
Recognizing and applying mathematics in contexts outside of mathematics

MATERIALS
- *Response Wheels
- Counters
- *Harder Shopping Game Mat

TECHNOLOGY
Presentation Lesson 7.9
Building Blocks Word Problems 10

TEST PREP

Cumulative Review
- Mental Math reviews multiplying by 10, 100, and 1,000 (Lesson 7.1).
- Problems 1 and 2 review subtracting two-digit numbers (Lesson 2.4).
- Problem 10 reviews perimeter (Lesson 3.6).

Extended Response
Problems 6 and 11

Problem-Solving Applications

Context of the Lesson In this lesson students will solve word problems, some of which require skills from this chapter (multidigit multiplication and division). Such applications for problem solving are incorporated throughout the entire *Real Math* program.

See page 248B for Math Background for teachers for this lesson.

Planning for Learning ● DIFFERENTIATE INSTRUCTION

INTERVENTION

If . . . students lack the prerequisite skill of multidigit addition and subtraction,

Then . . . teach *Intervention* Lesson 7.C.

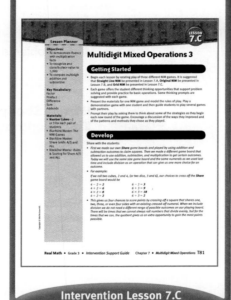

Intervention Lesson 7.C

ENGLISH LEARNER

Preview

If . . . students need language support,

Then . . . use Lesson 7.9 in *English Learner Support Guide* to preview lesson concepts and vocabulary.

English Learner Lesson 7.9

ENRICH

If . . . students are proficient in the lesson concepts,

Then . . . emphasize the student pages.

PRACTICE

If . . . students would benefit from additional practice,

Then . . . extend Strategy Building before assigning the student pages.

RETEACH

If . . . students are having difficulty understanding problem-solving applications,

Then . . . extend Strategy Building before assigning the student pages.

Spanish Cognates
mathematical matemático

Teaching Lesson 7.9

Mental Math 10

  Review multiplying by 10, 100, or 1,000. Use examples such as the following:

a. $100 \times 5 = 500$ **b.** $10 \times 20 = 200$

c. $10 \times 266 = 2{,}660$ **d.** $9 \times 100 = 900$

e. $25 \times 1{,}000 = 25{,}000$ **f.** $261 \times 100 = 26{,}100$

g. $100 \times 12 = 1{,}200$ **h.** $100 \times 138 = 13{,}800$

i. $1{,}000 \times 99 = 99{,}000$ **j.** $18 \times 10 = 180$

k. $134 \times 100 = 13{,}400$ **l.** $1{,}000 \times 10 = 10{,}000$

1 Develop 25

Tell Students In Today's Lesson They Will

solve word problems.

Strategy Building UNDERSTANDING Whole Group

Read a problem aloud, and ask students which operation (if any) they would use to solve the problem. Ask why they would use the operation(s) they decided upon. Have students solve the problem and check to see that the answer makes sense (with respect to the original problem). If students have difficulty, draw a picture or have them act out the story with objects. Also, consider using smaller numbers in the problems at first.

Use examples such as the following:

- **There are 4 chairs at each table in the room. There are 8 tables in the room. How many chairs are in the room?** multiply, because there are 8 groups of 4 chairs each; $8 \times 4 = 32$; there are 32 chairs
- **There are 32 chairs in the room and 27 people. If each person sits in a chair, how many chairs will be unused?** subtract, because each person who sits uses a chair; $32 - 27 = 5$; there are 5 unused chairs
- **Each window in the room has 6 panes of glass. There are 5 windows in the room. How many panes are there?** multiply; $5 \times 6 = 30$; there are 30 panes in the room

- **Dwight can reach to a height of 2 meters with his hand when he jumps. Merika can also reach to a height of 2 meters when she jumps. How high can they reach when they jump at the same time?** no operation needed; When they both jump, they don't go any higher than when they jump alone; the best answer here is 2 meters.

2 Assign Student Pages 20

Pages 276–277 APPLYING

Have students complete the exercises on pages 276 and 277 independently. Modeling the problems or drawing a picture may help discover the operation.

Monitoring Student Progress

If . . . students have difficulty completing pages 276 and 277,	**Then . . .** read the problems to students. Assist them in acting out or modeling the problem. If students can determine the correct operation to use when appropriate, but get wrong answers, you may want to give appropriate extra computation remediation.

As Students Finish

Building **B**locks Word Problems 10

 Game **Harder Shopping Game** This is a harder version of **The Shopping Game** from Chapter 6.

LESSON 7.9 Problem-Solving Applications

Key Ideas

When solving a problem, be sure you understand the situation, and be sure your answer makes sense when you finish. After deciding which operation to use, estimate your answer. Once you have solved the problem or exercise, be sure to compare your answer to your estimation. Some problems may not be possible to solve, but be sure to try all of your options before deciding an answer cannot be found.

Solve.

 1 Three months ago Chris weighed 89 pounds. Now he weighs 92 pounds. How many pounds did he gain in the last 3 months? 3

 2 Chelsea had 24 balloons. Some of them burst. Now she has 4 balloons. How many burst? 20

3 Mrs. James bought 13 packages of candles. Each package holds 6 candles. How many candles did she buy? 78

4 It usually takes Benjamin 2 hours to do his homework. It usually takes his twin sister 1 hour to do hers. If they work together, how long will it take to do their homework?
can't tell; probably less than 2 hours

5 Stickers cost 11¢ each. Lana has 45¢. How many stickers can she buy? Will she have any change and if so, how much? 4; yes; 1¢

6 **Extended Response** Abigail used a calculator to calculate 345 × 3. Her answer was 105. What mistake did Abigail most likely make?
She most likely didn't push the 4 or the calculator did not register the 4.

276 **Textbook** This lesson is available in the *eTextbook.*

Solve.

7 Jorge, Phillip, and Cody had a race. Each child finished the race in about 20 seconds. About how long did the race take?
about 20 seconds

8 Maria bought 9 packages of paper cups. Each package has 25 cups. How many paper cups did Maria buy?
225 cups

9 The area of a rectangle is 72 square meters. One side is 9 meters long. How long is the adjacent side?

10 What is the perimeter of the rectangle in Problem 9?
34 meters

Solve.

Most years have 365 days. Leap years have 366 days. Leap years come every four years. In a leap year, February has 29 days instead of 28 days. The years 1988, 1992, 1996, 2000, 2004, and 2008 are leap years.

February						
SUN	MON	TUE	WED	THU	FRI	SAT
			1	2	3	4	5
6	7	8	9	10	11	12
13	14	15	16	17	18	19
20	21	22	23	24	25	26
27	28	29				

11 **Extended Response** Mohammed just had his second birthday. Could he have been alive during a leap year? Explain your answer.

12 Bridget was born exactly 4 years before her cousin Angie. One of those years was a leap year. Bridget is how many days older than her cousin? 1,461

9 8 meters because the area of a rectangle is the product of the two adjacent sides; 72 divided by 9 = 8, or 9 × 8 = 72

11 The answer will depend on the year in which the question is answered.

277

Problem-Solving Applications LESSON 7.9

3 Reflect 5

Guided Discussion UNDERSTANDING Whole Group

Present this problem to the class:

Suppose a field trip cost $132 and there are 12 students sharing the cost equally. What would each student's share be?

Point out, if necessary, that the class has not yet learned to do 132 ÷ 12, which is the necessary calculation.

Allow students to discuss possible solutions and praise all correct or near-correct strategies. Point out that half of 132 is 66 if students don't suggest it. Also point out, if necessary, that they know how to divide 66 by 6; 66 ÷ 6 = 11.

■ **If 66 ÷ 6 = 11, then how much is twice that or what is 132 ÷ 12?**
11

Have students check the answer. How much is 11 × 12?

$10 \times 12 = 120$

$1 \times 12 = 12$

$120 + 12 = 132$

Use Mastery Checkpoint 16 found in **Assessment** to evaluate student mastery of arithmetic applications. By this time students should be able to correctly answer eighty percent of the Mastery Checkpoint items.

 Curriculum Connection: Students may be interested in researching the history of leap years, such as when it started, why we have them, which countries have leap years, and so on.

 Cumulative Review: For cumulative review of previously learned skills, see page 279–280.

 Family Involvement: Assign the **Practice, Reteach,** or **Enrichment** activities depending on the needs of your students.

Encourage students to play the **Harder Shopping Game** with a friend or a relative.

Concept/Question Board: Have students attempt to answer any unanswered questions on the Concept/Question Board.

 Math Puzzler: Christy ate 12 pancakes, Stefano ate 6, and Josh ate 13. If they started with 60 pancakes, how many pancakes are left? Describe how to solve the problem using words and a formula. add to get the number eaten and subtract that from 60; 12 + 6 + 13 = 31; 60 − 31 = 29

4 Assess and Differentiate

 Assess Use *eAssess* to record and analyze evidence of student understanding.

A Gather Evidence

Use the Daily Class Assessment Records in *Assessment* or *eAssess* to record daily observations.

Formal Assessment
✓ **Mastery Checkpoint**

Did the student
- ☐ use correct procedures?
- ☐ respond with at least 80% accuracy?

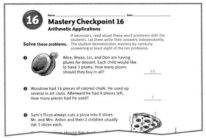

Assessment Page T68

B Summarize Findings

Analyze and summarize assessment data for each student. Determine which Assessment Follow-Up is appropriate for each student. Use the Student Assessment Record in *Assessment* or *eAssess* to update assessment records.

Assessment Page T41

C Assessment Follow-Up • DIFFERENTIATE INSTRUCTION

Based on your observations, use these teaching strategies for assessment follow-up.

INTERVENTION	ENRICH	PRACTICE	RETEACH
Review student performance on *Intervention* Lesson 7.C to see if students have mastered prerequisite skills for this lesson.	**If . . .** students are proficient in the lesson concepts, **Then . . .** encourage them to work on chapter projects or *Enrichment* Lesson 7.9.	**If . . .** students would benefit from additional practice, **Then . . .** assign *Practice* Lesson 7.9.	**If . . .** students struggle with choosing the correct operation for a word problem, **Then . . .** have them draw pictures or act out the situations described in the problems. For students who determine the correct operation but get wrong answers, give appropriate extra practice.

ENGLISH LEARNER
Review

Use Lesson 7.9 in *English Learner Support Guide* to review lesson concepts and vocabulary.

Enrichment Lesson 7.9

Practice Lesson 7.9

Exploring Problem Solving

Objectives
- To provide practice applying multiplication and division to a nonroutine, real-world problem
- To explore how the arrangement of objects may or may not affect how many can fit in a box

Materials
- Rulers
- Coin holder (optional)

Context of the Lesson This lesson provides an opportunity for students to think flexibly about spatial arrangements and to use in a new way what they have been learning about multiplication and division. The lesson also continues the theme of money and banking introduced in the chapter opener.

1 Develop 5

Tell Students In Today's Lesson They Will
find out how many coin holders can fit in a box.

Guided Discussion
Have students talk about collections and how people display their collections. Ask students whether they have ever had to pack their collections or other things into boxes. Tell them they will be figuring out how to pack a coin collection into a box.

2 Exploring Problem Solving 30

Using Student Pages
Read the problem on page 278 with the class. If possible, show an example of the kind of plastic coin case illustrated on the page. Make sure students understand the problem by asking questions such as the following:

- **What is the problem asking?** how many coin holders can fit in the box
- **Does the problem tell you how to pack the holders in the box?** no
- **What information does the problem give?** the exact size of each holder and of the box
- **Do all the holders have to face the same way?** no

Exploring Problem Solving

Elliot's grandfather gave him a coin collection. Each coin is in a clear plastic holder. Elliot will store the holders in a box until he gets a display cabinet. How many holders can he pack in the box?

Work with your group to solve the following problems.

1. Is there more than one way to arrange the holders in the box?
2. How will you arrange the coin holders in the box? *See Teacher's Edition*
3. If you arrange the holders that way, how many can fit in the box? *See Teacher's Edition.*
4. What is the greatest number of holders that will fit in the box? How do you know? There is room for 168 coin holders. *See Teacher's Edition.*

278

Textbook This lesson is available in the *eTextbook.*

Then read and discuss Problems 1 and 2, emphasizing the following points:

- There are different ways to pack the box.
- If space is left over on the sides or ends of the box, more holders can be packed there.
- It will be important to keep track of how the holders are packed and how many there are in the box.

Have students work in small groups on Problems 3 and 4. Circulate around the room to observe their approaches. Allow them to struggle with the problem for a while, complimenting their efforts. If a group seems frustrated or at an impasse, ask questions such as the following:

- **Would a model or diagram of the holders and the box help?**
- **What are some ways you could stack the holders?**
- **How tall would a stack of two holders be? Of three holders?**
- **How might you use a ruler to make a diagram to show the bottom of the box?**
- **How many coin holders would fit on the bottom of the box?**
- **How many layers of coin holders will fit in the box?**
- **How can you use the spaces that are left over?**

Answer to Problem 4

Here is one way to pack the box to fit 168 holders:

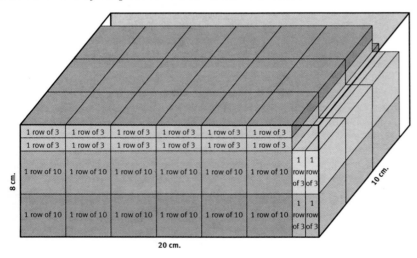

Reflect

Knowledge Age Skills

Problem Formulation, Planning, and Strategizing Have each group share their answer and their strategy for finding the answer. Help students understand the following points:

- When tackling a difficult problem, it often helps to break the problem into parts. In this example, you might think first of packing as many holders as you can facing one way. Then you might think about filling the empty spaces.
- You can make it easier to keep track of what you are doing by recording the things you do in a clear and organized way.

- Recording a three-dimensional situation such as this example is more challenging than a two-dimensional situation. People sometimes use diagrams that look three-dimensional. Sometimes they use words, equations, and a combination of different views, such as a side view, front view, and top view.
- Even though there were several ways to arrange the coin holders in the box, it always held the same number. That is not always true. In many situations, the way you pack affects how many can fit.

Sample Solutions Strategies

Students might use one or more of the following strategies to help solve the problem.

Make a Physical Model

Students might look for books or other objects that have a shape like the coin holders. They might stack them to get an idea of how they go together.

Students might fold paper to make a model of the box and mark off the number of holders that could fit on the bottom and along the side.

Make a Diagram

Students might outline the bottom of the box on graph paper and draw in the holders to see how many can fit flat on the bottom.

Break the Problem into Parts

Students might section off parts of the box and figure out how many coin holders will fit in each section. For example, they might figure out how many holders will fit into a section that is $9 \times 18 \times 6$, and then how many will fit in the 2-inch high section above that and how many will fit into the 2-inch section on the end.

Assess

When evaluating student work, think not only about whether the answer was correct, but consider whether the student thought rationally about the problem. Questions to consider include the following:

- Did the student understand the problem?
- Did the student use division and/or multiplication in appropriate ways to work on the problem?
- Was the student able to find a way to visualize the holders in the box?
- Did the student check the answer?
- Was the student able to find more than one way to pack the box?
- If the student made a model or diagram, was it used appropriately?

Cumulative Review

Assign Pages 279–280

Use the Cumulative Review as a review of concepts and skills that students have previously learned.

Here are different ways that you can assign these problems to your students as they work through the chapter:

- With some of the lessons in the chapter, assign a set of cumulative review problems to be completed as practice or for homework.
  Lesson 7.5—Problems 1–10
  Lesson 7.6—Problems 11–12
  Lesson 7.7—Problems 13–14
  Lesson 7.8—Problems 15–16
  Lesson 7.9—Problems 17–18
- At any point during the chapter, assign part or all of the cumulative review problems to be completed as practice or for homework.

Cumulative Review

Problems 1–10 review rounding to tens and thousands, Lesson 1.8.

Problems 11–12 review missing factors and division, Lesson 5.7.

Problems 13–14 review division and multiplication functions, Grade 2 Lesson 11.9.

Problems 15–16 review writing multiplication sentences, Lesson 4.8.

Problems 17–18 review functions with mixed operations, Grade 2 Lesson 12.3.

Monitoring Student Progress

If . . . students miss more than one problem in a section,

Then . . . refer to the indicated lesson for remediation suggestions.

Rounding Lesson 1.8

Round to the nearest ten in Problems 1–5. Round to the nearest thousand in Problems 6–10.

❶ 54	50	❻ 5,137	5,000
❷ 29	30	❼ 4,713	5,000
❸ 369	370	❽ 7,248	7,000
❹ 888	890	❾ 3,634	4,000
❺ 537	540	❿ 2,492	2,000

Missing Factors and Division I Lesson 5.7

Solve each problem.

⓫ There are 36 employees and 4 banks. How many employees are there for each bank?

$4 \times \blacksquare = 36$ 9 $36 \div 4 = \blacksquare$ 9

⓬ There are 30 ATMs in the entire county. There are 6 ATMs in each city in the county. How many cities are in the county?

$6 \times \blacksquare = 30$ 5 $30 \div 6 = \blacksquare$ 5

Division and Multiplication Functions Grade 2 Lesson 11.9

Find the function rules.

⓭ in → ÷3 → out

18	6
33	11
42	14
9	3

⓮ ÷4

40	10
36	9
32	8
28	7

Cumulative Review

Commutative Law of Multiplication Lesson 4.8

Write the multiplication sentence for each problem. Then solve the problem.

⓯ Rosa has eight $5 bills. How much money does she have in dollars? $8 \times 5 = 40$; $40

⓰ Moisha drove to 4 different banks each day for 6 days. How many banks did she visit? $4 \times 6 = 24$; 24 banks

More Functions with Mixed Operations Grade 2 Lesson 12.3

Find the simplified function rules.

⓱ The rule is ×8 ÷ 2. The simplified rule is ■.

×4

2	8
4	16
6	24
8	32

⓲ The rule is ×9 ÷ 3. The simplified rule is ■.

in → ×3 → out

3	9
6	18
7	21
8	24

Wrap-Up

1 Discuss 5

Concept/Question Board

Review the Concept/Question Board with students.
- Discuss students' contributions to the Concept side of the Board.
- Have students re-pose their questions, and lead a discussion to find satisfactory answers.

Chapter Projects APPLYING

Provide an opportunity for students who have worked on one or more of the projects outlined on page 249C to share their work with the class. Allow each student or student group five minutes to present or discuss their projects. For formal assessment, use the rubrics found in *Across the Curriculum Math Connections;* the rubric for **Create a Monetary System** is on page 77, and the rubric for **Research Coin Minting** is on page 81. For informal assessment, use the following rubric and questions.

	Exceeds Expectations	Meets Expectations	Minimally Meets Expectations
Applies mathematics in real-world situations:	❑	❑	❑
Demonstrates strong engagement in the activity:	❑	❑	❑

Create a Monetary System

- What name did you give your currency? Is it paper money or coin money?
- How did you use multiplication to create your monetary system?
- What subdivisions does your money have?
- How did you use the decimal system to create your subdivisions?
- What design did you use for your currency? Why did you choose that design?
- How did you use a spreadsheet program to calculate the subdivisions of your currency?

Research Coin Minting

- How are coins minted?
- What physical changes occur to the metal during the minting process?
- How many coins has the United States Treasury produced since the year 2000? How did you find this information?
- How did you use a search engine to find information about the history of coins?
- What details did you include in your report?
- How is the Internet a useful tool in writing a report?

2 Assign Student Pages 25

Key Ideas Review ✓ UNDERSTANDING

Have students complete the Review questions independently or in small groups. Then discuss each question as a class.

Possible Answers

Problem ❶ Problems 1–4 review multidigit multiplication. The answer to Problem 1 is 300.

Problem ❷ The answer is 615.

Problem ❸ The answer is 28.

Problem ❹ The answer is 2,703.

Problem ❺ Problems 5–8 review multidigit division. The answer to Problem 5 is 4 R1.

Problem ❻ The answer is 26.

Problem ❼ The answer is 9 R1.

Problem ❽ The answer is 34 R1.

`Extended Response`

Problem ❾ This problem reviews applications of multidigit division. The answer is 1. Students should refer to the remainder of the division problem.

`Extended Response`

Problem ❿ This problem reviews applications of multidigit multiplication and division. The answer is 112. Possible answers as to how Jurgen would divide his marbles include 2 piles of 56, 4 piles of 28, 7 piles of 16, and 8 piles of 14.

CHAPTER 7 Key Ideas Review

In this chapter you learned multidigit multiplication and division.

You learned two- and three-digit multiplication before exploring applications of multiplication.

You learned about remainders in division before being introduced to two-digit and three-digit division, as well as applications of division.

Solve the following multiplication problems.

❶ $100 \times 3 =$ ■ 300

❷ $123 \times 5 =$ ■ 615

❸ $14 \times 2 =$ ■ 28

❹ $901 \times 3 =$ ■ 2,703

Solve the following division problems. Write the remainders if necessary.

❺ $9 \div 2$ 4 R1

❻ $78 \div 3$ 26

❼ $64 \div 7$ 9 R1

❽ $103 \div 3$ 34 R1

Provide a detailed answer for the following exercises. `Extended Response`

❾ Josh and Mary want to divide a pile of 28 baseball cards into 3 equal piles. Are there any extra baseball cards after they divide them into piles? How do you know?

❿ Jurgen has 28 marbles, and Juan gave him 3 times as many marbles. How many marbles does Jurgen have now? If Jurgen wants to divide all of his marbles into equal piles, what is one way he could divide them?

Ⓒ Textbook This lesson is available in the *eTextbook*. 281

Chapter Review

Use the Chapter 7 Review to indicate areas in which each student is having difficulty or in which the class may need help. If students do well on the Chapter 7 Review, you may wish to skip directly to the Chapter Test; if not, you may want to spend a day or so helping students overcome their individual difficulties before taking the Practice Test.

Next to each set of problems is a list of the lessons in the chapter that covered those concepts. If they need help, students can refer to a specific lesson for additional instruction. You can also use this information to make additional assignments based on the previous lesson concepts.

Have students complete pages 282–283 on their own. For review purposes, you may want to do some of the word problems on page 283 as a class.

Monitoring Student Progress

Problems 1–5 Lessons 7.1–7.2

If . . . students miss one of these addition and multiplication problems,

Then . . . explain the relationship between addition and multiplication by 10s and 100s to show how addition can be used to find the answers to the multiplication problems and vice versa.

Problems 6–9 Lesson 7.3

If . . . students miss more than one of these multiplication problems,

Then . . . review the algorithm for multiplying three-digit numbers by one-digit numbers.

Problems 10–18 Lessons 7.5–7.9

If . . . students miss more than three of these division and multiplication problems,

Then . . . clarify the concept of a remainder and point out the relationship between multiplication and division.

CHAPTER 7 · Chapter Review

Lesson 7.1 **Find** the missing terms.

1. 1,000; 2,000; 3,000; ▮; 5,000   4,000

   8,000; 9,000; 10,000; ▮; 12,000   11,000

   120; 110; 100; ▮; 80   90

2. 90; 100; 110; ▮; 130   120

   500; 600; 700; ▮; 900   800

   160; 170; 180; ▮; 200   190

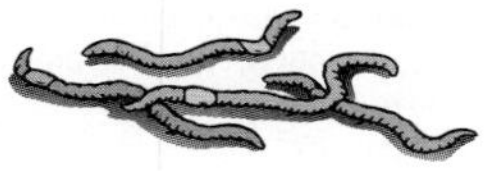

Lesson 7.2 3. At a bait shop, Bonnie bought 4 bags of earthworms. Each bag had 46 earthworms.

   a. How many earthworms did Bonnie buy?   184

   b. If Sue and Nancy each bought 2 bags of earthworms with 46 earthworms in each bag, how many earthworms do Bonnie, Sue, and Nancy have altogether?   368

   c. If Jon buys 3 bags of earthworms with 10 earthworms in each bag, how many earthworms do Jon and Sue have altogether?   122

Lesson 7.3 **Multiply.**

4. 123 × 2 = ▮ 246   5. 500 × 3 = ▮ 1,500

   123 × 3 = ▮ 369   250 × 3 = ▮ 750

   123 × 4 = ▮ 492   125 × 3 = ▮ 375

Lesson 7.5 **Determine** the remainder.

6. 34 ÷ 5 R4   7. 38 ÷ 3 R2   8. 48 ÷ 6 0   9. 13 ÷ 7 R6

282   Textbook This lesson is available in the *eTextbook*.

Lesson 7.6

Choose the correct answer.

10. Lance has 32 buttons, and he wants to make suits with 4 buttons each. How many suits can he make?

    a. 2
    b. 4
    c. 6
    d. 8

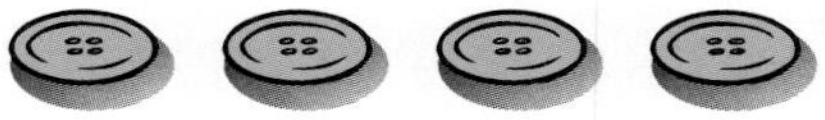

11. Andy wants to split a pizza among 3 friends and himself. The pizza has a total of 10 slices. If each receives an equal number of whole slices, how many whole slices will each person have?

    a. 1
    b. 2
    c. 3
    d. 4

Lessons 7.7 and 7.8

Divide.

12. 32 ÷ 2 16   13. 32 ÷ 8 4   14. 126 ÷ 6 21   15. 120 ÷ 5 24

Lesson 7.9

Answer the questions.

16. Marilyn bought a pack of 36 crayons. Danielle took 2 crayons, Bob took 6 crayons, and Matt took 7 crayons. How many crayons does Marilyn have left?   21

17. Bob bought 3 times more crayons than he took from Marilyn. Matt bought 4 times more crayons than he took from Marilyn. How many crayons did Bob and Matt buy?   46

18. Matt wants to divide his 28 crayons among Marilyn, Danielle, Bob, and himself. How many crayons does each person get?   7

Chapter Tests

40

Practice Test

Student Pages 284–287

- The Chapter 7 Practice Test on *Student Edition* pages 284–287 provides an opportunity to formally evaluate students' proficiency with concepts developed in this chapter.
- The content is similar to the Chapter 7 Review, in standardized format.

Problem 31 Extended Response

Students practice their multiplication and division skills. The answer to Part a of Problem 31 is 12 roses and 8 carnations. The explanations will vary such as this: $3 + 2 = 5$, $20 \div 5 = 4$, so $3 \times 4 = 12$ roses and $2 \times 4 = 8$ carnations. The answer to Part b of Problem 31 is 160 flowers in all; $12 \times 8 = 96$ roses and $8 \times 8 = 64$ carnations; $96 + 64 = 160$ flowers in all.

Problem 32 Extended Response

The answer to Part a of Problem 32 is 24; $3 \times 8 = 24$. The answer to Part b of Problem 32 is yes; 6. For both problems, students decide which operation(s) to use to solve problems in practical situations. They practice multidigit multiplication and division skills.

CHAPTER **7** **Practice Test**

Solve.

1. $9 \times 1,000 = $ ▢   9,000

2. $142 \times 100 = $ ▢   14,200

3. Grandpa gave each of his 5 grandchildren a $10 bill. How much money did he give away? $50

4. One of the children will exchange his $10 for dimes. How many dimes will he get? 100

5. Georgia's brother spends $8 a day on lunch. If he spends the same amount every day, how much does he spend on lunch in 1 year? $2,920

6. Lisa made 6 batches of cookies. Each batch makes 96 cookies. How many cookies did Lisa make altogether? 576

7. Marc's brother is 4 years old. How many months old is he? 48

8. Marc's brother is 4 years old. How many days old is he? (Hint: Count one leap year.) 1,461

9. $63 \div 9 = $ ▢   7

10. $155 \div 4 = $ ▢   38 R3

11. Sara's aunt gave her $40 to share evenly with her sister. How much will Sara and her sister each get? $20

12. How many feet are there in 187 yards? 561

284   📖 Textbook This lesson is available in the *eTextbook*.

Find the correct answer.

13. $74 \times 7 = $ ▢
    Ⓐ 141   Ⓑ 518
    Ⓒ 718   Ⓓ 441

14. $100 \times 18 = $ ▢
    Ⓐ 18   Ⓑ 180
    Ⓒ 1,800   Ⓓ 18,000

15. $46 \times 1,000 = $ ▢
    Ⓐ 460   Ⓑ 4,600
    Ⓒ 46,000   Ⓓ 60,000

16. $153 \times 5 = $ ▢
    Ⓐ 312   Ⓑ 515
    Ⓒ 155   Ⓓ 765

17. $218 \times 7 = $ ▢
    Ⓐ 225   Ⓑ 1,308
    Ⓒ 1,519   Ⓓ 1,526

18. $231 \times 4 = $ ▢
    Ⓐ 824   Ⓑ 924
    Ⓒ 1,024   Ⓓ 876

19. $144 \times 8 = $ ▢
    Ⓐ 1,152   Ⓑ 1,072
    Ⓒ 832   Ⓓ 152

20. $87 \div 3 = $ ▢
    Ⓐ 18   Ⓑ 29
    Ⓒ 30   Ⓓ 20

CHAPTER 7 Practice Test

In the equations below, *a* stands for the unknown number. Find the value of *a*.

21. $78 \div a = 13$
Ⓐ 10   Ⓑ 8
Ⓒ 6   Ⓓ 3

22. $175 \div 5 = a$
Ⓐ 35   Ⓑ 25
Ⓒ 15   Ⓓ 5

23. There were 102 pairs of shoes in the storeroom. They were arranged equally on 6 shelves. How many pairs of shoes were on each shelf?
Ⓐ 17   Ⓑ 17 R3
Ⓒ 18 R3   Ⓓ 19

24. What is the perimeter?

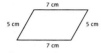

Ⓐ 12 centimeters
Ⓑ 14 centimeters
Ⓒ 24 centimeters
Ⓓ 35 centimeters

25. Would this temperature be high, low, or comfortable?

Ⓐ high
Ⓑ low
Ⓒ comfortable

Complete the following comparison using <, >, or =.

26. 47,142 ▨ 48,142
Ⓐ <
Ⓑ >
Ⓒ =

27. Which shows the same product as 3×8?
Ⓐ 9×2 Ⓑ 8×3
Ⓒ 8×4 Ⓓ 7×4

📖Textbook This lesson is available in the *eTextbook*.

---

28. What is 58,004 in expanded form?
Ⓐ $50,000 + 8,000 + 0 + 0 + 4$
Ⓑ $50,000 + 800 + 0 + 4$
Ⓒ $500,000 + 80,000 + 0 + 0 + 4$
Ⓓ $500,000 + 0 + 800 + 0 + 0 + 4$

29. How would you write 1,410 as a Roman numeral?
Ⓐ CCXXX   Ⓑ DDDDX
Ⓒ DCDX   Ⓓ MCDX

30. Find the sum.
$819 + 236 =$ ▨
Ⓐ 1,275   Ⓑ 1,255
Ⓒ 1,155   Ⓓ 1,055

Extended Response ▸ **Solve.**

31. Ralph is making small bouquets for Mother's Day. He groups 3 roses with 2 carnations. Each bouquet has 20 flowers.

a. How many roses and how many carnations does he use for each bouquet? Explain your answer.

b. Ralph made 8 bouquets. How many flowers did he use in all? How many were roses? How many were carnations? Explain your answer.

32. Ralph later got 30 orchids. He put 3 orchids in each bouquet.

a. How many orchids did he use in the bouquets? Explain your answer.

b. Did he have any orchids left over? If so, how many?

Chapter Test ✓ COMPUTING

For further evaluation instead of or in addition to this test, you might want to have students take the Chapter 7 Test provided in *Assessment*.

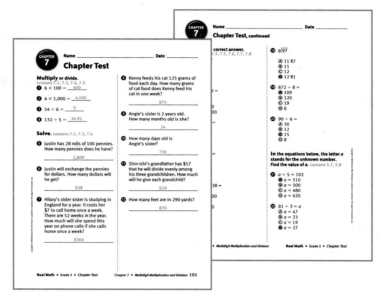

Assessment Pages 101–102

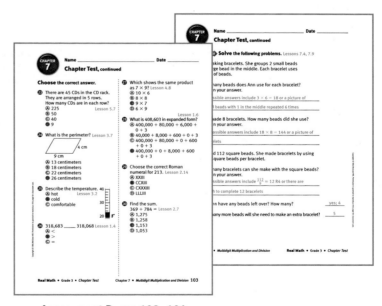

Assessment Pages 103–104

Assessment

4 Assess and Differentiate

 Assess Use **eAssess** to record and analyze evidence of student understanding.

A Gather Evidence

Use the Daily Class Assessment Records in **Assessment** or **eAssess** to record Informal and Formal Assessments.

Informal Assessment

☑ **Key Ideas Review** UNDERSTANDING

Did the student
- ❑ make important observations?
- ❑ extend or generalize learning?
- ❑ provide insightful answers?
- ❑ pose insightful questions?

Informal Assessment

☑ **Project** APPLYING

Did the student
- ❑ meet the project objectives?
- ❑ communicate clearly?
- ❑ complete the project accurately?
- ❑ connect mathematics to real-world situations?

Formal Assessment

☑ **Chapter Test** COMPUTING

Score the test, and record the results.

B Summarize Findings

Analyze and summarize assessment data for each student. Determine which Chapter Follow-Up is appropriate for each student. Use the Student Assessment Record in **Assessment** or **eAssess** to update assessment records.

C Chapter Follow-Up ● DIFFERENTIATE INSTRUCTION

Based on your observations, use these teaching strategies for chapter follow-up.

ENRICH	PRACTICE	RETEACH	INTERVENTION
If . . . students demonstrate a **secure understanding** of chapter concepts,	**If . . .** students demonstrate **competent understanding** of chapter concepts,	**If . . .** students demonstrate **emerging understanding** of chapter concepts,	**If . . .** students demonstrate **minimal understanding** of chapter concepts,
Then . . . move on to the next chapter.	**Then . . .** move on to the next chapter.	**Then . . .** move on to the next chapter, but continue to provide cumulative review.	**Then . . .** intensive intervention is still needed before they start the next chapter.

Clever Consuela

Context of the Thinking Story Manolita writes a program that makes the computer do tricky things with numbers.

Lesson Planner

OBJECTIVES
To develop logical thinking while integrating reading skills with mathematics

NCTM STANDARDS
Algebra
- Describing, extending, and making generalizations about numeric patterns
- Analyzing patterns and functions
- Representing the idea of a variable as an unknown quantity
- Investigating how a change in one variable relates to a change in a second variable

READING STANDARDS
- Listening for details
- Predicting what will happen in a story
- Drawing conclusions
- Making inferences
- Evaluating information

Using the Thinking Story

The Thinking Story may be used anytime throughout the chapter. Read the Thinking Story "Clever Consuela" to your class as they follow along in the **Student Edition** on pages 288–291. As you read the story, give students time to think about each question, but not so much that they forget the point being made. To help students follow the mathematics in this story, either have the students write down the numbers as they are entered into the computer, or write them down on the board for all to see.

Thinking Story

Manolita's mother worked with computers. She did part of her computer work at home, but she let Manolita use the computer when she wasn't working. She even taught Manolita how to write programs that would make the computer do what Manolita wanted it to do. Manolita loved number tricks, so she wrote a program that made the computer do tricky things with numbers. When the computer was running her programs, Manolita thought of it as her computer. She even gave it a name. She called it Clever Consuela. When she wrote a new program, she thought of that as teaching Clever Consuela a new trick.

"Come see the new trick I have taught Clever Consuela," she said to Marcus one day.

"I didn't know you have a dog," Marcus said.

What would make Marcus think Clever Consuela was a dog? ❶

288

"Clever Consuela is my computer," Manolita said. "When I write programs for it, it does neat things that I want it to do. That's like teaching it to do new tricks. Type any number, and see what Clever Consuela does."

Marcus typed the number 1, and it started dancing across the screen. "That's nice," Marcus said, "but I wouldn't call it clever. It just shows the number that you press and makes it dance."

"Type another number," Manolita said.

Marcus typed a 2, and immediately a number 3 started dancing across the screen. "It made a mistake," Marcus said. "I typed a 2, and a 3 came up instead."

"That's no mistake," Manolita said. "That's what it's supposed to do."

What could the computer be doing that made a 3 come up? ❷

Guided Discussion

As students answer the questions in the story, ask them to communicate how they decided on their answers. Allow students to debate the answers if necessary.

1 People name dogs and teach them tricks.

2 It is adding the numbers that are being typed.

3 It adds the last two numbers typed.

4 The number 4 was already in the computer when Marcus typed a 10: 10 + 4 = 14; the number 10 was already in the computer when Marcus typed a 4: 10 + 4 = 14.

5 3

6 It adds Old Number plus New Number to get Dancing Number.

7 Let students discuss it.

"I get it," Marcus said. "It's adding the numbers. What's so great about that? My little calculator can do that."

"Type another number," Manolita said.

"I'm typing a 4," he said, "so a 7 should come up." But a 6 came up instead. "See, it is making mistakes; 1 plus 2 plus 4 is 7, not 6."

"Clever Consuela never makes mistakes," Manolita said.

What could the computer be doing that made a 6 come up? **3**

"I don't get it," Marcus said.

"Type another number," Manolita said.

This time Marcus typed a 10, and the number that danced across the screen was 14. "I'm starting to get an idea," Marcus said. He typed a 4 and a 14 danced across the screen, just as it had before.

"That's just what I expected," Marcus said.

What could the computer be doing that made 14 come up after Marcus typed 10, and that also made 14 come up after he typed 4? **4**

Marcus typed again. "This time an 8 should come up," he said, and he was right. "Consuela is clever, but not too clever for me," he said. "Now I know what the computer will do every time. If I type a 3, 7 will come up. See, it did. Now if I type 2, 5 will come up. Now if I type 1 . . . "

What number will dance across the screen if Marcus types 1 after he typed 2 the time before? **5**

"Three comes up, just the way it should," Marcus said. "Consuela just adds the number I type to the number I typed before. That's all there is to it. But how did you get the computer to do that?"

"There are things called variables," Manolita said. "I programmed Clever Consuela to recognize three variables. One is

290

called *Old Number*, one is called *New Number*, and one is called *Dancing Number*. New Number is the number you type in. The computer figures out what Dancing Number is."

How could the computer figure out what Dancing Number should be? **6**

"That part is easy," said Marcus. "Dancing Number equals Old Number plus New Number. But how does the computer know what Old Number is? It keeps changing."

"That's the tricky part," said Manolita. "When you start the program, Old Number is always 0. That's why, when you typed 1 the first time, a 1 danced across the screen. Zero plus 1 is 1. When you type a number, two things happen. First, Consuela adds the New Number to the Old Number, like

you said. Then Consuela changes the New Number into the Old Number."

"I get it," said Marcus. "When I typed 2 after typing 1 the time before, 1 became Old Number, New Number was 2, and Dancing Number was 1 plus 2, which is 3."

"That's right," said Manolita. "And then Old Number became 2, and when you type in another number, Dancing Number is 2 plus that new number."

"Now that I understand it," said Marcus, "I don't think Consuela is very clever at all. The clever one is Manolita."

Do you agree that Manolita is the clever one, not the computer? Why or why not? **7**

The End

Lesson Study

Reflect on each of the lessons you taught in this chapter. Rate each one on the following scale, and then consider ways to maintain or improve positive teaching experiences in the future.

Lessons	Very Effective	Effective	Less Effective	What Worked	Ways to Improve
7.1 Multiplying by 10, 100, and 1,000					
7.2 Multiplying Two-Digit Numbers by One-Digit Numbers					
7.3 Multiplying Three-Digit Numbers by One-Digit Numbers					
7.4 Applications of Multiplication					
7.5 Division with Remainders					
7.6 Reasonable Answers to Division Problems					
7.7 Dividing Two-Digit Numbers by One-Digit Numbers					
7.8 Dividing Three-Digit Numbers by One-Digit Numbers					
7.9 Problem-Solving Applications					

Fractions

Teaching for Understanding

This chapter formally introduces fractions. Students will learn to represent fractions using geometric figures, sets, and time. Students will become acquainted with comparing, adding, and subtracting fractions. Students will also be introduced to percentages.

Prerequisite Skills and Concepts

- Recognizing Equal Parts ● Reading and Writing Fractions ● Estimating Fractional Parts

Fractions Skills Trace

Before Grade 3	Grade 3	After Grade 3
Grades K–2 Introduction to fractions of sets, areas, lengths, and time	**This chapter** introduces informal addition and subtraction of fractions.	Formal explorations of fractions, decimals, and percent as different ways of expressing rational numbers. Exploration of addition, subtraction, multiplication, and division of fractions and mixed numbers

Problem solving is in every lesson. This chapter includes the following:

CHAPTER INTRODUCTION Students apply what they learned about graphs in the previous chapter to solving a nonroutine problem involving visual models of fractions (pp. 292I–293C).

EXPLORING PROBLEM SOLVING The first lesson focuses on the Use Simple Numbers and Draw a Diagram strategies (pp. 310–311, 311A). The second lesson relates fractions in a mixture of pigments to the resulting color (pp. 328–328A).

THINKING STORY In "Bargains Galore" students help a character develop strategies for a summer job in a store (pp. 340–343).

Games

Develop reasoning skills, and provide extensive practice.

- **Fraction Game** (Lessons 8.3–8.11)

Math Background

Fractions

What are Fractions, Decimals, and Percents?

- At this level a fraction is understood by students as an operator used to indicate a part of a whole or set. In Grade 4 of **Real Math** students will learn more about fractions, ratios, decimals, and percentages as names of rational numbers.

- A *rational number* is the result of dividing two integers (with the divisor, or denominator, greater than 0), and can be placed on the number line.

- Decimals are written as numbers using place values of tenths, hundredths, thousandths, and so on. They are sometimes used to describe parts of measurement units (for example, 0.3 meters or 12.27 seconds).

- Percent means "out of 100." Percents almost always refer to part of something.

Key Ideas about Fractions

There are several key ideas about fractions that students must understand in order to avoid common errors.

- A fraction is expressed using two numbers, although it represents a single quantity. The bottom number (denominator) names the total number of equal parts, and the top number (numerator) names the number of parts being considered.

- It is important to reinforce the idea that when dividing things into thirds (or any other fraction), the group is divided into three equal parts called thirds (as represented by the denominator). For sets divided into fractional parts, the number of objects in each third depends on the size of the set—this understanding will develop slowly over time.

- It is also important to foster an understanding of fractional parts as objects that can be counted. If you know the kind of part you are counting, then you know how many parts are needed for one whole, and how many are more than one whole. This is a crucial understanding to make sense of improper fractions.

- Two fractions are *equivalent* if they describe the same proportion or number. For example, since two parts out of four equal parts is the same portion as one part out of two equal parts, the fractions $\frac{2}{4}$ and $\frac{1}{2}$ are equivalent.

- *Improper fractions* represent quantities greater than one whole. For example, if a number of oranges are each cut into four equal slices, then seven slices represent $\frac{7}{4}$ of an orange, or $1\frac{3}{4}$ oranges. Of course, there is nothing improper about using improper fractions. The term comes from the idea that a "proper" part of the whole is less than or equal to the whole.

Models for Fractions

Several different models for fractions are used in this chapter, to help students build a strong understanding of the meaning of fractions.

- Linear measurement
  This model was introduced in Grade 1 of **Real Math**. Fractions can represent the distance along a path. For example, $\frac{1}{4}$ of a length is the length of one part when the length is divided into four equal parts.

- Area
  An area model uses fractions to describe equal parts of a geometric figure. In this model, $\frac{1}{4}$ is the size of one part when the whole is separated into four identical parts. A key concept with fractions of area is that the figure may be divided in any way, as long as all parts are equal. For example, a square can be divided in halves with a horizontal line, a vertical line, or a diagonal.

- Sets
  A fraction of a set is a more concrete concept than a fraction of a continuous length or area. However, this model may be more confusing to students because numbers of objects are involved. Students may run into difficulty when considering fractions in terms of dividing up sets because the answer "what fraction of the set" may be confused with "how many objects" in the sub-set. For example, when thinking about dividing a set of six objects into thirds, students may divide the set into two groups of three instead of three groups of two.

- Time
  Using time is a way to connect the area model and the fractions of a number model. In $\frac{1}{2}$ of an hour, the minute hand travels through half the area of the circle. Because an hour is 60 minutes long, and 30 + 30 = 60, we can say that $\frac{1}{2}$ of an hour is 30 minutes.

What Research Says

About Fractional Parts of a Whole

How Children Develop Part-Whole Concepts for Numbers

"We know from extensive research that many people—adults, students, even teachers—find the rational-number system to be very difficult. Introduced in early elementary school, this number system requires that students reformulate their concept of number in a major way. They must go beyond whole-number ideas, in which a number expresses a fixed quantity, to understand numbers that are expressed in relationship to other numbers. These new proportional relationships are grounded in multiplicative reasoning that is quite different from the additive reasoning that characterizes whole numbers."

Moss, Joan. "Pipes, Tubes, and Beakers: New Approaches to Teaching the Rational-Number System" in Donovan, M. Suzanne and John D. Bransford, eds. *How Students Learn: Mathematics in the Classroom.* Washington, D.C.: National Research Council/National Academies Press, 2005, p. 310.

Research-Based Teaching Techniques

The highly complex and abstract nature of mathematics requires the use of representations, especially as our youngest mathematicians are still developing their number sense. Representations to support the ability to use numbers for ordering or comparing objects or collections might include the use of counters, coins, symbols, words, actions, or pictures. These physical representations of what is occurring abstractly in the child's thoughts support meaningful mathematical conversations, calculations, and thoughts.

Kilpatrick, J., J. Swafford, and B. Findell, eds. *Adding It Up: Helping Children Learn Mathematics.* Washington, D.C.: National Research Council/National Academy Press, 2001, pp. 94–95.

"Children need to learn that rational numbers are numbers in the same way that whole numbers are numbers. For children to use rational numbers to solve problems, they need to learn that the same rational number may be represented in different ways, as a fraction, a decimal, or a percent. Decimal and fractional representations need to be connected and understood. Building these connections takes extensive experience with rational numbers over a substantial period of time. Instructional sequences in which more time is spent at the outset on developing meaning for the various representations of rational numbers and the concept of unit have been shown to promote mathematical proficiency."

Kilpatrick, J., J. Swafford, and B. Findell, eds. *Adding It Up: Helping Children Learn Mathematics.* Washington, D.C.: National Research Council/National Academy Press, 2001, pp. 415–416.

 RESEARCH IN ACTION

Fractions Chapter 8 continues to reinforce the development of part-whole number concepts and an understanding of what fractional parts of a whole represent.

Combining and Separating Collections Throughout Chapter 8 students will develop strategies, concepts, contexts, and procedures for developing understanding of fractions as representing parts of sets, parts of figures, or portions of time.

Equivalence Chapter 8 provides activities and contexts for thinking about part-whole relationships between different fractions or between fractions and percents or decimals.

Vocabulary

denominator (Lesson 8.1) the part of a fraction written below the line; the denominator tells how many equal parts something is divided into

equivalent (Lesson 8.5) having the same value

improper fraction (Lesson 8.8) a fraction whose numerator is greater than or equal to its denominator

mixed number (Lesson 8.8) a number consisting of a whole number and a fraction

numerator (Lesson 8.1) the part of a fraction written above the line; the numerator tells how many parts are being referred to

percent (Lesson 8.11) a fraction with a denominator of 100; the number of parts in every hundred

quarter (Lesson 8.4) one-fourth of an hour; fifteen minutes

set (Lesson 8.3) a collection of numbers, points, objects, or other things that are grouped together

English Learners

Cognates

For English learners, a quick way to acquire new English vocabulary is to build on what is known in the primary language.

English	Spanish
numerator	numerador
denominator	denominador
fractions	fracciones
sections	secciones
hour	hora
minute	minuto
second	segundo
equivalent	equivalente
represent	representar
to compare	comparar
to decide	decidir
parts	partes
example	ejemplo
comparing	comparando
other type of number	otro tipo de número
100 equal parts	100 partes iguales
divided	dividir
percent	por ciento

Access Vocabulary

English learners may understand words in different contexts or not understand idioms. Review chapter vocabulary for this concern. For example:

foot, yard	types of linear measurement
quarter hour	$\frac{1}{4}$ of the whole hour
make a true statement	change the facts of a math problem to make it correct
mixed number	a combination of a whole number and a fraction
benchmark	a reference point for measurement

Chapter Planner

Lessons	Objectives	NCTM Standards	State Standards
8.1 Fractions of Geometric Figures pages 294A–297B	To familiarize students with fractions using geometric figures	Number and Operations, Communications	
8.2 Fractions of Linear Measure pages 298A–299A	To explore fractions using linear measurements	Number and Operations, Connections	
8.3 Fractions of Sets pages 300A–303B	To deepen understanding of fractions using sets	Number and Operations, Connections	
8.4 Fractions of Time pages 304A–305A	To broaden knowledge of fractions using time	Number and Operations, Connections	
8.5 Equivalent Fractions pages 306A–307A	To introduce equivalent fractions	Number and Operations, Communication	
8.6 Comparing Fractions pages 308A–309A	To introduce comparing fractions less than one whole	Number and Operations, Connections	
8.7 Adding and Subtracting Fractions pages 314A–317B	To introduce adding and subtracting fractions	Number and Operations, Connections	
8.8 Fractions Greater Than a Whole pages 318A–319A	To introduce fractions greater than one whole	Number and Operations, Connections	
8.9 Comparing Fractions Greater Than a Whole pages 320A–321A	To introduce comparing fractions greater than one whole	Number and Operations, Connections	
8.10 Tenths and Hundredths pages 322A–323A	To explore the relationship between tenths and hundredths in fractional form	Number and Operations, Connections	
8.11 Percents and Hundredths pages 324A–327B	To explore the relationship between percents and fractions	Number and Operations, Algebra, Data Analysis and Probability	

Vocabulary	Manipulatives and Materials	Games to reinforce skills and concepts
numerator denominator	• Response Wheels • Unlined paper, 1 piece per student • Coloring item such as crayon, pencil, or marker	
	• Response Wheels • String about 1 meter in length for the teacher and each student • Scissors for the teacher and each student • Length of string as long as the length of the classroom	
set	• Response Wheels • Fraction Game Mat • Number Cubes (two 0–5) • Overhead pattern blocks (or cut-outs) • Manipulatives of any kind	Fraction Game
quarter	• Response Wheels • Manipulatives, 60 per group • Fraction Game Mat	Fraction Game
equivalent	• Response Wheels • Unlined piece of paper for each student • Shading items, such as colored pencil or crayon • Fraction Game Mat	Fraction Game
	• Response Wheels • Overhead transparency of Blackline Master of Fraction Game • Fraction Game Mat	Fraction Game
	• Response Wheels • Fraction Tiles • Fraction Game Mat	Fraction Game
mixed number improper fraction	• Response Wheels • Fraction Tiles • Fraction Game Mat	Fraction Game
	• Overhead transparency of Blackline Master of Fractions Game • Fraction Tiles	Fraction Game
	• Response Wheels • 50 manipulatives • A set of coins per group, with a minimum of 10 dimes and 100 pennies • Fraction Game Mat	Fraction Game
percent	• An overhead transparency of the Hundredths Circle from Lesson 8.10 (optional) • Fraction Game Mat	Fraction Game

Additional Resources

Differentiated Instruction

Intervention Support Guide Provides instruction for the following prerequisite skills:

- Lesson 8.A Recognizing Equal Parts
- Lesson 8.B Reading and Writing Fractions
- Lesson 8.C Estimating Fractional Parts

Enrichment Support Guide Extends lesson concepts

Practice Reinforces lesson skills and concepts

Reteach Support Guide Provides alternate instruction for lesson concepts

English Learner Support Guide Previews and reviews lesson concepts and vocabulary for English learners

Technology

The following electronic resources are available:

Ⓔ **Planner** Lessons 8.1–8.11

Ⓔ **Presentation** Lessons 8.1–8.11

Ⓔ **Textbook** Lessons 8.1–8.11

Ⓔ **Assess** Lessons 8.1–8.11

Ⓔ **MathTools** *Fractions* Lessons 8.7 and 8.8

Ⓔ **Games** *Fraction Game* Lessons 8.3–8.11

Assessment

Informal Assessment rubrics at the end of each lesson provide daily evaluation of student math proficiency.

Chapter Planner, continued

Problem Solving

Problem Solving	When to use	Objectives	NCTM Standards	Skills Covered
Chapter Introduction pp. 292I–293C 15–30 minutes	Use after the Chapter 8 Pretest.	To introduce chapter concepts in a problem-solving setting	Number and Operations	Analyze visual models
Exploring Problem Solving pp. 310–311, 311A 30–45 minutes	Use anytime during the chapter.	To explore methods of solving nonroutine problems	Number and Operations, Connections	Adding and subtracting fractions
Exploring Problem Solving pp. 328–328A 45–60 minutes	Use anytime after the first Exploring Problem Solving.	To explore methods of solving nonroutine problems	Number and Operations, Connections	Adding, subtracting, and comparing fractions
Thinking Story—Bargains Galore pp. 338–339, 340–341 20–30 minutes	Use anytime during the chapter.	To develop logical reasoning while integrating reading skills with mathematics	Problem Solving, Communication	Computing, Comparing price

Review

Review	When to use	Objectives	NCTM Standards	Skills Covered
Cumulative Review p. 312–313 15–30 minutes	Use anytime after Lesson 8.6.	To review concepts and skills taught earlier in the year	Number and Operations, Connections	Adding and subtracting fractions
Cumulative Review p. 329–330 15–30 minutes	Use anytime after Lesson 8.11.	To review concepts and skills taught earlier in the year	Number and Operations, Connections	Adding, subtracting, and comparing fractions
Chapter 8 Review pp. 332A, 332–333 30–45 minutes	Use after Lesson 8.11.	To review concepts and skills taught in the chapter	Number and Operations, Connections, Communication	Adding, subtracting, and comparing fractions

Assessment

Assessment	When to use	Objectives	NCTM Standards	Skills Covered
Informal Assessment pp. 297B–327B 5 minutes per student	Use at the end of each lesson.	To provide daily evaluation of math proficiency	Number and Operations, Connections	Using fractions in visual diagrams
Pretest (Assessment pp. 106–107) 15–30 minutes	Use prior to Chapter 8.	To provide assessment of prerequisite and chapter topics	Number and Operations	Arithmetical operations, Fractions
Individual Oral Assessment p. 313A 5 minutes per student	Begin use after Lesson 8.6.	To provide alternate means of assessing students' progress	Number and Operations, Connections	Arithmetical operations, Fractions
Mastery Checkpoint (Assessment p. T70) 5 minutes per student	Use after Lesson 8.3.	To provide assessment of mastery of key skills	Number and Operations, Connections	Arithmetical operations, Fractions
Chapter 8 Practice Test pp. 334–335, 336–337 30–45 minutes	Use after or in place of the Chapter 8 Review.	To provide assessment or additional practice of the lesson concepts	Number and Operations, Connections, Communication	Arithmetical operations, Fractions
Chapter 8 Test (Assessment p. 114–117) 30–45 minutes	Use after or in place of the Chapter 8 Review.	To provide assessment of the chapter concepts	Number and Operations, Connections, Communication	Arithmetical operations, Fractions

Technology Resources and Support

Visit SRAonline.com for online versions of the **Real Math** eSuite.

Technology for Teachers

e Presentation	**Lessons 8.1-8.11** Use the *ePresentation* to interactively present chapter content.
e Planner	Use the Chapter and Lesson Planners to outline activities and time frames for Chapter 8.
e Assess	Students can take the following assessments in *eAssess*: • Chapter Pretest • Mastery Checkpoint **Lesson 8.3** • Chapter Test Teachers can record results and print reports for all assessments in this chapter.
e MathTools	*Fractions* **Lessons 8.7, 8.8**

Technology for Students

e Textbook	An electronic, interactive version of the **Student Edition** is available for all lessons in Chapter 8.
e MathTools	*Fractions* **Lessons 8.7, 8.8**
e Games	*Fraction Game* **Lessons 8.3–8.11**
TECH KNOWLEDGE	*TechKnowledge* Level 3 provides lessons that specifically teach the Unit 10 Internet and Unit 8 Database applications that students can use in this chapter's projects.

Fractions

1 Introduce Chapter 8 · 5

Chapter Objectives

Explain to students that in this chapter they will build on what they already know about fractions. They will

- name fractions of geometric figures, linear measure, sets, and time.
- compare fractions.
- add and subtract fractions.
- find tenths, hundredths, and percents.

Pretest COMPUTING

Administer the Pretest on *Assessment* pages 106 and 107.

The Pretest covers the following skills and topics from the chapter:

- Addition and subtraction facts (Problems 1–6)
- Multiplication facts (Problems 6–8)
- Greater than and less than (Problems 9–13)
- Fractions as parts of a whole or parts of a set (Problems 14–22)
- Addition and subtraction of fractions (Problems 16–22)

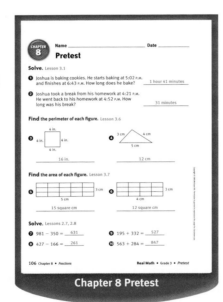

Chapter 8 Pretest

Access Prior Knowledge UNDERSTANDING

Have students talk about advertisements they have seen. Ask questions such as the following:

- **Which stores and restaurants do you like to go to? Why?**
- **What are some things stores and restaurants do so people will want to buy from them?**
- **What are some places where you see advertisements?**
- **What are your favorite advertisements?**
- **Have you ever seen advertisements painted on signs?**
- **How do advertisers try to make you want their product?**
- **What can be helpful about advertisements?**
- **What do you have to be aware of with advertisements?**

2 Exploring Problem Solving · 25

Tell Students In Today's Lesson They Will

figure out which paints should be used for which signs.

Materials

- Red, green, and blue counters
- Graph paper
- Red, green, and blue crayons, markers, or colored pencils

Using Student Pages

Read and discuss the information and illustrations on page 293 together. Make sure students understand the information by asking questions such as the following:

- **What do we know about the signs?** They are each supposed to be painted with different amounts of red, green, and blue paint.
- **What do the tubes show you?** the paint that will be used to paint each sign
- **What has happened?** The designer has lost her notes that tell which set of paints should be used for each sign.

Have students work alone or in pairs on Problems 1–3. Provide help as needed. To help students with Problem 3, have them recall what they already know about fractions by asking questions such as the following:

- **Which sign is half red?**
- **Which sign is divided into thirds?**
- **How much of sign 2 is green?**

Sample Answer to Problem 3

Half of sign 2 is blue, and half of the total amount of paint in set C is blue. Half of sign 3 is red, and half of the total amount of paint in set A is red. Sign 1 is a third red, a third blue, and a third green, and so is paint set B.

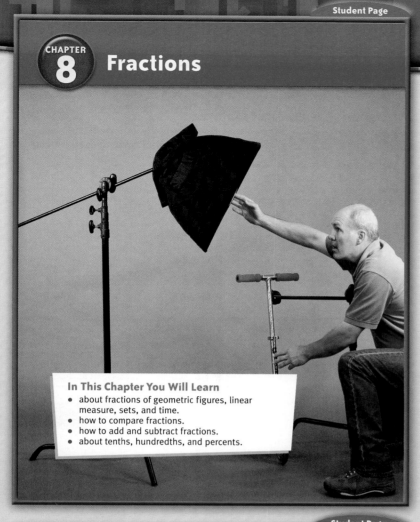

CHAPTER 8 Fractions

In This Chapter You Will Learn
- about fractions of geometric figures, linear measure, sets, and time.
- how to compare fractions.
- how to add and subtract fractions.
- about tenths, hundredths, and percents.

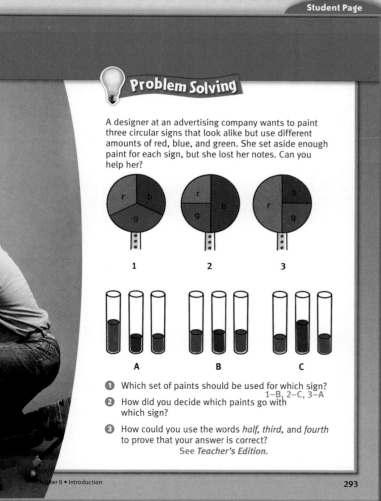

Problem Solving

A designer at an advertising company wants to paint three circular signs that look alike but use different amounts of red, blue, and green. She set aside enough paint for each sign, but she lost her notes. Can you help her?

1   2   3

A   B   C

❶ Which set of paints should be used for which sign?
   1–B, 2–C, 3–A
❷ How did you decide which paints go with which sign?

❸ How could you use the words *half*, *third*, and *fourth* to prove that your answer is correct?
   See *Teacher's Edition*.

Chapter 8 • Introduction   293

Concept/Question Board APPLYING

Questions
Have students think of and write three questions they have about fractions and how they can be used. Then have them select one question to post on the Question side of the Board.

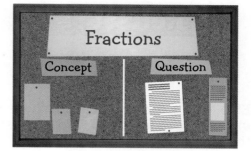

Concepts
As students work through the chapter, have them collect examples of how fractions are used in everyday situations. For each example, write a problem that relates to the item(s). Have them display their examples on the Concept side of the Board. Suggest the following:
- mixing beverages from concentrate
- sharing toys

Answers
Throughout the chapter, have students post answers to the questions and solutions to the problems on the Board.

Introduction

Knowledge Age Skills

Effective Communication Have students present and discuss their answers to Problems 1–3. In discussion, bring out the following points:

- Fractions can help us talk about how something is part of a whole.
- There are different ways to show fractions.

Sample Solutions Strategies

Students might use one of these strategies or a combination of strategies.

Make a Physical Model

Students might use graph paper to reproduce the paint with the tubes laid end to end and then colored appropriately to help them see which colors would be most prevalent in the matching circle.

red	blue	green

They might also use colored counters or connecting cubes to represent the paint.

Use Spatial Sense/Use Proportional Reasoning

Students might see how one color relates to another. For example, in sign 2 there is twice as much blue as green, so sign 2 must go with paint set C, which also has twice as much blue as green.

Home Connection

At this time, you may want to send home the letter on pages 30–33 of **Home Connection.** This letter describes what students will be learning and what activities they can do at home to support their work in school.

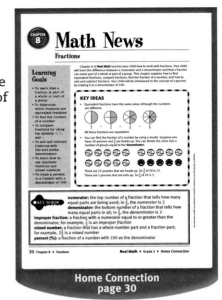

Home Connection page 30

Assess and Differentiate

 Assess Use *eAssess* to record and analyze evidence of student understanding.

Gather Evidence

Use the Daily Class Assessment Records in **Assessment** or *eAssess* to record informal and formal assessments.

Informal Assessment

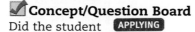 **Access Prior Knowledge**

Did the student `UNDERSTANDING`

- ❏ make important observations?
- ❏ extend or generalize learning?
- ❏ provide insightful answers?
- ❏ pose insightful questions?

Informal Assessment

✓ **Concept/Question Board**

Did the student `APPLYING`

- ❏ apply learning in new situations?
- ❏ contribute concepts?
- ❏ contribute answers?
- ❏ connect mathematics to real-world situations?

Formal Assessment

✓ **Pretest** `COMPUTING`

Review student answers in each problem set.

- ❏ Addition and subtraction facts (Problems 1–6)
- ❏ Multiplication facts (Problems 6–8)
- ❏ Greater than and less than (Problems 9–13)
- ❏ Fractions as parts of a whole or parts of a set (Problems 14–22)
- ❏ Addition and subtraction of fractions (Problems 16–22)

Summarize Findings

Analyze and summarize assessment data for each student. Determine which Assessment Follow-Up is appropriate for each student. Use the Student Assessment Record in **Assessment** or *eAssess* to update assessment records.

C Assessment Follow-Up ● DIFFERENTIATE INSTRUCTION

Based on your observations of each student, use these teaching strategies for a general approach to the chapter. Look for specific Differentiate Instruction and Monitoring Student Progress strategies in each lesson that relate specifically to the lesson content.

ENRICH	PRACTICE	RETEACH	INTERVENTION	ENGLISH LEARNER
If . . . students demonstrate a **secure understanding** of chapter concepts, **Then . . .** use *Enrichment* Lessons 8.1–8.11 as assessment follow-up to extend and apply understanding.	**If . . .** students grasp chapter concepts with **competent understanding,** **Then . . .** use *Practice* Lessons 8.1–8.11 as a lesson follow-up to develop fluency.	**If . . .** students have prerequisite understanding but demonstrate **emerging understanding** of chapter concepts, **Then . . .** use *Reteach* Lessons 8.5 and 8.6 to reteach lessons concepts.	**If . . .** students are not competent with prerequisite skills, **Then . . .** use *Intervention* Lessons 8.A–8.C before each lesson to develop fluency with prerequisite skills.	Use *English Learner Support Guide* Lessons 8.1–8.11 for strategies to preteach lesson vocabulary and concepts.

Chapter Projects

Math Across the Curriculum

Preview the chapter projects with students. Assign projects or have students choose from the projects to extend and enrich concepts in this chapter.

Create an Advertisement

 ART

3–4 weeks

MATH OBJECTIVE
To reinforce studies of fractions by finding and using a fraction in a product design

FINE ARTS OBJECTIVE
To use the principle of emphasis in a product design and advertisement

TECHNOLOGY OBJECTIVE
To use gadgets such as digital cameras and printers to create an advertisement

· ·

Have students use mathematics to create an advertisement for a product. To broaden the fine arts concept, have students incorporate elements of visual art you are currently studying.

As part of the project, students should consider the following issues:

- methods advertisers use to sell products
- applications of fractions in advertisements
- the intended audience for cereal advertisements
- use of a digital camera and printer

For specific step-by-step instructions for this project, see *Across the Curriculum Math Connections* pages 82–85.

High-Level Responsibility Students both design and create products and advertisements.

Creative Work with Ideas Students position elements to create emphasis in advertising photographs.

Categorize Toy Advertisements

 LANGUAGE ARTS WebQuest

3–4 weeks

MATH OBJECTIVE
To reinforce studies of halves, fourths, and eighths by using them to express time and size

LANGUAGE ARTS OBJECTIVE
To reinforce studies of the use of examples by categorizing examples of toy advertisements

TECHNOLOGY OBJECTIVE
To use a database program to categorize toy advertisements

· ·

Have students use technology to

- find examples of Internet toy advertising.
- research advertising strategies.
- categorize and organize advertising examples.

For this project, students use the Internet to investigate the following information:

- examples of Internet toy advertising
- views on advertising as it relates to children
- common advertising strategies

For specific step-by-step instructions for this project, see *Across the Curriculum Math Connections* pages 86–91.

Teamwork Have students work in groups to create a database of toy advertisements.

Creative Work with Ideas Students explore the information within the role of a toy company employee.

TECH KNOWLEDGE **TechKnowledge** Level 3 provides lessons that specifically teach the Unit 10 Internet and Unit 8 Database applications that students can use in this project.

Lesson Planner

OBJECTIVES
To review the concept of fractions (halves, thirds, fourths, and fifths) using geometric figures

NCTM STANDARDS
Number and Operations
Developing understanding of fractions as parts of unit wholes, as parts of a collection, as locations on number lines, and as divisions of whole numbers

Communication
Organizing and consolidating students' mathematical thinking through communication

MATERIALS
- *Response Wheels
- Unlined paper, one piece per student
- Coloring item such as crayon, pencil, or marker

TECHNOLOGY
ⓔ Presentation Lesson 8.1

TEST PREP
Cumulative Review
Mental Math reviews basic multiplication facts (Chapter 5).

Writing + Math
Journal

Fractions of Geometric Figures

Context of the Lesson In this introductory lesson on fractions, students review what the parts of a fraction are, what a fraction represents, and how to write fractions. At this grade level it is important to understand that a fraction is viewed as a part of a whole. In Grade 4, students will develop a deeper understanding of fractions and their relationships to decimals and percents.

See page 292B for Math Background for teachers for this lesson.

Planning for Learning ● DIFFERENTIATE INSTRUCTION

INTERVENTION

If . . . students lack the prerequisite skill of recognizing equal parts,

Then . . . teach **Intervention** Lesson 8.A.

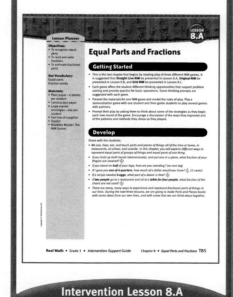

Intervention Lesson 8.A

ENGLISH LEARNER

Preview

If . . . students need language support,

Then . . . use Lesson 8.1 in **English Learner Support Guide** to preview lesson concepts and vocabulary.

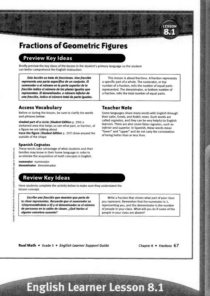

English Learner Lesson 8.1

ENRICH

If . . . students are proficient in the lesson concepts,

Then . . . emphasize the student pages.

PRACTICE

If . . . students would benefit from additional practice,

Then . . . extend Guided Discussion before assigning the student pages.

RETEACH

If . . . students are having difficulty understanding fractions of geometric figures,

Then . . . extend Guided Discussion before assigning the student pages.

Vocabulary
numerator \nü´ mə rā tər\ *n.* the part of a fraction written above the line; The numerator tells how many parts are being referred to.

denominator \di nom´ ə nā tər\ *n.* the part of a fraction written below the line; The denominator tells how many equal parts something is divided into.

Spanish Cognates
numerator numerador
denominator denominador

*Manipulative Kit Item

Mental Math 10

  Review basic multiplication facts. Have students show thumbs-up if the product of the expression on the left is greater than the number on the right, thumbs-down if it is less than, or open hand if the product and number are equal. Use examples such as the following:

a. 5×5 ☐ 30 down   **b.** 10×4 ☐ 47 down
c. 4×3 ☐ 11 up   **d.** 8×7 ☐ 57 down
e. 6×1 ☐ 6 open hand   **f.** 10×3 ☐ 20 up
g. 9×3 ☐ 28 down   **h.** 9×6 ☐ 50 up

1 Develop 25

Tell Students In Today's Lesson They Will
review the concept of fractions, using geometric figures.

Guided Discussion UNDERSTANDING Whole Group

1. Draw a circle on the board. Tell students to imagine it is their favorite kind of pizza. Ask a student to come to the board and divide the pizza into 2 equal parts (or halves). Ask questions such as the following:

   ■ **How many equal parts are there?** 2
   ■ **What fraction would each part be labeled?** $\frac{1}{2}$
   ■ **Which part would you rather have?** If they are equal, it doesn't matter.

2. Follow a similar procedure with a different pizza, having a student divide it into thirds (3 equal parts). This may be harder for students to do. If the sectioning is not reasonably equal, ask whether there would be a difference among the parts if they were equal. The students should respond *no*. Tell students we usually refer to something being divided into 3 equal parts as having been divided into *thirds*.

3. Follow a similar procedure with another pizza, having a student divide it into fourths. Looking at all 3 pizzas, ask questions such as the following to help students visually compare fractional amounts:

   ■ **Which piece would be the largest piece?** $\frac{1}{2}$
   ■ **Which would be the smallest piece?** $\frac{1}{4}$
   ■ **Which would be greater, $\frac{1}{2}$ or $\frac{2}{4}$?** They are the same.
   ■ **Which would be greater, $\frac{1}{3}$ or $\frac{1}{4}$?** $\frac{1}{3}$

It is recommended to also do the previous three steps with a figure that is not circular (i.e., a square or rectangle). The most common demonstration is with circles, and often students limit their perception of fractions to circular figures.

Using Student Pages ✓ APPLYING

Have each student copy or trace the following six figures from student page 294. Then have students follow each direction for the six figures. Walk around the room to see that students are doing this correctly.

1. Have students color in $\frac{1}{2}$ of the circle.
2. Have students color in $\frac{1}{2}$ of the triangle.
3. Have students color in $\frac{1}{3}$ of the circle.
4. Have students color in $\frac{3}{4}$ of the square.
5. Have students color in $\frac{2}{4}$ of the triangle.
6. Have students color in $\frac{3}{5}$ of the circle.

If students are in need of more guided practice, have them draw a rectangle, divide it into fourths, and color in $\frac{1}{4}$. Continue this process with other shapes such as circles, squares, or rectangles. If helpful, have students trace Problems 1–6 again from their text. Check for understanding before assigning student pages.

Monitoring Student Progress

If . . . students struggle with coloring the correct fractions, **Then . . .** work with manipulatives (fraction circles or tiles) to identify the correct fractions.

2 Assign Student Pages

20

Pages 294–295 APPLYING

Have students complete page 295 independently.

RESEARCH IN ACTION

"The number line has potential for organizing thinking about numbers and making connections with geometry. The number line is a line with points labeled by numbers. The potential of the number line does not stop at providing a simple way to picture all rational numbers geometrically. It also lets you form geometric models for the operations of arithmetic. Numbers on the number line have a dual nature: They are simultaneously points and oriented segments. A deep understanding of numbers and operations on the number line requires flexibility in using each interpretation."

Kilpatrick, J., J. Swafford, and B. Findell, eds. *Adding It Up: Helping Children Learn Mathematics.* Washington, D.C.: National Research Council/National Academy Press, 2001, pp. 87–92.

Student Page

LESSON 8.1 **Fractions of Geometric Figures**

Key Ideas

A fraction represents a specific part of a whole. The numerator, or top number of a fraction, tells the number of equal parts being referenced. The denominator, or bottom number of a fraction, tells the total number of equal parts.

Look at the following picture and its related fraction.

The fraction $\frac{1}{3}$, read as *one-third,* represents the shaded part of this circle.

The 1 is the numerator, showing we are referring to 1 part of the entire circle.

The 3 is the denominator, showing there are 3 equal parts total in the circle.

Copy the following shapes. Then listen as your teacher gives you specific directions for the following figures.

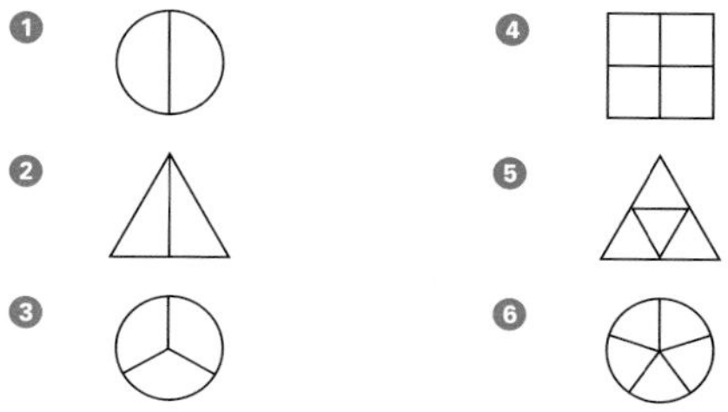

294

Textbook This lesson is available in the *eTextbook.*

Student Page

What fraction of each figure is shaded?

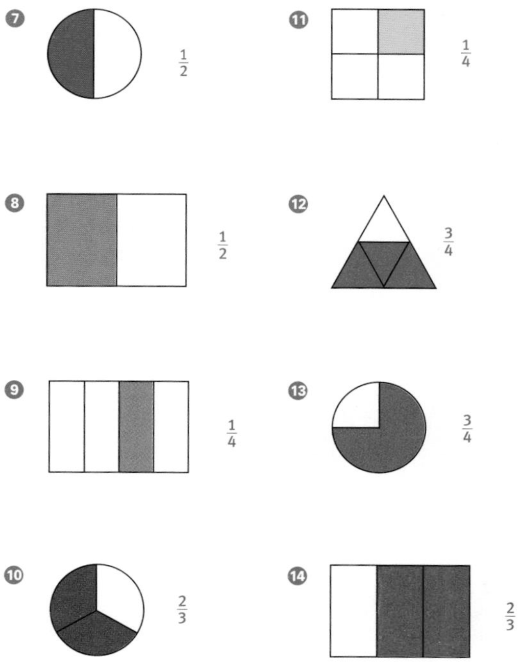

7. $\frac{1}{2}$
8. $\frac{1}{2}$
9. $\frac{1}{4}$
10. $\frac{2}{3}$
11. $\frac{1}{4}$
12. $\frac{3}{4}$
13. $\frac{3}{4}$
14. $\frac{2}{3}$

Chapter 8 • Lesson 1

295

Teaching Lesson 8.1

Assign Student Pages, continued

Pages 296–297 APPLYING

Have students complete pages 296 and 297 independently.

As Students Finish

 Have students play a previously introduced game.

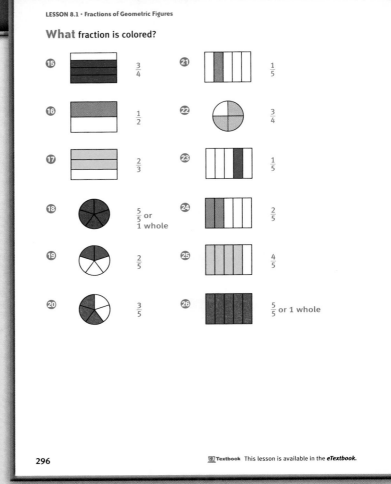

LESSON 8.1 · Fractions of Geometric Figures

What fraction is colored?

15. $\frac{3}{4}$ 21. $\frac{1}{5}$

16. $\frac{1}{2}$ 22. $\frac{3}{4}$

17. $\frac{2}{3}$ 23. $\frac{1}{5}$

18. $\frac{5}{5}$ or 1 whole   24. $\frac{2}{5}$

19. $\frac{2}{5}$ 25. $\frac{4}{5}$

20. $\frac{3}{5}$ 26. $\frac{5}{5}$ or 1 whole

296   Textbook This lesson is available in the *eTextbook*.

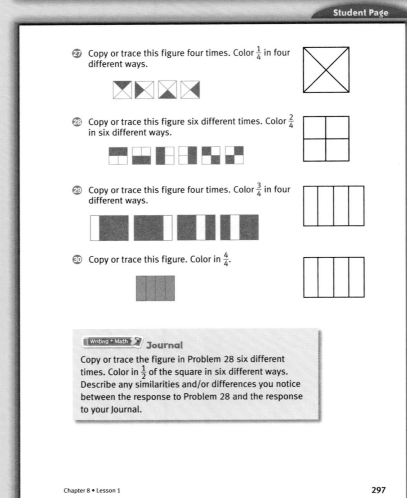

27. Copy or trace this figure four times. Color $\frac{1}{4}$ in four different ways.

28. Copy or trace this figure six different times. Color $\frac{2}{4}$ in six different ways.

29. Copy or trace this figure four times. Color $\frac{3}{4}$ in four different ways.

30. Copy or trace this figure. Color in $\frac{4}{4}$.

Writing + Math Journal

Copy or trace the figure in Problem 28 six different times. Color in $\frac{1}{2}$ of the square in six different ways. Describe any similarities and/or differences you notice between the response to Problem 28 and the response to your Journal.

Chapter 8 • Lesson 1   297

Reflect 5

Guided Discussion  Whole Group

Ask students whether there would be other ways to answer Problem 18 (or Problem 26). Yes, it could be $\frac{3}{3}$, $\frac{4}{4}$, $\frac{6}{6}$, and so on. In general, the answer is $\frac{n}{n}$, where n is any counting number.

Writing + Math **Journal**

Most students should notice the squares with $\frac{2}{4}$ shaded look like the squares with $\frac{1}{2}$ shaded.

 Cumulative Review: For cumulative review of previously learned skills, see page 312–313.

 Family Involvement: Assign the *Practice, Reteach,* or *Enrichment* activities depending on the needs of your students.

Encourage students to find real-world examples of fractions with a friend or a relative.

 Concept/Question Board: Have students look for additional examples using fractions and post them on the Concept/Question Board.

 Math Puzzler: Ask students to find the missing digits in this problem:

	3		4	3
−	1	0		9
		2	5	2

4 Assess and Differentiate

 Assess Use *eAssess* to record and analyze evidence of student understanding.

A Gather Evidence

Use the Daily Class Assessment Records in *Assessment* or *eAssess* to record daily observations.

Informal Assessment

☑ Student Pages

Did the student **APPLYING**
- ❑ apply learning in new situations?
- ❑ contribute concepts?
- ❑ contribute answers?
- ❑ connect mathematics to real-world situations?

Informal Assessment

☑ Guided Discussion

Did the student **UNDERSTANDING**
- ❑ make important observations?
- ❑ extend or generalize learning?
- ❑ provide insightful answers?
- ❑ pose insightful questions?

B Summarize Findings

Analyze and summarize assessment data for each student. Determine which Assessment Follow-Up is appropriate for each student. Use the Student Assessment Record in *Assessment* or *eAssess* to update assessment records.

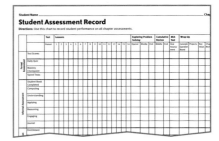

Assessment page T41

C Assessment Follow-Up • DIFFERENTIATE INSTRUCTION

Based on your observations, use these teaching strategies for assessment follow-up.

INTERVENTION

Review student performance on *Intervention* Lesson 8.A to see if students have mastered prerequisite skills for this lesson.

ENGLISH LEARNER

Review

Use Lesson 8.1 in *English Learner Support Guide* to review lesson concepts and vocabulary.

ENRICH

If . . . students are proficient in the lesson concepts,

Then . . . encourage them to work on chapter projects or *Enrichment* Lesson 8.1.

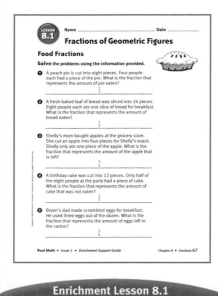

Enrichment Lesson 8.1

PRACTICE

If . . . students would benefit from additional practice,

Then . . . assign *Practice* Lesson 8.1.

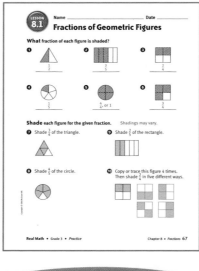

Practice Lesson 8.1

RETEACH

If . . . students struggle with fractions of geometric figures,

Then . . . provide statements involving fractions with only the denominator written, such as " /5 of a circle." Ask students how many equal parts the circle should be divided into (5), and then have them draw and divide the circle. Give more examples. When students understand denominators, go back to your examples and fill in numerators to form fractions. Then have students shade in the appropriate part of the circle.

Lesson Planner

OBJECTIVES
- To review the concept of fractions (halves, fourths, and eighths) using linear measurements
- To recognize sections of a ruler as fractional parts

NCTM STANDARDS

Number and Operations
Developing understanding of fractions as parts of unit wholes, as parts of a collection, as locations on number lines, and as divisions of whole numbers

Connections
Recognizing and using connections among mathematical ideas

MATERIALS
- *Response Wheels
- String about 1 meter in length for the teacher and each student
- Scissors for the teacher and each student
- Length of string as long as the length of the classroom

TECHNOLOGY
ⓔPresentation Lesson 8.2

TEST PREP

Cumulative Review
Mental Math reviews rounding to the nearest 1,000 (Lesson 1.8).

Fractions of Linear Measure

Context of the Lesson This lesson reintroduces the concepts of halves, fourths, and eighths using linear models. Students will explore halves and quarters by comparing line segments and different fractional lengths of string. In addition, in this lesson, two aspects of fractional parts are introduced—the denominator or bottom number tells how many equal parts something is cut into, while the top number (or numerator) tells how many of those parts are being discussed. Students will explore these aspects further in Grade 4.

See page 292B for Math Background for teachers for this lesson.

Planning for Learning ● DIFFERENTIATE INSTRUCTION

INTERVENTION

If . . . students lack the prerequisite skill of recognizing equal parts,

Then . . . teach *Intervention* Lesson 8.A.

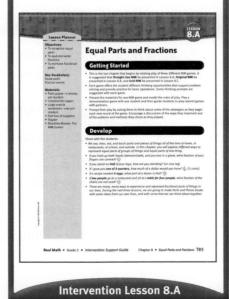

Intervention Lesson 8.A

ENGLISH LEARNER

Preview

If . . . students need language support,

Then . . . use Lesson 8.2 in *English Learner Support Guide* to preview lesson concepts and vocabulary.

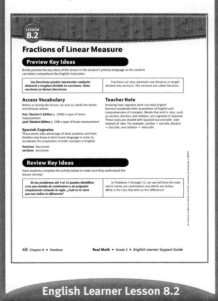

English Learner Lesson 8.2

ENRICH

If . . . students are proficient in the lesson concepts,

Then . . . emphasize the student pages.

PRACTICE

If . . . students would benefit from additional practice,

Then . . . extend Strategy Building before assigning the student pages.

RETEACH

If . . . students are having difficulty understanding fractions of linear measure,

Then . . . extend Guided Discussion before assigning the student pages.

Access Vocabulary
foot, yard types of linear measurement

Spanish Cognates
fractions fracciones
sections secciones

*Manipulative Kit Item

Mental Math 5

  Round to the nearest 1,000 using examples such as the following:

a. 1,247 1,000 **b.** 578 1,000 **c.** 3,427 3,000

d. 4,788 5,000 **e.** 1,578 2,000 **f.** 4,107 4,000

g. 9,788 10,000 **h.** 4,682 5,000 **i.** 1,000 1,000

1 Develop 25

Tell Students In Today's Lesson They Will
review the concept of fractions using linear measure and recognize the sections of a ruler as fractional parts.

Guided Discussion UNDERSTANDING Whole Group

Begin by asking students what they remember about halves. Ask questions such as the following:

- **What does it mean to divide something into halves?** to make 2 equal parts
- **How many equal parts do you have if something is divided into halves?** 2

Hold up a piece of string. Ask questions such as the following:

- **How would you cut the string in half?**
- **How can you ensure both sides are the same length?**

Discuss various solutions. If it is not mentioned, suggest folding the string in half to find the middle point. Cutting at the middle point would ensure both sides are even.

Hand out a string to each of the students. Have them cut their string in half, reminding them to make sure each length is equal. After the string has been cut, ask questions such as the following:

- **How many equal pieces are there?** 2
- **What would be the denominator for the fraction describing each piece of the string?** 2
- **If we hold 1 of these pieces of string, what fraction represents that piece of string?** $\frac{1}{2}$

These two pieces are called *halves*, and 2 halves make 1 whole piece of string. Write $\frac{1}{2}$ on the board. Have students name the fraction.

Ask questions such as the following about fourths:

- **What does it mean to divide something into *fourths*?** to make 4 equal parts
- **How many equal parts do you have if something is divided into fourths?** 4
- **How would you divide the string into fourths?** Possible answer: cut each of the halves into halves again

Cut the halves of your string into halves again. Demonstrate that you have created four equal parts and those 4 pieces make one whole piece of string. Write $\frac{1}{4}$ on the board. Have students name the fraction. Introduce the word *quarters* as another name for items divided into fourths. This vocabulary will become essential when students explore Fractions of Time in Lesson 8.4.

Strategy Building UNDERSTANDING Whole Group

Draw three line segments on the board.

1. Have a student come to the board and divide one line segment in half. Have the student write $\frac{1}{2}$ above each of the segments on the line.

2. Have another student come to the board and divide the second line segment into fourths. Review with students how the string was divided into fourths or quarters if the student is uncertain on how to proceed. Have the student write $\frac{1}{4}$ above each segment on the line.

3. Finally, have a third student divide the third line segment into eighths. Have the student write $\frac{1}{8}$ above each segment on the line. Make sure each student is marking the sections evenly.

If students are still uncertain about linear measure, have a student start at one end of the classroom and walk about halfway across the room while other members of the classroom decide if the estimate is about right. Check the estimate with a piece of string.

While the first student remains at the halfway point, have two other students walk $\frac{1}{4}$ of the way and $\frac{1}{8}$ of the way. Ask questions such as the following:

- **How did you decide how far to walk?** Possible answer: $\frac{1}{4}$ is half of $\frac{1}{2}$ and $\frac{1}{8}$ is half of $\frac{1}{4}$
- **Who did the most walking?** $\frac{1}{2}$
- **Who did the least walking?** $\frac{1}{8}$

2 Assign Student Pages 20

Pages 298–299 APPLYING
Have students complete pages 298 and 299 independently.

As Students Finish

 Game Have students play a previously introduced game.

LESSON
8.2 **Fractions of Linear Measure**

Key Ideas

Any distance or length can be divided into equal parts. A fraction can be used to tell how many equal parts there are and how many of those parts are being considered.

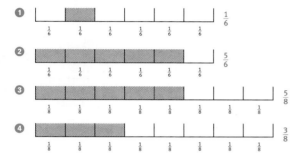

This section of a line is divided into 6 parts. Each part is $\frac{1}{6}$ of the specific section of the line.

What fraction of the line is shaded?

❶ $\frac{1}{6}$

❷ $\frac{5}{6}$

❸ $\frac{5}{8}$

❹ $\frac{3}{8}$

298   Textbook This lesson is available in the *eTextbook*.

A ruler is often divided into sections. To read the fractional parts on a ruler, first count the total parts, which will be your denominator. Then count the parts you are working with, which will be your numerator.

Each of the following rulers has been divided into twelfths, so each section is $\frac{1}{12}$. How much of a whole is each ribbon?

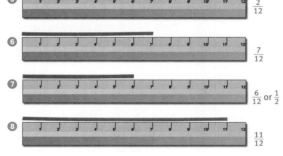

❺ $\frac{2}{12}$

❻ $\frac{7}{12}$

❼ $\frac{6}{12}$ or $\frac{1}{2}$

❽ $\frac{11}{12}$

Each of the following rulers has been divided into tenths, so each section is $\frac{1}{10}$. How much of a whole is each ribbon?

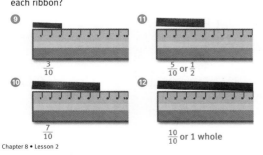

❾ $\frac{3}{10}$

⓫ $\frac{5}{10}$ or $\frac{1}{2}$

❿ $\frac{7}{10}$

⓬ $\frac{10}{10}$ or 1 whole

Chapter 8 • Lesson 2   299

---

3 **Reflect**   10

Guided Discussion

Whole Group

Look at the string that was cut into fourths and halves. Ask questions such as the following:

- **How many halves make one whole?** 2
- **How many fourths make one-half?** 2
- **How many eighths make one-fourth?** 2
- **If each of the eighths were cut in half again, how many pieces would there be?** 16

Make comparisons with the lengths of strings. For example, which is larger, $\frac{2}{4}$ or $\frac{1}{2}$?

Cumulative Review: For cumulative review of previously learned skills, see page 312–313.

Family Involvement: Assign the *Practice, Reteach,* or *Enrichment* activities depending on the needs of your students. Encourage students to practice finding $\frac{1}{2}$, $\frac{1}{4}$, and $\frac{1}{8}$ of various real-world objects with a friend or a relative.

Concept/Question Board: Have students look for additional examples using fractions and post them on the Concept/Question Board.

Math Puzzler: Joey's birthday is in a month that has 30 days. Juanita's and Stacey's birthdays are in months that have 31 days. Stacey was born one month after Juanita and one month before Joey. In which months were each born? Juanita—July; Stacey—August; Joey—September

Chapter 8 • Lesson 2   **298–299**

Assess and Differentiate

 Assess Use *eAssess* to record and analyze evidence of student understanding.

A Gather Evidence

Use the Daily Class Assessment Records in *Assessment* or *eAssess* to record daily observations.

Informal Assessment
☑ **Strategy Building**

Did the student **UNDERSTANDING**
❏ make important observations?
❏ extend or generalize learning?
❏ provide insightful answers?
❏ pose insightful questions?

Informal Assessment
☑ **Student Pages**

Did the student **APPLYING**
❏ apply learning in new situations?
❏ contribute concepts?
❏ contribute answers?
❏ connect mathematics to real-world situations?

B Summarize Findings

Analyze and summarize assessment data for each student. Determine which Assessment Follow-Up is appropriate for each student. Use the Student Assessment Record in *Assessment* or *eAssess* to update assessment records.

Assessment page T41

C Assessment Follow-Up ● DIFFERENTIATE INSTRUCTION

Based on your observations, use these teaching strategies for assessment follow-up.

INTERVENTION	ENRICH	PRACTICE	RETEACH
Review student performance on *Intervention* Lesson 8.A to see if students have mastered prerequisite skills for this lesson.	**If . . .** students are proficient in the lesson concepts, **Then . . .** encourage them to work on chapter projects or *Enrichment* Lesson 8.2.	**If . . .** students would benefit from additional practice, **Then . . .** assign *Practice* Lesson 8.2.	**If . . .** students struggle with fractions of linear measures, **Then . . .** have them model each of the problems using a ruler and pieces of string. For example, have them make a $\frac{1}{12}$-foot standard piece by cutting a piece one inch long. Then they can mark how many of their 1-inch pieces make up the problem piece.

ENGLISH LEARNER

Review

Use Lesson 8.2 in *English Learner Support Guide* to review lesson concepts and vocabulary.

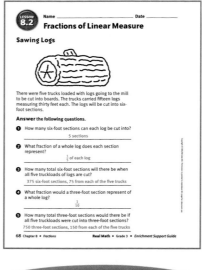

Enrichment Lesson 8.2

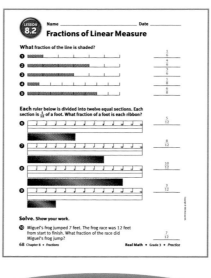

Practice Lesson 8.2

Lesson Planner

OBJECTIVES
- To find fractions of sets
- To relate finding fractions of sets to finding fractions of a number

NCTM STANDARDS

Number and Operations
Developing understanding of fractions as parts of unit wholes, as parts of a collection, as locations on number lines, and as divisions of whole numbers

Connections
Recognizing and using connections among mathematical ideas

MATERIALS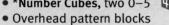
- *Response Wheels
- *Fraction Game Mat
- *Number Cubes, two 0–5
- Overhead pattern blocks (or cutouts)
- Manipulatives of any kind

TECHNOLOGY
- Presentation Lesson 8.3
- Games Fraction Game

TEST PREP

Cumulative Review
- Mental Math reviews Roman numerals (Lesson 2.14).
- Problem 38 reviews dividing three-digit numbers by one-digit numbers (Lesson 7.8).

Extended Response
Problem 38

Writing + Math
Journal

Fractions of Sets

Context of the Lesson In Grade 2 students explored parts of sets and fractions of numbers. In this lesson students extend that exploration to develop a method for finding fractions of sets. No algorithm is taught, as students are intuitively finding fractions of sets. In Grade 4 students will apply these same intuitive methods to finding fractions of numbers, and will be formally introduced to an algorithm.

See page 292B for Math Background for teachers for this lesson.

Planning for Learning ● DIFFERENTIATE INSTRUCTION

INTERVENTION

If . . . students lack the prerequisite skill of reading and writing fractions,

Then . . . teach *Intervention* Lesson 8.B.

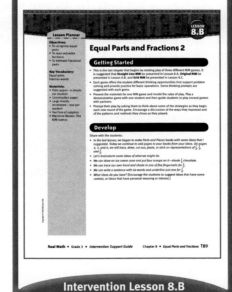

Intervention Lesson 8.B

ENGLISH LEARNER

Preview

If . . . students need language support,

Then . . . use Lesson 8.3 in *English Learner Support Guide* to preview lesson concepts and vocabulary.

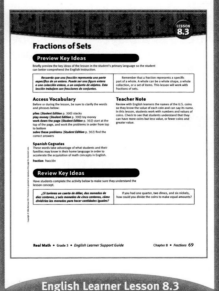

English Learner Lesson 8.3

ENRICH

If . . . students are proficient in the lesson concepts,

Then . . . emphasize the **Fraction Game.**

PRACTICE

If . . . students would benefit from additional practice,

Then . . . extend Strategy Building before assigning the student pages.

RETEACH

If . . . students are having difficulty understanding fractions of sets,

Then . . . extend Guided Discussion before assigning the student pages.

Vocabulary
set \set\ *n.* a collection of numbers, points, objects, or other things that are grouped together

Spanish Cognates
fraction fracción

*Manipulative Kit Item

Mental Math 10

 Review Roman numerals using examples such as the following:

a. X 10
b. V 5
c. XX 20
d. XV 15
e. IV 4
f. C 100
g. I 1
h. CIV 104

1 Develop 25

Tell Students In Today's Lesson They Will
find fractions of sets and relate fractions of sets to fractions of a number.

Skill and Strategy Building ENGAGING Whole Group

 **Fraction Game**
Have two students demonstrate the **Fraction Game Mat.** The object of this game is to own more circles at the end of the game. Players take turns rolling two 0–5 **Number Cubes** and making fractions equal to or less than 1. Remind students that they may divide their fraction between more than one circle (i.e., a player who rolls a 4 and a 5 may cover $\frac{1}{5}$ of a circle and $\frac{3}{5}$ of another circle). A circle is awarded to a player who has covered more than half of it. When actually playing a full game, students continue until all of the circles are either owned or covered completely.

Guided Discussion UNDERSTANDING Whole Group

Have six students come to the front of the class. Remind students that fractions refer to a part of a whole. When you divide a line or a shape, the line or the shape is the whole. When you divide a group of objects, the group is the whole.

Ask questions such as the following to lead the discussion, writing down the fraction for each answer (which will vary depending on the number of students in the group):

- **What fraction are boys?**
- **What fraction are girls?**
- **What fraction have on blue jeans?**
- **What fraction have brown hair?**

Draw 8 shapes on the board, or use overhead projector pattern blocks.

Have one student circle or separate the objects in half sections. Ask questions such as the following:

- **How many equal parts will there be?** 2
- **How many shapes are in $\frac{1}{2}$ of the group?** 4

Have another student circle or separate the objects in fourths. Ask questions such as the following:

- **How many equal parts will there be?** 4
- **How many shapes are in $\frac{1}{4}$ of the group?** 2

If students need more practice, have them divide into eighths and answer similar questions.

Strategy Building APPLYING Small Group

Remind students that when you are dividing sets of objects into fractional parts, you are dividing the objects into equal groups. For example, if you divide a set into fourths, you divide it into 4 equal groups. If you divide it into thirds, you divide it into 3 equal groups.

Divide students into groups of 2 or 3. Give each group 20 manipulatives. Have them find the answers to the following questions:

- **What is $\frac{1}{4}$ of 20?** 5
- **What is $\frac{2}{4}$ of 20?** 10
- **What is $\frac{3}{4}$ of 20?** 15
- **What is $\frac{4}{4}$ of 20?** 20
- **What pattern do you see in your answers?** Possible answer: They are multiples of 5.

Using 10 manipulatives, ask questions such as the following:

- **What is $\frac{1}{5}$ of 10?** 2
- **What is $\frac{2}{5}$ of 10?** 4
- **What is $\frac{3}{5}$ of 10?** 6
- **What is $\frac{4}{5}$ of 10?** 8
- **What is $\frac{5}{5}$ of 10?** 10
- **What pattern do you see in your answers?** Possible answer: They are multiples of 2.

If students need more practice, continue similar demonstrations of fractions of sets.

2 Assign Student Pages

20

Pages 300–301 APPLYING

Have students complete pages 300 and 301 independently. You might want to have manipulatives or play money available as necessary.

RESEARCH IN ACTION

"Students' informal notions of partitioning, sharing, and measuring provide a starting point for building the concept of rational number. Young children appreciate the idea of "fair shares," and they can use that understanding to partition quantities into equal parts. In some ways, sharing can play the role for rational numbers that counting does for whole numbers."

Kilpatrick, J., J. Swafford, and B. Findell, eds. *Adding it Up: Helping Children Learn Mathematics*. Washington, D.C.: National Research Council/National Academy Press, 2001, p. 7.

LESSON 8.3 Fractions of Sets

Key Ideas

Recall that a fraction represents a specific part of a whole. This can be a whole shape, or it can be a whole collection, or **set**, of items.

Rosalie divided 15 coins into 3 equal piles.

Because there are 3 equal piles total, we would say 1 pile is $\frac{1}{3}$ of the whole collection, or set, of pennies.

Count the number of pennies in 1 pile. There are 5 pennies in 1 pile.

$$\frac{1}{3} \text{ of } 15 = 5$$

Solve. You may use manipulatives to act out these problems.

Lola divided 10 coins into 5 equal piles.

❶ Draw the 5 piles.   Check students' work.

❷ How many coins are there in each pile?   2

❸ $\frac{1}{5}$ of 10 is ■.   2

❹ $\frac{1}{4}$ of 16 is ■.   4

300   ▣ **Textbook** This lesson is available in the *eTextbook.*

---

❺ $\frac{1}{2}$ of 12 = ■.   6

❻ $\frac{1}{5}$ of 15 = ■.   3

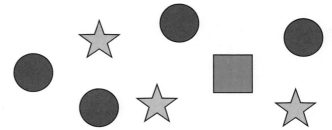

Use the picture to answer the questions.

❼ What fraction of the set is stars? $\frac{3}{8}$

❽ What fraction of the set is circles? $\frac{4}{8}$ or $\frac{1}{2}$

❾ What fraction of the set is squares? $\frac{1}{8}$

❿ What fraction of the set includes all the stars and all the circles? $\frac{7}{8}$

⓫ What fraction of the set includes all the stars, circles, and squares? $\frac{8}{8}$ or 1 whole

⓬ What fraction of the set includes no stars, circles, or squares? $\frac{0}{8}$ or 0

⓭ What fraction of the set is not squares? $\frac{7}{8}$

⓮ What fraction of the set is not circles? $\frac{4}{8}$ or $\frac{1}{2}$

Chapter 8 • Lesson 3   301

Assign Student Pages, continued

Pages 302–303 APPLYING

Have students complete pages 302 and 303 independently. Again, you might want to have manipulatives available as necessary.

As Students Finish

Game **Fraction Game**

eGames *Fraction Game*

Student Page

LESSON 8.3 • Fractions of Sets

You may use manipulatives to help you solve these problems. Work down the page.

15. $\frac{1}{6}$ of 12 is ■. 2
16. $\frac{2}{6}$ of 12 is ■. 4
17. $\frac{3}{6}$ of 12 is ■. 6
18. $\frac{4}{6}$ of 12 is ■. 8
19. $\frac{1}{8}$ of 24 is ■. 3
20. $\frac{2}{8}$ of 24 is ■. 6
21. $\frac{3}{8}$ of 24 is ■. 9
22. $\frac{4}{8}$ of 24 is ■. 12
23. $\frac{1}{5}$ of 25 is ■. 5
24. $\frac{2}{5}$ of 25 is ■. 10
25. $\frac{3}{5}$ of 25 is ■. 15
26. $\frac{4}{5}$ of 25 is ■. 20
27. $\frac{1}{5}$ of 30 is ■. 6
28. $\frac{3}{5}$ of 30 is ■. 18
29. $\frac{1}{3}$ of 30 is ■. 10
30. $\frac{2}{3}$ of 30 is ■. 20

302

eTextbook This lesson is available in the ***eTextbook***.

Student Page

Solve.

31. In Michael's class, $\frac{1}{3}$ of the students are boys. What fraction of the students are girls? $\frac{2}{3}$

There are 20 students in Bev's class; $\frac{1}{2}$ of them are girls.

32. How many girls are in Bev's class? 10
33. How many boys are in Bev's class? 10
34. Julius lives 30 miles from where he works. He has driven $\frac{1}{3}$ of the way there. How many miles has he driven? 10
35. Keiko and her 4 friends want to share a pizza equally. What fraction of the pizza should each person get? $\frac{1}{5}$
36. **Extended Response** There are 400 pages in the book Shamika is reading for her summer reading program. She has 8 weeks to read the book. How many pages should she read weekly if she wants to read an equal amount each week? Explain how you got your answer. 50; Accept all reasonable answers. See Reflect in *Teacher's Edition* for further explanations.

Writing + Math **Journal**

Determine what fraction each shape is of the whole area. Explain how you got your answer. Accept any reasonable answer.

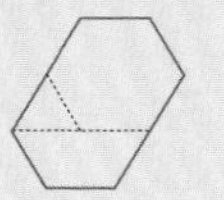

a. Hexagon $\frac{6}{10}$

b. Triangle $\frac{1}{10}$

c. Trapezoid $\frac{3}{10}$

Chapter 8 • Lesson 3 303

③ **Reflect**   5

Guided Discussion   UNDERSTANDING   Whole Group

Have students explain or demonstrate how they would find the following:

- $\frac{1}{2}$ of 60   30
- $\frac{1}{3}$ of 60   20
- $\frac{1}{4}$ of 60   15
- $\frac{1}{5}$ of 60   12

Extended Response

Problem 38 Acceptable answers include an understanding that if Shamika wants to read the same amount each week, she must divide 400 by 8, even though the method of obtaining the answer might vary. Some students may say there could be more writing on some pages than others, so this is only an approximation.

Writing + Math   Journal

The total is $\frac{10}{10}$. The hexagon is $\frac{6}{10}$, the triangle is $\frac{1}{10}$, and the trapezoid is $\frac{3}{10}$. Students should be able to break the entire shape into 10 triangles.

✓   Use Mastery Checkpoint 17 found in **Assessment** to evaluate student mastery of simple fractions. By this time, students should be able to correctly answer eighty percent of the Mastery Checkpoint items.

Cumulative Review: For cumulative review of previously learned skills, see page 312–313.

Family Involvement: Assign the **Practice, Reteach,** or **Enrichment** activities depending on the needs of your students.

Encourage students to play the **Fraction Game** with a friend or a relative.

Concept/Question Board: Have students look for additional examples using fractions and post them on the Concept/Question Board.

Math Puzzler: I am a number between 20 and 30. You say my name when you count by 3s, 4s, 6s, and 8s. Who am I? 24

Assess and Differentiate

 Assess Use **eAssess** to record and analyze evidence of student understanding.

A Gather Evidence

Use the Daily Class Assessment Records in **Assessment** or **eAssess** to record daily observations.

Formal Assessment
☑ **Mastery Checkpoint**

Did the student
- ❑ use correct procedures?
- ❑ respond with at least 80% accuracy?

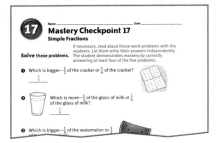

Assessment Page T70

B Summarize Findings

Analyze and summarize assessment data for each student. Determine which Assessment Follow-Up is appropriate for each student. Use the Student Assessment Record in **Assessment** or **eAssess** to update assessment records.

Assessment page T41

C Assessment Follow-Up • DIFFERENTIATE INSTRUCTION

Based on your observations, use these teaching strategies for assessment follow-up.

INTERVENTION	ENRICH	PRACTICE	RETEACH
Review student performance on **Intervention** Lesson 8.B to see if students have mastered prerequisite skills for this lesson.	**If . . .** students are proficient in the lesson concepts, **Then . . .** encourage them to work on chapter projects or **Enrichment** Lesson 8.3.	**If . . .** students would benefit from additional practice, **Then . . .** assign **Practice** Lesson 8.3.	**If . . .** students struggle with finding fractions of whole numbers, **Then . . .** have them partition a set of objects such as interlocking cubes into equal bunches or piles. Point out that the bottom number (denominator) represents the bunches or piles into which we divide the objects. Encourage students to use manipulatives to help them solve the problems.

ENGLISH LEARNER

Review

Use Lesson 8.3 in **English Learner Support Guide** to review lesson concepts and vocabulary.

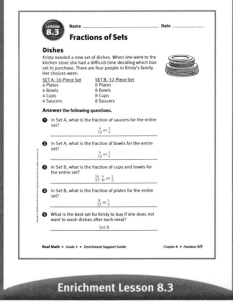

Enrichment Lesson 8.3

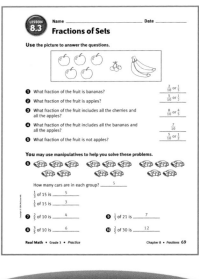

Practice Lesson 8.3

Lesson Planner

OBJECTIVES
- To apply knowledge of fractions of sets to fractions of time
- To find fractions of time in half hours, quarter hours, and thirds of an hour

NCTM STANDARDS
Number and Operations
Developing understanding of fractions as parts of unit wholes, as parts of a collection, as locations on number lines, and as divisions of whole numbers

Connections
Recognizing and using connections among mathematical ideas

MATERIALS

- *Response Wheels
- Manipulatives, 60 per group
- *Fraction Game Mat

TECHNOLOGY
- Presentation Lesson 8.4
- Games Fraction Game

TEST PREP
Cumulative Review
Mental Math reviews basic division facts (Chapter 5).

Writing + Math
Journal

Fractions of Time

Context of the Lesson In Grade 2 students incorporated the terms *half hour* and *quarter hour* when referring to telling time. In this lesson students will use their knowledge of fractions and minutes in an hour to create a description of the terms *half hour* and *quarter hour*. This lesson is a continuation of Lesson 8.3, Fractions of Sets.

See page 292B for Math Background for teachers for this lesson.

Planning for Learning ● DIFFERENTIATE INSTRUCTION

INTERVENTION	ENGLISH LEARNER	ENRICH
If . . . students lack the prerequisite skill of reading and writing fractions, **Then . . .** teach *Intervention* Lesson 8.B.	Preview **If . . .** students need language support, **Then . . .** use Lesson 8.4 in *English Learner Support Guide* to preview lesson concepts and vocabulary.	**If . . .** students are proficient in the lesson concepts, **Then . . .** emphasize the student pages.

ENRICH continued:

PRACTICE
If . . . students would benefit from additional practice, **Then . . .** extend Strategy Building before assigning the student pages.

RETEACH
If . . . students are having difficulty understanding fractions of time, **Then . . .** extend Guided Discussion before assigning the student pages.

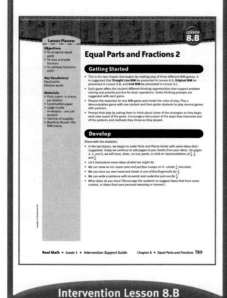

Intervention Lesson 8.B

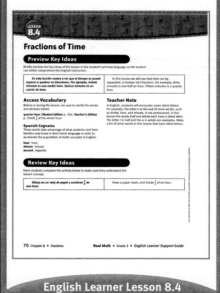

English Learner Lesson 8.4

Vocabulary
quarter \kwôr´ tər\ *n.*
one-fourth of an hour; fifteen minutes

Access Vocabulary
quarter hour $\frac{1}{4}$ of the whole hour

Spanish Cognates
hour hora
minute minuto
second segundo

Mental Math

  Provide practice with division facts. Use examples such as the following:

a. $28 \div 7$ 4
c. $30 \div 5$ 6
e. $6 \div 2$ 3
g. $64 \div 8$ 8
i. $54 \div 9$ 6

b. $100 \div 10$ 10
d. $72 \div 8$ 9
f. $49 \div 7$ 7
h. $80 \div 8$ 10
j. $0 \div 7$ 0

1 Develop 25

Tell Students In Today's Lesson They Will

apply their knowledge of fractions of sets to find fractions of time in half hours, quarter hours, and thirds of an hour.

Guided Discussion UNDERSTANDING Whole Group

Review with students what it means to find a fraction of a set. Make 5 stacks of 4 objects. These objects can be tangible objects or drawings. Ask students questions such as the following:

- **How many objects are there total?** 20
- **How do you know?** Possible answers: $5 \times 4 = 20$ or the student counted 20 objects
- **How many stacks are there?** 5
- **What fraction of the whole is 1 stack?** $\frac{1}{5}$
- **How many objects are in 1 stack?** 4

Write on the board $\frac{1}{5}$ of 20 is 4. Have students tell how many each of the following is: $\frac{2}{5}$ of 20, $\frac{3}{5}$ of 20, $\frac{4}{5}$ of 20, and $\frac{5}{5}$ of 20. Ask students how many minutes are in one hour. Place 60 objects on the table or overhead projector, or draw them on the board. Have one student come up and demonstrate $\frac{1}{2}$ of 60. Have a second student count and verify that the student has indeed found 30 to be $\frac{1}{2}$ of 60. On the board, write the equation $\frac{1}{2}$ of $60 = 30$.

Have a third student come up and demonstrate $\frac{1}{4}$ of 60. With the class, count and verify that $\frac{1}{4}$ of 60 is 15. Write on the board $\frac{1}{4}$ of $60 = 15$.

Have students give their answer to the question *What is $\frac{3}{4}$ of 60?* 45

Strategy Building REASONING Whole Group

Have students work as a class to answer questions such as the following.

a. $\frac{1}{2}$ of 60 30
c. $\frac{0}{2}$ of 60 0
e. $\frac{2}{4}$ of 60 30
g. $\frac{1}{3}$ of 60 20

b. $\frac{2}{2}$ of 60 60
d. $\frac{1}{4}$ of 60 15
f. $\frac{0}{4}$ of 60 0
h. $\frac{3}{3}$ of 60 60

If students understand the concept, feel free to ask questions dealing with sixths of the hour.

Using Student Pages APPLYING Small Group

Have students turn to student page 304. As a class or in small groups, go through the items in Key Ideas, emphasizing the fact that a face of a clock can be viewed in halves, thirds, and fourths. Have students work as a class or in small groups on Problems 1–4. Check for understanding before assigning student pages.

Monitoring Student Progress

If . . . students are having difficulty seeing the half-, third-, and quarter-hour divisions on the clock face,

Then . . . have students represent the exercise with fraction circles.

2 Assign Student Pages 20

Pages 304–305 APPLYING

Have students complete page 305 independently.

As Students Finish

Game Fraction Game

Games *Fraction Game*

LESSON 8.4 Fractions of Time

Key Ideas

Time can be represented as fractions of an hour. We often use the phrases *half hour* and *quarter hour*. What do these phrases actually mean when referring to fractions of time?

If we look at the face of a clock, we can see how it could be divided into halves and quarters.

This clock face is divided into 2 equal sections, so each section would be $\frac{1}{2}$ of the whole.

This clock face is divided into 4 equal sections, so each section would be $\frac{1}{4}$ of the whole. Another way of saying $\frac{1}{4}$ is to refer to it as one-quarter of the whole.

📖 **Textbook** This lesson is available in the *eTextbook*.

Think about how much time passes in an hour. There are 60 minutes in one hour.

$\frac{1}{2}$ of 60 = 30

Therefore, $\frac{1}{2}$ of an hour is 30 minutes.

What fraction is represented by the shaded part of each clock?

① $\frac{1}{2}$

② $\frac{3}{4}$

③ $\frac{2}{4}$ or $\frac{1}{2}$

How many minutes? The first one is done for you.

④ 1 hour = 60 minutes

⑤ $\frac{2}{2}$ of an hour   60 minutes

⑥ $\frac{2}{4}$ of an hour   30 minutes

⑦ $\frac{3}{4}$ of an hour   45 minutes

⑧ $\frac{4}{4}$ of an hour   60 minutes

⑨ $\frac{1}{3}$ of an hour   20 minutes

⑩ $\frac{2}{3}$ of an hour   40 minutes

Which is longer?

⑪ $\frac{1}{2}$ of an hour or $\frac{2}{4}$ of an hour?   same

⑫ $\frac{1}{2}$ of an hour or $\frac{1}{4}$ of an hour? $\frac{1}{2}$

⑬ $\frac{1}{2}$ of an hour or $\frac{3}{4}$ of an hour? $\frac{3}{4}$

⑭ $\frac{2}{2}$ of an hour or $\frac{1}{1}$ of an hour?   same

⑮ $\frac{2}{2}$ of an hour or $\frac{4}{4}$ of an hour?   same

⑯ $\frac{2}{4}$ of an hour or $\frac{2}{3}$ of an hour? $\frac{2}{3}$

Writing + Math Journal

Describe how you would find $\frac{1}{5}$ of an hour.

Divide 60 into 5 parts; $\frac{1}{5}$ of 60 would be 12 minutes.

LESSON 8.4 Fractions of Time

  3 Reflect   10

Guided Discussion   RESPONSE WHEEL

Whole Group

Show on the **Response Wheels** the following times:

a. quarter to 8   7:45

b. quarter after 9   9:15

c. half past 4   4:30

d. quarter after 3   3:15

e. half past 6   6:30

Writing + Math Journal

Students can use fractions of sets to find $\frac{1}{5}$ of 60 or divide the face of the clock into 5 equal parts.

Review **Cumulative Review:** For cumulative review of previously learned skills, see page 312–313.

Family Involvement: Assign the *Practice, Reteach,* or *Enrichment* activities depending on the needs of your students.

Encourage students to practice finding fractions of an hour with a friend or a relative.

Concept/Question Board: Have students look for additional examples using fractions and post them on the Concept/Question Board.

Math Puzzler: How many 4s do you add to find 16? 8? 24? 56?   4; 2; 6; 14

4 Assess and Differentiate

 Assess Use *eAssess* to record and analyze evidence of student understanding.

A Gather Evidence

Use the Daily Class Assessment Records in *Assessment* or *eAssess* to record daily observations.

Informal Assessment
☑ **Strategy Building**

Did the student **REASONING**
- ❏ provide a clear explanation?
- ❏ communicate reasons and strategies?
- ❏ choose appropriate strategies?
- ❏ argue logically?

Informal Assessment
☑ **Student Pages**

Did the student **APPLYING**
- ❏ apply learning in new situations?
- ❏ contribute concepts?
- ❏ contribute answers?
- ❏ connect mathematics to real-world situations?

B Summarize Findings

Analyze and summarize assessment data for each student. Determine which Assessment Follow-Up is appropriate for each student. Use the Student Assessment Record in *Assessment* or *eAssess* to update assessment records.

Assessment page T41

C Assessment Follow-Up ● DIFFERENTIATE INSTRUCTION

Based on your observations, use these teaching strategies for assessment follow-up.

INTERVENTION

Review student performance on *Intervention* Lesson 8.B to see if students have mastered prerequisite skills for this lesson.

ENGLISH LEARNER

Review

Use Lesson 8.4 in *English Learner Support Guide* to review lesson concepts and vocabulary.

ENRICH

If . . . students are proficient in the lesson concepts,

Then . . . encourage them to work on chapter projects or *Enrichment* Lesson 8.4.

Enrichment Lesson 8.4

PRACTICE

If . . . students would benefit from additional practice,

Then . . . assign *Practice* Lesson 8.4.

Practice Lesson 8.4

RETEACH

If . . . students struggle with envisioning fractions of time,

Then . . . have them take a clock face and divide it into 12 sections by putting lines at every five minutes. Then have them shade the portions for quarter hours and hours. Have them represent each of the problems using this model.

Lesson Planner

OBJECTIVES
- To give students an experience that will help them understand equivalent fractions
- To introduce in a more formal way the concept of equivalent fractions

NCTM STANDARDS
Number and Operations
Recognizing and generating equivalent forms of commonly used fractions

Communication
Using the language of mathematics to express mathematical ideas precisely

MATERIALS
- *Response Wheels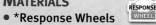
- Unlined piece of paper for each student
- Shading items, such as colored pencil or crayon
- *Fraction Game Mat

TECHNOLOGY
- Presentation Lesson 8.5
- Games Fraction Game

TEST PREP
Cumulative Review
Mental Math reviews fractions of time (Lesson 8.4).

Writing + Math
Journal

Looking Ahead
You will need to prepare an overhead transparency of the Blackline Master of the **Fraction Game** for Lesson 8.6.

Equivalent Fractions

Context of the Lesson Students have explored fraction equivalency in Grade 2 when the **Fraction Game** was first introduced. This lesson will allow students to further examine fractions and their equivalents. This concept will be extended in Grade 4 to include finding fractions in their lowest terms.

See page 292B for Math Background for teachers for this lesson.

Planning for Learning ● DIFFERENTIATE INSTRUCTION

INTERVENTION
If . . . students lack the prerequisite skill of reading and writing fractions,

Then . . . teach *Intervention* Lesson 8.B.

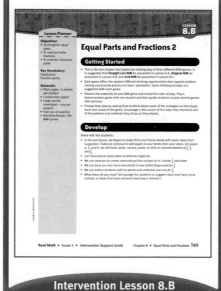

Intervention Lesson 8.B

ENGLISH LEARNER
Preview

If . . . students need language support,

Then . . . use Lesson 8.5 in *English Learner Support Guide* to preview lesson concepts and vocabulary.

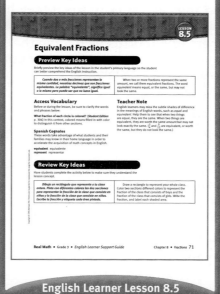

English Learner Lesson 8.5

ENRICH
If . . . students are proficient in the lesson concepts,

Then . . . emphasize the **Fraction Game.**

PRACTICE
If . . . students would benefit from additional practice,

Then . . . extend Guided Discussion before assigning the student pages.

RETEACH
If . . . students are having difficulty understanding equivalent fractions,

Then . . . extend Strategy Building before assigning the student pages.

Vocabulary
equivalent \i kwiv´ ə lənt\ *adj.*
having the same value

Spanish Cognates
equivalent equivalente
represent representar

---

*Manipulative Kit Item

Teaching Lesson 8.5

Mental Math

  Have students find fractions of time using examples such as the following:

a. $\frac{1}{2}$ of 60 30

b. $\frac{1}{3}$ of 60 20

c. $\frac{2}{3}$ of 60 40

d. $\frac{1}{4}$ of 60 15

e. $\frac{2}{4}$ of 60 30

f. $\frac{1}{6}$ of 60 10

g. $\frac{3}{6}$ of 60 30

h. $\frac{5}{6}$ of 60 50

1 Develop 25

Tell Students In Today's Lesson They Will

explore equivalent fractions.

Strategy Building UNDERSTANDING Whole Group

1. Distribute to each student an unlined piece of 8.5″ × 11″ paper, and have students fold the paper in half (either end to end or side to side). Tell everyone to shade $\frac{1}{2}$ of the sheet, and have them hold up their papers so you can check to see if they have done it correctly.

2. Have students fold their papers into fourths by folding the sheets in half again in the opposite direction. After they unfold their papers, ask questions such as the following:
   - **What fraction of the sheet is each part?** $\frac{1}{4}$
   - **How many of the fourths are shaded?** 2
   - **Which is bigger, the $\frac{1}{2}$ of the paper or the $\frac{2}{4}$ of the paper?** They are the same.

3. Have students fold their papers again, this time making one more fold in the first direction. Ask questions such as the following:
   - **How many parts are there?** 8
   - **What fraction represents each part?** $\frac{1}{8}$
   - **Which is bigger, the $\frac{1}{2}$ of the paper or the $\frac{4}{8}$ of the paper?** They are the same.

Have students find other equivalent fractions using their folded papers. Examples are $\frac{1}{4}$ and $\frac{2}{8}$, $\frac{3}{4}$ and $\frac{6}{8}$, or $\frac{2}{4}$ and $\frac{4}{8}$.

Guided Discussion   UNDERSTANDING Whole Group

Draw a circle on the board. Have a student shade $\frac{1}{2}$ of the circle. Then draw another circle the same size to the right of the first one, and ask another student to shade $\frac{2}{4}$ of it. Make sure each student is dividing the circle into equal parts before shading. Repeat this procedure for $\frac{3}{6}$, $\frac{4}{8}$, and $\frac{5}{10}$ of a circle. Label each circle. When you have finished, you should have five circles, one each with $\frac{1}{2}$ shaded, $\frac{2}{4}$ shaded, $\frac{3}{6}$ shaded, $\frac{4}{8}$ shaded, and $\frac{5}{10}$ shaded. If any of the students happen to shade in nonadjacent parts of the circle, commend them and point out there are many ways each circle could be shaded. In this exercise, however, they are going to shade adjacent parts to make it easier to see certain things.

Ask students questions such as the following to help them visualize equivalent fractions more clearly:

- **Which is larger, $\frac{1}{2}$ or $\frac{2}{4}$?** They are the same.
- **Which is larger, $\frac{5}{10}$ or $\frac{3}{6}$?** They are the same.
- **Which is larger, $\frac{4}{8}$ or $\frac{1}{2}$?** They are the same.

Introduce the term *equivalent fractions* to students. Point out that fractions that show the same amount are equivalent fractions.

2 Assign Student Pages 20

Pages 306–307 APPLYING

Have students complete pages 306 and 307 independently.

As Students Finish

 Fraction Game

 Games *Fraction Game*

LESSON 8.5 Equivalent Fractions

Key Ideas

When two or more fractions represent the same part of a whole, we call them **equivalent** fractions.

Each of the following circles has the same amount shaded. However, each shaded part is represented by a different fraction.

$\frac{3}{4}$ $\frac{6}{8}$

Because $\frac{3}{4}$ and $\frac{6}{8}$ represent the same amount, we would say they are equivalent fractions.

What fraction of each circle is colored?

① $\frac{1}{3}, \frac{2}{6}, \frac{3}{9}$

② $\frac{1}{2}, \frac{2}{4}, \frac{4}{8}$

③ $\frac{2}{3}, \frac{4}{6}, \frac{6}{9}$

306   Textbook This lesson is available in the **eTextbook**.

What fraction of each rectangle is colored?

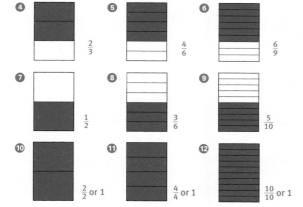

④ $\frac{2}{3}$ ⑤ $\frac{4}{6}$ ⑥ $\frac{6}{9}$

⑦ $\frac{1}{2}$ ⑧ $\frac{3}{6}$ ⑨ $\frac{5}{10}$

⑩ $\frac{2}{2}$ or 1   ⑪ $\frac{4}{4}$ or 1   ⑫ $\frac{10}{10}$ or 1

Writing + Math Journal

List or draw five fractions that are equivalent to $\frac{1}{2}$.

Possible answers: $\frac{1}{2}, \frac{2}{4}, \frac{3}{6}, \frac{4}{8}$, and $\frac{5}{10}$

---

③ Reflect   5

Guided Discussion   Whole Group

Have students identify which of the following fractions are equivalent (represent the same amount):  $\frac{1}{2}, \frac{2}{4}, \frac{3}{6}, \frac{4}{8}, \frac{5}{10}. \frac{1}{5}, \frac{2}{10}. \frac{1}{3}, \frac{2}{6}$

- $\frac{1}{2}$
- $\frac{2}{4}$
- $\frac{1}{5}$
- $\frac{1}{6}$
- $\frac{5}{10}$
- $\frac{1}{3}$
- $\frac{3}{6}$
- $\frac{2}{10}$
- $\frac{2}{7}$
- $\frac{2}{3}$
- $\frac{1}{4}$
- $\frac{4}{8}$
- $\frac{2}{6}$
- $\frac{3}{8}$
- $\frac{1}{10}$

List the remaining fractions in order from least to greatest. $\frac{1}{10}, \frac{1}{6}, \frac{1}{4}, \frac{2}{7}, \frac{3}{8}, \frac{2}{3}$

Writing + Math Journal

Students should note that there are infinite or unlimited possibilities.

 Cumulative Review: For cumulative review of previously learned skills, see page 312–313.

 Family Involvement: Assign the *Practice, Reteach,* or *Enrichment* activities depending on the needs of your students.

Encourage students to practice finding equivalent fractions with a friend or a relative.

 Concept/Question Board: Encourage students to continue to post questions, answers, and examples on the Concept/Question Board.

 Math Puzzler: Red flowers cost 30¢ each. White flowers and pink flowers cost 50¢ each. If Josephina plants 4 red flowers, 4 white flowers, and 4 pink flowers (in order in one row) in her garden, how much do the first 7 flowers in the row cost? $2.70

Assess and Differentiate

 Assess Use **eAssess** to record and analyze evidence of student understanding.

A Gather Evidence

Use the Daily Class Assessment Records in **Assessment** or **eAssess** to record daily observations.

Informal Assessment

☑ **Guided Discussion**

Did the student [UNDERSTANDING]

- ❏ make important observations?
- ❏ extend or generalize learning?
- ❏ provide insightful answers?
- ❏ pose insightful questions?

Portfolio Assessment

☑ **Journal**

Did the student [REASONING]

- ❏ provide a clear explanation?
- ❏ communicate reasons and strategies?
- ❏ choose appropriate strategies?
- ❏ argue logically?

B Summarize Findings

Analyze and summarize assessment data for each student. Determine which Assessment Follow-Up is appropriate for each student. Use the Student Assessment Record in **Assessment** or **eAssess** to update assessment records.

Assessment page T41

C Assessment Follow-Up ● DIFFERENTIATE INSTRUCTION

Based on your observations, use these teaching strategies for assessment follow-up.

INTERVENTION

Review student performance on **Intervention** Lesson 8.B to see if students have mastered prerequisite skills for this lesson.

ENGLISH LEARNER

Review

Use Lesson 8.5 in **English Learner Support Guide** to review lesson concepts and vocabulary.

ENRICH

If . . . students are proficient in the lesson concepts,

Then . . . encourage them to work on chapter projects or **Enrichment** Lesson 8.5.

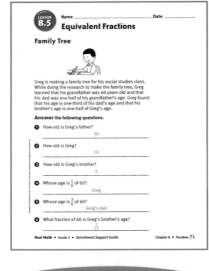

Enrichment Lesson 8.5

PRACTICE

If . . . students would benefit from additional practice,

Then . . . assign **Practice** Lesson 8.5.

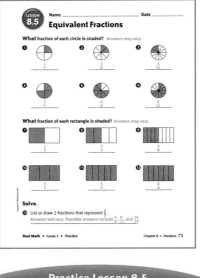

Practice Lesson 8.5

RETEACH

If . . . students are having difficulty understanding equivalent fractions,

Then . . . reteach the concept using **Reteach** Lesson 8.5.

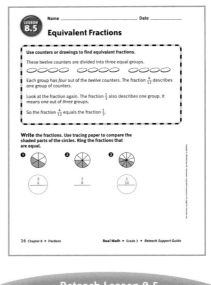

Reteach Lesson 8.5

Lesson Planner

OBJECTIVES
To compare fractions less than one whole

NCTM STANDARDS
Number and Operations
Using models, benchmarks, and equivalent forms to judge the size of fractions

Connections
Understanding how mathematical ideas interconnect and build on one another to produce a coherent whole

MATERIALS

- *Response Wheels
- Overhead transparency of Blackline Master of **Fraction Game**
- *Fraction Game Mat

TECHNOLOGY
- e Presentation Lesson 8.6
- e Games Fraction Game

TEST PREP
Cumulative Review
Mental Math reviews finding fractions of a set (Lesson 8.3).

Extended Response
Problem 8

Comparing Fractions

Context of the Lesson As students have worked with fractions in previous grades, they have developed an intuitive knowledge about which fractions are greater when comparing. In this lesson students will compare fractions using $<$, $>$, and $=$ without finding a common denominator. In Grade 4 students will apply this same intuitive knowledge to fractions and begin to find common denominators.

See page 292B for Math Background for teachers for this lesson.

Planning for Learning ● DIFFERENTIATE INSTRUCTION

INTERVENTION
If . . . students lack the prerequisite skill of recognizing equal parts,

Then . . . teach **Intervention** Lesson 8.A.

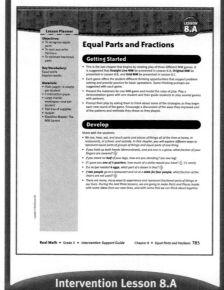

Intervention Lesson 8.A

ENGLISH LEARNER
Preview

If . . . students need language support,

Then . . . use Lesson 8.6 in **English Learner Support Guide** to preview lesson concepts and vocabulary.

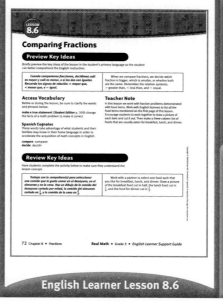

English Learner Lesson 8.6

ENRICH
If . . . students are proficient in the lesson concepts,

Then . . . emphasize the student pages.

PRACTICE
If . . . students would benefit from additional practice,

Then . . . extend Skill Building before assigning the student pages.

RETEACH
If . . . students are having difficulty understanding how to compare fractions,

Then . . . extend Guided Discussion before assigning the student pages.

Access Vocabulary
make a true statement change the facts of a math problem to make it correct

Spanish Cognates
compare comparar
decide decidir

Mental Math   10

  Practice finding fractions of a set. Write problems such as the following on the board as you present them to students.

a. $\frac{1}{2}$ of 10   5   **b.** $\frac{1}{2}$ of 20   10

c. $\frac{1}{3}$ of 15   5   **d.** $\frac{2}{3}$ of 15   10

e. $\frac{1}{5}$ of 20   4   **f.** $\frac{3}{5}$ of 20   12

g. $\frac{4}{4}$ of 12   12   **h.** $\frac{0}{4}$ of 12   0

1   Develop   25

Tell Students In Today's Lesson They Will

compare fractions less than one whole.

Guided Discussion   UNDERSTANDING   Whole Group

Review with students what it means to compare numbers. Ask questions such as the following:

- **What does > represent?** greater than
- **What does < represent?** less than
- **What does it mean to say two things are equal?** They have the same value.

If students are uncertain about which symbol to use when writing, remind them to place the open end or larger end of the symbol near the larger number. Encourage students to read their answer from left to right to check for accuracy. For example, 3 > 4 would be read *three is greater than four,* and that would be an incorrect statement.

Skill Building   APPLYING   Whole Group

 On the board or by using the circles on the overhead transparency copy of the **Fraction Game,** draw circles **THUMBS UP** divided into halves, thirds, fourths, and fifths. Starting with numerators of 1, compare various fractions with students. Have students respond with thumbs-up if the answer is greater

than, thumbs-down if the answer is less than, and open hand if the answer is equal to. Use examples such as the following:

- $\frac{1}{2}$ ____ $\frac{1}{3}$ up
- $\frac{1}{4}$ ____ $\frac{1}{3}$ down
- $\frac{1}{3}$ ____ $\frac{1}{5}$ up
- $\frac{1}{5}$ ____ $\frac{1}{4}$ down
- $\frac{1}{2}$ ____ $\frac{1}{5}$ up

When students are comfortable with numerators of 1, move to fractions with numerators greater than 1, but make sure the fractions are less than a whole. Use examples such as the following:

- $\frac{1}{2}$ ____ $\frac{2}{4}$ open hand
- $\frac{2}{4}$ ____ $\frac{1}{3}$ up
- $\frac{1}{3}$ ____ $\frac{2}{3}$ down
- $\frac{2}{3}$ ____ $\frac{2}{2}$ down
- $\frac{3}{5}$ ____ $\frac{1}{2}$ up

Ask students to explain how they might determine the larger of two numbers if the numerator of both is 1. For example, ask, *Which is greater, $\frac{1}{2}$ or $\frac{1}{3}$?* $\frac{1}{2}$ because the smaller the denominator is, the larger the fraction is

2   Assign Student Pages   20

Pages 308–309   APPLYING

Have students complete pages 308 and 309 independently. Encourage students to use the pictures on page 309 to assist with visualization of fractions.

Monitoring Student Progress

If . . . students are struggling with determining which symbol to use,	**Then . . .** have them write down only the larger of the two fractions (or both if they are equal). As a class, review the symbols on a regular basis.

As Students Finish

 Game   Fraction Game

 Games *Fraction Game*

LESSON 8.6 Comparing Fractions

Key Ideas

When we compare fractions, we decide which fraction of something is bigger and which is smaller, or if both fractions of a thing are the same.

Which is bigger, $\frac{1}{2}$ of the cake or $\frac{1}{3}$ of the cake?

We could draw a picture using circles for the two cakes.

By looking at the pictures, we can see that $\frac{1}{2}$ is bigger.

Answer these questions.

1. Which is bigger, $\frac{1}{2}$ of the pie or $\frac{1}{5}$ of the pie? $\frac{1}{2}$
2. Which is bigger, $\frac{1}{3}$ of the loaf of bread or $\frac{1}{5}$ of the loaf? $\frac{1}{3}$
3. Which is bigger, $\frac{1}{3}$ of the pizza or $\frac{1}{4}$ of the pizza? $\frac{1}{3}$
4. Which is bigger, $\frac{1}{2}$ of the muffin or $\frac{1}{4}$ of the muffin? $\frac{1}{2}$
5. Which is bigger, $\frac{1}{4}$ of the apple or $\frac{1}{2}$ of the apple? $\frac{1}{2}$
6. Which is bigger, $\frac{1}{5}$ of the banana or $\frac{1}{2}$ of the banana? $\frac{1}{2}$
7. Which is bigger, $\frac{1}{3}$ of the sandwich or $\frac{1}{4}$ of the sandwich? $\frac{1}{3}$
8. **Extended Response** Explain how you got your answer to Problem 7.   Accept all reasonable answers.

308   Ⓔ Textbook This lesson is available in the *eTextbook*.

Symbols are also used sometimes to compare fractions. These symbols are $<$, $>$, or $=$.

Copy each statement, and replace the ▇ with $<$, $>$, or $=$ to make a true statement. The pictures may help you.

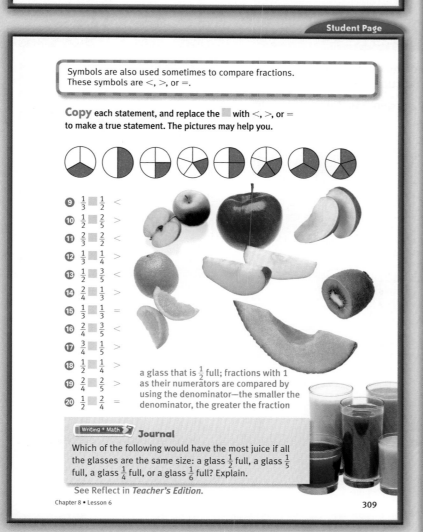

9. $\frac{1}{3}$ ▇ $\frac{1}{2}$ $<$
10. $\frac{1}{2}$ ▇ $\frac{2}{5}$ $>$
11. $\frac{2}{3}$ ▇ $\frac{2}{2}$ $<$
12. $\frac{1}{3}$ ▇ $\frac{1}{4}$ $>$
13. $\frac{1}{2}$ ▇ $\frac{3}{5}$ $<$
14. $\frac{2}{4}$ ▇ $\frac{1}{3}$ $>$
15. $\frac{1}{3}$ ▇ $\frac{1}{3}$ $=$
16. $\frac{2}{4}$ ▇ $\frac{3}{5}$ $<$
17. $\frac{3}{4}$ ▇ $\frac{1}{5}$ $>$
18. $\frac{1}{2}$ ▇ $\frac{1}{4}$ $>$
19. $\frac{2}{4}$ ▇ $\frac{2}{5}$ $>$
20. $\frac{1}{2}$ ▇ $\frac{2}{4}$ $=$

a glass that is $\frac{1}{2}$ full; fractions with 1 as their numerators are compared by using the denominator—the smaller the denominator, the greater the fraction

Writing + Math Journal

Which of the following would have the most juice if all the glasses are the same size: a glass $\frac{1}{2}$ full, a glass $\frac{1}{5}$ full, a glass $\frac{1}{4}$ full, or a glass $\frac{1}{6}$ full? Explain.

See Reflect in *Teacher's Edition.*

---

3 Reflect   5 ⏱

Guided Discussion ✓ REASONING   Whole Group

Pose the following problem for discussion: Mark and Sarah were ordering pizza. Mark asked for the pizza to be cut into 4 equal pieces. Sarah said she was so hungry she wanted the pizza cut into 8 equal pieces so she could have more pieces. What's right and what's wrong with Sarah's thinking? Accept all answers that show an understanding of equivalent fractions and that Sarah will get more pieces, but they will be smaller pieces.

Extended Response

Problem 8 Students should discuss the fact that the larger the denominator, the smaller the fraction.

Writing + Math Journal

Discuss with students how they can compare other fractions with common numerators. The larger the denominator, the smaller the fraction. Therefore, a glass $\frac{1}{2}$ full would have the most juice.

$$\frac{1}{2} > \frac{1}{3} > \frac{1}{4} > \frac{1}{6}$$

Cumulative Review: For cumulative review of previously learned skills, see page 312–313.

Family Involvement: Assign the **Practice, Reteach,** or **Enrichment** activities depending on the needs of your students.

Encourage students to play the **Fraction Game** with a friend or a relative.

Concept/Question Board: Encourage students to continue to post questions, answers, and examples on the Concept/Question Board.

Math Puzzler: Lucinda's older brother weighs 4 times as much as she does. Her older sister, Darlene, is 50 pounds heavier than she is, and weighs 95 pounds. How much does Lucinda's older brother weigh? 180 pounds

4 Assess and Differentiate

e Assess Use **eAssess** to record and analyze evidence of student understanding.

A Gather Evidence

Use the Daily Class Assessment Records in **Assessment** or **eAssess** to record daily observations.

Informal Assessment
☑ **Skill Building**

Did the student **APPLYING**
- ☐ apply learning in new situations?
- ☐ contribute concepts?
- ☐ contribute answers?
- ☐ connect mathematics to real-world situations?

Informal Assessment
☑ **Guided Discussion**

Did the student **REASONING**
- ☐ provide a clear explanation?
- ☐ communicate reasons and strategies?
- ☐ choose appropriate strategies?
- ☐ argue logically?

B Summarize Findings

Analyze and summarize assessment data for each student. Determine which Assessment Follow-Up is appropriate for each student. Use the Student Assessment Record in **Assessment** or **eAssess** to update assessment records.

Assessment page T41

C Assessment Follow-Up ● DIFFERENTIATE INSTRUCTION

Based on your observations, use these teaching strategies for assessment follow-up.

INTERVENTION

Review student performance on **Intervention** Lesson 8.A to see if students have mastered prerequisite skills for this lesson.

ENGLISH LEARNER

Review

Use Lesson 8.6 in **English Learner Support Guide** to review lesson concepts and vocabulary.

ENRICH

If . . . students are proficient in the lesson concepts,

Then . . . encourage them to work on chapter projects or **Enrichment** Lesson 8.6.

Enrichment Lesson 8.6

PRACTICE

If . . . students would benefit from additional practice,

Then . . . assign **Practice** Lesson 8.6.

Practice Lesson 8.6

RETEACH

If . . . students are having difficulty understanding how to compare fractions,

Then . . . reteach the concept using **Reteach** Lesson 8.6.

Reteach Lesson 8.6

Exploring Problem Solving

Objectives
- To analyze the Use Simple Numbers and Draw a Diagram strategies
- To generalize about a fraction
- To apply skills and concepts of fraction off in a sales promotion

Materials
- Grid paper
- Rulers
- Scissors
- Counters

Context of the Lesson While analyzing problem-solving strategies, students apply what they have been learning about fractions to a real-world, nonroutine problem.

Develop 5

Tell Students In Today's Lesson They Will
- figure out how much people can save at a toy robot sale.
- decide how to advertise the sale.

Skill Building

Discuss with students what fractional savings mean. Ask questions such as the following:

- **Suppose you bought something that usually costs $1, but you got it on sale for 50¢. How much did you save?** 50¢
- **What fraction of the regular price did you save?** $\frac{50}{100}$, or $\frac{1}{2}$
- **How do you know?** because 50¢ is half of $1; 50 + 50 = 100
- **What would half off something that costs $4 be?** $2

Have students work together for a few minutes to come up with several more regular prices and their half-off sale prices. On the board draw a table such as the one below, and use it to keep track.

Regular Price	Fraction Off the Regular Price	Sale Price	Amount Saved
$10.00	$\frac{1}{2}$	$5.00	$5.00
$3.00	$\frac{1}{2}$	$1.50	$1.50
$5.00	$\frac{1}{2}$	$2.50	$2.50

Exploring Problem Solving

Read the problem. Think about how you might solve it.

You are going to advertise a sale where a customer can buy one robot at the regular price and then buy an identical one for half off. What fraction of the cost of two robots will people save if they take advantage of this sale?

❶ One dollar is an easy amount to work with, and we know how to find fractions of a dollar.

❷ She can subtract how much she will pay for 2 robots on sale, $1.50, from the regular price of 2 robots, $2.00.

Claudia used simple numbers to solve the problem.

> **My Plan**
> A. I will choose a simple number for the price: $1.
> B. I will figure out how much I would pay for 2 robots with the sale.
> C. I will figure out how much I save from the regular price for 2 robots.
> D. I will compare the amount I save to the regular price.

Think about Claudia's strategy. Answer the following questions.

❶ What do you think of Claudia's choice for a simple number?

❷ How can Claudia figure out the amount in step C?

❸ How do you think Claudia will figure out the fraction off the whole price in step D?

❸ To find what fraction of $2 is 50¢, she could think about how many half dollars are in $2 or how many 50s are in 200.

310   Textbook   This lesson is available in the *eTextbook*.

Trenton made a diagram to solve the problem.

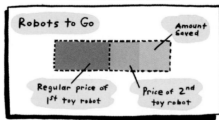

Think about Trenton's strategy. Answer these questions.

❹ What did Trenton use to stand for the regular price of a robot? a rectangle

❺ What did Trenton use to stand for the price of the second robot at Robots to Go?
a rectangle half the size of the first

❻ Should you compare the amount saved to the regular price of 1 robot or 2 robots? Why? 2 robots, because you have to buy 2 robots to get the savings

❼ How will Trenton figure out what fraction of the regular price is saved in the sale? He can see how many "amount saved" portions there are in the whole diagram, because he knows he saved one of these amounts.

Work with a partner to solve these problems.

❽ Finish solving the problem. Use Claudia's strategy, Trenton's strategy, or a strategy of your own.

❾ Would you write in your advertisement that this is a $\frac{1}{2}$-off sale? Why or why not?

❿ What strategy did you use to solve the problem? Why?

❾ Answers may vary, although students should agree that the term $\frac{1}{2}$-off sale in this case can easily be misleading. Some may think the term is acceptable because you do get $\frac{1}{2}$ off the cost of something. Others may point out that customers may feel deceived and then have a negative reaction toward the store.

Ask questions such as the following:

- **What do you notice about the sale price and the amount saved?** No matter what the regular price is, the sale price and amount saved are equal.
- **Why is that?** When you take away half of something, you have half left. Two halves of something are always the same.

Exploring Problem Solving 15

Using Student Pages

Tell students they are going to use what they know about fractions to examine a common type of sale and see what fraction of the price is really saved. Read the problem on page 310 together.

Tell students they are going to have a chance to figure out the savings on their own, but first they will look at student pages 310 and 311 to see how two other students are trying to solve the problem.

Analyzing Sample Strategy 1

Discuss Claudia's strategy. Ask questions such as the following:

- **Why is Claudia making up the price of a toy robot?** because the price is not given
- **Can Claudia use any price, even if it is not close to a real price?** Claudia can use any price because she is just using the price to explore what the fraction is that is saved.
- **If Claudia uses $1 as the regular price of a toy robot, how much will the second robot cost at Robots to Go?** 50¢

Give students time to think about Problems 1–3. Then discuss them.

Analyzing Sample Strategy 2

With the class, examine Trenton's strategy by giving students time to think about Problems 4–7 and then discussing them.

Have students work individually or in small groups on Problems 8–10.

Reflect 10

Effective Communication Call on students or groups to explain their answers, reasons, and methods.

In discussion, bring out the following points:

- Fractions can be used in misleading or confusing ways. It is important to be clear about what the fraction refers to. If you get half off the price of only one of several items, your savings is less than if you get half off everything you buy.

- Even if you do not know the regular price of a toy robot, you can still figure out how much you save relative to what you would have paid.
- Students may disagree on what should be included in the advertisement. There are various correct ways to advertise the sale, such as "buy one, get one for half off." The job of the advertiser is to help the store sell its robots, but customers might feel cheated if the advertisement is deceptive.

Sample Solutions Strategies

Students might use one or more of the following strategies.

Make a Physical Model

Students might take graph paper and draw and cut out models similar to the diagram on page 311. Students might also use counters to represent the cost of the robots: two counters for the cost of the first one and then one counter for the cost of the second one.

Use Number Sense

Students might see that if the savings is $\frac{1}{2}$ of 1 robot, that's the same as $\frac{1}{4}$ of 2 robots.

Write an Equation

Students might use words, numbers, and symbols to help them keep track of how the quantities in the problem are related:

$$\text{fraction you save} = \frac{\text{amount you save}}{\text{amount you pay without the sale}}$$

Assess 15

When evaluating student work, focus not only on the correctness of the answer but also on whether students thought rationally about the problem and the various solutions presented. Questions to consider include the following:

- Did the student understand the problem?
- Did the student show all the steps the group took in solving the problem?
- Could the student explain his or her strategy, including why his or her answer works even though the regular price of a toy robot is not known?
- If a strategy did not work, could the student recognize that and change the strategy or try something else?
- Did the student look back to see if the reasoning and the answer made sense?

Cumulative Review

Assign Pages 312–313

Use the Cumulative Review as a review of concepts and skills that students have previously learned.

Here are different ways that you can assign these problems to your students as they work through the chapter:

- With some of the lessons in the chapter, assign a set of cumulative review problems to be completed as practice or for homework.
  Lesson 8.1—Problems 1–3
  Lesson 8.2—Problem 4
  Lesson 8.3—Problems 5–6
  Lesson 8.4—Problems 7–8
  Lesson 8.5—Problems 9–12
  Lesson 8.6—Problems 13–17
- At any point during the chapter, assign part or all of the cumulative review problems to be completed as practice or for homework.

Cumulative Review

Problems 1–3 review skip counting to multiply, Lesson 4.2.

Problem 4 reviews measuring length in inches, feet, and yards, Lesson 3.5.

Problems 5–6 review adding with three or more addends, Lesson 2.10.

Problems 7–8 review telling time, Lesson 3.1.

Problems 9–12 review multiplying by 2, 1, and 0, Lesson 5.1.

Problems 13–17 review estimating and dividing in word problems, Lesson 7.6.

Monitoring Student Progress

If . . . students miss more than one problem in a section,
Then . . . refer to the indicated lesson for remediation suggestions.

Cumulative Review

Skip Counting Lesson 4.2

Find the missing numbers. Then use the completed exercise to help multiply.

1. 6, 12, 18, ■, 30, ■, ■, 48   24; 36; 42
2. $12 \times 3 =$ ■   36
3. $6 \times 6 =$ ■   36

4. 4 feet tall; $1\frac{1}{3}$ yards tall; There are 3 feet in 1 yard. One foot would be $\frac{1}{3}$ of a yard.

Measuring Length—Inches, Feet, and Yards Lesson 3.5

Solve.

4. Extended Response ► This ad shows a stuffed animal. Use the scale in the ad to determine the height of the stuffed animal. How tall is it in feet? How tall is it in yards? Explain your answer.

Adding with Three or More Addends Lesson 2.10

Add. Use shortcuts if you can.

5. $444 + 263 + 188 =$ ■   895
6. $130 + 230 + 430 + 630 =$ ■   1,420

Telling Time Lesson 3.1

Write the time in two ways.

7.   ■ 1:35
   ■ minutes after ■   35; 1:00

8.   ■ 6:19
   ■ minutes after ■   19; 6:00

312   Textbook This lesson is available in the *eTextbook*.

Multiplying by 2, 1, and 0 Lesson 5.1

Find the product.

9. $8 \times 0 =$ ■   0
10. $12 \times 2 =$ ■   24
11. $8 \times 7 =$ ■   56
12. $100 \times 0 =$ ■   0

Estimating/Reasonable Answers to Division Problems Lesson 7.6

Extended Response ► **Answer** the problems. If it is not possible to solve the problem, explain why.

13. There were 20 advertisements. The teacher wanted to divide them equally among 3 students. How many did each student get?   You can't divide the advertisements equally. Each student would get 6 ads with 2 remaining.

14. There are 28 pairs of white shorts. Each volleyball player will get 2 pairs of shorts. How many players are there?   14 players

15. Ms. Reeve said each student could check out 5 books. There are 35 books in the checkout pile. How many students are checking out books?   7 students

16. Our neighborhood is having a community yard sale. There are 7 people hanging the 28 signs for the sale. How many signs will each person hang?   4 signs

17. The students wanted to make a picture for the craft show. They wanted an equal number of girls and boys in the picture. They wanted a total of 37 students in the photo. How many girls and how many boys are in the picture?   This is not possible. You cannot have 18.5 girls and 18.5 boys.

Individual Oral Assessment

Purpose of the Test

The Individual Oral Assessment is designed to measure students' growing knowledge of chapter concepts. It is administered individually to each student, and it requires oral responses from each student. The test takes about five minutes to complete. See **Assessment** for detailed instructions for administering and interpreting the test, and record students' answers on the Student Assessment Recording Sheet.

Assessment Page T34

Directions

Read each question to the student and record his or her oral response. If the student answers correctly, go to the next question. Stop when the student misses two questions at the same level. Students should not use scrap paper.

Materials

2 pencils

2 pens

4 erasers, paper

Questions

Level 1: Prerequisite

1. (Show $\frac{1}{2}$.) Read this fraction. one-half

2. (Show $\frac{1}{5}$.) Read this fraction. one-fifth

3. (Show a square divided into fourths with one section shaded.) What fraction of the square is shaded? $\frac{1}{4}$

4. (Show a square divided into halves with one section shaded.) What fraction of the square is shaded? $\frac{1}{2}$

Level 2: Basic

5. (Show a circle divided into fifths with one section shaded.) What fraction of the shape is shaded? $\frac{1}{5}$

6. (Show a circle divided into fourths with two sections shaded.) What fraction of the shape is shaded? $\frac{2}{4}$ or $\frac{1}{2}$

7. (Show a circle divided into fourths.) How would you show $\frac{1}{4}$? Shade one section.

8. (Show a circle divided into fifths.) How would you show $\frac{2}{5}$? Shade two sections.

Level 3: At Level

9. (Show a clock.) How many minutes are equal to $\frac{1}{2}$ of an hour? 30 minutes

10. Which is greater, $\frac{1}{2}$ or $\frac{1}{5}$? $\frac{1}{2}$

11. Which is greater, $\frac{1}{3}$ or $\frac{1}{4}$? $\frac{1}{3}$

12. (Show 2 pencils, 2 pens, and 4 erasers.) What fraction of this set is erasers? $\frac{1}{2}$

Level 4: Challenge Application

13. How many minutes are in $\frac{3}{4}$ of an hour? 45

14. Which is greater, $\frac{3}{6}$ or $\frac{1}{2}$? They are equal.

15. There are 12 inches in a foot. What fraction would represent 5 inches? $\frac{5}{12}$

16. Tell me a fraction that is equal to $\frac{1}{2}$. Possible answers: $\frac{2}{4}$, $\frac{3}{6}$, $\frac{4}{8}$

Level 5: Content Beyond Mid-Chapter

17. Warrick worked for $\frac{1}{2}$ of an hour and took a break. Then he worked $\frac{1}{4}$ of an hour longer. How many minutes did he work total? 45 minutes

18. In Jeanette's class $\frac{1}{3}$ of the students did not play sports, $\frac{1}{3}$ of them played soccer, and the other third played basketball. Tell me the fraction of children that played sports. $\frac{2}{3}$

19. If there were 21 children in Jeanette's class, what number of children did not play soccer or basketball? 7

20. What fraction would 35% be? $\frac{35}{100}$

Lesson Planner

OBJECTIVES
- To introduce the addition and subtraction of common fractions with same denominators, using pictures and manipulatives
- To introduce the addition and subtraction of fractions with different denominators, using pictures and manipulatives

NCTM STANDARDS
Number and Operations
Using visual models, benchmarks, and equivalent forms to add and subtract commonly used fractions

Connections
Recognizing and applying mathematics in contexts outside of mathematics

MATERIALS
- *Response Wheels
- *Fraction Tiles
- *Fraction Game Mat

TECHNOLOGY
- Ⓔ Presentation Lesson 8.7
- Ⓔ Games Fraction Game
- Ⓔ MathTools Fractions

TEST PREP
Cumulative Review
Mental Math reviews square facts (Lesson 5.4).

Writing + Math
Journal

Adding and Subtracting Fractions

Context of the Lesson In this lesson students will add and subtract fractions with like and unlike denominators, using manipulatives and/or drawings. The fractions in this lesson will be less than a whole, although in Lesson 8.9 students will compare fractions greater than a whole. Students will also begin to develop a stronger sense of how fractions relate to one another and how they relate to a whole.

See page 292B for Math Background for teachers for this lesson.

Planning for Learning ● DIFFERENTIATE INSTRUCTION

INTERVENTION

If . . . students lack the prerequisite skill of reading and writing fractions,

Then . . . teach *Intervention* Lesson 8.B.

Intervention Lesson 8.B

ENGLISH LEARNER

Preview

If . . . students need language support,

Then . . . use Lesson 8.7 in *English Learner Support Guide* to preview lesson concepts and vocabulary.

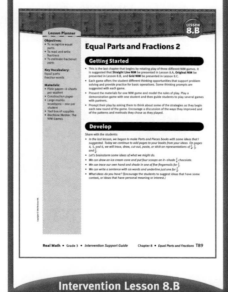

English Learner Lesson 8.7

ENRICH

If . . . students are proficient in the lesson concepts,

Then . . . emphasize the student pages.

PRACTICE

If . . . students would benefit from additional practice,

Then . . . extend Strategy Building before assigning the student pages.

RETEACH

If . . . students are having difficulty understanding adding and subtracting fractions,

Then . . . extend Guided Discussion before assigning the student pages.

Spanish Cognates
parts partes
example ejemplo

*Manipulative Kit Item

Teaching Lesson 8.7

Mental Math 5

  Review with students the square facts using examples such as the following:

a. 3×3 9 **b.** 7×7 49
c. 6×6 36 **d.** 10×10 100
e. 1×1 1 **f.** 9×9 81
g. 5×5 25 **h.** 0×0 0

1 Develop 25

Tell Students In Today's Lesson They Will

add and subtract fractions with like and unlike denominators, using pictures and manipulatives.

Guided Discussion UNDERSTANDING
Whole Group

Although we are teaching students to add fractions with different denominators in this lesson, we do not introduce a standard step-by-step procedure or algorithm. By helping students to visualize these problems and to understand them, we are helping them to use common sense with the use of fractions. By following this approach, students will be much better prepared when the algorithms are introduced in Grade 4. Introducing the algorithm too early usually has students memorizing rules without understanding, a situation that often leads to failure when students forget the rules.

Present statements such as the following to students. Ask students to decide, using common sense, which statements could be true and which could not. Allow time for discussion with each.

- In Pricilla's class $\frac{1}{4}$ of the students are boys, and $\frac{1}{2}$ are girls. doesn't make sense; If half are girls, then the other half must be boys.

- Max read about $\frac{1}{4}$ of the book. He still has more than $\frac{1}{2}$ to read. makes sense; Max still has about $\frac{3}{4}$ of the book to read, and $\frac{3}{4}$ is more than $\frac{1}{2}$.

- In Michella's homeroom class $\frac{2}{3}$ of the students in the class are wearing sneakers, and $\frac{3}{4}$ of the students are not wearing sneakers. doesn't make sense; The number wearing sneakers and not wearing sneakers should equal 1, and $\frac{2}{3} + \frac{3}{4} > 1$.

- In Juan's math class $\frac{2}{3}$ of the students in the class are wearing sneakers, and $\frac{3}{4}$ of the students say mathematics is their favorite subject. could be true; Students who wear sneakers can also think mathematics is their favorite subject.

Strategy Building UNDERSTANDING
Small Group

Have fraction bars and/or fraction circles available, or use **eMathTools: Fractions** to present addition statements on the board. Have students find the sum. For each problem, allow students to show, using the manipulatives, how they were able to find the sum. Use examples such as the following:

- $\frac{1}{2} + \frac{1}{2}$ 1
- $\frac{1}{8} + \frac{3}{8}$ $\frac{4}{8}$ or $\frac{1}{2}$
- $\frac{1}{2} + \frac{1}{4}$ $\frac{3}{4}$
- $\frac{3}{4} + \frac{1}{4}$ $\frac{4}{4}$ or 1
- $\frac{1}{4} + \frac{1}{4} + \frac{1}{4}$ $\frac{3}{4}$
- $\frac{3}{4} + \frac{1}{8}$ $\frac{7}{8}$

Using Student Pages APPLYING
Whole Group

Do page 314 as a class activity. For each problem, draw a corresponding figure on the board, and call on different students to describe how they were able to solve the problem. Check for understanding before assigning student pages.

2 Assign Student Pages 20 ⏱

Pages 314–315 `APPLYING`

Have students complete page 315 independently. Fraction tiles should be available as needed.

📋 RESEARCH IN ACTION

"We know from extensive research that many people—adults, students, even teachers—find the rational-number system to be very difficult. Introduced in early elementary school, this number system requires that students reformulate their concept of number in a major way. They must go beyond whole-number ideas, in which a number expresses a fixed quantity, to understand numbers that are expressed in relationship to other numbers. These new proportional relationships are grounded in multiplicative reasoning that is quite different from the additive reasoning that characterizes whole numbers."

Moss, Joan. "Pipes, Tubes, and Beakers: New Approaches to Teaching the Rational-Number System" in Donovan, M., Suzanne and John D. Bransford, eds. *How Students Learn: Mathematics in the Classroom*. Washington, D.C. National Research Council/National Academies Press. 2005, p. 310.

LESSON 8.7 Adding and Subtracting Fractions

Key Ideas

When we add fractions, we are combining the number of parts of the whole.

For example, if you ate $\frac{1}{3}$ of a pizza and your brother ate $\frac{1}{3}$ of the same pizza, together the two of you have eaten $\frac{2}{3}$ of the pizza.

$\frac{1}{3} + \frac{1}{3} = \frac{2}{3}$

Use the following illustrations to complete the addition sentences.

❶ $\frac{2}{5} + \frac{1}{5} = \blacksquare$ $\frac{3}{5}$

❷ $\frac{1}{8} + \frac{6}{8} = \blacksquare$ $\frac{7}{8}$

314 📖 **Textbook** This lesson is available in the *eTextbook*.

Solve. You may draw pictures to help.

❸ Randoph's mom divided her vegetable garden into sixths. She planted $\frac{2}{6}$ with green beans and $\frac{3}{6}$ with tomatoes. What fraction of her total garden is planted with beans or tomatoes? $\frac{5}{6}$

❹ Alfonso walked $\frac{5}{8}$ of the way to school. He stopped for a rest, and then walked another $\frac{3}{8}$. What fraction of the way to school did Alfonso walk? $\frac{8}{8}$ or all the way

❺ Mary Ann lined up her stuffed animals on her shelf. She noticed $\frac{1}{3}$ of them are teddy bears and $\frac{1}{3}$ of them are polar bears. The remaining stuffed animals are dolphins. What fraction of her total stuffed-animal collection is bears? $\frac{2}{3}$

❻ If Mary Ann has 30 stuffed animals total, how many are teddy bears? How many are polar bears? How many are dolphins? 10 of each

Replace each ▨ with $<$, $=$, or $>$ to make a true statement. The pictures may help you.

❼ $\frac{1}{4} + \frac{1}{4} \blacksquare \frac{1}{2}$ $=$

❽ $\frac{4}{8} + \frac{1}{8} \blacksquare \frac{1}{2}$ $>$

❾ $\frac{1}{3} + \frac{1}{3} \blacksquare \frac{1}{2}$ $>$

❿ $\frac{2}{8} + \frac{1}{8} \blacksquare \frac{1}{2}$ $<$

⓫ $\frac{1}{2} + \frac{1}{8} \blacksquare \frac{3}{4}$ $<$

⓬ $\frac{2}{3} + \frac{1}{3} \blacksquare \frac{3}{4}$ $>$

⓭ $\frac{2}{8} + \frac{1}{4} \blacksquare \frac{1}{2}$ $=$

⓮ $\frac{1}{4} + \frac{1}{4} \blacksquare \frac{3}{4}$ $<$

⓯ $\frac{1}{2} + \frac{2}{8} \blacksquare \frac{3}{4}$ $=$

Assign Student Pages, continued

Pages 316–317 APPLYING

Have students complete pages 316 and 317 independently. Students should be able to complete page 316, but fraction tiles should be available as needed. Page 317 might be difficult for some students. Allow some students to work by themselves or in small groups while you use manipulatives with the students who are having difficulty.

As Students Finish

 Fraction Game

 Games *Fraction Game*

LESSON 8.7 · Adding and Subtracting Fractions

Replace each ▢ with <, >, or = to make a true statement. The pictures may help you.

16. $\frac{1}{4} + \frac{1}{4}$ ▢ $\frac{1}{2}$ =

21. $\frac{1}{4} + \frac{1}{4}$ ▢ $\frac{3}{4}$ <

17. $\frac{1}{4} + \frac{1}{2}$ ▢ $\frac{1}{8}$ >

22. $\frac{1}{4} + \frac{1}{8}$ ▢ $\frac{1}{2}$ <

18. $\frac{1}{8} + \frac{1}{8} + \frac{1}{8}$ ▢ $\frac{1}{2}$ <

23. $\frac{1}{2} + \frac{1}{8}$ ▢ $\frac{3}{4}$ <

19. $\frac{1}{8} + \frac{1}{8}$ ▢ $\frac{1}{4}$ =

24. $\frac{1}{2} + \frac{1}{4} + \frac{1}{8}$ ▢ $\frac{3}{4}$ >

20. $\frac{3}{8} + \frac{1}{8}$ ▢ $\frac{1}{2}$ =

Textbook This lesson is available in the *eTextbook*.

Add. The pictures may help you.

25. $\frac{1}{2} + \frac{1}{2} =$ ▢ $\frac{2}{2}$ or 1

26. $\frac{1}{2} + \frac{1}{4} =$ ▢ $\frac{3}{4}$

27. $\frac{1}{4} + \frac{1}{4} + \frac{1}{4} =$ ▢ $\frac{3}{4}$

28. $\frac{1}{4} + \frac{1}{8} =$ ▢ $\frac{3}{8}$

29. $\frac{1}{4} + \frac{1}{8} + \frac{1}{8} =$ ▢ $\frac{4}{8}, \frac{2}{4}$, or $\frac{1}{2}$

30. $\frac{1}{3} + \frac{1}{3} =$ ▢ $\frac{2}{3}$

31. $\frac{2}{6} + \frac{1}{3} =$ ▢ $\frac{4}{6}$ or $\frac{2}{3}$

32. $\frac{1}{6} + \frac{1}{6} + \frac{1}{6} =$ ▢ $\frac{3}{6}$ or $\frac{1}{2}$

33. $\frac{1}{3} + \frac{1}{6} + \frac{1}{6} =$ ▢ $\frac{4}{6}$ or $\frac{2}{3}$

34. $\frac{3}{6} + \frac{2}{6} =$ ▢ $\frac{5}{6}$

35. $\frac{1}{2} + \frac{1}{3} =$ ▢ $\frac{5}{6}$

Subtract. The pictures may help you.

36. $\frac{3}{4} - \frac{1}{2} =$ ▢ $\frac{1}{4}$

37. $\frac{3}{8} - \frac{1}{4} =$ ▢ $\frac{1}{8}$

38. $\frac{1}{3} - \frac{1}{6} =$ ▢ $\frac{1}{6}$

39. $\frac{1}{2} - \frac{1}{6} =$ ▢ $\frac{2}{6}$ or $\frac{1}{3}$

40. $1 - \frac{1}{3} =$ ▢ $\frac{2}{3}$

> Writing + Math **Journal**
>
> Which picture is $\frac{3}{5}$ shaded? Explain why the other pictures don't show $\frac{3}{5}$.
>
> a. b. c.
>
>
>
> c; Choices *a* and *b* aren't divided into fifths.

Chapter 8 • Lesson 7

3 Reflect

10

Guided Discussion

Whole Group

Suppose somebody wanted to add $\frac{1}{3}$ of a pie and $\frac{1}{5}$ of a pie. How might they do this? Possible answer: They could try to find fractions equivalent to $\frac{1}{3}$ and $\frac{1}{5}$.

If students have fun with this, encourage them to continue. Otherwise, stop before students become frustrated. $\frac{5}{15} + \frac{3}{15} = \frac{8}{15}$

Writing + Math **Journal**

Some students might try to overanalyze this problem. Remind students of the meanings of *denominator* and *numerator* from Lesson 8.1.

RESEARCH IN ACTION

"Children need to learn that rational numbers are numbers in the same way that whole numbers are numbers. For children to use rational numbers to solve problems, they need to learn that the same rational number may be represented in different ways, as a fraction, a decimal, or a percent. Fraction concepts and representations need to be related to those of division, measurement, and ratio. Decimal and fractional representations need to be connected and understood. Building these connections take extensive experience with rational numbers over a substantial period of time. Researchers have documented that difficulties in working with rational numbers can often be traced to weak conceptual understanding . . . . Instructional sequences in which more time is spent at the outset on developing meaning for the various representations of rational numbers and the concept of unit have been shown to promote mathematical proficiency."

Kilpatrick, J., J. Swafford, and B. Findell, eds. *Adding It Up: Helping Children Learn Mathematics*. Washington, D.C.: National Research Council/National Academy Press, 2001, pp. 415–416.

 Curriculum Connection: Students might be interested in researching how fractions are used in cooking and baking.

 Cumulative Review: For cumulative review of previously learned skills, see page 329–330.

 Family Involvement: Assign the *Practice, Reteach,* or *Enrichment* activities depending on the needs of your students. Encourage students to play the **Fraction Game** with a friend or a relative.

 Concept/Question Board: Encourage students to continue to post questions, answers, and examples on the Concept/Question Board.

 Math Puzzler: I am a fraction. My numerator is 2 less than my denominator. The sum of my numerator and denominator is 8. What fraction am I? $\frac{3}{5}$

Assess and Differentiate

 Assess Use *eAssess* to record and analyze evidence of student understanding.

A Gather Evidence

Use the Daily Class Assessment Records in *Assessment* or *eAssess* to record daily observations.

Informal Assessment
Student Pages

Did the student **APPLYING**
- apply learning in new situations?
- contribute concepts?
- contribute answers?
- connect mathematics to real-world situations?

Portfolio Assessment
☑**Journal**

Did the student **REASONING**
- provide a clear explanation?
- communicate reasons and strategies?
- choose appropriate strategies?
- argue logically?

B Summarize Findings

Analyze and summarize assessment data for each student. Determine which Assessment Follow-Up is appropriate for each student. Use the Student Assessment Record in *Assessment* or *eAssess* to update assessment records.

Assessment page T41

C Assessment Follow-Up • DIFFERENTIATE INSTRUCTION

Based on your observations, use these teaching strategies for assessment follow-up.

INTERVENTION

Review student performance on *Intervention* Lesson 8.A to see if students have mastered prerequisite skills for this lesson.

ENGLISH LEARNER

Review

Use Lesson 8.7 in *English Learner Support Guide* to review lesson concepts and vocabulary.

ENRICH

If . . . students are proficient in the lesson concepts,

Then . . . encourage them to work on chapter projects or *Enrichment* Lesson 8.7.

Enrichment Lesson 8.7

PRACTICE

If . . . students would benefit from additional practice,

Then . . . assign *Practice* Lesson 8.7.

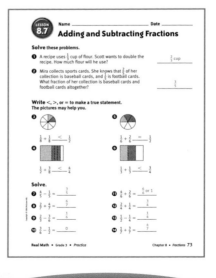

Practice Lesson 8.7

RETEACH

If . . . students struggle with equivalent fractions,

Then . . . have them use lined paper to make an organized list of equivalent fractions starting with $\frac{1}{2}$, then $\frac{1}{3}$, $\frac{1}{4}$, and so on. Encourage students to use this list while working on the lesson.

OBJECTIVES
To discuss fractions greater than a whole

NCTM STANDARDS

Number and Operations
Understanding numbers, ways of representing numbers, relationships among numbers, and number systems

Connections
Recognizing and using connections among mathematical ideas

MATERIALS

- *Response Wheels
- *Fraction Tiles
- *Fraction Game Mat

TECHNOLOGY
- Presentation Lesson 8.8
- Games Fraction Game
- MathTools Fractions

TEST PREP
Cumulative Review
Mental Math reviews finding fractions of sets (Lesson 8.3).

Writing + Math
Journal

Looking Ahead

You may want to prepare an overhead transparency of the Blackline Master of the **Fraction Game** for Lesson 8.9.

Fractions Greater Than a Whole

Context of the Lesson This is the first of two lessons on fractions greater than a whole. Fractions greater than one were introduced in Grade 2. Students began to see they must be able to name amounts that are greater than a whole. In this lesson common terminology will be introduced, and students will explore various ways of finding equivalent fractions greater than a whole. In Grade 4 students will explore this concept further.

See page 292B for Math Background for teachers for this lesson.

Planning for Learning ● DIFFERENTIATE INSTRUCTION

INTERVENTION

If . . . students lack the prerequisite skill of reading and writing fractions,

Then . . . teach *Intervention* Lesson 8.A.

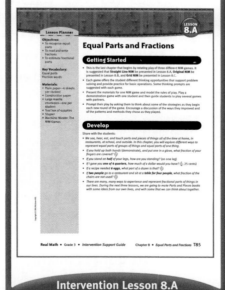

Intervention Lesson 8.A

ENGLISH LEARNER

Preview

If . . . students need language support,

Then . . . use Lesson 8.8 in *English Learner Support Guide* to preview lesson concepts and vocabulary.

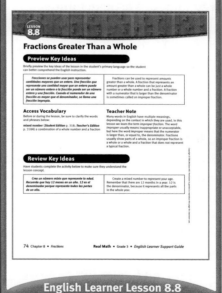

English Learner Lesson 8.8

ENRICH

If . . . students are proficient in the lesson concepts,

Then . . . emphasize the **Fraction Game.**

PRACTICE

If . . . students would benefit from additional practice,

Then . . . extend Guided Discussion before assigning the student pages.

RETEACH

If . . . students are having difficulty understanding fractions greater than a whole,

Then . . . extend Strategy Building before assigning the student pages.

Vocabulary
mixed number *n.* a number consisting of a whole number and a fraction

improper fraction *n.* a fraction whose numerator is greater than or equal to its denominator

Access Vocabulary
mixed number a combination of a whole number and a fraction

Mental Math 5

  Practice finding fractions of sets using examples such as the following:

a. $\frac{1}{2}$ of 10 5

b. $\frac{1}{3}$ of 9 3

c. $\frac{1}{2}$ of 4 2

d. $\frac{1}{3}$ of 6 2

e. $\frac{2}{3}$ of 6 4

f. $\frac{1}{5}$ of 10 2

g. $\frac{2}{5}$ of 10 4

h. $\frac{5}{5}$ of 10 10

1 Develop 25

Tell Students In Today's Lesson They Will

identify fractions greater than a whole.

Guided Discussion UNDERSTANDING Whole Group

Review with students what it means to use a fraction. Ask questions such as the following:

- **What does it mean when something is divided into fourths?** There are 4 equal parts.
- **What is the denominator going to be if we divide something into fourths?** 4
- **How many fourths are in 1 whole?** 4

On the board or overhead transparency, draw a square and divide it into fourths, either diagonally or vertically and horizontally.

 or

Shade in the entire square.

Ask questions about the shape, such as how many fourths there are and what fraction is represented by the whole. $\frac{4}{4}$ Write on the board the fraction $\frac{4}{4}$. Ask students to state the number of whole shapes. 1

Leaving the whole shaded square, draw an equal square beside it and shade $\frac{1}{4}$ of it. Ask questions such as the following:

- **How many fourths are shaded?** 5
- **What fraction would describe how many parts are shaded?** $\frac{5}{4}$ or $1\frac{1}{4}$

Because there is 1 whole and $\frac{1}{4}$ of another whole, we can call this $1\frac{1}{4}$ or $\frac{5}{4}$. Read it as *one and one-fourth*. Explain to the class that sometimes we use fractions for amounts or numbers greater than a whole. When the fraction has a whole number and a fraction, we often use the term *mixed number*. A mixed number,

however, is still considered a fraction. When we have a fraction that has a numerator larger than the denominator, we often use the term *improper fraction*. However, it is important to note that there is nothing "wrong" or improper about the fraction; it is just another way to write a fraction greater than a whole.

Using *eMathTools: Fractions* or fraction tiles, place 10 fourths on the screen. You may need to cover up the mixed number given by the *eMathTool*. Ask students questions such as the following:

- **How many fourths are there?** 10
- **What will be the denominator for these fractions?** 4
- **How many wholes are there?** 2
- **How many remaining fractions are there?** 2
- **What fraction names the total amount?** $\frac{10}{4}$, $2\frac{2}{4}$, or $2\frac{1}{2}$

Reinforce to students the fact that no matter which type of fraction they choose to use, all three fractions represent the same amount.

Strategy Building REASONING Small Group

Divide students into small groups. Pass out fractional items of any kind (fraction tiles, fraction circles, and so on). Have the groups determine the fraction names for various fractions, for example, 12 fifths, 7 halves, 9 fourths, 8 thirds, and so on. Have students draw and record their answers. Encourage students to find improper fractions, mixed numbers, and equivalent fractions.

2 Assign Student Pages 20

Pages 318–319 APPLYING

Have students complete page 319 independently. Fraction tiles should be available as needed.

Monitoring Student Progress

| **If . . .** students are struggling with finding appropriate fractions, | **Then . . .** assist them with grouping the pieces into the correct number of wholes and drawing a picture of the results. Have students describe orally how many wholes and how many remaining pieces there are. Write this amount and the total pieces next to a picture. |

As Students Finish

  Fraction Game

 Games *Fraction Game*

LESSON 8.8 Fractions Greater Than a Whole

Key Ideas

Fractions can be used to represent amounts greater than a whole. A fraction that represents an amount greater than a whole can be just a whole number, or the fraction can be a whole number *and* a fraction.

The amount represented by the above fraction circles can be written two ways. If we count the shaded parts, there are 12 shaded parts total. Each circle is divided into 6 sections. We can write this fraction as $\frac{12}{6}$.

We also can tell there are 2 whole fraction circles that are shaded. We can write this fraction as 2.

If we count the shaded parts of these fractions, we find there are 7 shaded parts total. Each circle is divided into 5 equal sections. We can write this fraction as $\frac{7}{5}$.

We can also tell there is 1 whole fraction circle shaded, and $\frac{2}{5}$ of another fraction circle is shaded. We can write this fraction as $1\frac{2}{5}$.

A fraction with a numerator that is greater than the denominator is often called an improper fraction. A fraction that has a whole number and a fraction is often called a mixed number. It is important to remember that the amount is the same whether the fraction is written as an improper fraction or a mixed number.

Textbook This lesson is available in the *eTextbook*.

Name the fraction represented by the shaded sections in two ways.

1
$1\frac{3}{4}, \frac{7}{4}$

4
$2, \frac{6}{3}$

2
$2, \frac{4}{2}$

5
$1\frac{1}{2}, \frac{3}{2}$

3
$1\frac{1}{5}, \frac{6}{5}$

6
$1\frac{1}{2}, 1\frac{2}{4}, \frac{6}{4}, \text{ or } \frac{3}{2}$

Writing + Math **Journal**
Which is greater, $2\frac{1}{2}$ or $3\frac{1}{3}$? Explain.

$3\frac{1}{3}$; See Reflect in *Teacher's Edition*.

---

3 Reflect
10

Guided Discussion
Whole Group

Have students find the equivalent fractions from the following fractions: $1\frac{1}{2}, 1\frac{2}{4}, 1\frac{3}{6}, 2\frac{1}{3}, 2\frac{2}{6}$

- $1\frac{1}{2}$
- $1\frac{1}{10}$
- $2\frac{1}{3}$
- $2\frac{2}{6}$
- $1\frac{2}{4}$
- $2\frac{7}{9}$
- $1\frac{8}{10}$
- $2\frac{1}{5}$
- $1\frac{3}{6}$

Have students list the remaining fractions in order from least to greatest. $1\frac{1}{10}, 1\frac{8}{10}, 2\frac{1}{5}, 2\frac{7}{9}$

 **Journal**

The most obvious reason is that 3 wholes is greater than 2 wholes. However, if students do not list this explanation, encourage them to validate the answers they give with manipulatives, drawings, or whatever way students choose that is convincing.

Curriculum Connection: Students may be interested in researching how fractions are used in the sciences.

Cumulative Review: For cumulative review of previously learned skills, see page 329–330.

Family Involvement: Assign the *Practice, Reteach,* or *Enrichment* activities depending on the needs of your students.

Encourage students to play the **Fraction Game** with a friend or a relative.

Concept/Question Board: Have students attempt to answer any unanswered questions on the Concept/Question Board.

Math Puzzler: Use the digits 2, 4, 7, and 8 to complete the following number sentence. Use each digit only once, and make the greatest possible sum, then the least possible sum. $84 + 72$ or $82 + 74 = 156$; $28 + 47$ or $27 + 48 = 75$

_____ _____ + _____ _____ = _____

_____ _____ + _____ _____ = _____

4 Assess and Differentiate

 e Assess Use *eAssess* to record and analyze evidence of student understanding.

A Gather Evidence

Use the Daily Class Assessment Records in *Assessment* or *eAssess* to record daily observations.

Informal Assessment
☑ **Guided Discussion**

Did the student **UNDERSTANDING**
- ☐ make important observations?
- ☐ extend or generalize learning?
- ☐ provide insightful answers?
- ☐ pose insightful questions?

Performance Assessment
☑ **Game**

Did the student **ENGAGING**
- ☐ pay attention to others' contributions?
- ☐ contribute information and ideas?
- ☐ improve on a strategy?
- ☐ reflect on and check the accuracy of his or her work?

B Summarize Findings

Analyze and summarize assessment data for each student. Determine which Assessment Follow-Up is appropriate for each student. Use the Student Assessment Record in *Assessment* or *eAssess* to update assessment records.

Assessment page T41

C Assessment Follow-Up • DIFFERENTIATE INSTRUCTION

Based on your observations, use these teaching strategies for assessment follow-up.

INTERVENTION

Review student performance on *Intervention* Lesson 8.A to see if students have mastered prerequisite skills for this lesson.

ENGLISH LEARNER

Review

Use Lesson 8.8 in *English Learner Support Guide* to review lesson concepts and vocabulary.

ENRICH

If . . . students are proficient in the lesson concepts,

Then . . . encourage them to work on chapter projects or *Enrichment* Lesson 8.8.

Enrichment Lesson 8.8

PRACTICE

If . . . students would benefit from additional practice,

Then . . . assign *Practice* Lesson 8.8.

Practice Lesson 8.8

RETEACH

If . . . students struggle with visualizing mixed numbers,

Then . . . have them work with inch rulers. Have students draw a 12-inch line on paper. Then have them find and compare various points for mixed numbers on the line. For example, say "Find $3\frac{1}{2}$ inches on the line and mark it. Now find and mark $3\frac{3}{4}$ inches. Which measurement is greater?" Repeat this procedure with other mixed numbers.

Lesson Planner

OBJECTIVES
To provide practice determining which of two mixed numbers is greater

NCTM STANDARDS
Number and Operations
Using models, benchmarks, and equivalent forms to judge the size of fractions

Connections
Understanding how mathematical ideas interconnect and build on one another to produce a coherent whole

MATERIALS
- Overhead transparency of Blackline Master of **Fraction Game**
- *Fraction Tiles
- *Fraction Game Mat

TECHNOLOGY
 Presentation Lesson 8.9
Games Fraction Game

TEST PREP
Cumulative Review
- Mental Math reviews comparing fractions less than a whole (Lesson 8.6).
- Problems 17 and 18 review fractions greater than a whole (Lesson 8.8).

Writing + Math
Journal

Looking Ahead
You may want to prepare a set of coins per group, with a minimum of 10 dimes and 100 pennies for the Strategy Building in Lesson 8.10. You may also want multiple copies of the Hundredths Circle for Lesson 8.10.

Comparing Fractions Greater Than a Whole

Context of the Lesson This is the second of two lessons on fractions greater than a whole. In this lesson students will use manipulatives and/or drawings to compare fractions greater than a whole. This concept will be further explored in Grade 4.

See page 292B for Math Background for teachers for this lesson.

Planning for Learning ● DIFFERENTIATE INSTRUCTION

INTERVENTION

If . . . students lack the prerequisite skill of reading and writing fractions,

Then . . . teach **Intervention** Lesson 8.A.

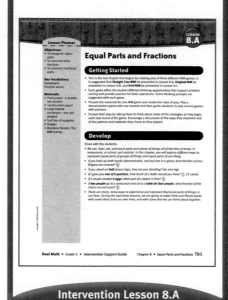

Intervention Lesson 8.A

ENGLISH LEARNER

Preview

If . . . students need language support,

Then . . . use Lesson 8.9 in **English Learner Support Guide** to preview lesson concepts and vocabulary.

English Learner Lesson 8.9

ENRICH

If . . . students are proficient in the lesson concepts,

Then . . . emphasize the student pages.

PRACTICE

If . . . students would benefit from additional practice,

Then . . . extend Strategy Building before assigning the student pages.

RETEACH

If . . . students are having difficulty understanding comparing fractions greater than a whole,

Then . . . extend Mental Math before assigning the student pages.

Spanish Cognates
comparing comparando
other type of number otro tipo de número

Mental Math 10

Provide practice in the relative sizes of fractions with numerators greater than one, but fractions less than a whole. Have students respond with thumbs-up if the first fraction is greater than the second fraction, thumbs-down if the first fraction is less than the second fraction, and open hand if the fractions are equal. Use examples such as the following:

a. $\frac{3}{4}$ ▭ $\frac{1}{2}$ up   **b.** $\frac{2}{6}$ ▭ $\frac{2}{3}$ down

c. $\frac{1}{4}$ ▭ $\frac{1}{3}$ down   **d.** $\frac{1}{2}$ ▭ $\frac{3}{5}$ down

e. $\frac{3}{4}$ ▭ $\frac{2}{3}$ up   **f.** $\frac{1}{3}$ ▭ $\frac{2}{6}$ open hand

g. $\frac{1}{2}$ ▭ $\frac{5}{10}$ open hand   **h.** $\frac{2}{5}$ ▭ $\frac{1}{2}$ down

1 Develop 25

Tell Students In Today's Lesson They Will

compare fractions greater than a whole.

Strategy Building ✔ UNDERSTANDING   Whole Group

On the board or by using the circles on the overhead transparency of the Blackline Master for the **Fraction Game,** draw a circle divided into $\frac{1}{2}$, $\frac{1}{3}$, $\frac{1}{4}$, and $\frac{1}{5}$. Starting with numerators of 1, compare various fractions greater than a whole. Write the comparison on the board with a blank between each fraction. Color in the appropriate fractions to assist students in visualizing the fractions. Have students respond with thumbs-up if the answer is greater than, thumbs-down if the answer is less than, and open hand if the answer is equal to. Use examples such as the following:

- $1\frac{1}{2}$ ▭ $1\frac{1}{3}$ up
- $1\frac{1}{4}$ ▭ $1\frac{1}{3}$ down
- $2\frac{1}{3}$ ▭ $2\frac{1}{5}$ up
- $2\frac{1}{5}$ ▭ $2\frac{1}{4}$ down
- $3\frac{1}{2}$ ▭ $2\frac{1}{5}$ up

When students are comfortable with numerators of 1, move to fractions with numerators greater than 1. Use examples such as the following:

- $1\frac{1}{2}$ ▭ $1\frac{2}{4}$ open hand
- $2\frac{2}{4}$ ▭ $2\frac{1}{3}$ up
- $1\frac{1}{3}$ ▭ $2\frac{2}{3}$ down
- $1\frac{2}{3}$ ▭ $1\frac{2}{2}$ down
- $2\frac{3}{5}$ ▭ $3\frac{1}{2}$ down

Using Student Pages APPLYING   Whole Group

Have students open their books to page 320. Review the information in the Key Ideas, emphasizing the fact that reading a mathematical statement aloud may help them check to see if a statement is correct. Have students complete Problems 2–4, reading their answers aloud to the class. Check for understanding before assigning student pages.

2 Assign Student Pages 20

Pages 320–321 APPLYING

Have students complete pages 320 and 321 independently.

As Students Finish

Game Fraction Game

e Games *Fraction Game*

LESSON 8.9 **Comparing Fractions Greater Than a Whole**

Key Ideas

Even though fractions greater than a whole may contain a whole number or a whole number and a fraction, compare them as you would any other type of number.

Look at the following fractions. Determine which fraction is larger.

The fraction represented here is $1\frac{1}{3}$, read *one and one-third*.

The fraction represented here is $1\frac{3}{4}$, read *one and three-fourths*.

We can determine by looking at the fraction circles that $1\frac{3}{4}$ is the larger fraction. This mathematical statement can be written as $1\frac{3}{4} > 1\frac{1}{3}$, read *one and three-fourths is greater than one and one-third*, or $1\frac{1}{3} < 1\frac{3}{4}$, read *one and one-third is less than one and three-fourths*.

Copy and replace the ■ with $<$, $>$, or $=$ to make a true statement. The first one has been done for you.

1. $5 < 5\frac{2}{3}$. This is read *5 is less than five and two-thirds*.
2. $\frac{4}{5}$ ■ $\frac{3}{4}$ $>$
3. $2\frac{4}{5}$ ■ $2\frac{3}{4}$ $>$
4. $6\frac{2}{5}$ ■ $6\frac{3}{4}$ $<$

320   Textbook This lesson is available in the *eTextbook*.

Copy and replace the ■ with $<$, $>$, or $=$ to make a true statement. Use fraction circles, fraction tiles, or drawings if needed.

5. $4\frac{1}{2}$ ■ $3\frac{1}{3}$ $>$ 11. $5\frac{4}{5}$ ■ $6\frac{3}{4}$ $<$
6. $7\frac{2}{3}$ ■ $7\frac{4}{6}$ $=$ 12. $5\frac{2}{3}$ ■ $5\frac{3}{4}$ $<$
7. $5\frac{4}{5}$ ■ $5\frac{3}{4}$ $>$ 13. $\frac{3}{5}$ ■ $1\frac{1}{5}$ $<$
8. $\frac{2}{3}$ ■ $\frac{3}{4}$ $<$ 14. $7\frac{2}{3}$ ■ $6\frac{3}{4}$ $>$
9. $1\frac{1}{2}$ ■ $1\frac{2}{4}$ $=$ 15. $5\frac{4}{5}$ ■ $4\frac{3}{4}$ $>$
10. $7\frac{2}{3}$ ■ $7\frac{3}{4}$ $<$ 16. $3\frac{1}{5}$ ■ $2\frac{3}{5}$ $>$

Solve.

 17. Margaret has 3 boxes of green pens and $\frac{3}{4}$ of a box of red pens. How many boxes of pens does she have? $3\frac{3}{4}$

 18. Natasha has 3 boxes of green pens and $\frac{1}{2}$ box of red pens. How many boxes of pens does she have? $3\frac{1}{2}$

19. Which girl has more pens? Margaret

20. Write one mathematical statement comparing the fractions $3\frac{1}{4}$ and $2\frac{1}{2}$. $3\frac{1}{4} > 2\frac{1}{2}$ or $2\frac{1}{2} < 3\frac{1}{4}$

Writing + Math **Journal**

Explain how you determine which fraction is greater when comparing two or more fractions.

Accept all reasonable answers.

Chapter 8 • Lesson 9   321

---

3 Reflect   5

Guided Discussion

Whole Group

Ask students to explain how they might determine the larger of two fractions if the whole number of both fractions is the same. For example, *Which is greater, $1\frac{1}{2}$ or $1\frac{1}{3}$? $1\frac{1}{2}$ because $\frac{1}{2}$ is greater than $\frac{1}{3}$*

Ask students to explain how they might determine the larger of two fractions if the whole numbers of both fractions are not the same. For example, *Which is greater, $2\frac{1}{2}$ or $3\frac{1}{3}$? $3\frac{1}{3}$ because 3 wholes is greater than 2 wholes*

Discuss with students their answers to student page 321. Address any uncertainties or confusions regarding methods and/or answers.

 Writing + Math **Journal**

Accept all reasonable answers such as if the fractions are mixed numbers, compare the whole number parts. If the whole numbers are equal, compare the fractions.

Curriculum Connection: Students may be interested in researching how fractions are used in carpentry and architecture.

Cumulative Review: For cumulative review of previously learned skills, see page 329–330.

Family Involvement: Assign the *Practice, Reteach,* or *Enrichment* activities depending on the needs of your students.

Encourage students to play the **Fraction Game** with a friend or a relative.

Concept/Question Board: Have students attempt to answer any unanswered questions on the Concept/Question Board.

Math Puzzler: There are 24 students in Anitra's class, and one-third of them are boys. How many boys are in Anitra's class? How many girls? $8; 24 - 8 = 16$

4 Assess and Differentiate

 Assess Use *eAssess* to record and analyze evidence of student understanding.

A Gather Evidence

Use the Daily Class Assessment Records in *Assessment* or *eAssess* to record daily observations.

Informal Assessment

☑ **Strategy Building**

Did the student UNDERSTANDING

- ☐ make important observations?
- ☐ extend or generalize learning?
- ☐ provide insightful answers?
- ☐ pose insightful questions?

Portfolio Assessment

☑ **Journal**

Did the student REASONING

- ☐ provide a clear explanation?
- ☐ communicate reasons and strategies?
- ☐ choose appropriate strategies?
- ☐ argue logically?

B Summarize Findings

Analyze and summarize assessment data for each student. Determine which Assessment Follow-Up is appropriate for each student. Use the Student Assessment Record in *Assessment* or *eAssess* to update assessment records.

Assessment page T41

C Assessment Follow-Up ● DIFFERENTIATE INSTRUCTION

Based on your observations, use these teaching strategies for assessment follow-up.

INTERVENTION

Review student performance on *Intervention* Lesson 8.A to see if students have mastered prerequisite skills for this lesson.

ENGLISH LEARNER

Review

Use Lesson 8.9 in *English Learner Support Guide* to review lesson concepts and vocabulary.

ENRICH

If . . . students are proficient in the lesson concepts,

Then . . . encourage them to work on chapter projects or *Enrichment* Lesson 8.9.

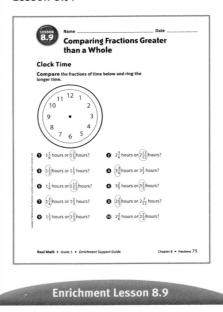

Enrichment Lesson 8.9

PRACTICE

If . . . students would benefit from additional practice,

Then . . . assign *Practice* Lesson 8.9.

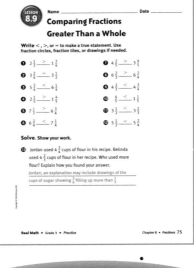

Practice Lesson 8.9

RETEACH

If . . . students struggle with comparing fractions,

Then . . . have them use models such as 10 × 10 grids or circles. Have students work in pairs. Have each student choose a number and then compare them and see which is larger.

Lesson Planner

OBJECTIVES
To explore the relationship of tenths and hundredths in fractional form

NCTM STANDARDS
Number and Operations
- Developing an understanding of fractions as parts of unit wholes, as parts of a collection, as locations on number lines, and as divisions of whole numbers
- Using models, benchmarks, and equivalent forms to judge the size of fractions

Connections
Recognizing and using connections among mathematical ideas

MATERIALS

- *Response Wheels
- 50 manipulatives
- A set of coins per group, with a minimum of 10 dimes and 100 pennies
- *Fraction Game Mat

TECHNOLOGY
- Presentation Lesson 8.10
- Games Fraction Game

TEST PREP
Cumulative Review
- Mental Math reviews multiplying by powers of 10 (Lesson 7.1).
- Problems 7–15 review fractions of sets (Lesson 8.3).

Writing + Math
Journal

Looking Ahead
You may want to prepare an overhead transparency of the Hundredths Circle on page 322 of the *Student Edition* to be used in Lesson 8.11.

Tenths and Hundredths

Context of the Lesson This is the first of two lessons on tenths and hundredths. Students will extend their knowledge of tenths to explore the relationship to hundredths. In Lesson 8.11 students will relate hundredths to percents. In Grade 4 students will work more extensively with percents as they explore the relationships between hundredths, fractions, percents, and decimals.

See page 292B for Math Background for teachers for this lesson.

Planning for Learning • DIFFERENTIATE INSTRUCTION

INTERVENTION
If . . . students lack the prerequisite skill of estimating fractional parts,

Then . . . teach *Intervention* Lesson 8.C.

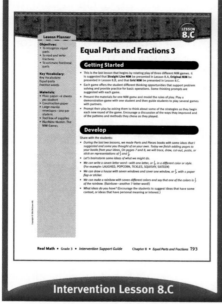

Intervention Lesson 8.C

ENGLISH LEARNER
Preview

If . . . students need language support,

Then . . . use Lesson 8.10 in *English Learner Support Guide* to preview lesson concepts and vocabulary.

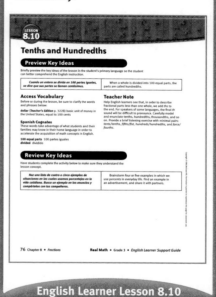

English Learner Lesson 8.10

ENRICH
If . . . students are proficient in the lesson concepts,

Then . . . emphasize the student pages.

PRACTICE
If . . . students would benefit from additional practice,

Then . . . extend Strategy Building before assigning the student pages.

RETEACH
If . . . students are having difficulty understanding tenths and hundredths,

Then . . . extend Guided Discussion before assigning the student pages.

Spanish Cognates
100 equal parts 100 partes iguales
divided dividido

Mental Math 10

  Practice multiplying by 10, 100, and 1,000. Use examples such as the following:

a. 8×10 80
b. $9 \times 1{,}000$ 9,000
c. 100×7 700
d. 100×10 1,000
e. 91×100 9,100
f. 10×425 4,250
g. $42 \times 1{,}000$ 42,000
h. 701×10 7,010
i. $1{,}000 \times 0$ 0
j. $10 \times 1{,}000$ 10,000

1 Develop 25

Tell Students In Today's Lesson They Will

explore the relationship of tenths and hundredths in fractional form.

Guided Discussion UNDERSTANDING Whole Group

Review with students how to find fractions of sets. Without grouping manipulatives, ask students to find $\frac{1}{5}$ of 50. Place or draw 50 manipulatives, and have students calculate what $\frac{1}{5}$ would be. Once students have reached an agreed-upon answer of 10, ask questions such as the following:

- **What is $\frac{2}{5}$ of 50?** 20
- **What is $\frac{3}{5}$ of 50?** 30
- **What is $\frac{5}{5}$ of 50?** 50
- **What is $\frac{0}{5}$ of 50?** 0
- **What does the denominator of any fraction represent?** how many equal parts each whole is divided into
- **What does the numerator of any fraction represent?** how many equal parts are being referenced

Write on the board the fraction $\frac{1}{10}$. Read the fraction as *one-tenth*. Have students explain what the fraction represents. There are 10 parts to the whole; only 1 part is being referenced

Write on the board the fraction $\frac{1}{100}$. Read the fraction as *one-hundredth*. Have students explain what the fraction represents. There are 100 equal parts to the whole; only 1 part is being referenced.

Have students think of any real-world situations where the whole is divided into tenths or hundredths. For example, some students may recall having used meters, kilometers, and centimeters in Chapter 3. Our number system is base-ten, and if they are familiar with decimal numbers, they may recognize tenths and hundredths. Tenths of a mile on an odometer of a car is recognizable. The most common real-world situation is our money system. The dollar can be broken into dimes and pennies.

Strategy Building REASONING Small Group

Divide the class into small groups. Give each group a collection of pennies and dimes. Each group should have a minimum of 10 dimes and 100 pennies, but preferably more. If needed, divide the class into only 2 or 3 groups, and give them large amounts of each of the two coins.

Ask students questions such as the following:

- **How many dimes are in a dollar?** 10
- **If we have 1 dime, what fraction of the dollar do we have?** $\frac{1}{10}$
- **How many cents is a dollar worth?** 100
- **If we have 1 penny, what fraction of the value of a dollar do we have?** $\frac{1}{100}$

Have students in each group ask questions of each other. For example, if they hold up 2 dimes, what fraction of a dollar is that? $\frac{2}{10}$

When students are comfortable with this activity, have them determine what fraction describes the dimes they have and what fraction describes the pennies they have. Students can use a fraction, an improper fraction, or a mixed number.

Using Student Pages APPLYING Whole Group

Have students turn to student page 322. As a class read through the Key Ideas, emphasizing that the circle is divided into 100 parts and each part is $\frac{1}{100}$ of the whole. Help students to notice that the circle is also divided into 10 parts, and each of those parts is $\frac{1}{10}$ of the whole. Have students work as a class on Problems 1–6. Check for understanding before assigning student pages.

2 Assign Student Pages 20

Pages 322–323 APPLYING

Have students complete page 323 independently.

Monitoring Student Progress

If . . . students are having a difficult time visualizing the tenths sections,	**Then . . .** make a copy of the circle, and have them color each tenth a different color.

As Students Finish

 Game Fraction Game

 **Games** *Fraction Game*

LESSON 8.10 Tenths and Hundredths

Key Ideas

This circle is divided into 100 equal parts.

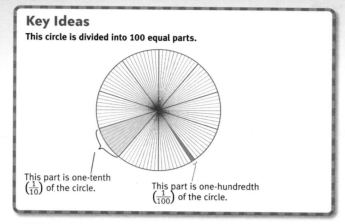

This part is one-tenth $\left(\frac{1}{10}\right)$ of the circle.

This part is one-hundredth $\left(\frac{1}{100}\right)$ of the circle.

Use the circle graph to help answer the following questions.

1. How many $\frac{1}{100}$ sections are there in this graph?   100
2. How many $\frac{1}{10}$ sections are there in this graph?   10
3. In $\frac{1}{10}$ of the circle, how many $\frac{1}{100}$ sections are there?   10
4. In $\frac{3}{10}$ of the circle, how many $\frac{1}{100}$ sections are there?   30
5. In $\frac{5}{10}$ of the circle, how many $\frac{1}{100}$ sections are there?   50
6. What is another fraction to represent $\frac{5}{10}$ of the circle?
   Possible answers: $\frac{1}{2}$ or $\frac{50}{100}$

322   Textbook This lesson is available in the *eTextbook*.

Fill in the table.

Tenths		Hundredths		Tenths		Hundredths
$\frac{1}{10}$	=	$\frac{10}{100}$		$\frac{6}{10}$	=	■ $\frac{60}{100}$
$\frac{2}{10}$	=	$\frac{20}{100}$		■ $\frac{7}{10}$	=	$\frac{70}{100}$
$\frac{3}{10}$	=	■ $\frac{30}{100}$		■ $\frac{8}{10}$	=	$\frac{80}{100}$
$\frac{4}{10}$	=	■ $\frac{40}{100}$		$\frac{9}{10}$	=	■ $\frac{90}{100}$
■ $\frac{5}{10}$	=	$\frac{50}{100}$		■ $\frac{10}{10}$	=	$\frac{100}{100}$ or ■ whole 1

Solve.

7. What is $\frac{1}{10}$ of 100?   10
8. What is $\frac{1}{10}$ of 200?   20
9. What is $\frac{1}{10}$ of 300?   30
10. What is $\frac{2}{10}$ of 100?   20
11. What is $\frac{2}{10}$ of 200?   40
12. What is $\frac{2}{10}$ of 300?   60
13. What is $\frac{3}{10}$ of 100?   30
14. What is $\frac{5}{10}$ of 200?   100
15. What is $\frac{10}{10}$ of 300?   300

 Journal
Describe how to find $\frac{1}{10}$ of 500.

Accept any reasonable answer. See Reflect in *Teacher's Edition* for further explanations.

3 Reflect   5

Guided Discussion

Whole Group

Do you know of any way to write $\frac{1}{10}$ and $\frac{1}{100}$ other than as fractions?
Some students may recall that 0.1 is read *one-tenth* and 0.01 is read *one one-hundredths*.

 Journal

Possible answers include $\frac{1}{10}$ of 100 is 10 and $10 \times 50 = 500$; 500 can be divided into 10 groups of 50.

Cumulative Review: For cumulative review of previously learned skills, see page 329–330.

Family Involvement: Assign the *Practice, Reteach,* or *Enrichment* activities depending on the needs of your students.
Encourage students to play the **Fraction Game** with a friend or a relative.

Concept/Question Board: Have students attempt to answer any unanswered questions on the Concept/Question Board.

 Math Puzzler: One day Bruce and John Lee ate half a loaf of bread together. Chuck ate $\frac{2}{4}$ of the same loaf all by himself. Who ate more bread, Chuck by himself, or Bruce and John Lee together?
neither; $\frac{1}{2}$ is the same amount as $\frac{2}{4}$

4 Assess and Differentiate

 Assess Use *eAssess* to record and analyze evidence of student understanding.

A Gather Evidence

Use the Daily Class Assessment Records in **Assessment** or **eAssess** to record daily observations.

Informal Assessment
☑ **Mental Math**

Did the student **COMPUTING**
- ❏ respond accurately?
- ❏ respond quickly?
- ❏ respond with confidence?
- ❏ self-correct?

Portfolio Assessment
☑ **Journal**

Did the student **REASONING**
- ❏ provide a clear explanation?
- ❏ communicate reasons and strategies?
- ❏ choose appropriate strategies?
- ❏ argue logically?

B Summarize Findings

Analyze and summarize assessment data for each student. Determine which Assessment Follow-Up is appropriate for each student. Use the Student Assessment Record in **Assessment** or **eAssess** to update assessment records.

Assessment page T41

C Assessment Follow-Up ● DIFFERENTIATE INSTRUCTION

Based on your observations, use these teaching strategies for assessment follow-up.

INTERVENTION

Review student performance on *Intervention* Lesson 8.C to see if students have mastered prerequisite skills for this lesson.

ENGLISH LEARNER

Review

Use Lesson 8.10 in *English Learner Support Guide* to review lesson concepts and vocabulary.

ENRICH

If . . . students are proficient in the lesson concepts,

Then . . . encourage them to work on chapter projects or *Enrichment* Lesson 8.10.

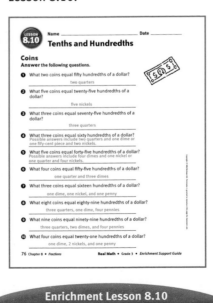

Enrichment Lesson 8.10

PRACTICE

If . . . students would benefit from additional practice,

Then . . . assign *Practice* Lesson 8.10.

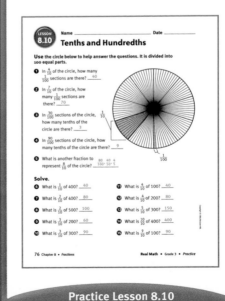

Practice Lesson 8.10

RETEACH

If . . . students struggle with tenths and hundredths,

Then . . . have them use 10 × 10 grids. Shade three tenths of a grid on the board. How many tenths are in the grid? 10 How many tenths are shaded? 3 What decimal can you write for the shaded part on your grid? 0.3

Next, have students color some squares on their hundredths grids. How many hundredths are in the grid? 100 What decimal can you write for the colored part of the grid?

OBJECTIVES
- To explore the relationship between percents and fractions
- To read and interpret circle graphs with percent data

NCTM STANDARDS
Number and Operations
Recognizing and generating equivalent forms of commonly used fractions, decimals, and percents

Algebra
Using representations such as graphs, tables, and equations to draw conclusions

Data Analysis and Probability
Developing and evaluating inferences and predictions that are based on data

MATERIALS
- An overhead transparency of the Hundredths Circle from Lesson 8.10 (optional)
- *Fraction Game Mat
- *Response Wheels

TECHNOLOGY
⊡ **Presentation** Lesson 8.11
⊡ **Games** Fraction Game

TEST PREP
Cumulative Review
Mental Math reviews comparing fractions (Lesson 8.6).

Extended Response
Problems 21–22, 25, 27–29, and 33–35

Writing + Math
Journal

Percents and Hundredths

Context of the Lesson This is the second of two lessons on hundredths. In this lesson students will begin to explore the relationship between fractions and percents. In Grade 4 students will relate fractions, percents, and decimals as equivalent forms of the same rational number.
See page 292B for Math Background for teachers for this lesson.

Planning for Learning ● DIFFERENTIATE INSTRUCTION

INTERVENTION

If . . . students lack the prerequisite skill of estimating fractional parts,

Then . . . teach *Intervention* Lesson 8.C.

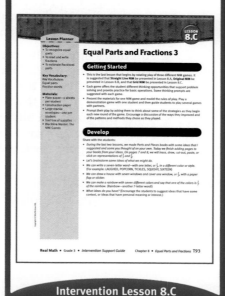

Intervention Lesson 8.C

ENGLISH LEARNER

Preview

If . . . students need language support,

Then . . . use Lesson 8.11 in *English Learner Support Guide* to preview lesson concepts and vocabulary.

English Learner Lesson 8.11

ENRICH

If . . . students are proficient in the lesson concepts,

Then . . . emphasize the student pages.

PRACTICE

If . . . students would benefit from additional practice,

Then . . . extend Skill Building before assigning the student pages.

RETEACH

If . . . students are having difficulty understanding tenths and percents,

Then . . . extend Strategy Building before assigning the student pages.

Vocabulary
percent \pər sent´\ *n.* a fraction with a denominator of 100; the number of parts in every hundred

Access Vocabulary
benchmark a reference point for measurement

Spanish Cognates
percent porciento

Mental Math 10

Compare fractions with numerators greater than 1 but values less than a whole. Have students show thumbs-up if the first fraction is greater, thumbs-down if the second fraction is greater, or open hand if both fractions are equivalent. Use examples such as the following:

a. $\frac{1}{2}$ ▢ $\frac{1}{3}$ up

b. $\frac{1}{2}$ ▢ $\frac{2}{4}$ open hand

c. $\frac{1}{3}$ ▢ $\frac{1}{4}$ up

d. $\frac{1}{4}$ ▢ $\frac{1}{2}$ down

e. $\frac{2}{3}$ ▢ $\frac{1}{2}$ up

f. $\frac{3}{4}$ ▢ $\frac{3}{5}$ up

g. $\frac{2}{4}$ ▢ $\frac{2}{5}$ up

h. $\frac{3}{4}$ ▢ $\frac{5}{5}$ down

1 Develop 25

Tell Students In Today's Lesson They Will

explore the relationship between percents and fractions through reading and interpreting circle graphs with percent data.

Guided Discussion UNDERSTANDING   Whole Group

It is important throughout this lesson to stress that percentages are often estimates. However, because a percent is a fraction with a denominator of 100, it may not be possible to find the exact fraction. Explain that percent means *per 100*. Percents can be thought of as fractions with a denominator of 100.

Draw on the board a circle graph. Divide the graph in half, and ask how many of the $\frac{1}{100}$ sections it would be. 50 Now, mark each side with 50%. Ask questions such as the following:

■ **How much does the entire circle represent?** 1 whole
■ **How many parts or sections are there?** 2
■ **How many of the sections do we need to make the whole?** 2
■ **If we add the percents, what is the total?** 100%

Draw another circle graph on the board, but divide this one into three sections of your choosing. Estimate an appropriate percent for each of the three sections. Ask students some of the same questions as with the previous circle graph. Emphasize that the total is going to be 100%. Because the whole circle is 100, we can represent a section of the circle with a fraction that has 100 as the denominator (the total sections for the whole). Introduce the term *percent* as a fraction with the denominator of 100. Ask students questions such as the following:

■ **In the first drawing, what would the fractions be for each part?** $\frac{50}{100}$
■ **In the second drawing, what would the fractions be for each part?** varies depending on percents

■ **If you add the fractions for the first drawing, what is the total?** $\frac{100}{100}$
■ **If you add the fractions for the second drawing, what is the total?** $\frac{100}{100}$

Skill Building   UNDERSTANDING   Whole Group

 Practice benchmark percents with examples such as the following. Have students show with their percent slider if the percent is nearest to 0%, 25%, 50%, 75%, or 100%. This type of percent recognition will be used later in the book, especially in the area of Mental Math.

a. 10% 0%

b. 91% 100%

c. 24% 25%

d. 1% 0%

e. 51% 50%

f. 28% 25%

g. 79% 75%

h. 60% 50%

i. 89% 100%

j. 99% 100%

Strategy Building REASONING   Whole Group

Draw on the board a graph of U.S. medals won in the 2004 Olympics. Divide the graph into the following appropriate sections with percentages of Gold—34%, Silver—38%, and Bronze—28%.

Have students look at the graph and explain it in their own words. Have them add the percents to verify they equal 100% (one whole). Ask questions such as the following:

Olympic Graph

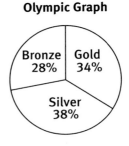

■ **Are there any medal percents that were more than 50%?** no
■ **Are there any medal percents more than 25%?** yes, all three
■ **Which medal had the largest percent?** silver
■ **Which medal had the smallest percent?** bronze
■ **Were the gold and silver medals together, more than 50%?** yes
■ **If there were 103 medals won altogether by the U.S., will the number of gold medals be more or less than 103? Explain your answer.** less; A percentage less than a whole cannot be more than the sum total.

Check for understanding before assigning student pages.

2 Assign Student Pages 20

Pages 324–325 ✓ APPLYING

Have students complete pages 324–325 independently. On Problems 13–18, students can have the option to show the answers on the Percent Slider *(Response Wheel)*.

LESSON 8.11 Percents and Hundredths

Key Ideas

A **percent** is a fraction with 100 as the denominator.

The term 1% is read *one percent*.

The term 1% can be written as the fraction $\frac{1}{100}$. The fraction $\frac{1}{100}$ is read *one one-hundredth*.

Write the fraction for the following percents.
Remember, a percent is a fraction with a denominator of 100.

1. 46% $\frac{46}{100}$ 4. 100% $\frac{100}{100}$ or 1
2. 6% $\frac{6}{100}$ 5. 89% $\frac{89}{100}$
3. 21% $\frac{21}{100}$ 6. 0% $\frac{0}{100}$

Write the percent for the following fractions.

7. $\frac{87}{100}$ 87%   10. $\frac{2}{100}$ 2%
8. $\frac{19}{100}$ 19%   11. $\frac{100}{100}$ 100%
9. $\frac{33}{100}$ 33%   12. $\frac{99}{100}$ 99%

Determine which of the following benchmark percents, 0%, 25%, 50%, 75%, or 100%, would be closest to the given fraction.

13. $\frac{5}{100}$ 0%   16. $\frac{60}{100}$ 50%
14. $\frac{98}{100}$ 100%   17. $\frac{21}{100}$ 25%
15. $\frac{76}{100}$ 75%   18. $\frac{75}{100}$ 75%

324 Textbook This lesson is available in the *eTextbook*.

Use the graph to answer the following questions. Remember, a percent is a fraction with a denominator of 100.

19. What fraction is each section of this circle graph?
    a. Recycle $\frac{37}{100}$
    b. Make my family more aware $\frac{8}{100}$
    c. Research $\frac{17}{100}$
    d. Make posters and signs $\frac{21}{100}$
    e. Plant trees $\frac{17}{100}$

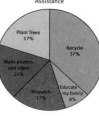

Environmental Assistance

20. What was the most popular way to help the environment? What was the least popular way? recycle; make family aware

21. **Extended Response** If there were 5,829 students in grades K–5 surveyed in all, would the number who chose recycling be more or less than 5,000? Explain.

    21. less; 5,000 is more than 50% and the recycling is only 37%, which is less than 50%.

22. **Extended Response** Of the following percents, 0%, 25%, 50%, or 100%, which would you choose to describe about how many students voted for *make posters*, *research*, or *make* family *more aware*? Explain.
    50%; the actual total is 45%, which is closer to 50% than to other benchmarks.

Chapter 8 • Lesson 11   325

Assign Student Pages, continued

Pages 326–327 APPLYING

Have students complete pages 326–327 independently.

As Students Finish

 Fraction Game

 **Games** *Fraction Game*

Lesson 8.11 Percents and Hundredths

Use the graph to answer the following questions.

23 What fraction is each section of this circle graph?
   a. Preprimary School $\frac{3}{100}$
   b. Elementary or High School $\frac{21}{100}$
   c. College or Graduate School $\frac{5}{100}$
   d. Not in School $\frac{71}{100}$

Preprimary School 3% Elementary or High School 21% College or Graduate School 5% Not in School 71% *Alaska School Population*

24 **Extended Response** This is a graph of the population of Alaska during the 2000 Census. There were 626,932 residents in Alaska. Why do you think 71% of the residents are not enrolled in school? See Reflect in *Teacher's Edition*.

25 Of the three sections representing Alaskan residents *in school* for the 2000 Census (ages 3 and up), which group had the greatest number of students? Elementary or High School

26 **Extended Response** If there were 185,760 students enrolled in school in Alaska during the 2000 Census, would the number who were in the *College or Graduate School* section be more or less than 100,000? Explain.

27 **Extended Response** In 2000, the percent of Alaskans in elementary or high school was closest to which of these: 0%, 25%, 50%, 75%, or 100%? 27 25%

28 **Extended Response** In 2000, the percent of Alaskans not in school was closest to which of these: 0%, 25%, 50%, 75%, 100%? 28 75%

326 **Textbook** This lesson is available in the *eTextbook*.

Use the graph to answer the following questions.

29 What fraction is each section of this circle graph?
   a. Mom $\frac{52}{100}$
   b. Dad $\frac{21}{100}$
   c. Sibling $\frac{14}{100}$
   d. Grandparent $\frac{4}{100}$
   e. Other $\frac{9}{100}$

Other 9% Grandparent 4% Sibling 14% Dad 21% Mom 52% *Time Spent with Family Member*

30 In this survey, who is the family member the students spend the most amount of time with? Mom

31 In this survey, who is the family member the students spend the least amount of time with? Grandparent

32 **Extended Response** If there were 428 students surveyed, would the number who chose *Other* be more or less than 500? Explain how you know. less; 500 is more than the total number of students surveyed

33 **Extended Response** Of the following percents, 0%, 25%, 50%, 75%, or 100%, which would you choose to describe about how many students chose *Sibling* as the family member they spend the most time with? Explain. 33 25%; The actual total is 14%, which is closer to 25% than 0%.

34 **Extended Response** Of the following percents, 0%, 25%, 50%, 75%, or 100%, which would you choose to describe about how many students chose *Mom* or *Dad* as the family member they spend the most time with? Explain. 34 75%; The actual total is 73%, which is closer to 75% than 50%.

Writing + Math Journal
Write one true statement and one false statement about the graph above. Accept all reasonable answers.

Chapter 8 • Lesson 11 327

 **Reflect** 5 (V)

Guided Discussion
Whole Group

Referring to the circle graph in the Strategy Building section, ask students if the number of silver medals would be less than, equal to, or greater than 38? greater than 38—probably 39

Problem 24 A possible answer is that most residents of Alaska have already completed school.

Writing + Math **Journal**

Discuss students' statements to verify the validity of each.

 Curriculum Connection: Students may be interested in researching other items of the 2004 Olympics and creating percentage graphs of their own to display their findings.

 Cumulative Review: For cumulative review of previously learned skills, see page 329–330.

 Family Involvement: Assign the *Practice, Reteach,* or *Enrichment* activities depending on the needs of your students.

Encourage students to play the **Fraction Game** with a friend or a relative.

 Concept/Question Board: Have students attempt to answer any unanswered questions on the Concept/Question Board.

 Math Puzzler: Arnold has 7 more cans of soup than Josie has. Josie has 6 fewer cans than Julie. Julie has 16 cans. How many cans of soup did the three friends collect for the food drive? 43

Assess and Differentiate

 **Assess** Use *eAssess* to record and analyze evidence of student understanding.

A Gather Evidence

Use the Daily Class Assessment Records in *Assessment* or *eAssess* to record daily observations.

Informal Assessment

☑ **Skill Building**

Did the student UNDERSTANDING

❑ make important observations?
❑ extend or generalize learning?
❑ provide insightful answers?
❑ pose insightful questions?

Informal Assessment

☑ **Student Pages**

Did the student APPLYING

❑ apply learning in new situations?
❑ contribute concepts?
❑ contribute answers?
❑ connect mathematics to real-world situations?

B Summarize Findings

Analyze and summarize assessment data for each student. Determine which Assessment Follow-Up is appropriate for each student. Use the Student Assessment Record in *Assessment* or *eAssess* to update assessment records.

Assessment page T41

C Assessment Follow-Up • DIFFERENTIATE INSTRUCTION

Based on your observations, use these teaching strategies for assessment follow-up.

INTERVENTION

Review student performance on *Intervention* Lesson 8.C to see if students have mastered prerequisite skills for this lesson.

ENGLISH LEARNER

Review

Use Lesson 8.11 in *English Learner Support Guide* to review lesson concepts and vocabulary.

ENRICH

If . . . students are proficient in the lesson concepts,

Then . . . encourage them to work on chapter projects or *Enrichment* Lesson 8.11.

Enrichment Lesson 8.11

PRACTICE

If . . . students would benefit from additional practice,

Then . . . assign *Practice* Lesson 8.11.

Practice Lesson 8.11

RETEACH

If . . . students struggle with the benchmark percents,

Then . . . have them model each benchmark using a 10 × 10 grid. They can then use these models as a reference while they work their problems.

Exploring Problem Solving

Objectives

- To solve a nonroutine problem involving fractions
- To relate fractions in a mixture of pigments to the resulting color
- To provide practice using different forms to describe parts of wholes

Materials

- Markers, crayons, or paint in a variety of colors
- Construction paper or drawing paper (1 or 2 sheets for each student plus some extra)

Context of the Lesson This lesson provides an opportunity for students to apply what they have been learning about fractions (and percents) to a real-world situation.

1 Develop

5

Tell Students In Today's Lesson They Will

match up colors with the formulas that make those colors.

Skill Building

On the board or overhead projector, write $\frac{1}{2}$ *blue,* $\frac{1}{2}$ *red.* Tell students this is a formula for a dye used to color a T-shirt. Ask questions such as the following:

- **What color do you think the T-shirt will be if the manufacturer uses this formula?** purple
- **How do you know?** because red and blue make purple

Next write $\frac{1}{3}$ *blue,* $\frac{1}{3}$ *red,* $\frac{1}{3}$ *water.* Ask questions such as the following:

- **How will this color compare to the color from the first formula?** It will be lighter; it will be whiter.
- **How do you know?** You have added water, and there is less blue and less red than in the first formula.
- **What would you call the color the T-shirt will be with this dye?** light purple, lavender, orchid

Next write *75% red, the rest water.* Ask questions such as the following:

- **What color is most of the dye?** red, because 75% is red and that is more than half
- **What color will the T-shirt be with this dye?** dark pink, pink, light red
- **How do you know?** Red and white make pink. Most of the dye is red, but a fourth of it is white, which will lighten it.

Exploring Problem Solving

Your advertising agency has created four new T-shirt colors for a company that sells clothing on the Internet. The formulas for the four colors got mixed up. Your job is to figure out which formula goes with which shirt color. You also get to give each color a special name.

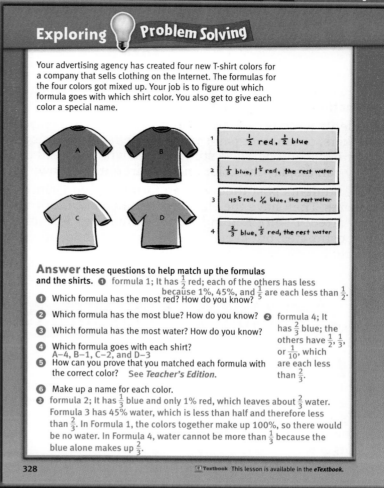

1. $\frac{1}{2}$ red, $\frac{1}{2}$ blue
2. $\frac{1}{3}$ blue, $1\frac{\%}{?}$ red, the rest water
3. $45\frac{?}{?}$ red, $\frac{?}{10}$ blue, the rest water
4. $\frac{2}{3}$ blue, $\frac{1}{5}$ red, the rest water

Answer these questions to help match up the formulas and the shirts.

1. Which formula has the most red? How do you know?

   ❶ formula 1; It has $\frac{1}{2}$ red; each of the others has less because 1%, 45%, and $\frac{1}{5}$ are each less than $\frac{1}{2}$.

2. Which formula has the most blue? How do you know?

   ❷ formula 4; It has $\frac{2}{3}$ blue; the others have $\frac{1}{2}$, $\frac{1}{3}$, or $\frac{1}{10}$, which are each less than $\frac{2}{3}$.

3. Which formula has the most water? How do you know?

4. Which formula goes with each shirt? A–4, B–1, C–2, and D–3

5. How can you prove that you matched each formula with the correct color? See *Teacher's Edition.*

6. Make up a name for each color.

   ❸ formula 2; It has $\frac{1}{3}$ blue and only 1% red, which leaves about $\frac{2}{3}$ water. Formula 3 has 45% water, which is less than half and therefore less than $\frac{2}{3}$. In Formula 1, the colors together make up 100%, so there would be no water. In Formula 4, water cannot be more than $\frac{1}{3}$ because the blue alone makes up $\frac{2}{3}$.

328 　Textbook This lesson is available in the *eTextbook.*

To give students more experience with fractions and color combinations, complete the following activity:

1. Students write their own formulas and then use crayons, markers, or tempera paint to see if the resulting colors match their expectations. Have students use white instead of water. They can display the color on a T-shirt outline drawn on paper.

2. Have students post their written formulas and T-shirt pictures. Then have the class try to match each formula to the correct T-shirt. Remind students that their formulas are only estimates, but even if they do not get them all right, they should be able to justify their choices.

 Exploring Problem Solving 30

Using Student Pages

Read the information and go over the illustrations on page 328 together. Give students access to graph paper and, if available, markers, crayons, or paints of the colors listed in the formulas. Have students work in small groups or individually on Problems 1–6.

If students seem to be having difficulty, encourage them to struggle with the problem for a while. When needed, ask guiding questions such as the following:

■ **How could you use the markers or crayons to help you?**
■ **What have you learned about fractions and percentages that can help you?**
■ **How could you use the graph paper to help you make a diagram of the formula?**

Sample Answer to Problem 5

Shirts A and C look bluest and formulas 2 and 4 have the most blue. Since shirt C is lighter, it would work with formula 2 because that has more water than formula 4. Shirt D is the reddest so that would go with formula 3, which is almost half red and hardly any blue. Shirt B looks the most like an even mixture of red and blue, which is formula 1.

 Reflect 10

Problem Formulation, Planning, and Strategizing Have each student or group share how they matched the formulas and shirts and present the names they created for each color. Help students understand the following points:

● Percents and fractions are different ways to describe the same thing. They both tell you what part of a whole something is.

● You can tell a lot about how something looks or tastes by knowing what fraction each ingredient is. You do not need to know how many ounces or cups of each ingredient is, just the relative amounts. For example, lemonade that is $\frac{1}{4}$ sugar will taste sweeter than lemonade that is $\frac{1}{100}$ sugar, no matter how much or how little of the lemonade you make.

● If you know all the fractions that make up a whole except for one of them, you can figure out that fraction because all the fractions must add up to 1.

Sample Solutions Strategies

Use a Physical Model

Students might act out the problem by using crayons, markers, or paints to make and compare the colors.

Draw a Diagram

Students might use circle graphs or color in 10 × 10 grids to help them visualize and compare formulas. For example, for formula 4 they might draw the following:

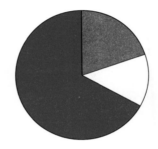 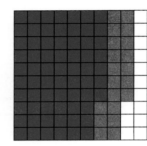

Use Logical Reasoning

Students might use the process of elimination to determine the last of the four match-ups.

 Assess 15

When evaluating student work, focus on whether students thought rationally about the problem. Questions to consider include the following:

● Did the student understand the problem?
● Did the student use an understanding of fractions and percents to try to make reasonable matches?
● Was the student able to explain his or her reasoning?

Cumulative Review

Assign Pages 329–330

Use the Cumulative Review as a review of concepts and skills that students have previously learned.

Here are different ways that you can assign these problems to your students as they work through the chapter:

- With some of the lessons in the chapter, assign a set of cumulative review problems to be completed as practice or for homework.
  Lesson 8.7—Problems 1–2
  Lesson 8.8—Problems 3–4
  Lesson 8.9—Problems 5–12
  Lesson 8.10—Problems 13–17
  Lesson 8.11—Problems 18–25
- At any point during the chapter, assign part or all of the cumulative review problems to be completed as practice or for homework.

Cumulative Review

Problems 1–2 review reading a thermometer, Lesson 3.2.

Problems 3–4 review multiplying by 2, 1, and 0, Lesson 5.1.

Problems 5–12 review multiplying by 10, 100, and 1,000, Lesson 7.1.

Problems 13–17 review adding with three or more addends, Lesson 2.10.

Problems 18–25 review inverse functions of addition, subtraction, multiplication, and division, Lesson 6.4.

> ### Monitoring Student Progress
>
> **If . . .** students miss more than one problem in a section,
> ⋮ **Then . . .** refer to the indicated lesson for remediation suggestions.

Cumulative Review

Reading a Thermometer Lesson 3.2

Use the Fahrenheit scale on the thermometers shown to answer the questions.

1 What temperature is it? Is it comfortable, cold, or hot?   98°F; hot

2 What temperature is it? Is it comfortable, cold, or hot?   78°F; comfortable

Multiplying by 2, 1, and 0 Lesson 5.1

Solve each problem.

3 Each student is making 2 signs for the craft fair. If there are 24 students, how many signs will there be altogether?   48

4 Adina and her sister are making 6 loaves of banana bread. Each loaf requires 2 bananas. How many bananas do they need?   12

Multiplying by 10, 100, and 1,000 Lesson 7.1

Multiply.

5 $1,000 \times 10 =$ ▮   10,000
6 $60 \times 10 =$ ▮   600
7 $10 \times 110 =$ ▮   1,100
8 $100 \times 83 =$ ▮   8,300
9 $240 \times 1,000 =$ ▮   240,000
10 $1,000 \times 16 =$ ▮   16,000
11 $1,000 \times 43 =$ ▮   43,000
12 $100 \times 2 =$ ▮   200

Cumulative Review

Adding with Three or More Addends Lesson 2.10

Add. Use shortcuts if you can.

13 Tia had two errands on Monday. She had to go to the grocery store and to her Aunt Kaya's house. How far did she travel to get to the store?   830 feet

14 When she stops by her aunt's house, her aunt asks her to drop off a check at the bank. How many feet must she go to get to the bank from her Aunt Kaya's house?   540 feet

15 On Tuesday, Tia made two stops. First, she stopped at the dentist. The dentist asked Tia to get a special toothpaste at the grocery store. Tia went to the grocery store and then went home. If she took the shortest route, how many feet did Tia travel altogether on Tuesday?   1,220 feet

16 On Wednesday, Tia went to the post office. When the bridge was not under construction, the distance to the post office was only 343 feet. How many feet is it now?   513 feet

17 **Extended Response** Which one-way route is a total distance of 610 feet? Explain how you found your answer.

17 from Tia's house to the grocery passing the bank; By looking at the map, students should add up distances until they find a route that is 610 feet one way.

Inverse Functions (Reversing the Arrow) Lesson 6.4

Write the inverse operation.

18 +20   −20
19 +3   −3
20 ×6   ÷6
21 ÷9   ×9
22 ÷30   ×30
23 +100   −100
24 +4   −4
25 ÷14   ×14

📖 Textbook This lesson is available in the *eTextbook*.

Wrap-Up

1 Discuss

Concept/Question Board

Review the Concept/Question Board with students.

- Discuss students' contributions to the Concept side of the Board.
- Have students re-pose their questions, and lead a discussion to find satisfactory answers.

Chapter Projects APPLYING

Provide an opportunity for students who have worked on one or more of the projects outlined on page 293C to share their work with the class. Allow each student or student group five minutes to present or discuss their projects. For formal assessment, use the rubrics found in *Across the Curriculum Math Connections;* the rubric for **Create an Advertisement** is on page 85, and the rubric for **Categorize Toy Advertisements** is on page 91. For informal assessment, use the following rubric and questions.

	Exceeds Expectations	Meets Expectations	Minimally Meets Expectations
Applies mathematics in real-world situations:	❏	❏	❏
Demonstrates strong engagement in the activity:	❏	❏	❏

Create an Advertisement

- How do advertisers sell products?
- What fraction did you write and use in your advertisement?
- How did you use color and emphasis in your cereal box design?
- How did you set up your photographic shot? How did you create emphasis in the photograph?
- What photograph did you use? Why did you choose that photograph?
- Are print advertisements a good way to advertise a product? How else could you advertise your cereal?

Categorize Toy Advertisements

- Did you find more examples of television, print, or Internet advertising?
- How long were the television advertisements? What size were the print advertisements?
- How did you express the measurements of the advertisements?
- How did you organize your examples? What fields did you create in your database?
- Was a database a good way to categorize and organize your examples? What would be another way to do this?
- What recommendations did you include in your paper?
- What do you think is the best way to advertise a product? Why?

2 Assign Student Pages 25

Key Ideas Review   UNDERSTANDING

Have students complete the Review questions independently or in small groups. Then discuss each question as a class.

Possible Answers

Problem ❶ Problems 1–4 review fractions using diagrams. The answer to Problem 1 is to divide the circle into 5 equal sections and shade 2 sections.

Problem ❷ The answer is to shade 2 counters.

Problem ❸ The answer is to shade 6 blocks.

Problem ❹ The answer is to shade 2 crayons.

Problem ❺ Problems 5–6 involves adding and subtracting fractions. The answer to Problem 5 is $\frac{5}{8}$.

Problem ❻ The answer to Problem 6 is $\frac{1}{6}$.

Problem ❼ Problems 7–8 review concepts in comparing fractions. The answer is false.

Problem ❽ The answer is true.

Extended Response

Problem ❾ This problem focuses on the students' comprehension of computing fractional amounts of whole numbers. The answer to Part a is 12 pens, and the answer to Part b is 6 pens.

Extended Response

Problem ❿ Students added and subtracted fractions with common denominators in this chapter. They should understand that when $\frac{4}{8}$ is added to $\frac{2}{8}$ the answer is $\frac{6}{8}$; however, Charles has reduced the answer to an equivalent fraction—$\frac{3}{4}$ is equivalent to $\frac{6}{8}$. Therefore, Charles's answer is correct.

CHAPTER **8** Key Ideas Review

In this chapter you learned about fractions.

You learned about properties of fractions.

You learned how to compute with fractions.

Copy the following. Shade the fractional amounts.

❶ $\frac{2}{5}$ Check students' work to be sure their drawings are representative of the fractional amounts.

❸ $\frac{6}{10}$

❷ $\frac{1}{2}$

❹ $\frac{2}{5}$

Add or subtract.

❺ $\frac{4}{8} + \frac{1}{8} = \blacksquare$ $\frac{5}{8}$

❻ $\frac{4}{6} - \frac{3}{6} = \blacksquare$ $\frac{1}{6}$

Answer true or false.

❼ $\frac{1}{2}$ is greater than $\frac{3}{4}$.   false

❽ $\frac{5}{6}$ is less than $\frac{6}{6}$.   true

Extended Response **Provide** a detailed answer for the following exercises.

❾ Mary bought a pack of 16 pens and gave $\frac{1}{4}$ of them away.

  a. How many pens does she have now?   12 pens
  b. Then she gave $\frac{1}{2}$ of her leftover pens away. How many pens does she have left?   6 pens

❿ Charles added the following:

  $\frac{4}{8} + \frac{2}{8} = \frac{3}{4}$

Explain how you know Charles is correct.
See the *Teacher's Edition*.

Chapter Review

Use the Chapter 8 Review to indicate areas in which each student is having difficulty or in which the class may need help. If students do well on the Chapter 8 Review, you may wish to skip directly to the Chapter Test; if not, you may want to spend a day or so helping students overcome their individual difficulties before taking the Practice Test.

Next to each set of problems is a list of the lessons in the chapter that covered those concepts. If they need help, students can refer to a specific lesson for additional instruction. You can also use this information to make additional assignments based on the previous lesson concepts.

Have students complete pages 332–333 on their own. For review purposes, you may want to do the word problem on page 333 as a class.

Monitoring Student Progress

Problems 1–4 Lessons 8.1 and 8.4

If . . . students miss two or more of these fraction problems,

Then . . . invite the entire class to draw different diagrams on the board, and then divide the diagrams into fractions that you choose at random.

Problems 5–9 Lessons 8.5–8.7

If . . . students miss two or more of these comparison problems,

Then . . . clarify the difference between greater than, less than, or equal to. Invite the class to draw diagrams of the fractions before comparing them.

Problems 10–13 Lesson 8.10

If . . . students miss more than one of these money problems,

Then . . . review the relationship between decimals and fractions.

Problem 14 Lesson 8.11

If . . . students miss this percentage problem,

Then . . . draw different diagrams on the board, divide the diagrams into fractional amounts with percent equivalents, and shade various sections of each diagram. Label either the shaded or nonshaded sections of each diagram, asking comparison and computation questions of each diagram.

CHAPTER 8 Chapter Review

Lesson 8.1 **Divide** the figures.

One possible answer:

❶

Copy the figure, and shade in about two-thirds of the figure.

One possible answer:

❷

Copy the figure, and shade in half of the figure.

Lesson 8.4 **Determine** the fractions of time.

❸

a. How many minutes is it until 4:00? 45
b. What fraction of an hour is left until 4:00? $\frac{3}{4}$

❹

a. What time is it? 5:30
b. What fraction of an hour has passed since 5:00? $\frac{1}{2}$

Lesson 8.5 **State** true or false.

❺ $\frac{1}{2} = \frac{5}{8}$ ▢ false

❻ $\frac{2}{10} = \frac{1}{5}$ ▢ true

Lesson 8.6 **Fill** in the blank using <, =, or >.

❼ $\frac{3}{3}$ ▢ $\frac{1}{2}$ >

❽ $\frac{6}{18}$ ▢ $\frac{1}{2}$ <

🅒 Textbook This lesson is available in the *eTextbook*.

Lesson 8.7

❾ **Extended Response** Tricia, Patty, Mike, and Josh want to split a pizza equally among themselves.

Draw a diagram showing how they would split the pizza.   Diagrams should show a circle or a rectangle divided into fourths.

Lesson 8.10

Fill in the blank with *tenths* or *hundredths*.

❿ 80¢ = 8 ▢ of a dollar   tenths

⓫ 1¢ = one ▢ of a dollar   hundredth

⓬ 40¢ = 4 ▢ of a dollar   tenths

⓭ 95¢ = 9 ▢ and 5 ▢ of a dollar   tenths, hundredths

Lesson 8.11

Answer the questions.

⓮

a. If 40% of this circle is shaded, what percent is *not* shaded? 60%

b. What fraction of the circle is shaded? $\frac{2}{5}$

CHAPTER 8 Assessment

3 Chapter Tests

40

Practice Test

Student Pages 334–337

- The Chapter 8 Practice Test on **Student Edition** pages 334–337 provides an opportunity to formally evaluate students' proficiency with concepts developed in this chapter.
- The content is similar to the Chapter 8 Review, in standardized format.

Problem ㉙   Extended Response ▶

Students apply their understanding of fractional parts and their knowledge of fractional operations as they solve these problems. For Problem 33, students determine fractional parts based on percentages in a circle graph. The answer to Part a is blue and $\frac{28}{100}$. The answer to Part b is yellow and $\frac{14}{100}$. The answer to Part c is pink and red, and $\frac{36}{100}$. The answer to Part d is 25%.

Problem ㉚   Extended Response ▶

For Problem 34, students add and subtract fractions to solve realistic problem situations. The answer to Part a is $\frac{6}{4}$, or $1\frac{1}{2}$ yards. The answer to Part b is $2\frac{3}{4}$ yards. The answer to Part c is $4\frac{1}{4}$ yards.

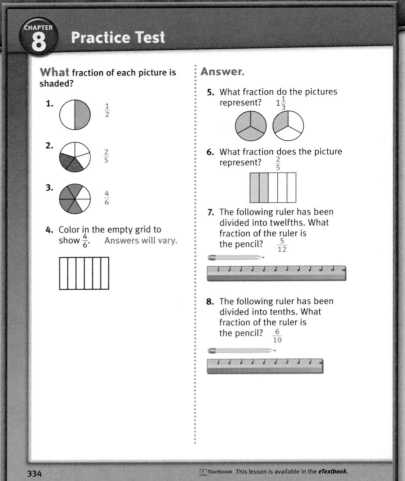

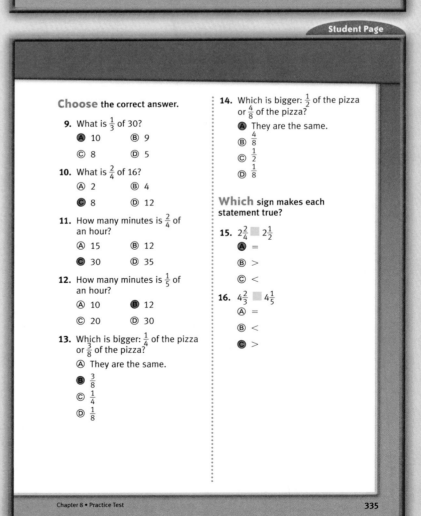

CHAPTER 8 Practice Test

Solve.

17. $\frac{3}{4} - \frac{2}{4} = \blacksquare$
Ⓐ $\frac{6}{8}$ Ⓑ $\frac{5}{8}$
Ⓒ $\frac{1}{4}$ Ⓓ $\frac{1}{8}$

18. $\frac{5}{8} + \frac{2}{8} = \blacksquare$
Ⓐ $\frac{7}{8}$ Ⓑ $\frac{6}{8}$
Ⓒ $\frac{3}{8}$ Ⓓ $\frac{2}{8}$

19. $\frac{2}{3} + \frac{1}{3} = \blacksquare$
Ⓐ $\frac{1}{3}$ Ⓑ $\frac{2}{3}$
Ⓒ $\frac{3}{3}$ Ⓓ $\frac{4}{3}$

20. Which mixed number is equal to $\frac{13}{5}$?
Ⓐ $1\frac{1}{5}$ Ⓑ $1\frac{3}{5}$
Ⓒ $2\frac{2}{5}$ Ⓓ $2\frac{3}{5}$

21. What is the value of the 4 in 83,142?
Ⓐ 4 ten thousands
Ⓑ 4 thousands
Ⓒ 4 hundreds
Ⓓ 4 tens

22. Find the sum. $299 + 173 = \blacksquare$
Ⓐ 492   Ⓑ 472
Ⓒ 461   Ⓓ 453

23. Find the difference.
$912 - 347 = \blacksquare$
Ⓐ 565   Ⓑ 574
Ⓒ 635   Ⓓ 646

24. Find the product of 7×8.
Ⓐ 15   Ⓑ 32
Ⓒ 49   Ⓓ 56

25. Harrison has 7 dimes in his pocket. How much money does he have?
Ⓐ 70¢   Ⓑ 75¢
Ⓒ 80¢   Ⓓ 90¢

26. Find the quotient of $81 \div 9$.
Ⓐ 12   Ⓑ 11
Ⓒ 9   Ⓓ 8

27. Find the inverse function of -3.
Ⓐ $+3$ Ⓑ -3
Ⓒ $\div 3$ Ⓓ $\times 3$

28. $2 + 8 + 5 + 7 = \blacksquare$
Ⓐ 22   Ⓑ 30
Ⓒ 28   Ⓓ 19

336   Textbook This lesson is available in the *eTextbook*.

Use the graph to answer the following questions.

29. Ari surveyed his classmates about their favorite colors. He made a circle graph to show the results of his survey.

Favorite Colors

a. What color did the most of Ari's classmates choose as their favorite? What percent of his classmates chose it?   blue; 28%

b. What color did the fewest of Ari's classmates choose as their favorite? What percent of his classmates chose it?   yellow; 14%

c. Which two colors were equally popular among Ari's classmates? What percent of his classmates chose them?   red and pink; 18% each

d. Of the following benchmark percents, 0%, 5%, 25%, 50%, 75%, or 100%, which percent benchmark is closest to how many of Ari's classmates chose green as their favorite color?   25%

30. Ryan and his friends are making wall hangings out of cloth and felt. A small wall hanging uses $\frac{3}{4}$ yard of black felt and $\frac{1}{4}$ yard each of red, blue, and green felt. A large wall hanging uses $1\frac{1}{4}$ yards of black felt and $\frac{1}{2}$ yard each of red, blue, and green felt.

a. How much felt does a small wall hanging use altogether? Explain. $1\frac{1}{2}$ yards

b. How much felt does a large wall hanging use altogether? Explain. $2\frac{3}{4}$ yards

c. Ryan wants to make a small wall hanging and a large wall hanging. How much felt will he need altogether? $4\frac{1}{4}$ yards

Chapter Test COMPUTING

For further evaluation instead of or in addition to this test, you might want to have students take the Chapter 8 Test provided in **Assessment**.

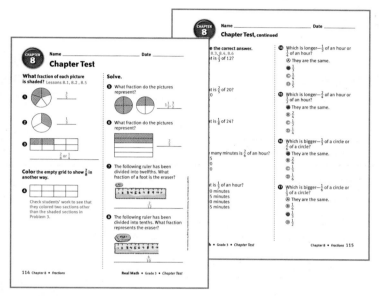

Assessment Pages 114–115

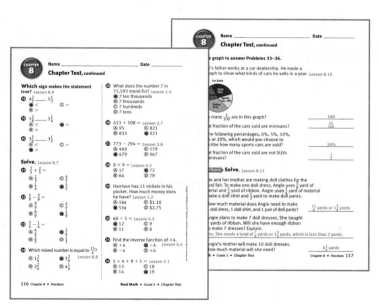

Assessment Pages 116–117

4 Assess and Differentiate

 Assess Use *eAssess* to record and analyze evidence of student understanding.

A Gather Evidence

Use the Daily Class Assessment Records in **Assessment** or **eAssess** to record Informal and Formal Assessments.

Informal Assessment

☑ **Key Ideas Review** UNDERSTANDING

Did the student
- ❏ make important observations?
- ❏ extend or generalize learning?
- ❏ provide insightful answers?
- ❏ pose insightful questions?

Informal Assessment

☑ **Project** APPLYING

Did the student
- ❏ meet the project objectives?
- ❏ communicate clearly?
- ❏ complete the project accurately?
- ❏ connect mathematics to real-world situations?

Formal Assessment

☑ **Chapter Test** COMPUTING

Score the test, and record the results.

B Summarize Findings

Analyze and summarize assessment data for each student. Determine which Chapter Follow-Up is appropriate for each student. Use the Student Assessment Record in **Assessment** or **eAssess** to update assessment records.

C Chapter Follow-Up ● DIFFERENTIATE INSTRUCTION

Based on your observations, use these teaching strategies for chapter follow-up.

ENRICH	PRACTICE	RETEACH	INTERVENTION
If . . . students demonstrate **secure understanding** of chapter concepts,	**If . . .** students demonstrate **competent understanding** of chapter concepts,	**If . . .** students demonstrate **emerging understanding** of chapter concepts,	**If . . .** students demonstrate **minimal understanding** of chapter concepts,
Then . . . move on to the next chapter.	**Then . . .** move on to the next chapter.	**Then . . .** move on to the next chapter, but continue to provide cumulative review.	**Then . . .** intensive intervention is still needed before they start the next chapter.

CHAPTER 8 · Thinking Story

Bargains Galore

Context of the Thinking Story Cousin Trixie has a summer job in a store where the bargains are not really bargains.

Lesson Planner

OBJECTIVES
To develop logical thinking while integrating reading skills with mathematics

NCTM STANDARDS
Problem Solving
- Building new mathematical knowledge through problem solving
- Solving problems that arise in mathematics and in other contexts

Communication
- Communicating mathematical thinking coherently and clearly
- Analyzing and evaluating the mathematical thinking and strategies of others

READING STANDARDS
- Listening for details
- Drawing conclusions
- Making inferences
- Evaluating information

Using the Thinking Story

The Thinking Story may be used anytime throughout the chapter. Read the Thinking Story "Bargains Galore" to your class as they follow along in the **Student Edition** on pages 340–343. As you read the story, give students time to think about each question, but not so much that they forget the point being made.

Thinking Story

Bargains Galore

Portia and Ferdie's cousin Trixie had a summer job in a store. One day Willy and his mother went to the store.

"Hi, Willy!" said Cousin Trixie when they walked in the door. "You've come to the perfect store. I have bargains galore."

"I don't know what that means," said Willy.

"It's what our advertising manager told me to say. I don't know what it means either," said Cousin Trixie. "But I know you'll save money by shopping in my store."

"I'm getting more confused," said Willy. "How can I save money by spending it?"

What does it mean when people say that you'll save money by shopping somewhere? ❶

"What I mean," said Trixie, "is that you'll get more for your money if you buy things from me

338

than if you buy them someplace else. For instance, I have a special on big packs of chewing gum. They usually cost 30¢ apiece, but today you can buy 3 packs for a dollar."

Will Willy save money if he buys 3 packs of gum? ❷

Why or why not? ❸

"I think I'll buy 3 packs at the regular price," said Willy. "Then I'll save 10¢."

Will Willy really save 10¢? ❹

Willy's mother was standing nearby. She whispered to Willy, "You can buy 3 packs of chewing gum in any store for 90¢, so you're not saving any money."

"Thanks," said Willy. "Then I guess I won't buy the gum. I want to save money."

"I'll tell you what I'll do," said Trixie. "If you buy 3 packs of gum for a dollar, I'll throw in a 10¢ package of mints free. You can't turn down a bargain like that!"

Is that a real bargain? ❺

Why or why not? ❻

As Willy left the store with his 3 packs of gum and the mints, he began thinking out loud. "I didn't really save money. I got 3 packs of gum worth 30¢ each and a 10¢ package of mints for a dollar. That's just what they usually cost. Besides, I don't like mints very much, and I don't need all this gum."

Trixie's next customer was Manolita. "I need a pound of salted peanuts," she said. "We're having a party."

"You're in luck," said Cousin Trixie. "I have a special bargain today. Usually I sell a pound bag of peanuts for $2, but today peanuts are half off."

"Half off!" said Manolita. "That's great. My dad will be happy when he finds out I've saved him money."

Cousin Trixie opened a pound bag of peanuts and poured half of them out. "That will be $2," she said, handing the half-empty bag to Manolita.

What did Trixie do wrong? ❼

"Didn't you take half off the wrong thing?" asked Manolita. "You should charge me half as much money, not give me half as many peanuts."

"Just to make you happy, I'll take half off the price too," Trixie said. "That will be $1 for half a pound of peanuts. You can't say that doesn't save you money. You've saved a whole dollar."

Does that really save Manolita money? ❽

Why or why not? ❾

"It sounds as if I'm saving money," said Manolita, "but I'm not sure. Now I have to take the dollar I saved and buy another half pound of peanuts with it. So I'm still spending $2 and getting only a pound of peanuts. I don't think my dad will be very impressed."

Guided Discussion

As students answer the questions in the story, ask them to communicate how they decided on their answers. Allow students to debate the answers if necessary.

1 You will not pay as much there as you would for the same item somewhere else.

2 no

3 The sale price is more than the regular price.

4 No, he is buying the gum at the regular price.

5 no

6 Willy is buying everything at the regular price.

7 She took half off the amount of peanuts but not the price.

8 no

9 She is still not getting half off the price, which should be $1 for a pound of peanuts.

10 $1

11 $2

12 no

13 He is spending $2 on paint, so the lamp is actually costing $1 more.

Later that afternoon, Mr. Eng went to Trixie's store to buy a purple lamp for his favorite purple room. "You came to the right store," said Cousin Trixie. "I have bargains galore on lamps. All the lamps are a dollar less than the regular price."

"Very good," said Mr. Eng, "but I can't find any purple lamps."

"In that case, you're luckier yet," said Trixie. "I also have a bargain on purple paint. A $3 spray can of paint will cost you only $2. You're really saving money today, Mr. Eng. You're saving money on the lamp and on the paint too."

How much is Mr. Eng saving on the lamp? **10**

How much money does he have to spend for the paint? **11**

Is he really saving money? **12**

Why or why not? **13**

When Mr. Eng got back home, he told his wife about his lucky bargain. "But," said Ms. Eng, "you saved a dollar on the lamp and had to spend $2 for paint. So the lamp is costing a dollar more than the regular price. What kind of bargain is that?"

"It's a Trixie-type bargain," said Mr. Eng. "That means you spend more than you should to get more than you need."

The End

340

Chapter 8 • Thinking Story

341

CHAPTER 8 — Teacher Reflection

Lesson Study

Reflect on each of the lessons you taught in this chapter. Rate each one on the following scale, and then consider ways to maintain or improve positive teaching experiences in the future.

Lessons	Very Effective	Effective	Less Effective	What Worked	Ways to Improve
8.1 Fractions of Geometric Figures					
8.2 Fractions of Linear Measure					
8.3 Fractions of Sets					
8.4 Fractions of Time					
8.5 Equivalent Fractions					
8.6 Comparing Fractions					
8.7 Adding and Subtracting Fractions					
8.8 Fractions Greater Than a Whole					
8.9 Comparing Fractions Greater Than a Whole					
8.10 Tenths and Hundredths					
8.11 Percents and Hundredths					

Measurement

Lessons

- **9.1** Metric Length
- **9.2** Customary Length
- **9.3** Metric Weight
- **9.4** Customary Weight
- **9.5** Metric Capacity
- **9.6** Customary Capacity
- **9.7** Choosing the Correct Unit
- **9.8** Measuring Elapsed Time
- **9.9** Understanding the Metric System

Teaching for Understanding

This chapter builds on students' previous knowledge of fractions to deepen their understanding of metric and customary units of measurement. Students will become familiar with the basic units of length, weight, and capacity within the metric and customary systems. Students will also learn measurement conversions in each system.

Prerequisite Skills and Concepts

- Measuring in Centimeters and Inches • Telling Time to the Nearest Minute
- Multiplying by 10, 100, and 1,000

Measurement Skills Trace

Before Grade 3	Grade 3	After Grade 3
Grades K–2 Formally introduced to metric and customary units of measurement	**Chapter 8** formally introduced fractions and arithmetic operations involving fractions. **This chapter** illustrates real-world applications of fractions.	Use measurement conversions as a context for operations with fractions and decimals.

Problem solving is in every lesson. This chapter includes the following:

CHAPTER INTRODUCTION Students learn the practicality of using measurement units of appropriate size (pp. 342I–343C).

EXPLORING PROBLEM SOLVING The first lesson focuses on the Make a Diagram and Write an Equation strategies (pp. 352–353, 353A). The second lesson solves a real-world problem involving customary measures and elapsed time (pp. 366–366A).

THINKING STORY In "Mosquito Lake" students help a character develop strategies for camping (pp. 376–377, 378–379).

Games

Develop reasoning skills, and provide extensive practice.

- **Find the Distance Game 2** (Lesson 9.1)
- **Checkbook Game** (Lesson 9.3)
- **Shopping Game** (Lesson 9.4)
- **Roll a 15 Game** (Lesson 9.5)
- **Metric Unit Game** (Lesson 9.7)
- **Minutes Game** (Lesson 9.8)
- **Harder Minutes Game** (Lesson 9.8)
- **Metric Unit Game** (Lesson 9.9)

Math Background

Measurement

The Metric System

- Most of the world uses the metric system. The only countries not on this system are the United States, Myanmar, and Liberia. Even in the United States the metric system is used routinely for scientific applications, although customary units are used more frequently for road signs, retail pricing, and so on.

- Both the metric and the customary systems of measurement are introduced and developed in **Real Math.** We do not ask students to convert from one system to another; we encourage them to think in terms of each system independently. Each system is taught independently so that students will not think of one as "growing out of" the other or in some way being dependent on the other.

- Metric usage in **Real Math** is derived from a modernized version of the metric system called *le Systeme International d'Unites* (SI), which was established by international agreement in 1966 to standardize usage throughout the world and create a truly international system of measure. The system is built on a foundation of seven basic units, and all other units are derived from them. We have made some minor modifications in SI based on pedagogical considerations. For example, we use the capital letter L rather than the lowercase letter l for *liter* to avoid confusion with the numeral 1.

Weight and Mass

- For simplicity, **Real Math** follows the common convention of measuring both weight and mass in pounds and kilograms.

- Technically, the pound is a unit of weight, and a kilogram is a unit of mass. Weight is the amount of heaviness of an object, caused by gravity's pull on it. Mass is the amount of matter an object contains. Mass is measured on a balance scale in kilograms (or slugs, in the customary system), whereas weight is measured on a spring scale in newtons (or pounds, in the customary system).

- A person's mass is the same whether it is measured on Earth or on the moon, but his or her weight changes because of the change in gravity. However, this is a subtle distinction and the effort to teach it to students is typically too great for the potential benefits.

Metrix Prefixes

Units smaller than a meter have Latin prefixes:

Deci- means 10; 10 decimeters make a meter.

Centi- means 100; 100 centimeters make a meter.

Milli- means 1,000; 1,000 millimeters make a meter.

Units larger than a meter have Greek prefixes:

Deka- means 10; a dekameter is 10 meters.

Hecto- means 100; a hectometer is 100 meters.

Kilo- means 1,000; a kilometer is 1,000 meters.

SI Units

- In the metric system, the "official" units include meter for length (defined as the length of the path traveled by light in a vacuum during a time interval of $\frac{1}{299,792,458}$ of a second) and kilogram for mass (defined as the mass of a specific metal bar in a vault in France).

- Although the kilogram is the officially-defined unit, metric prefixes for mass are attached to the root "gram."

- The liter is derived from the meter. Specifically, a volume of 1 milliliter ($\frac{1}{1000}$ of a liter) is defined as the volume of 1 cubic centimeter (a cubic 1 centimeter on each side). So, a volume of 1 liter is equal to the volume of 1000 cubic centimeters, or a cube 10 centimeters on each side.

What Research Says

About Measurement

How Children Develop Measurement Skills and Concepts

"Children's development of [measurement] skills is a slow process…. Recent research suggests that children benefit from using objects and rulers to measure at any age. Not only do children prefer using rulers, but they can use them meaningfully and in combination with manipulable units to develop understanding of length measurement. Even if they do not understand rulers fully or use them accurately, they can use rulers *along with* manipulable units such as centimeter cubes and arbitrary units to develop their measurement skills."

Clements, Douglas and J. Sarama, eds. *Engaging Young Children in Mathematics: Standards for Early Childhood Mathematics Education.* Mahwah, New Jersey: Lawrence Erlbaum Associates, Publishers, 2004, pp. 51–52.

Learning Trajectories for Measurement

Children typically follow an observable developmental progression in learning to measure with recognizable stages or levels. This developmental path can be described as part of a learning trajectory. Key steps in the learning trajectory for measurement from the second-grade range are described below. For the complete trajectory, see Appendix B.

Strand	Age	Level Name	Level	Description
Measuring	7	Length Unit Iterater	6	A significant change occurs when a child can use a ruler and see the need for identical units.
Measuring	6	Length Unit Relater	7	At the next level, a child can relate size and number of units. For example, the child may explain, "If you measure with centimeters instead of inches, you'll need more of them, because each one is smaller."

Clements, D. H., J. Sarama, & A. M. DiBiase, eds. *Engaging Young Children in Mathematics: Standards for Early Childhood Mathematics Education.* Mahwah, NJ: Lawrence Erlbaum Associates, 2004, pp. 51–52.

Research-Based Teaching Techniques

Research has shown that the development of measurement ability and understandings in children is a complex … process. [Children] must develop a recognition that attributes such as length, height, weight, and capacity can be measured formally and informally. They must gain experience in using nonstandard and standard units for measuring and then learn various strategies for using those units to accurately assign values to the attributes being measured.

They gradually acquire knowledge and language associated with standard systems and units of measure. They gain an appreciation of the benefits of using one system or unit over another and become more skillful in using tools of measurement to accurately determine numbers of units when measuring.

A foundation in measurement concepts enables students to use measurement systems, tools, and techniques. This foundation needs to be established by the teacher as he or she provides children with direct experiences with comparing objects, counting units, and making connections between spatial concepts and number. Children will come to recognize attributes by looking at, touching, or directly comparing objects.

Teachers should guide students' experiences by making the resources for measuring available, planning opportunities to measure, and encouraging students to explain the results of their actions.

National Council of Teachers of Mathematics. *Principles and Standards for School Mathematics.* Reston, VA: NCTM, 2000.

 RESEARCH IN ACTION

Measurement In Chapter 9 students will gain greater awareness of the tools and procedures used to measure and compare attributes of time, temperature, length, weight, and capacity.

Attributes Throughout Chapter 9 students will gain greater awareness of attributes associated with the measurement of time, temperature, length, weight, and capacity.

Communication and Language Development In Chapter 9 students develop greater fluency with and awareness of the language of measurement. Students will use the language of measurement to compare, classify, and describe objects in the world around them.

Vocabulary

capacity (Lesson 9.5) the amount of liquid a container has the potential to hold

cup (Lesson 9.6) a customary measure of capacity equal to 8 fluid ounces

elapsed (Lesson 9.8) the amount of time that has passed

foot (Lesson 9.2) a customary measure of length equal to 12 inches

gallon (Lesson 9.6) a customary measure of capacity equal to 4 quarts

hour (Lesson 9.8) a measure of time equal to 60 minutes

kilogram (Lesson 9.3) a metric measure of weight equal to 1,000 grams

kilometer (Lesson 9.1) a metric measure of length equal to 1,000 meters

mile (Lesson 9.2) a customary measure of length equal to 5,280 feet

milliliter (Lesson 9.5) a metric measure of capacity equal to one-thousandth of a liter

millimeter (Lesson 9.1) a metric measure of length equal to one-thousandth of a meter

minute (Lesson 9.8) a measure of time equal to 60 seconds

pint (Lesson 9.6) a customary measure of capacity equal to 2 cups

pound (Lesson 9.4) a customary measure of weight equal to 16 ounces

quart (Lesson 9.6) a customary measure of capacity equal to 2 pints

yard (Lesson 9.2) a customary measure of length equal to 3 feet

English Learner

Cognates

For English learners a quick way to acquire new English vocabulary is to build on what is known in the primary language.

English	Spanish
metric system	sistema métrico
units	unidades
correct unit	unidad correcta
depends on	depende en
to convert	convertir
to report	reportar
has passed	ha pasado

Access Vocabulary

English learners may understand words in different contexts or not understand idioms. Review chapter vocabulary for this concern. For example:

metric	having to do with meters, like the metric system
customary	common
weight	describes how much something weighs
convert each measure	change each measure

Chapter Planner

Lessons	Objectives	NCTM Standards	State Standards
9.1 Metric Length pages 344A–345A	To familiarize students with meters, centimeters, millimeters, and kilometers and converting units	Measurement Problem Solving	
9.2 Customary Length pages 346A–347A	To practice measuring to the nearest $\frac{1}{2}$ and $\frac{1}{4}$ inch and converting units	Measurement Problem Solving	
9.3 Metric Weight pages 348A–349A	To explore metric units of weight and measurement conversions	Measurement Problem Solving	
9.4 Customary Weight pages 350A–351A	To deepen understanding of customary units of weight and conversions	Measurement Problem Solving	
9.5 Metric Capacity pages 356A–357A	To explore and introduce practical applications of metric units of capacity	Measurement Problem Solving	
9.6 Customary Capacity pages 358A–359A	To develop familiarity with customary units of capacity	Measurement Problem Solving	
9.7 Choosing the Correct Unit pages 360A–361A	To clarify concepts of length, weight, and capacity in metric and customary units of measurement	Measurement Problem Solving	
9.8 Measuring Elapsed Time pages 362A–363A	To strengthen knowledge of units of time by calculating elapsed time	Measurement Communication	
9.9 Understanding the Metric System pages 364A–365A	To solidify knowledge of the relationship between metric units of measurement	Measurement Connections	

Vocabulary	Manipulatives and Materials	Games to reinforce skills and concepts
• kilometer • millimeter	• Response Wheels • Metersticks • 30-centimeter rulers • Find the Distance 2 Game Mat	Find the Distance Game 2 (Lesson 3.4)
• foot • yard	• Response Wheels • 12-inch rulers • Yardsticks • 20–25 pencils and pens of different lengths (in a box)	
kilogram	• Response Wheels • Platform scale • Small spring scale or double-pan balance • Checkbook Game Mat	Checkbook Game (Lesson 2.6)
pound	• Response Wheels • Platform scale • Small spring scale or double-pan balance • Shopping Game Mat	Shopping Game (Lesson 7.1)
• capacity • milliliters	• Response Wheels • One 1-liter soda bottle (label removed) • One 2-liter soda bottle (label removed) • One clear 1-liter measuring cylinder • Small graduated cylinder (for measuring in milliliters) • Pitcher of water • Various sizes of plastic containers (labels removed)	Roll a 15 Game (Lessons 1.2–1.5)
• cup • gallon • pint • quart	• Response Wheels • Various sizes of containers labeled with volume measures	Multigo 1 (Lesson 5.8)
	• Response Wheels • Metric Unit Game Mat	
• elapsed • hour • minute	• Response Wheels • Minutes Game Mat • Demonstration clock	Harder Minutes Game (Lessons 3.1–3.2)
	• Response Wheels • Metric Unit Game Mat	Metric Unit Game

Additional Resources

Differentiated Instruction

Intervention Support Guide Provides instruction for the following prerequisite skills:

- Lesson 9.A Measuring in Centimeters and Inches
- Lesson 9.B Telling Time to the Nearest Minute
- Lesson 9.C Multiplying by 10, 100, and 1,000

Enrichment Support Guide Extends lesson concepts

Practice Reinforces lesson skills and concepts

Reteach Support Guide Provides alternate instruction for lesson concepts

English Learner Support Guide Previews and reviews lesson concepts and vocabulary for English learners

Technology

The following electronic resources are available:

Planner Lessons 9.1–9.9

Presentation Lessons 9.1–9.9

Textbook Lessons 9.1–9.9

Assess Lessons 9.1–9.9

MathTools *Metric/Customary Conversion* Lessons 9.1–9.6

Games *Roll a 15 Game* Lesson 9.5
 Multigo 1 Lesson 9.6

Building Blocks *Reptile Ruler* Lessons 9.1–9.2

Assessment

Informal Assessment rubrics at the end of each lesson provide daily evaluation of student math proficiency.

Chapter Planner, continued

Problem Solving	When to use	Objectives	NCTM Standards	Skills Covered
Chapter Introduction pp. 342I–343C 15–30 minutes	Use after the Chapter 9 Pretest	To introduce chapter concepts in a problem-solving setting	Measurement Problem Solving	Addition, Subtraction, Measurement
Exploring Problem Solving pp. 352–353, 353A 30–45 minutes	Use anytime during the chapter	To explore methods of solving nonroutine problems	Measurement Problem Solving	Measurement, Computation, and Algebraic thinking
Exploring Problem Solving pp. 366, 366A 45–60 minutes	Use anytime during the chapter	To explore methods of solving nonroutine problems	Measurement Problem Solving	Proportional Reasoning, Fractions
Thinking Story— Mosquito Lake pp. 376–377, 378–379 20–30 minutes	Use anytime during the chapter	To develop logical reasoning while integrating reading skills with mathematics	Problem Solving Communication	Reasoning

Review				
Cumulative Review p. 354–355 15–30 minutes	Use anytime after Lesson 9.4	To review concepts and skills taught in Lessons 9.1–9.4	Measurement and Problem Solving	Measuring length, Fractions of geometric figures, Customary length, Multiplying two-digit numbers by one-digit numbers
Cumulative Review p. 367–368 15–30 minutes	Use anytime after Lesson 9.9	To review concepts and skills taught in Lessons 9.1–9.9	Measurement	Multiplying three-digit numbers by one-digit numbers, Perimeter and area, Metric length, Fractions of time, Customary weight
Chapter 9 Review pp. 370A, 370–371 30–45 minutes	Use after Lesson 9.9	To review concepts and skills taught in the chapter	Measurement Number and Operations Problem Solving	Metric and customary conversions (length, weight, capacity), Choosing the correct unit, Measuring elapsed time

Assessment				
Informal Assessment Rubrics pp. 344A–365A 5 minutes per student	Use at the end of the lesson	To provide daily evaluation of math proficiency	Measurement Problem Solving	Estimation, Measurement, Problem Solving
Pretest (*Assessment* pp. 119–120) 15–30 minutes	Use prior to Chapter 9	To provide assessment of prerequisite and chapter topics	Measurement Problem Solving	Arithmetical Operations, Visualizing Data
Individual Oral Assessment p. 355A 5 minutes per student	Use after Lesson 9.4	To provide alternate means of assessing students' progress	Measurement Problem Solving	Measuring, Unit Conversions
Mastery Checkpoint (*Assessment* p. T60) 5 minutes per student	Begin after Lesson 9.4	To provide assessment of mastery of key skills	Measurement Problem Solving	Estimation, Measurement, Unit Conversions
Chapter 9 Practice Test pp. 372–373, 374–375 30–45 minutes	Use after or in place of the Chapter 9 Review	To provide assessment or additional practice of the lesson concepts	Measurement Problem Solving	Estimation, Measurement, Problem Solving
Chapter 9 Test (*Assessment* pp. 126–129) 30–45 minutes	Use after or in place of the Chapter 9 Review	To provide assessment of the chapter concepts	Measurement Problem Solving	Estimation, Measurement, Problem Solving

Technology Resources and Support

Visit SRAonline.com for the online versions of the **Real Math eSuite.**

Technology for Teachers

Presentation — **Lessons 9.1–9.9** Use the **ePresentation** to interactively present chapter content.

Planner — Use the Chapter and Lesson Planners to outline activities and time frames for Chapter 9.

Assess — Students can take the following assessments in **eAssess:**
- Chapter Pretest
- Mastery Checkpoint **Lesson 9.4**
- Chapter Test

Teachers can record results and print reports for all assessments in this chapter.

MathTools — **Metric/Customary Conversion Tool** Lessons 9.1–9.6

Technology for Students

Textbook — An electronic, interactive version of the **Student Edition** is available for all lessons in Chapter 9.

MathTools — **Metric/Customary Conversion Tool** Lessons 9.1–9.6

Games — **Roll a 15 Game** Lesson 9.5; **Multigo 1** Lesson 9.6

TechKnowledge Level 3 provides lessons that specifically teach the Unit 10 Internet and Unit 1 Computer Basics applications that students can use in this chapter's project.

Building Blocks — **Reptile Ruler** Lessons 9.1–9.2

Measurement

 1 | **Introduce Chapter 9** 5

Chapter Objectives

Explain to students that in this chapter they will build on what they already know about measurement. They will

- use standard units of metric length.
- use customary rulers to draw and measure lengths to the nearest inch, foot, or yard.
- measure elapsed time.

Pretest COMPUTING

Administer the Pretest on **Assessment** pages 119 and 120.

The Pretest covers the following skills and topics from the chapter:

- Time (Problems 1–3)
- Linear measurement (Problems 4 and 5)
- Multiplication and division of multidigit numbers (Problems 6–10)
- Addition and subtraction of multidigit numbers (Problems 11 and 12)
- Measurement conversions, customary and metric (Problems 13–20)
- Measurement units for length, weight, and capacity (Problems 21–25)

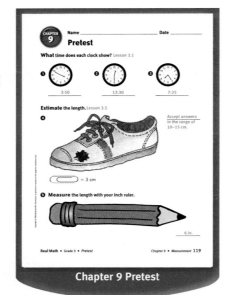

Chapter 9 Pretest

Access Prior Knowledge ✓ UNDERSTANDING

Use the photograph on page 342 to initiate a discussion of camping and campgrounds. Ask questions such as the following:

- Have you ever gone to a summer camp or known someone who has?
- Have you read any books about children who have gone to summer camp?
- What are some of the activities that camps offer?
- If you were to design a summer camp, what would you include?

 2 | **Exploring Problem Solving** 30

Tell Students In Today's Lesson They Will

- pretend to help build a summer camp.
- figure out how many bricks they will need for a border along a path.

Materials

- Long strips of paper such as adding machine tape, or large sheets of construction paper
- Crayons (one box per group)
- Scissors
- Rulers

Using Student Pages

Have students look at the picture and read the problem on page 343. Make sure students understand the problem by asking questions such as the following:

- **What is going on in the story?** We are helping build a camp. We are planning to lay bricks along the side of a path from the swimming pool to the ropes. We have to decide how many bricks we will need.
- **How long is each brick?** the same length as a new crayon
- **Will the border be along just one side of the path?** No, it will be along both sides.

Tell students they are going to pretend that the swimming pool is on one side of the classroom and the ropes are on the other side. Each group will have only one box of crayons to help them measure, but they may use paper and pencil or markers to help them. Ask questions such as the following:

- **How could you find out how many bricks it would take to go across the classroom?**

Give students time to think about strategies they might use, and then allow them to share their ideas. Students might suggest methods such as these:

- Line up and count the crayons, mark the spot at the end of the line, move the crayons to make a new line from the spot you mark, and keep doing this until you get to the other side of the classroom.
- Use paper to make a ruler equal to 10 crayons (or some other number), and then count how many times you have to place the ruler end to end to get across the classroom.

CHAPTER 9 Measurement

In This Chapter You Will Learn
- how to use standard units of metric length, weight, and capacity.
- how to estimate and measure lengths to the nearest inch, foot, or yard.
- how to calculate elapsed time.

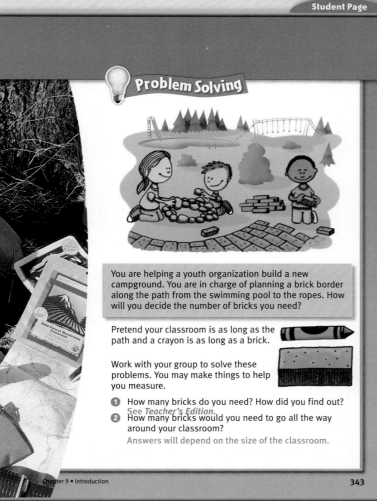

Problem Solving

You are helping a youth organization build a new campground. You are in charge of planning a brick border along the path from the swimming pool to the ropes. How will you decide the number of bricks you need?

Pretend your classroom is as long as the path and a crayon is as long as a brick.

Work with your group to solve these problems. You may make things to help you measure.

1. How many bricks do you need? How did you find out?
   See *Teacher's Edition*.
2. How many bricks would you need to go all the way around your classroom?
   Answers will depend on the size of the classroom.

Chapter 9 • Introduction   343

Continue the discussion by asking the following:

- **Once you find out how many bricks are needed, are you finished with the problem?** no, because we need to have the border on both sides of the path

Have students work on the problem in pairs or small groups, allowing them access to as much paper as they need. Circulate around the room, and provide support as needed. Be sure to allow students time to struggle with the problem before offering suggestions. If students seem to be unable to make progress, ask questions such as these:

- **What can you do if you do not have enough crayons to reach across the room?**
- **Suppose you had only 1 crayon. How could you figure out how many crayons long your desk is?**

Problem 1 Answers will depend on the size of the classroom. Methods may vary, but may include making a ruler equal to a set number of crayons and counting how many times the student has to place the ruler end to end to get across the classroom.

Concept/Question Board APPLYING

Questions

Have students think of and write three questions they have about measurement and how it can be used. Then have them select one question to post on the Question side of the Board.

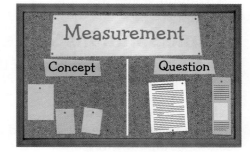

Concepts

As students work through the chapter, have them collect examples of how measurement is used in everyday situations. For each example, have them write a problem that relates to the item(s). Have them display their examples on the Concept side of the Board. Suggest the following:

- track and field events
- cooking
- traveling

Answers

Throughout the chapter, have students post answers to the questions and solutions to the problems on the Board.

Chapter 9 • Measurement   **342–343**

③ Reflect 10

Effective Communication Have groups present their results. Encourage students to ask for clarification if they do not understand what is being presented. After each presentation, ask students what they liked about the method and how it was presented. In discussion, bring out the following points:

- When measuring a large distance, a measuring tool that shows a group of the units can save time and effort.
- Some numbers, like 10, are easier to work with than other numbers.
- To make it easier to describe long distances, we can use longer units. Then we do not have to use such large numbers.
- In real-world problems, there are different ways to approach a solution. Some ways may be more efficient than others.

Sample Solutions Strategies

Students might use one or more of the following strategies to solve the problem.

Make a Physical Model

Students might lay the crayons end to end, and when they have used them all, they might reuse the same crayons starting where the last crayon ended.

Students might use paper to make a ruler that shows crayon lengths, and then use their ruler to measure the length of the room in "crayon units."

Use Skip Counting

Students might measure how many crayons long one step is and then skip count by that number as they step from one side of the room to the other.

Use Computation

Students might use a standard ruler to see how many crayons there are in a foot and how many feet long the room is. Then they could use that information to calculate how many crayons long the room is.

Home Connection

At this time, you may want to send home the letter on pages 34–37 of **Home Connection.** This letter describes what students will be learning and what activities they can do at home to support their work in school.

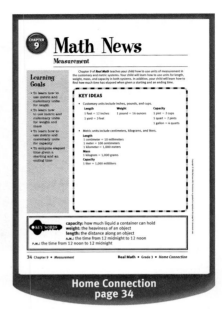

Home Connection page 34

4 Assess and Differentiate

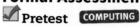 **Assess** Use *eAssess* to record and analyze evidence of student understanding.

A Gather Evidence

Use the Daily Class Assessment Records in *Assessment* or *eAssess* to record Informal and Formal Assessments.

Informal Assessment
 Access Prior Knowledge
Did the student **UNDERSTANDING**
- ❏ make important observations?
- ❏ extend or generalize learning?
- ❏ provide insightful answers?
- ❏ pose insightful questions?

Informal Assessment
Concept/Question Board
Did the student **APPLYING**
- ❏ apply learning in new situations?
- ❏ contribute concepts?
- ❏ contribute answers?
- ❏ connect mathematics to real-world situations?

Formal Assessment
Pretest **COMPUTING**
Review student answers in each problem set.
- ❏ Time (Problems 1–3)
- ❏ Linear measurement (Problems 4 and 5)
- ❏ Multiplication and division of multidigit numbers (Problems 6–10)
- ❏ Addition and subtraction of multidigit numbers (Problems 11 and 12)
- ❏ Measurement conversions, customary and metric (Problems 13–20)
- ❏ Measurement units for length, weight, and capacity (Problems 21–25)

B Summarize Findings

Analyze and summarize assessment data for each student. Determine which Assessment Follow-Up is appropriate for each student. Use the Student Assessment Record in *Assessment* or *eAssess* to update assessment records.

C Assessment Follow-Up • DIFFERENTIATE INSTRUCTION

Based on your observations of each student, use these teaching strategies for a general approach to the chapter. Look for specific Differentiate Instruction and Monitoring Student Progress strategies in each lesson that relate specifically to the lesson content.

ENRICH	PRACTICE	RETEACH	INTERVENTION	ENGLISH LEARNER
If . . . students demonstrate **secure understanding** of chapter concepts, **Then . . .** move quickly through the chapter or use *Enrichment* Lessons 9.1–9.9 as assessment follow-up to extend and apply understanding.	**If . . .** students grasp chapter concepts with **competent understanding,** **Then . . .** use *Practice* Lessons 9.1–9.9 as lesson follow-up to develop fluency.	**If . . .** students have prerequisite understanding but demonstrate **emerging understanding** of chapter concepts, **Then . . .** use *Reteach* Lesson 9.6 to reteach lesson concepts.	**If . . .** students are not competent with prerequisite skills, **Then . . .** use *Intervention* Lessons 9.A–9.C before each lesson to develop fluency with prerequisite skills.	Use *English Learner Support Guide* Lessons 9.1–9.9 for strategies to preteach lesson vocabulary and concepts.

Math Across the Curriculum

Preview the chapter projects with students. Assign projects to extend and enrich concepts in this chapter.

Evaluate Campfire Songs

2–3 weeks

MATH OBJECTIVE
To reinforce studies of measurement by measuring the length of a musical program

FINE ARTS OBJECTIVE
To reinforce studies of music by creating a campfire song program

TECHNOLOGY OBJECTIVE
To use computer basics to view and search Web sites for information

• •

Have students use technology to
- gather information about the history of camping and folk songs.
- create and apply evaluation criteria for their programs.

For this project, students use the Internet to investigate the following information:
- history of the conservation and camping movements
- databases of camp and sing-along songs

For specific step-by-step instructions for this project, see *Across the Curriculum Math Connections* pages 92–97.

Teamwork Students work in teams to select songs.

Problem Formulation and Planning Students must consider both time and diverse song selection as they create their programs.

TECH KNOWLEDGE *TechKnowledge* Level 3 provides lessons that specifically teach the Unit 10 Internet and Unit 1 Computer Basics applications that students can use in this project.

Plan a Family Camping Trip

2–3 weeks

SCIENCE

MATH OBJECTIVE
To reinforce studies of choosing the correct unit by choosing units to measure distance

SCIENCE OBJECTIVE
To reinforce studies of environment by considering the environment of a camping trip

TECHNOLOGY OBJECTIVE
To use a word processing program to create a camping plan and a checklist

• •

Have students use mathematics to plan a family camping trip. To broaden the science concept, have students incorporate and describe aspects of environments you are currently studying.

As part of the project, students should consider the following issues:
- National Parks in their state
- the distances to the parks
- choosing units of measure
- using a word processing program to make a bulleted checklist

For specific step-by-step instructions for this project, see *Across the Curriculum Math Connections* pages 98–101.

High-Level Responsibility Students organize lists including all needed gear for a camping trip.

Problem Formulation, Planning, and Strategizing Students must determine how to measure the approximate distances to campgrounds.

Lesson Planner

OBJECTIVES
- To give students more experience with estimating, measuring, and problem solving using metric units of length
- To introduce millimeters and kilometers
- To provide practice with converting meters to centimeters and centimeters to meters

NCTM STANDARDS
Measurement
- Selecting and using benchmarks to estimate measurements
- Selecting and applying appropriate standard units to measure length
- Carrying out simple unit conversions

Problem Solving
Applying a variety of appropriate strategies to solve problems

MATERIALS
- *Response Wheels
- Meterstick
- 30-centimeter rulers
- Yardstick
- Find the Distance 2 Game Mat

TECHNOLOGY
- **Presentation** Lesson 9.1
- **Building Blocks** Reptile Ruler
- **MathTools** Metric/Customary Conversion Tool

TEST PREP
Cumulative Review
Mental Math reviews comparing fractions (Lesson 8.6).

Extended Response
Problems 6–8

Looking Ahead
For the next lesson, you will need a box that contains 20–25 pencils and pens of different lengths.

Metric Length

Context of the Lesson In Chapter 3 students reviewed estimating and measuring in centimeters and meters. This lesson provides more applications for measuring in centimeters and meters and includes a discussion of and applications for millimeters and kilometers. The focus of the next lesson is on measuring in inches, feet, and yards.

See page 342B for Math Background for teachers for this lesson.

Planning for Learning ● DIFFERENTIATE INSTRUCTION

INTERVENTION
If . . . students lack the prerequisite skill of measuring in centimeters and inches,

Then . . . teach **Intervention** Lesson 9.A.

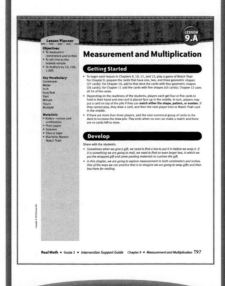

Intervention Lesson 9.A

ENGLISH LEARNER
Preview

If . . . students need language support,

Then . . . use Lesson 9.1 in **English Learner Support Guide** to preview lesson concepts and vocabulary.

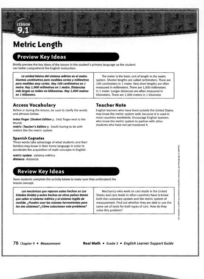

English Learner Lesson 9.1

ENRICH
If . . . students are proficient in the lesson concepts,

Then . . . emphasize exploring **eMathTools: Metric/Customary Conversion Tool**.

PRACTICE
If . . . students would benefit from additional practice,

Then . . . extend Guided Discussion about centimeters and meters before assigning the student pages.

RETEACH
If . . . students are having difficulty using metric units to measure length,

Then . . . extend Skill Building before assigning the student pages.

Vocabulary
Review from Lesson 3.4:
centimeter and **meter**
millimeter \miʹ lə mē tər\ *n.* a metric measure of length equal to one-thousandth of a meter
kilometer \kə läʹ mə tər\ *n.* a metric measure of length equal to 1,000 meters

Access Vocabulary
index finger finger next to the thumb
metric having to do with meters like the metric system

Spanish Cognates
metric system sistema métrico
distance distancia

Mental Math | 5

  Write pairs of fractions on the board, leaving a circle where the relation sign belongs. Have students show thumbs-up if the fraction on the left is greater than the fraction on the right, thumbs-down if it is less, and open hand if the fractions are equal. Possible examples include the following:

a. $\frac{1}{2} \bigcirc \frac{1}{3}$ up

b. $\frac{1}{4} \bigcirc \frac{3}{4}$ down

c. $\frac{1}{3} \bigcirc \frac{3}{4}$ down

d. $\frac{2}{4} \bigcirc \frac{1}{2}$ open hand

e. $\frac{2}{4} \bigcirc \frac{1}{4}$ up

f. $\frac{3}{6} \bigcirc \frac{2}{4}$ open hand

1 Develop | 25

Tell Students In Today's Lesson They Will

- estimate and measure length in millimeters, centimeters, and meters.
- understand the approximate length of a kilometer.

Guided Discussion  UNDERSTANDING | Whole Group

Centimeters and Meters

1. Hold up a meterstick. Remind students that the meter is the basic unit of measure in the metric system, which is based on multiples of ten. Explain that a meter is used to measure length. Point out that one way to remember the length of 1 meter is to recall the height from the floor to the doorknob on a standard-sized door. Use the meterstick to show students that the height of the doorknob is about 1 meter.

2. Ask a student to bring a centimeter ruler to the front of the room and measure the meterstick to find out how many centimeter rulers it takes to make one meterstick.

   $3\frac{1}{3}$ centimeter rulers Then ask the class to explain how they could have determined this without actually measuring the meterstick. A centimeter ruler is 30 centimeters long. The length of three rulers is 30 + 30 + 30 = 90, so a meterstick is 3 rulers plus 10 more centimeters because 30 + 30 + 30 + 10 = 100.

3. Ask students how many centimeters are in 1 meter. 100 Then ask questions such as the following, and have students show their answers with their *Response Wheels:*

   - **How many centimeters are in 2 meters?** 200
   - **How many centimeters are in $\frac{1}{2}$ meter?** 50
   - **How many meters are in 300 centimeters?** 3

Skill Building ENGAGING | Whole Group

Estimating and Measuring in Centimeters

Guide students through the following activity on estimating and measuring in centimeters. This activity was introduced in Lesson 3.4 and is reintroduced here to help students continue to refine their measurement skills.

1. Select an object or a student in the classroom, and ask students to estimate the object's or person's length or height in centimeters.

2. Have students record their estimates.

3. Have one or more students measure the object or the student to the nearest centimeter and report the measure to the class.

4. Write the name of the object or the student and the corresponding measure on the board.

5. Repeat Steps 1 through 4 for other objects or students. For example, have students estimate and measure the height of one student. Then ask a second student to stand next to the first student. Have students estimate and then measure the height of the second student. Repeat with a third, fourth, and fifth student.

Guided Discussion UNDERSTANDING | Whole Group

Millimeters and Kilometers

1. Explain that there are metric units of measure that are smaller than the centimeter. Direct students to notice the marks between the centimeters on the rulers, and tell them that the space between each mark stands for 1 millimeter. Explain that there are 10 millimeters in 1 centimeter and 1,000 millimeters in 1 meter. Have students estimate and then measure the lengths of various small objects (paper clips, pencils, crayons, and so on) in millimeters.

2. Finally, explain that a kilometer is 1,000 meters and is used to measure distances. Tell students that it takes about 12 minutes to walk 1 kilometer at a reasonable pace.

2 Assign Student Pages | 25

Pages 344–345 APPLYING

Have students complete student page 344 independently. Then have them do page 345 as a group activity. Spend a few minutes discussing the students' answers for the first three discussion questions. Have students work in groups of two or three to complete the estimating and measuring activity.

As Students Finish

 Find the Distance Game 2 (introduced in Lesson 3.4)

Building Blocks *Reptile Ruler* Student can practice using a ruler to measure length.

LESSON 9.1 Metric Length

Key Ideas

The meter is the basic unit of length in the metric system. The height from the floor to the doorknob of your classroom door is probably about 1 meter.

1 meter

We often measure shorter lengths using centimeters. There are 100 centimeters in 1 meter. Each edge of your **Number Cube** is about 2 centimeters long.

Very short lengths are often measured in millimeters. There are 1,000 millimeters in 1 meter. A nickel is about 2 millimeters thick.

Longer distances are often measured in kilometers. There are 1,000 meters in 1 kilometer.

Which unit (millimeters, centimeters, meters, or kilometers) would you use to measure these lengths or distances?

HARTSVILLE
1 Kilometer
DARLINGTON
15 Kilometers
MYRTLE BEACH
100 Kilometers

1. the length of a large pool   meters
2. the distance from where you live to the next town or city   kilometers
3. the length of your index finger   centimeters
4. the length of a sharp pencil point   millimeters
5. the wingspan of a monarch butterfly   centimeters

344   ⊡ **Textbook** This lesson is available in the *eTextbook*.

Grady is 125 centimeters tall. The apple he is about to pick is 160 centimeters high.

Discuss and solve these problems.

6. **Extended Response** Can Grady pick the apple without standing on something to make him taller? Explain. See *Teacher's Edition.*
7. **Extended Response** What if the apple were 200 centimeters high? Would Grady be able to reach it without standing on something? Explain. No, his arms would not be long enough.
8. **Extended Response** If he jumped, could Grady reach the apple that is 200 centimeters high? Explain. He could possibly reach it if he jumped. A few, but not all, students can jump that high.

Do this activity. Work in groups of two or three.

* Measure and record your height in centimeters.
* Estimate how high you can reach. Record your estimate.
* Reach as high as you can, and measure the height. Record that measurement.
* Estimate how high you can reach if you jump. Record your estimate.
* Measure how high you can reach if you jump. Record that measurement.

Discuss the following questions with your group.

* Were your estimates accurate? Why or why not?
* How much higher will you be able to reach next year? In five years? In twenty years? Explain.

During the discussion, students should present reasonable estimates for their growth over the years given.

Chapter 9 • Lesson 1   345

---

3 Reflect   5

Guided Discussion ☑ REASONING   Whole Group

Discuss the last question on page 345. Allow students to make estimates of how tall they will be, but be sure to challenge them to explain why they think so. Expect varied but legitimate estimates. For example, some students will make estimates based on the heights of their parents or older siblings, while other students might try to extend the growth patterns they have recently experienced. They must, of course, note that growth slows down and stops at a certain age. The goal of the discussion is not so much to make accurate estimates, but to have students actively thinking about height and length using centimeter units.

Extended Response

Problem 6 Students should explain that Grady can probably pick the apple without standing on something because his arms will likely extend about 30–40 centimeters above his head. If that's not enough, he can likely jump the few extra centimeters.

Curriculum Connection: Students might be interested in investigating the wingspans, in centimeters, of various birds and butterflies.

Cumulative Review: For cumulative review of previously learned skills, see page 354–355.

Family Involvement: Assign the *Practice, Reteach,* or *Enrichment* activities depending on the needs of your students.

Encourage students to practice measuring the lengths of various items in millimeters, centimeters, and meters with a friend or a relative.

Concept/Question Board: Have students look for additional examples using measurement in millimeters, centimeters, meters, and kilometers and post them on the Concept/Question Board.

Math Puzzler: A seven-digit number has three 7s, two 3s, two 6s, and is the same backward and forward. None of the 7s are next to another 7. What is the number? 6,737,376 or 3,767,673

Assess and Differentiate

 Assess Use *eAssess* to record and analyze evidence of student understanding.

A Gather Evidence

Use the Daily Class Assessment Records in *Assessment* or *eAssess* to record daily observations.

Informal Assessment
☑ **Guided Discussion**

Did the student `UNDERSTANDING`
- ❑ make important observations?
- ❑ extend or generalize learning?
- ❑ provide insightful answers?
- ❑ pose insightful questions?

Informal Assessment
☑ **Guided Discussion**

Did the student `REASONING`
- ❑ provide a clear explanation?
- ❑ communicate reasons and strategies?
- ❑ choose appropriate strategies?
- ❑ argue logically?

B Summarize Findings

Analyze and summarize assessment data for each student. Determine which Assessment Follow-Up is appropriate for each student. Use the Student Assessment Record in *Assessment* or *eAssess* to update assessment records.

Assessment page T41

C Assessment Follow-Up ● DIFFERENTIATE INSTRUCTION

Based on your observations, use these teaching strategies for assessment follow-up.

INTERVENTION

Review student performance on *Intervention* Lesson 9.A to see if students have mastered prerequisite skills for this lesson.

ENGLISH LEARNER

Review

Use Lesson 9.1 in *English Learner Support Guide* to review lesson concepts and vocabulary.

ENRICH

If . . . students are proficient in the lesson concepts,

Then . . . encourage them to work on chapter projects or *Enrichment* Lesson 9.1.

Enrichment Lesson 9.1

PRACTICE

If . . . students would benefit from additional practice,

Then . . . assign *Practice* Lesson 9.1.

Practice Lesson 9.1

RETEACH

If . . . students struggle with understanding metric measurements,

Then . . . have them work with a centimeter ruler and a meterstick to measure objects around the classroom and around the school. They need to develop a sense of how long a centimeter is and how long a meter is to be able to estimate these measurements. Encourage them to make the connection that the metric system is based on powers of ten.

Lesson Planner

OBJECTIVES
- To give students more experience with estimating, measuring, and problem solving using customary units of length
- To provide practice with measuring length to the nearest $\frac{1}{2}$ inch and $\frac{1}{4}$ inch
- To provide practice with simple unit conversions in the customary system

NCTM STANDARDS
Measurement
- Selecting and using benchmarks to estimate measurements
- Selecting and applying appropriate standard units to measure length
- Carrying out simple unit conversions

Problem Solving
Applying a variety of appropriate strategies to solve problems

MATERIALS
- *Response Wheels
- 12-inch rulers
- Yardsticks
- 20–25 pencils and pens of different lengths (in a box)

TECHNOLOGY
- Presentation Lesson 9.2
- MathTools Metric/Customary Conversion Tool
- Building Blocks Reptile Ruler

TEST PREP
Cumulative Review
- Mental Math reviews comparing fractions (Lesson 8.6).
- Problem 4 reviews perimeter (Lesson 3.6).

Multistep Problems
Problem 5

Extended Response
Problems 5 and 11

*Manipulative Kit Item

Customary Length

Context of the Lesson In Chapter 3 students reviewed estimating and measuring in inches and feet. This lesson provides more applications for measuring length in inches, feet, and yards and includes practice with measuring length to the nearest $\frac{1}{2}$ inch and $\frac{1}{4}$ inch. The focus of the next lesson is on measuring weight in grams and kilograms. See page 342B for Math Background for teachers for this lesson.

Planning for Learning ● DIFFERENTIATE INSTRUCTION

INTERVENTION
If . . . students lack the prerequisite skill of measuring in centimeters and inches,

Then . . . teach *Intervention* Lesson 9.A.

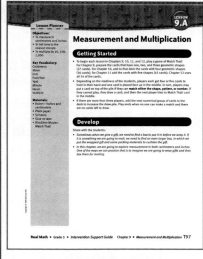

Intervention Lesson 9.A

ENGLISH LEARNER
Preview

If . . . students need language support,

Then . . . use Lesson 9.2 in *English Learner Support Guide* to preview lesson concepts and vocabulary.

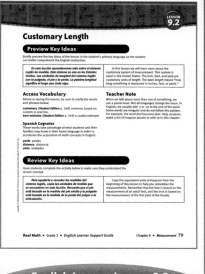

English Learner Lesson 9.2

ENRICH
If . . . students are proficient in the lesson concepts,

Then . . . have them design a wall table that lists and illustrates conversions for customary units of length.

PRACTICE
If . . . students would benefit from additional practice,

Then . . . extend Guided Discussion before assigning the student pages.

RETEACH
If . . . students are having difficulty using customary units to measure length,

Then . . . extend Skill Building (estimating and measuring in inches and feet) before assigning the student pages.

Vocabulary
foot\fu̇t\n. a customary measure of length equal to 12 inches
yard\yärd\n. a customary measure of length equal to 3 feet

Access Vocabulary
customary common, based on custom or practice
best estimate a careful estimate

Spanish Cognates
yards yardas
distance distancia
units unidades

Mental Math — 5

  As in the previous lesson, write pairs of fractions on the board, leaving a circle where the relation sign belongs. Have students show thumbs-up if the fraction on the left is greater than the fraction on the right, thumbs-down if it is less, and open hand if the fractions are equal. Possible examples include the following:

a. $\frac{1}{3} \bigcirc \frac{1}{8}$ up

b. $\frac{1}{8} \bigcirc \frac{1}{4}$ down

c. $\frac{1}{4} \bigcirc \frac{3}{4}$ down

d. $\frac{4}{8} \bigcirc \frac{1}{5}$ up

e. $\frac{1}{2} \bigcirc \frac{4}{8}$ open hand

f. $\frac{3}{4} \bigcirc \frac{1}{5}$ up

1 Develop — 30

Tell Students In Today's Lesson They Will

- review estimating and measuring length in inches and feet.
- measure length to the nearest $\frac{1}{2}$ inch and $\frac{1}{4}$ inch.
- decide whether to use inches, feet, or yards to measure various lengths.

Skill Building ENGAGING
Whole Group

Estimating and Measuring in Inches and Feet

 Guide students through the following activity in estimating and measuring in inches and feet. This activity was introduced in Lesson 3.5 and is reintroduced here to help students continue to refine their measurement skills. Spend an equal amount of time working with each of the two units.

1. Select an object or a student in the classroom, and ask students to estimate the object's or person's length in inches or feet.

2. Have students record their estimates or show them with their **Response Wheels.**

3. Have one or more students measure the object or the student to the nearest inch or foot, and report the measure to the class. When it seems appropriate, have students estimate and measure in feet *and* inches (for example, 4 feet, 2 inches).

4. Write the name of the object or the student and the corresponding measure on the board.

5. Repeat Steps 1 through 4 for other objects or students. For example, have students estimate and then measure the height of one student. Then ask a second student to stand next to the first student. Have students estimate and measure the height of the second student. Repeat with a third, fourth, and fifth student.

Skill Practice ENGAGING
Whole Group

Measuring to the Nearest $\frac{1}{2}$ Inch and $\frac{1}{4}$ Inch

1. Have each student choose a pen or a pencil from the box you prepared in advance.

2. Ask each student to use an inch ruler to measure the length of the pen or pencil to either the nearest $\frac{1}{2}$ inch or the nearest $\frac{1}{4}$ inch. Explain that as they measure, students should determine whether it makes more sense to report the measurement to the nearest $\frac{1}{2}$ inch or $\frac{1}{4}$ inch. Have students record their measurements on paper.

3. After students finish, ask questions to determine who recorded the shortest measurement. Have that student place his or her pen or pencil vertically on a long desk or table. Then call out measurements in $\frac{1}{4}$-inch intervals, starting with the shortest measurement, and have students place their pens or pencils in order of length next to the first pen or pencil. Say, for example, *Krista's pencil is $4\frac{1}{2}$ inches long. Does anyone else have a pencil or pen that is that long? How about $4\frac{3}{4}$ inches long?*

4. When all pens and pencils have been placed on the desk, have students check to see if the pattern matches their measurements. If any pens or pencils are out of order, have students measure those objects again and attempt to place them in the correct order.

Guided Discussion REASONING
Whole Group

1. Remind students there are 12 inches in 1 foot and 3 feet in 1 yard. Ask questions to assess students' abilities to select an appropriate unit of measure to determine the length of a given object. Possible examples include the following:

   ■ **Which unit would you use to measure the length of a stapler?** inch

   ■ **Which unit would you use to measure the height of a tree?** foot or yard

2 Assign Student Pages — 20

Pages 346–347 APPLYING
Small Group

Review the information at the top of page 346. Then allow students to work in small groups to answer the questions on pages 346 and 347. If students do not have time to research the actual distances on page 347, provide the distances to them after they have made their estimates. They will need the actual distances to correctly answer the questions that follow the chart.

As Students Finish

Building Blocks *Reptile Ruler*

 MathTools *Metric/Customary Conversion Tool* Have students explore converting customary units of length.

LESSON 9.2 Customary Length

Key Ideas

The inch, foot, and yard are customary units of length.

There are 12 inches in 1 foot.

12 in. = 1 ft

There are 3 feet in 1 yard.

There are 36 inches in 1 yard.

There are 1,760 yards in 1 mile.

3 feet or 1 yard

12 inches or 1 foot

Answer the following questions.

1. Edward was able to jump about 36 inches. How many feet is that? **3**

2. David's desk is 6 feet long. How many yards is that? **2**

3. Shawn's garden is about 3 yards long. How many feet is that? **9**

Review 4. Darlene wants to buy fencing for her tomato garden. The garden is shaped like a rectangle and is 3 yards wide and 6 yards long. How many yards of fencing does she need? **18**

Multistep 5. **Extended Response** The type of fence Darlene wants to buy is packaged in 6-foot rolls. How many rolls must she buy? Explain.

346   **Textbook** This lesson is available in the *eTextbook*.

REAL WORLD Shea Stadium is located in Flushing, New York. It is the home ballpark of the New York Mets.

Study the map of Shea Stadium. Then make your best estimates of the distances shown on the table. Check your estimates by researching the distances in an almanac or on the Internet.

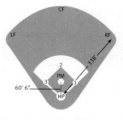

Distance	Estimate	Actual
Pitcher's mound to home plate		60 feet, 6 inches
Home plate to right field post		338 feet
First base to second base		6. 90 feet
Second base to third base		7. 90 feet
First base to third base		8. about 127 feet, 3 inches
Home plate to farthest point in center field		9. 410 feet

10. About how many yards is it from first base to second base? **30**

11. **Extended Response** How many yards is it from home plate to the farthest point in center field? Tell how you know. **about 130–140 yards; 410 feet divided by 3 feet equals about 137 yards.**

12. How many inches is it from first base to second base? How do you know? **1,080 inches; 12 × 90 = 1,080**

13. If you could draw lines from home plate to first base to second base to third base and back to home plate, what shape would you make? **a square**

14. About how far does a player run if he or she hits a home run? **a bit more than 360 feet because 4 × 90 = 360 and the player would run a bit more than that as he or she rounds the bases**

Chapter 9 • Lesson 2   347

---

3 Reflect 5

Guided Discussion **REASONING** Whole Group

1. Tell students that there are 5,280 feet in 1 mile. Ask students how they could determine how many yards are in 1 mile. Students should suggest dividing 5,280 by 3 because there are 3 feet in 1 yard. If students are unsure of how to do this because they have divided only three-digit numbers, help them to see that they can divide 528 by 3 and multiply the quotient by 10. The answer is 1,760 yards.

2. Have students work in pairs to convert customary units of length. Ask questions such as the following:

- **How many feet are there in $\frac{1}{2}$ mile?** 2,640
- **How many yards are there in $\frac{1}{2}$ mile?** 880
- **How many yards are there in 2 miles?** 3,520
- **How many feet are there in 2 miles?** 10,560

Extended Response

Problem 5 The answer is 9. Students should explain that Darlene needs 18 yards of fencing, which is equal to 54 feet (there are 3 feet in 1 yard, and 18 × 3 = 54). Because thare are 6 feet in each roll of fencing, she needs 9 rolls of fencing because 54 ÷ 6 = 9.

REAL WORLD Curriculum Connection: Students may wish to do research to find the height in feet of the top five tallest buildings in the world.

Review Cumulative Review: For cumulative review of previously learned skills, see page 354–355.

Family Involvement: Assign the *Practice, Reteach,* or *Enrichment* activities depending on the needs of your students.

Encourage students to practice measuring the lengths of various items in inches, feet, and yards with a friend or a relative.

Concept/Question Board: Have students look for additional examples using measurement in inches, feet, and yards and post them on the Concept/Question Board.

Math Puzzler: Vinny had 5 sticks that he laid end to end. He measured the total length, which was 50 centimeters. He got 2 more sticks of the same length from his friend Freddie and added them to his 5 sticks. What was the length of the 7 sticks altogether? **70 cm: 50 ÷ 5 = 10; 10 × 2 = 20; 50 + 20 = 70**

Chapter 9 • Lesson 2   **346–347**

Assess and Differentiate

 Assess Use **eAssess** to record and analyze evidence of student understanding.

Gather Evidence

Use the Daily Class Assessment Records in **Assessment** or **eAssess** to record daily observations.

Informal Assessment
☑ **Skill Practice**

Did the student **ENGAGING**
- ❑ pay attention to others' contributions?
- ❑ contribute information and ideas?
- ❑ improve on a strategy?
- ❑ reflect on and check the accuracy of his or her work?

Informal Assessment
☑ **Guided Discussion**

Did the student **REASONING**
- ❑ provide a clear explanation?
- ❑ communicate reasons and strategies?
- ❑ choose appropriate strategies?
- ❑ argue logically?

B Summarize Findings

Analyze and summarize assessment data for each student. Determine which Assessment Follow-Up is appropriate for each student. Use the Student Assessment Record in **Assessment** or **eAssess** to update assessment records.

Assessment page T41

Assessment Follow-Up • DIFFERENTIATE INSTRUCTION

Based on your observations, use these teaching strategies for assessment follow-up.

INTERVENTION

Review student performance on **Intervention** Lesson 9.A to see if students have mastered prerequisite skills for this lesson.

ENGLISH LEARNER

Review

Use Lesson 9.2 in **English Learner Support Guide** to review lesson concepts and vocabulary.

ENRICH

If . . . students are proficient in the lesson concepts,

Then . . . encourage them to work on chapter projects or **Enrichment** Lesson 9.2.

Enrichment Lesson 9.2

PRACTICE

If . . . students would benefit from additional practice,

Then . . . assign **Practice** Lesson 9.2.

Practice Lesson 9.2

RETEACH

If . . . students struggle with measuring length in customary units,

Then . . . have them use a ruler and a yardstick to measure objects around the classroom and the school. Have them write their measurements in inches, in feet and in yards, as appropriate. Discuss with them the fact that converting between customary measurements is not as easy as converting between metric measurements. Encourage them to copy the conversion amounts into their notebooks for easy reference.

Lesson Planner

OBJECTIVES
- To give students experience with estimating, measuring, and problem solving using metric units of weight
- To provide practice with simple unit conversions in the metric system

NCTM STANDARDS
Measurement
- Selecting and using benchmarks to estimate measurements
- Selecting and applying appropriate standard units to measure weight
- Carrying out simple unit conversions

Problem Solving
Applying a variety of appropriate strategies to solve problems

MATERIALS

- *Response Wheels
- Platform scale
- Small spring scale or double-pan balance
- Metric weights
- **Checkbook Game Mat**

TECHNOLOGY
- **ⓔPresentation** Lesson 9.3
- **ⓔMathTools** Metric/Customary Conversion Tool

TEST PREP
Cumulative Review
Mental Math reviews adding fractions (Lesson 8.7).

Extended Response
Problem 24

Writing + Math
Journal

Metric Weight

Context of the Lesson This is the third lesson in a sequence of six lessons that focus on metric and customary measures. In this lesson students estimate and measure in grams and kilograms and learn to convert between the two units. A parallel lesson using ounces and pounds follows, but at this time we do not ask students to convert between systems. Rather, we ask them to think in metric units now and think in customary units in the next lesson. Later, in fourth grade, we do include lessons on converting between systems. Students were introduced to grams and kilograms in the second grade program.

See page 342B for Math Background for teachers for this lesson.

Planning for Learning ● DIFFERENTIATE INSTRUCTION

INTERVENTION
If . . . students lack the prerequisite skill of multiplying by 10, 100, and 1,000,

Then . . . teach *Intervention* Lesson 9.C.

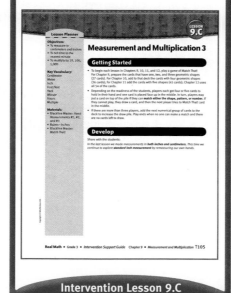

Intervention Lesson 9.C

ENGLISH LEARNER
Preview

If . . . students need language support,

Then . . . use Lesson 9.3 in *English Learner Support Guide* to preview lesson concepts and vocabulary.

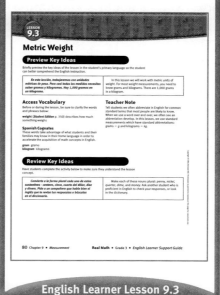

English Learner Lesson 9.3

ENRICH
If . . . students are proficient in the lesson concepts,

Then . . . allow them time for playing a game of their choice from a previous lesson.

PRACTICE
If . . . students would benefit from additional practice,

Then . . . extend Skill Building before assigning the student pages.

RETEACH
If . . . students are having difficulty using metric units to measure weight,

Then . . . extend Guided Discussion before assigning the student pages.

Vocabulary	Access Vocabulary	Spanish Cognates
kilogram\kē´lō\ *n.* a metric measure of weight equal to 1,000 grams	**weight** describes how much something weighs	**gram** gramo **kilogram** kilogramo

Mental Math 5

  Write addition statements with fractions on the board. Have students show the sums on their **Response Wheels** by using a finger to indicate the fraction bar. Possible examples include the following:

a. $\frac{1}{2} + \frac{1}{2} = 1$

b. $\frac{1}{4} + \frac{1}{4} = \frac{1}{2}$

c. $\frac{1}{2} + \frac{1}{4} = \frac{3}{4}$

d. $\frac{1}{3} + \frac{1}{3} = \frac{2}{3}$

e. $\frac{1}{8} + \frac{1}{8} = \frac{1}{4}$

f. $\frac{1}{6} + \frac{1}{6} + \frac{1}{6} = \frac{1}{2}$

1 Develop 25

Tell Students In Today's Lesson They Will

estimate and measure weight in grams and kilograms.

Guided Discussion UNDERSTANDING   Whole Group

1. Have appropriate weighing instruments available. This will include a platform scale for weighing heavy objects and a small spring scale or double-pan balance for weighing lighter objects.

2. Think aloud as you weigh a few objects using the appropriate scales, and report the weights to the class using gram and kilogram units. Use examples such as the following:
   - This stack of three textbooks weighs about 3 kilograms.
   - This notebook weighs about 247 grams. That's just about $\frac{1}{4}$ of 1 kilogram.
   - Two notebooks must weigh about $\frac{1}{2}$ of 1 kilogram, or 500 grams. Let's see if that is correct. (Weigh the two notebooks.) Yes, together they weigh a bit less than 500 grams.

3. Tell students that there are 1,000 grams in 1 kilogram, and spend a few minutes helping students learn how to convert between the two units.

Skill Building   ENGAGING   Whole Group

Estimating and Measuring in Grams and Kilograms

  Guide students through the following activity in estimating and measuring in grams and kilograms.

1. Select an object in the classroom, and ask students to estimate its weight in grams or kilograms.

2. Have students show their estimates with their **Response Wheels.**

3. Have one or more students measure the object to the nearest gram or kilogram and report the measure to the class.

4. Write the name of the object and its corresponding measure on the board.

5. Choose an object related to the first object (for example, if the first object was a book, choose a different-sized book as the second object), and have students estimate and measure to check again.

6. Repeat the activity several times to allow students time to refine their estimates.

2 Assign Student Pages 25

Pages 348–349 APPLYING   Small Group

Before asking students to complete pages 348–349, have a volunteer use a double-pan balance to determine the approximate weight, in grams, of 10 nickels. about 50 grams Record this weight on the board. Then have students complete pages 348–349 independently.

Monitoring Student Progress

| **If . . .** students consistently give wrong answers during the Skill-Building activity, | **Then . . .** distinguish between those students who cannot estimate with reasonable accuracy and those whose estimates are contrary to reason. Students in the former category will benefit from additional practice. Students in the latter category will likely need individual tutoring on the use of weighing instruments followed by practice with estimating and measuring to check. |

As Students Finish

 Checkbook Game (introduced in lesson 2.6)

 MathTools *Metric/Customary Conversion Tool* Have students explore converting metric units of weight.

LESSON 9.3 Metric Weight

Key Ideas

The gram and the kilogram are metric units of weight.

There are 1,000 grams in 1 kilogram.

1,000 g = 1 kg

Convert each measure from kilograms to grams or from grams to kilograms. Write the new measure.

1. ☐ g = 5 kg   5,000
2. ☐ g = 2 kg   2,000
3. 1 kg = ☐ g   1,000
4. 4 kg = ☐ g   4,000
5. 6 kg = ☐ g   6,000
6. ☐ g = 3 kg   3,000
7. ☐ g = 10 kg   10,000
8. 11 kg = ☐ g   11,000

Write whether you would use grams or kilograms to report the weight of each of the following.

9. a slice of bread   grams
10. an adult cat   kilograms
11. a dime   grams
12. a bag of groceries   kilograms

Textbook This lesson is available in the *eTextbook*.

Copy and complete the table.

Number of Nickels	Weight (grams)	Number of Dollars
20	about 100	1
100	13 about 500	5
1,000	14 about 5,000	50
2,000	15 about 10,000	100
10,000	16 about 50,000	500
100,000	17 about 500,000	5,000

Write the weight in kilograms.

18. 1,000 nickels = about ☐ kilograms   5
19. 2,000 nickels = about ☐ kilograms   10
20. 3,000 nickels = about ☐ kilograms   15
21. 10,000 nickels = about ☐ kilograms   50
22. 100,000 nickels = about ☐ kilograms   500
23. 1000,000 nickels = about ☐ kilograms   5,000
24. **Extended Response** Because 1 nickel weighs about 5 grams, do you think 1 dime weighs about 10 grams? Why or why not?   no; A dime is clearly smaller and lighter than a nickel, so it could not possibly weigh 10 grams.

Writing + Math **Journal**

One penny weighs about $2\frac{1}{2}$ grams. If most third-grade students can carry about 2,000 nickels (10 kilograms), about how many pennies do you think you can carry? Explain your answer. How much money is that?

See *Teacher's Edition* for explanation.

---

3 Reflect   5

Guided Discussion ✓ REASONING   Whole Group

1. Discuss the methods students used to find the answer to the Journal question on student page 349. For example, they may have determined that 4 pennies weigh about 10 grams ($2\frac{1}{2} + 2\frac{1}{2} + 2\frac{1}{2} + 2\frac{1}{2} = 10$), and because there are 10,000 grams in 10 kilograms, they multiplied 4 by 1,000 to get 4,000 pennies. To find the amount of money in pennies, students should have remembered that there are 100 pennies in $1 and 1,000 pennies in $10, so there are 4,000 pennies in $40 ($10 + $10 + $10 + $10 = $40).

2. Have students try lifting a stack of 5 textbooks that each weigh about 4 kilograms (or 2 pounds) to see if they could, in fact, carry 2,000 nickels or 4,000 pennies.

Writing + Math **Journal**

Students should explain that because the weight of a penny is one-half the weight of a nickel, most third-grade students can probably carry about 4,000 pennies (4,000 is twice as many as 2,000). The amount of money in pennies is $40.

Review **Cumulative Review:** For cumulative review of previously learned skills, see page 354–355.

Family Involvement: Assign the **Practice, Reteach,** or **Enrichment** activities depending on the needs of your students.

Encourage students to practice measuring the weight of various items in grams and kilograms with a friend or a relative.

Concept/Question Board: Have students look for additional examples using measurement in grams and kilograms and post them on the Concept/Question a Board.

Math Puzzler: Write the following patterns on the board, and have students give the answers.

2, 4, 8, 16, _____ 32

3, 9, 6, 18, 15, _____ 45

87, 77, 67, _____ 57

Assess and Differentiate

e Assess Use *eAssess* to record and analyze evidence of student understanding.

A Gather Evidence

Use the Daily Class Assessment Records in *Assessment* or *eAssess* to record daily observations.

Informal Assessment
☑ **Skill Building**

Did the student **ENGAGING**
- ❏ pay attention to others' contributions?
- ❏ contribute information and ideas?
- ❏ improve on a strategy?
- ❏ reflect on and check the accuracy of his or her work?

Informal Assessment
☑ **Guided Discussion**

Did the student **REASONING**
- ❏ provide a clear explanation?
- ❏ communicate reasons and strategies?
- ❏ choose appropriate strategies?
- ❏ argue logically?

B Summarize Findings

Analyze and summarize assessment data for each student. Determine which Assessment Follow-Up is appropriate for each student. Use the Student Assessment Record in *Assessment* or *eAssess* to update assessment records.

Assessment page T41

C Assessment Follow-Up ● DIFFERENTIATE INSTRUCTION

Based on your observations, use these teaching strategies for assessment follow-up.

INTERVENTION

Review student performance on *Intervention* Lesson 9.C to see if students have mastered prerequisite skills for this lesson.

ENGLISH LEARNER

Review

Use Lesson 9.3 in *English Learner Support Guide* to review lesson concepts and vocabulary.

ENRICH

If . . . students are proficient in the lesson concepts,

Then . . . encourage them to work on chapter projects or *Enrichment* Lesson 9.3.

Enrichment Lesson 9.3

PRACTICE

If . . . students would benefit from additional practice,

Then . . . assign *Practice* Lesson 9.3.

Practice Lesson 9.3

RETEACH

If . . . students struggle with weighing objects,

Then . . . have them work in teams to learn how to use a pan balance. Make sure they have the balance calibrated correctly and use the appropriate masses. Each student should have a chance to weigh a variety of objects. Encourage students to handle each of the weights so that they can get a feel for how much a gram is and how much a kilogram is. Remind them that converting between the metric weights is just like converting between the metric lengths.

Lesson Planner

OBJECTIVES
- To give students experience with estimating, measuring, and problem solving using customary units of weight
- To provide practice with simple unit conversions in the customary system

NCTM STANDARDS

Measurement
- Selecting and using benchmarks to estimate measurements
- Selecting and applying appropriate standard units to measure weight
- Carrying out simple unit conversions

Problem Solving
Applying a variety of appropriate strategies to solve problems

MATERIALS

- *Response Wheels
- Platform scale
- Small spring scale or double-pan balance
- Customary weights
- Shopping Game Mat

TECHNOLOGY
[e] **Presentation** Lesson 9.4
[e] **MathTools** Metric/Customary Conversion Tool

TEST PREP

Cumulative Review
Mental Math reviews subtracting fractions (Lesson 8.7).

Looking Ahead

For the next lesson, you will need the following materials: one 1-liter soda bottle (label removed), one 2-liter soda bottle (label removed), one clear 1-liter (4-cup) measuring cup, one small graduated cylinder (for measuring in milliliters), a pitcher of water, and various sizes of plastic containers used for food and other grocery products.

*Manipulative Kit Item

Customary Weight

Context of the Lesson This is the fourth lesson in a sequence of six lessons that focus on customary and metric units of measure. In this lesson students estimate and measure in ounces and pounds. They also learn to convert between them, but at this time are not expected to use standard algorithms for doing so. The preceding lesson dealt with grams and kilograms in a parallel manner. The next lessons in this chapter deal with estimating and measuring capacity. This lesson contains a Mastery Checkpoint.

See page 342B for Math Background for teachers for this lesson.

Planning for Learning · DIFFERENTIATE INSTRUCTION

INTERVENTION

If . . . students lack the prerequisite skill of measuring in centimeters and inches,

Then . . . teach *Intervention* Lesson 9.A.

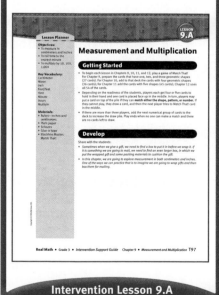

Intervention Lesson 9.A

ENGLISH LEARNER

Preview

If . . . students need language support,

Then . . . use Lesson 9.4 in *English Learner Support Guide* to preview lesson concepts and vocabulary.

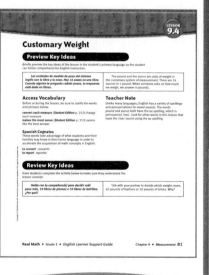

English Learner Lesson 9.4

ENRICH

If . . . students are proficient in the lesson concepts,

Then . . . emphasize chapter projects.

PRACTICE

If . . . students would benefit from additional practice,

Then . . . extend Skill Building before assigning the student pages.

RETEACH

If . . . students are having difficulty using customary units to measure weight,

Then . . . extend Guided Discussion before assigning the student pages.

Vocabulary
pound \paund\ *n.* a customary measure of weight equal to 16 ounces

Access Vocabulary
convert each measure change each measure
makes the most sense seems like the best answer

Spanish Cognates
to convert convertir
to report reportar

Mental Math 5

Write subtraction statements with fractions on the board. Have students show the differences on their **Response Wheels** by using a finger to indicate the fraction bar. Possible examples include the following:

a. $\frac{3}{4} - \frac{1}{4} = \frac{1}{2}$ **b.** $\frac{1}{2} - \frac{1}{4} = \frac{1}{4}$

c. $\frac{3}{4} - \frac{1}{2} = \frac{1}{4}$ **d.** $1 - \frac{1}{4} = \frac{3}{4}$

e. $1 - \frac{3}{4} = \frac{1}{4}$ **f.** $1 - \frac{1}{3} = \frac{2}{3}$

1 Develop 25

Tell Students In Today's Lesson They Will

estimate and measure weight in ounces and pounds.

Guided Discussion UNDERSTANDING Whole Group

1. As in the previous lesson, have a platform scale available for weighing heavy objects and a small spring scale or double-pan balance available for weighing lighter objects, but use customary weights (oz. and lb.).
2. Think aloud as you weigh a few objects using the appropriate scales, and report the weights to the class using pound and ounce units. Use examples such as the following:
   - This stack of three textbooks weighs about 6 pounds.
   - This notebook weighs about 8 ounces. That's just about $\frac{1}{2}$ of 1 pound.
   - Two notebooks must weigh about 1 pound. Let's see if that is correct. (Weigh the two notebooks.) Yes, together they weigh about 1 pound—perhaps a bit more.
3. Tell students that there are 16 ounces in 1 pound, and spend a few minutes helping students learn how to convert between the two units.

Skill Building ENGAGING Whole Group

Estimating and Measuring in Ounces and Pounds

 Guide students through the following activity in estimating and measuring in ounces and pounds.

1. Select an object in the classroom, and ask students to estimate its weight in ounces or pounds.
2. Have students show their estimates with their **Response Wheels.**
3. Have one or more students measure the object to the nearest ounce or pound and report the measure to the class.
4. Write the name of the object and its corresponding measure on the board.
5. Choose an object related to the first object (for example, if the first object was a book, choose a different-sized book as the second object), and have students estimate and measure to check again.
6. Repeat the activity several times to allow students time to refine their estimates.

2 Assign Student Pages 20

Pages 350–351 APPLYING

Have students complete pages 350–351 independently. Make sure students understand that the photographs on page 351 represent life-sized people, animals, and objects.

Monitoring Student Progress

| **If . . .** students give estimates that are contrary to reason, | **Then . . .** those students will likely need individual instruction with the use of weighing instruments followed by practice with estimating weight—perhaps for just 2 to 3 minutes a day. |

As Students Finish

 Shopping Game (introduced in Lesson 7.1)

 **Metric/Customary Conversion Tool** Have students explore converting customary units of weight.

LESSON 9.4 Customary Weight

Key Ideas

The ounce and the pound are customary units of weight.

There are 16 ounces in 1 pound.

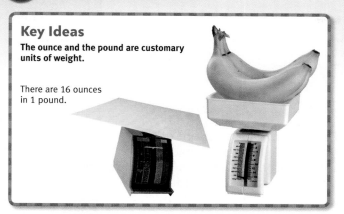

Convert each measure from pounds to ounces or from ounces to pounds. Write the new measure.

① 2 lb = ☐ oz   32
② 10 lb = ☐ oz   160
③ 8 oz = ☐ lb $\frac{1}{2}$
④ 24 oz = ☐ lb $1\frac{1}{2}$
⑤ 4 lb = ☐ oz   64
⑥ 8 lb = ☐ oz   128
⑦ 100 lb = ☐ oz   1,600
⑧ 50 lb = ☐ oz   800

Write whether you would use ounces or pounds to report the weight of each of the following.

⑨ a bag of flour   ounces or pounds
⑩ a paper clip   ounces
⑪ an adult dog   pounds
⑫ a toothbrush   ounces

350   **Textbook** This lesson is available in the *eTextbook*.

Choose the number that makes the most sense.

⑬ weighs about ☐ pounds
   a. 10   **b.** 100   **c.** 1,000

⑭ weighs about ☐ pounds
   a. 2   **b.** 25   **c.** 250

⑮ weighs about ☐ ounces
   a. 32   **b.** 16   **c.** 1

⑯ weighs about ☐ ounces
   a. 25   **b.** 250   **c.** 2,500

⑰ weighs about ☐ pounds
   a. 400   **b.** 40   **c.** 4

⑱ weighs about ☐ ounces
   a. 10   **b.** 100   **c.** 1,000

---

3 Reflect   10

Guided Discussion REASONING   Whole Group

Discuss how students determined their answers for student page 351. If students do not mention a systematic method, point out that they could proceed by comparing each picture in the following way:

- You can determine that the horse weighs about 1,000 pounds because an adult horse weighs much more than an adult person, who on average weighs more than 100 pounds and less than 200 pounds.
- An adult beagle must weigh about 25 pounds because a beagle clearly weighs much less than an adult person and much more than 2 pounds.
- A glue stick clearly weighs less than 1 pound (16 ounces), so it must weigh a little more than 1 ounce.

Continue this line of thinking for the remaining pictures on the page, and have students contribute ideas as you proceed.

☑ Use Mastery Checkpoint 18 found in *Assessment* to evaluate student mastery of measuring length and weight. By this time, students should be able to correctly answer eighty percent of the Mastery Checkpoint items.

REAL WORLD **Curriculum Connection:** Have students weigh small objects they find in their homes and report their measures to the class.

Review **Cumulative Review:** For cumulative review of previously learned skills, see page 354–355.

Family Involvement: Assign the *Practice, Reteach,* or *Enrichment* activities depending on the needs of your students.

Encourage students to practice measuring the weight of various items in ounces and pounds with a friend or a relative.

Math **Concept/Question Board:** Have students look for additional examples using measurement in ounces and pounds and post them on the Concept/Question Board.

Math Puzzler: Tara starts at 5 and counts up by 7s. Trent starts at 52 and counts down by 5s. What numbers do Tara and Trent both say? 12, 47

4 Assess and Differentiate

eAssess Use **eAssess** to record and analyze evidence of student understanding.

A Gather Evidence

Use the Daily Class Assessment Records in **Assessment** or **eAssess** to record daily observations.

Formal Assessment

☑ **Mastery Checkpoint**

Did the student
- ❑ use correct procedures?
- ❑ respond with at least 80% accuracy?

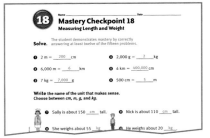

Assessment Page T71

B Summarize Findings

Analyze and summarize assessment data for each student. Determine which Assessment Follow-Up is appropriate for each student. Use the Student Assessment Record in **Assessment** or **eAssess** to update assessment records.

Assessment Page T41

C Assessment Follow-Up ● DIFFERENTIATE INSTRUCTION

Based on your observations, use these teaching strategies for assessment follow-up.

INTERVENTION

Review student performance on **Intervention** Lesson 9.A to see if students have mastered prerequisite skills for this lesson.

ENGLISH LEARNER

Review

Use Lesson 9.4 in **English Learner Support Guide** to review lesson concepts and vocabulary.

ENRICH

If . . . students are proficient in the lesson concepts,

Then . . . encourage them to work on chapter projects or **Enrichment** Lesson 9.4.

Enrichment Lesson 9.4

PRACTICE

If . . . students would benefit from additional practice,

Then . . . assign **Practice** Lesson 9.4.

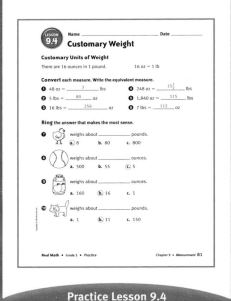

Practice Lesson 9.4

RETEACH

If . . . students struggle with understanding customary weights,

Then . . . have them bring in examples of different weights from home. Cans of soup, boxes of mix, or bags of chips will give them a sense of common weights. Provide examples of other weights they may not see at home. You may be able to borrow large bags of potatoes or other pre-marked food items from the cafeteria. Avoid weighing students or comparing weights to body weight.

Exploring Problem Solving

Objectives
- To analyze the Make a Diagram and Write an Equation strategies
- To provide practice with measurement, computation, and algebraic thinking
- To provide practice solving and analyzing solutions to a real-world, nonroutine problem

Materials
- Cubes
- Graph paper

Context of the Lesson This lesson provides an opportunity for students to apply what they have been learning about measurement in this chapter and what they learned about division in Chapter 7. The lesson also continues the camping theme introduced in the Chapter Introduction.

1 Develop 5

Tell Students In Today's Lesson They Will
- figure out how many campsites will fit in a new campground.
- look at how two students are trying two different strategies to solve the problem.
- solve the problem themselves and share how they did it.

Guided Discussion
Have students talk about camping experiences they have had. Ask questions such as the following:

■ **Have you ever been camping?**

■ **What do people usually bring with them for camping?** Possible answers: tents, sleeping bags, food

■ **What might you find at a campsite?** Possible answers: a campfire, fishing equipment, backpacks

■ **Why would people want to camp at a campsite?** Possible answers: to relax, to be outdoors, to do something new

---

Exploring Problem Solving

The owners of Cherry Lake are going to build a campground. They plan to put campsites around three sides of the lake. Each campsite will be a square 10 meters wide. How many campsites will fit?

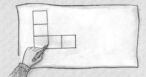

200 meters
200 meters
200 meters

Cherry Lake

N

❷ Possible answer: The diagram helps her see that a corner campsite is part of two sides, and she should be careful not to count it twice.

❸ Possible answer: She could divide to figure out how many campsites are in each section.

Gloria made a diagram to solve the problem

Think about Gloria's strategy. Answer the following questions.

❶ What do the squares in Gloria's diagram represent? campsites

❷ How could Gloria use her diagram to help solve the problem?

❸ How could Gloria solve the problem without drawing every campsite?

352   📱Textbook This lesson is available in the *eTextbook*.

James wrote an equation to solve the problem.

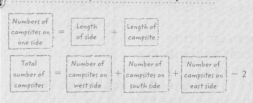

| Numbers of campsites on one side | = | Length of side | ÷ | Length of campsite |

| Total number of campsites | = | Number of campsites on west side | + | Number of campsites on south side | + | Number of campsites on east side | − 2 |

Think about James's strategy. Answer the following questions.

❹ Does James's first equation make sense? Why or why not? yes; Dividing the total length by the length of each piece tells you how many pieces will fit.

❺ What numbers should James use in his first equation to find the number of campsites along one side of the lake? 200 for the length of a side and 10 for the length of a campsite

❻ In James's second equation, why is he subtracting 2 from the sum? When you add the campsites on each side, you are counting the 2 corner campsites twice.

❼ How might James write his equation in a shorter way?

❽ Finish solving the problem. Use Gloria's strategy, James's strategy, or a strategy of your own.   58 campsites

❾ What strategy did you use? Why?

❿ How many fewer campsites would fit if each campsite was 20 meters wide instead of 10 meters wide? 30 fewer; Only 28 would fit instead of 58.

❼ Possible answer: He could use a letter or a word or two instead of several words, such as *W*, *west*, or *west sites* for the number of campsites on the west side.

❾ Possible answer: James's strategy helped me keep track of how the different quantities in the problem are related.

Chapter 9 • Exploring Problem Solving   353

Using Student Pages

As students look at the illustration on page 352, have them follow in their books as you read the problem together.

Analyzing Sample Solution 1

Guide students through Gloria's solution by reviewing Problems 1–3.

Gloria could keep drawing squares until she has enough to make a row 200 meters long. She could count by tens to keep track. Gloria could draw her diagram on graph paper and let each space stand for 10 meters.

In discussion, bring out the following points:

- Gloria's diagram helps her see that a corner campsite is part of two sides and that she should be careful not to count it twice.
- There are many ways that drawing a diagram can help solve a problem. It can help you understand the problem. It can help you think of a shorter way to solve the problem.
- Flexible thinking helps solve problems. For example, because you start using a strategy does not mean you cannot change. Often one strategy gives you an idea for using a completely different strategy or a different version of the one you are using.

Analyzing Sample Solution 2

Guide students through James's strategy by reviewing Problems 4–7. In discussion, bring out these points:

- Equations can help students keep track of how the different quantities in a problem are related.
- Equations can be a useful guide for doing computations, especially when there are several computations.
- Equations can be written in many different forms. It is important that students make them clear enough to be helpful for them.
- Equations should model the problem accurately. The relationships among the parts of the equation should be the same as the relationships among those parts of the problem.

Have students work individually or in groups on Problems 8–10.

Students who finish early may make up and exchange their own campground word problems.

Reflect 10

Effective Communication Have individuals or groups present their solutions, especially those that used methods that are different from the methods shown on pages 352 and 353.

In discussion, bring out the following points:

- Diagrams do not need to be artistic. Students should try to make diagrams that represent the relationships in the problem in a clear enough way to help them solve the problem.
- Equations can be a handy way to outline a problem because they can show how the pieces of the problem fit together.
- Whatever form you use for equations, check that the equation matches what is in the problem.
- Good problem solvers look for efficient methods for solving problems.

Sample Solutions Strategies

Students might use one or more of these strategies instead of or in conjunction with the strategies presented on pages 352 and 353.

Use Mental Math

Students might realize that $200 \div 10$ is the same as $20 \div 1$ and determine that there would be 20 campsites per side. They could then multiply 20 by 3 (for each side) and get 60. They might then subtract the 2 corners and get 58.

Students might decide that the east and west sides have 19 campsites each, and the south side has 20. To add $19 + 19$ mentally, they could think: $20 + 20 = 40$, so $19 + 19$ is 2 less, or 38. They can then add 20 to 38 mentally to get 58.

Make a Physical Model

Students might use cubes to represent the campsites. They can count by tens as they lay down the first row of cubes until they get to 200.

Guess, Check, and Revise

Students might guess how many campsites will fit along a side and then skip count or multiply to check.

Assess 15

When evaluating student work, focus on whether students thought rationally about the problem and the solutions. Questions to consider include the following:

- Did the student understand the problem?
- Did the student understand the sample solutions?
- Did the student persist when stuck?
- Did the student use operations appropriately?
- Did the student check to see that answers made sense?

Although expressing mathematical ideas is an ability that continues to develop over time, by this stage you should begin to see signs of improvement in most students.

Cumulative Review

Assign Pages 354–355

Use this Cumulative Review as a review of concepts and skills that students have previously learned.

Here are different ways that you can assign these problems to your students as they work through the chapter:

- With some of the lessons in the chapter, assign a set of cumulative review problems to be completed as practice or for homework.
  Lesson 9.1—Problems 1–4
  Lesson 9.2—Problems 5–10
  Lesson 9.3—Problems 11–14
  Lesson 9.4—Problem 15
- At any point during the chapter, assign part or all of the cumulative review problems to be completed as practice or for homework.

Cumulative Review

Problems 1–4 review lengths in inches, feet, and yards, Lesson 3.5.

Problems 5–10 review fractions of sets, Lesson 8.3.

Problems 11–14 review converting customary lengths, Lesson 9.2.

Problem 15 reviews multiplying two-digit numbers by one-digit numbers, Lesson 7.2.

Monitoring Student Progress

If . . . students miss more than one problem in a section,

Then . . . refer to the indicated lesson for remediation suggestions.

Cumulative Review

Measuring Length—Inches, Feet, and Yards Lesson 3.5

Solve these problems.

1. **Extended Response** Angel put his tent 5 yards from the creek. Sofía put her tent 15 feet from the creek. Whose tent is closer to the creek? Neither tent is closer. They are the same distance from the creek.

2. How do you know? There are 3 feet in 1 yard, so both tents are 15 feet or 5 yards away.

3. Taylor has a wooden board that is 1 yard long. He needs pieces that are 6 inches long. How many 6-inch pieces can he get from the board? 6

4. How long will the leftover piece be? There won't be any left over.

Fractions of Sets Lesson 8.3

What fraction is colored?

5. $\frac{3}{5}$

8. $\frac{3}{4}$

6. $\frac{1}{5}$

9. $\frac{5}{5}$ or 1 whole

7.  $\frac{1}{3}$

10. $\frac{2}{5}$

354　Textbook This lesson is available in the *eTextbook*.

Customary Length Lesson 9.2

3 feet = 1 yard

Answer the following questions.

11. Élan has a rope that is 72 inches long. How many feet is that? 6

12. Fátima must stay 6 feet from the campfire. How many yards is that? 2

13. My family's camper is about 6 yards long. How many feet is that? 18

14. Each table is 6 feet or 2 yards long. There are 3 tables; $3 \times 2 = 6$ yards.

14. **Extended Response** For her camping trip, Jo wants to make tablecloths for the picnic tables. There will be 3 picnic tables at her campsite. Each table is 6 *feet* long. How many *yards* of fabric does she need? Explain your answer. 6

Multiplying Two-Digit Numbers by One-Digit Numbers Lesson 7.2

Read the problem, and answer the question.

15. The Cho family wants to buy a tarp to put under their tent. One tarp is 2 yards long and 2 yards wide. Another tarp is 3 yards long and 3 yards wide. The tent is 90 inches by 108 inches. Which tarp will be closer in size to covering the bottom of the tent completely?

a. 2 yards by 2 yards

b. 3 yards by 3 yards

Individual Oral Assessment

Purpose of the Test

The Individual Oral Assessment is designed to measure students' growing knowledge of chapter concepts. It is administered individually to each student, and it requires oral responses from each student. The test takes about five minutes to complete.

See **Assessment** for detailed instructions for administering and interpreting the test, and for recording students' answers on the Student Assessment Recording Sheet.

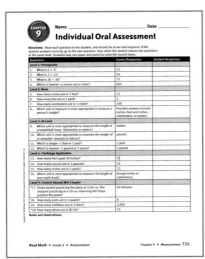

Assessment Page T35

Directions

Read each question to the student, and record his or her oral response. If the student answers correctly, go to the next question. Stop when the student misses two questions at the same level. Students should not use scrap paper.

Materials

None

Questions

Level 1: Prerequisite

1. What is 4 × 3? 12
2. What is 2 × 12? 24
3. What is 36 + 36? 72
4. Which is heavier, a house cat or a lion? lion

Level 2: Basic

5. How many inches are in 1 foot? 12
6. How many feet are in 1 yard? 3
7. How many centimeters are in 1 meter? 100
8. Which unit of measure is most appropriate for measuring a person's height? Possible answers include inches, feet and inches, centimeters, or meters.

Level 3: At Level

9. Which unit is more appropriate for measuring the height of a basketball hoop, kilometers or meters? meters
10. Which unit is more appropriate for measuring the weight of a computer, pounds or ounces? pounds
11. Which is longer, 1 foot or 1 yard? 1 yard
12. Which is heavier, 1 pound or 1 ounce? 1 pound

Level 4: Challenge Application

13. How many feet equal 30 inches? $2\frac{1}{2}$
14. How many ounces are in 2 pounds? 32
15. How many inches are in 2 yards? 72
16. Which unit is most appropriate for measuring the length of your math book? Accept inches or centimeters.

Level 5: Content beyond Mid-Chapter

17. Tonya started practicing the piano at 3:30 P.M. She stopped practicing at 4:10 P.M. How long did Tonya practice the piano? 40 minutes
18. How many pints are in 4 quarts? 8
19. How many milliliters are in 3 liters? 3,000
20. How many dimes are in $7.00? 70

Lesson Planner

OBJECTIVES
- To give students experience with estimating and measuring using metric units of capacity
- To provide measurement applications for metric capacity
- To provide practice with simple unit conversions in the metric system

NCTM STANDARDS
Measurement
- Selecting and using benchmarks to estimate measurements
- Selecting and applying appropriate standard units to measure capacity
- Carrying out simple unit conversions

Problem Solving
Applying a variety of appropriate strategies to solve problems

MATERIALS

- *Response Wheels
- One 1-liter soda bottle (label removed)
- One 2-liter soda bottle (label removed)
- One clear 1-liter measuring cylinder
- Small graduated cylinder (for measuring in milliliters)
- Pitcher of water
- Various sizes of plastic containers (labels removed)

TECHNOLOGY
- e Presentation Lesson 9.5
- e MathTools Metric/Customary Conversion Tool
- e Games *Roll a 15 Game*

TEST PREP
Cumulative Review
- Mental Math reviews comparing fractions greater than a whole (Lesson 8.9).
- Problem 9 reviews multidigit multiplication (Chapter 7).

Multistep Problems
Problem 9

Extended Response
Problem 9

*Manipulative Kit Item

Metric Capacity

Context of the Lesson This lesson is part of a series of lessons that deal with metric and customary units. In this lesson, students estimate and measure capacity in liters and milliliters. Metric capacity was last studied in Lesson 10.7 of Grade 2. Here we extend the practice to include more work with measuring capacity to the nearest milliliter. The discussion of volume continues in Chapter 11, where we develop the concept through the use of cubic centimeters, which for practical purposes are the same as milliliters.

See page 342B for Math Background for teachers for this lesson.

Planning for Learning ● DIFFERENTIATE INSTRUCTION

INTERVENTION
If . . . students lack the prerequisite skill of multiplying by 10, 100, and 1,000,

Then . . . teach *Intervention* Lesson 9.C.

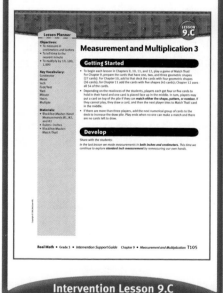

Intervention Lesson 9.C

ENGLISH LEARNER
Preview

If . . . students need language support,

Then . . . use Lesson 9.5 in *English Learner Support Guide* to preview lesson concepts and vocabulary.

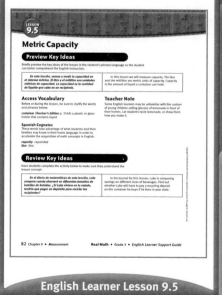

English Learner Lesson 9.5

ENRICH
If . . . students are proficient in the lesson concepts,

Then . . . emphasize exploring *eMathTools: Metric/ Customary Conversion Tool*.

PRACTICE
If . . . students would benefit from additional practice,

Then . . . extend Skill Building before assigning the student pages.

RETEACH
If . . . students are having difficulty using metric units to measure capacity,

Then . . . extend Guided Discussion before assigning the student pages.

Vocabulary
capacity\kə pa´sə tē\ *n.* the amount of anything a container can hold

milliliter \mi´lē\ *n.* a metric measure of capacity equal to one-thousandth of a liter

Access Vocabulary
container a plastic or glass holder

Spanish Cognates
capacity capacidad
liter litro

Mental Math 5

Present exercises that require students to compare fractions greater than a whole. Write exercises such as the following on the board, leaving a circle where the relation sign belongs. Have students show thumbs-up if the fraction on the left is greater than the fraction on the right, thumbs-down if it is less, and open hand if the fractions are equal.

a. $1\frac{1}{2} \bigcirc 1\frac{2}{4}$ open hand

b. $4\frac{1}{2} \bigcirc 4\frac{1}{4}$ up

c. $5\frac{4}{5} \bigcirc 6\frac{3}{4}$ down

d. $3\frac{1}{3} \bigcirc 3\frac{2}{6}$ open hand

e. $5\frac{1}{2} \bigcirc 5\frac{3}{4}$ down

f. $4\frac{3}{4} \bigcirc 2\frac{3}{4}$ up

1 Develop 30

Tell Students In Today's Lesson They Will

estimate and measure capacity in liters and milliliters.

Guided Discussion UNDERSTANDING Whole Group

1. Have the following containers and measurement tools available: one 1-liter soda bottle (label removed), one 2-liter soda bottle (label removed), and one clear 1-liter measuring cylinder.

2. Fill the 1-liter bottle full with water, and then think aloud as you pour the water from the bottle into the measuring cylinder. Say, for example, *There is 1 liter of water in this bottle. So, the capacity of this bottle is 1 liter.* Show students how to read the measure using the marks on the measuring cylinder. Repeat this process for the 2-liter bottle, filling the measuring cylinder twice.

3. Tell students that there are 1,000 milliliters in 1 liter, and spend a few minutes helping students learn how to convert between the two units. Ask questions such as the following:

   ■ **How many milliliters of water will the 1-liter bottle hold?**
   1,000

   ■ **How many milliliters of water will the 2-liter bottle hold?**
   2,000

Skill Building REASONING Whole Group

Estimating and Measuring in Liters and Milliliters

 Guide students through the following activity in estimating and measuring in liters and milliliters. Have available various sizes of plastic containers, a pitcher of water, a clear 1-liter measuring cylinder, and a small graduated cylinder to measure milliliters. Label each plastic container with a different letter of the alphabet.

1. Select a container, and ask students to estimate its capacity in milliliters or liters, depending on the size of the container.

2. Have students show their estimates with their **Response Wheels.**

3. Have one or more students fill the container with water, use the measuring cylinder (or the graduated cylinder) to find the capacity to the nearest milliliter or the nearest 10 mL, and report the measure to the class.

4. Write the letter of the container and its corresponding measure on the board.

5. Choose another container, and have students estimate and measure to check again.

6. Repeat the activity several times to allow students time to refine their estimates.

Skill and Strategy Building   REASONING Whole Group

1. Have available a number of containers—the kind used for soap, soft drinks, shampoo, peanut butter, and so on. Provide different containers from the ones used in the previous activities, if possible. Try to find containers that have different shapes, heights, and capacities. Remove the labels.

2. Show about 5 of the containers, and have the class discuss and estimate how to place the containers in order according to how much liquid they hold. When an order has been determined, pose the question of how the order can be checked. Students might suggest filling the containers with water and then pouring the water into capacity measuring containers. Other students might suggest filling the container thought to have the greatest capacity with water and then pouring that water successively into the smaller containers. If the order is correct, there should be enough water to fill each of the containers, in turn.

2 Assign Student Pages 20

Pages 356–357 APPLYING

Have students complete pages 356–357 independently.

As Students Finish

 Roll a 15 Game (reviews addition and subtraction)

Games *Roll a 15 Game*

LESSON 9.5 Metric Capacity

Key Ideas

The liter and the milliliter are metric units of capacity.
Capacity is the amount (of anything) a container can hold.

There are 1,000 milliliters in 1 liter.

1000 mL = 1 L

Convert each measure from liters to milliliters or from milliliters to liters. Write the new measure.

① 1 L = ▉ mL   **1,000**   ⑤ 7 L = ▉ mL   **7,000**

② ▉ L = 1,000 mL   **1**   ⑥ ▉ L = 5,000 mL   **5**

③ 2 L = ▉ mL   **2,000**   ⑦ 4 L = ▉ mL   **4,000**

④ ▉ L = 3,000 mL   **3**   ⑧ ▉ L = 8,000 mL   **8**

 ⑨ **Extended Response** Ming sells lemonade at her juice stand. Each glass contains 240 milliliters of **Review** lemonade. If she sold 20 glasses of lemonade, about how many liters is that?   Ming sold 4,800 milliliters because 240 × 20 = 4,800. There are 1,000 milliliters in 1 liter, so Ming sold a little less than 5 liters.

356   Textbook This lesson is available in the *eTextbook*.

Write the name of the unit that makes sense. Use milliliters or liters.

⑩ About 250 ▉ of juice   milliliters   ⑫ About 100 ▉ of perfume
                                                      milliliters

⑪ About 10 ▉ of water   liters   ⑬ About 1 ▉ of stew   liter

⑭ About 800 ▉ of water   liters

Chapter 9 • Lesson 5   357

---

3 Reflect   5

Guided Discussion   REASONING   Whole Group

1. Ask students what the combined volume will be if you mix two volumes of water that contain 50 milliliters each. As students agree that the combined volume will be 100 milliliters, use a measuring glass to demonstrate that this is true. Repeat one or two more times using different volumes.

2. Repeat what you just did, but now use a known volume of water (50 milliliters, for example) and a known volume of rubbing alcohol (50 milliliters, for example). Ask students to predict what the combined volume will be. Most students will predict the combined volume will be 100 milliliters, but this will not be true. Demonstrate the mixing, and have students note that the combined volume is just a bit more than 90 milliliters. Ask the following question:

   ■ **What happened to the lost 8 or so milliliters?**

3. To help students understand what happened, point out that volume is kept the same (conserved) only if we combine the same kinds of liquids or other materials. Ask, for example, what the combined volume will be from mixing sand and water, marbles and water, sand and marbles. Help students to see that in each of these cases the combined volume is less than the sum of the two starting volumes because the particles or liquids tend to fill up the empty spaces. For your information, in the case of water and rubbing alcohol, the water molecules and the alcohol molecules can fit together to take up "empty" space.

 Cumulative Review: For cumulative review of previously learned skills, see page 367–368.

 Family Involvement: Assign the **Practice, Reteach,** or **Enrichment** activities depending on the needs of your students.

Encourage students to practice measuring the capacity of various containers in liters and milliliters with a friend or a relative.

 Concept/Question Board: Have students look for additional examples using measurement in liters and milliliters and post them on the Concept/Question Board.

 Math Puzzler: Four runners were in a race. John ran faster than George. George ran faster than Cindy. Dwight ran faster than John. Who won the race?   Dwight

Assess and Differentiate

e Assess Use **eAssess** to record and analyze evidence of student understanding.

A Gather Evidence

Use the Daily Class Assessment Records in **Assessment** or **eAssess** to record daily observations.

Informal Assessment
☑ **Skill and Strategy Building**

Did the student **REASONING**
- ❏ provide a clear explanation?
- ❏ communicate reasons and strategies?
- ❏ choose appropriate strategies?
- ❏ argue logically?

Informal Assessment
☑ **Concept/Question Board**

Did the student **APPLYING**
- ❏ apply learning in new situations?
- ❏ contribute concepts?
- ❏ contribute answers?
- ❏ connect mathematics to real-world situations?

B Summarize Findings

Analyze and summarize assessment data for each student. Determine which Assessment Follow-Up is appropriate for each student. Use the Student Assessment Record in **Assessment** or **eAssess** to update assessment records.

Assessment page T41

C Assessment Follow-Up ● DIFFERENTIATE INSTRUCTION

Based on your observations, use these teaching strategies for assessment follow-up.

INTERVENTION
Review student performance on **Intervention** Lesson 9.C to see if students have mastered prerequisite skills for this lesson.

ENGLISH LEARNER
Review
Use Lesson 9.5 in **English Learner Support Guide** to review lesson concepts and vocabulary.

ENRICH
If . . . students are proficient in the lesson concepts,

Then . . . encourage them to work on chapter projects or **Enrichment** Lesson 9.5.

Enrichment Lesson 9.5

PRACTICE
If . . . students would benefit from additional practice,

Then . . . assign **Practice** Lesson 9.5.

Practice Lesson 9.5

RETEACH
If . . . students struggle with understanding metric capacity,

Then . . . have them look at and hold a variety of containers that show metric capacity. Also allow them to use metric measuring cylinders and containers to verify the comparison between milliliters and liters.

Lesson Planner

OBJECTIVES
- To give students experience with estimating and measuring using customary units of capacity
- To provide measurement applications for customary capacity
- To provide practice with simple unit conversions in the customary system

NCTM STANDARDS
Measurement
- Selecting and using benchmarks to estimate measurements
- Selecting and applying appropriate standard units to measure capacity
- Carrying out simple unit conversions

Problem Solving
Applying a variety of appropriate strategies to solve problems

MATERIALS

- *Response Wheels
- Various sizes of containers labeled with volume measures

TECHNOLOGY
- ⓔ **Presentation** Lesson 9.6
- ⓔ **MathTools** Metric/Customary Conversion Tool
- ⓔ **Games** *Multigo 1*

TEST PREP
Cumulative Review
Mental Math reviews comparing fractions greater than a whole (Lesson 8.9).

Customary Capacity

Context of the Lesson In this lesson, students estimate and measure capacity in fluid ounces, cups, pints, quarts, and gallons. This lesson continues a series of lessons that deal with metric and customary units. Customary capacity was last studied in Lesson 10.6 of Grade 2. Metric units of capacity were covered in the previous lesson, but at this time it is best not to have students convert measures between systems.

See page 342B for Math Background for teachers for this lesson.

Planning for Learning • DIFFERENTIATE INSTRUCTION

INTERVENTION

If . . . students lack the prerequisite skill of measuring in centimeters and inches,

Then . . . teach *Intervention* Lesson 9.A.

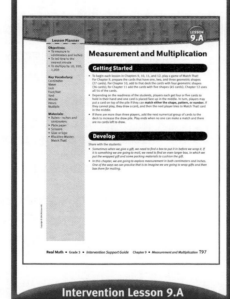

Intervention Lesson 9.A

ENGLISH LEARNER

Preview

If . . . students need language support,

Then . . . use Lesson 9.6 in *English Learner Support Guide* to preview lesson concepts and vocabulary.

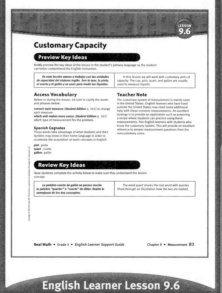

English Learner Lesson 9.6

ENRICH

If . . . students are proficient in the lesson concepts,

Then . . . emphasize chapter projects.

PRACTICE

If . . . students would benefit from additional practice,

Then . . . extend Skill Building before assigning the student pages.

RETEACH

If . . . students are having difficulty using customary units to measure capacity,

Then . . . extend Guided Discussion before assigning the student pages.

Vocabulary
cup\kəp\ *n.* a customary measure of capacity equal to 8 fluid ounces
pint\pīnt\ *n.* a customary measure of capacity equal to 2 cups

quart\kwort\ *n.* a customary measure of capacity equal to 2 pints
gallon\gaʹ lən\ *n.* a customary measure of capacity equal to 4 quarts

Spanish Cognates
pint pinta
quart cuarto
gallon galón

Mental Math 5

  As in the previous lesson, present exercises that require students to compare fractions greater than a whole. Write exercises such as the following on the board, leaving a circle where the relation sign belongs. Have students show thumbs-up if the fraction on the left is greater than the fraction on the right, thumbs-down if it is less, and open hand if the fractions are equal.

a. $2\frac{1}{8} \bigcirc 1\frac{3}{4}$ up

b. $7\frac{1}{8} \bigcirc 7\frac{1}{4}$ down

c. $7\frac{2}{8} \bigcirc 7\frac{1}{4}$ open

d. $1\frac{3}{4} \bigcirc 1\frac{2}{5}$ up

e. $2\frac{4}{6} \bigcirc 2\frac{2}{3}$ open

f. $3\frac{1}{5} \bigcirc 2\frac{3}{5}$ up

1 Develop 25

Tell Students In Today's Lesson They Will

estimate and measure capacity in fluid ounces, cups, pints, quarts, and gallons.

Guided Discussion UNDERSTANDING   Whole Group

1. Ask students to name some of the units of capacity that products are labeled in, other than liters and milliliters. Possible questions include the following:

   ■ **What is the common unit of capacity for measuring gasoline in the United States?** gallon

   ■ **What units of capacity are often used for containers of milk?** pint, quart, gallon; $\frac{1}{2}$ gallon is the most common

   ■ **What units of capacity are often used in recipes?** cup, tablespoon, teaspoon

   Focus students' attention on *cup, pint, quart,* and *gallon,* and write these four units on the board.

2. Point out that *quart* sounds like *quarter*. Therefore, it is reasonable to suggest that a quart is a quarter (or one-fourth) of some other unit. Explain that a quart is one-fourth of a gallon, and write *4 quarts = 1 gallon* on the board.

3. You may wish to have students refer to page 358 as you discuss the remaining customary units. Explain (and demonstrate, using a measuring cup and containers) the following relationships. Write each relationship on the board after each demonstration.

   - 1 gallon = 4 quarts
   - 1 quart = 2 pints = 4 cups
   - 1 pint = 2 cups
   - $\frac{1}{2}$ pint = 1 cup
   - 1 cup = 8 fluid ounces
   - 1 fluid ounce = 2 tablespoons

Skill Building REASONING   Whole Group

Estimating and Measuring in Cups, Pints, Quarts, and Gallons

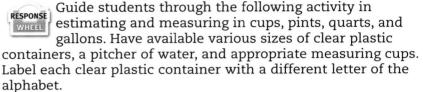 Guide students through the following activity in estimating and measuring in cups, pints, quarts, and gallons. Have available various sizes of clear plastic containers, a pitcher of water, and appropriate measuring cups. Label each clear plastic container with a different letter of the alphabet.

1. Select a container, and ask students to estimate its capacity in cups, pints, quarts, or gallons, depending on the size of the container.

2. Have students show their estimates with their **Response Wheels.**

3. Have one or more students fill the container with water, use the appropriate measuring cup to find the capacity to the nearest cup, pint, quart, or gallon, and report the measure to the class.

4. Write the letter of the container and its corresponding measure on the board.

5. Choose another container, and have students estimate and measure to check again.

6. Repeat the activity several times to allow students the opportunity to refine their estimates.

2 Assign Student Pages 20

Pages 358–359 APPLYING

Have students complete page 359 independently.

As Students Finish

 Multigo 1 (reviews multiplication facts and solving missing-factor problems)

 Games *Multigo 1*

MathTools *Metric Customary Conversion Tool* Have students explore converting customary units of capacity.

RESEARCH IN ACTION

"The idea of a unit of measure is fundamental as is the notion that measurement involves the organized accumulation of standard units. Further, *conservation* of length, area, and volume (understanding that the quantities do not change under transformations such as reflection or other rigid motion) was considered both a hallmark of, and a constraint on, children's development in each domain of spatial measure."

Kilpatrick, J., J. Swafford, and B. Findell. eds. *Adding it Up: Helping Children Learn Mathmatics.* Washington, D.C.: National Research Council/National Academy Press, 2001, p. 281.

LESSON 9.6 Customary Capacity

Key Ideas

The cup, pint, quart, and gallon are customary units of capacity. They are usually used for measuring liquids.

There are 2 cups in 1 pint.

There are 2 pints in 1 quart.

There are 4 quarts in 1 gallon.

358   📖 **Textbook** This lesson is available in the *eTextbook*.

Convert each measure. Write the new measure.

1. 1 quart = ▇ cups   4
2. $\frac{1}{2}$ gallon = ▇ pints   4
3. 2 quarts = ▇ cups   8
4. $\frac{1}{2}$ gallon = ▇ quarts   2

5. 1 gallon = ▇ cups   16
6. $\frac{1}{4}$ gallon = ▇ quart   1
7. 1 gallon = ▇ pints   8
8. 8 pints = ▇ quarts   4

Which unit makes more sense?

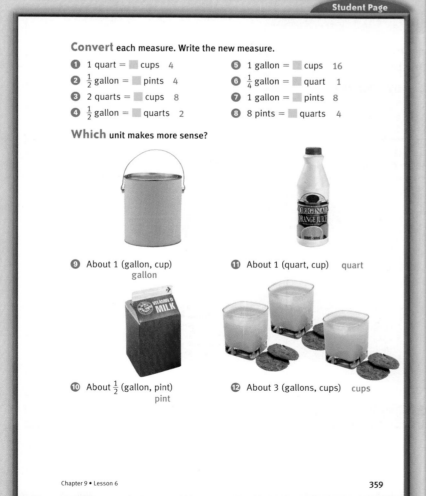

9. About 1 (gallon, cup)
   gallon

10. About $\frac{1}{2}$ (gallon, pint)
    pint

11. About 1 (quart, cup)   quart

12. About 3 (gallons, cups)   cups

---

3 Reflect   5 🕐

Guided Discussion REASONING   Whole Group

1. Have available several containers that are labeled with volume measures, such as cans and bottles found in a grocery store. Point out that most labels give the measure in both metric and customary units. Through discussion, have students explain which measure, metric or customary, was used by the company to decide how much to put into the container. Possible examples include the following:

   - A container that is labeled 1 liter or 33.8 fluid ounces was clearly intended to be 1 liter. The 33.8 ounces is calculated.
   - A container that is labeled 20 fluid ounces or 591 milliliters was clearly intended to be 20 fluid ounces.

2. Explain that most of the world is using the metric system, and although we in the United States are not doing so for everyday measures, all businesses that buy or sell in other countries do use the metric system. For now, most containers in this country have their contents labeled in both systems.

Review **Cumulative Review:** For cumulative review of previously learned skills, see page 367–368.

Family Involvement: Assign the *Practice, Reteach,* or *Enrichment* activities depending on the needs of your students.

Encourage students to practice measuring the capacity of various containers in cups, pints, quarts, and gallons with a friend or a relative.

Concept/Question Board: Encourage students to continue to post questions, answers, and examples on the Concept/Question Board.

Math Puzzler: Marjorie has 7 times as many pennies as Jack. Jack has 4 times as many pennies as Susan. Susan has 2 pennies. How many pennies does Marjorie have? 56; $2 \times 4 \times 7 = 56$

Chapter 9 • Lesson 6   358–359

4 Assess and Differentiate

 e Assess Use **eAssess** to record and analyze evidence of student understanding.

A Gather Evidence

Use the Daily Class Assessment Records in **Assessment** or **eAssess** to record daily observations.

Informal Assessment
☑ **Guided Discussion**

Did the student **UNDERSTANDING**

❏ make important observations?
❏ extend or generalize learning?
❏ provide insightful answers?
❏ pose insightful questions?

Informal Assessment
☑ **Skill Building**

Did the student **REASONING**

❏ provide a clear explanation?
❏ communicate reasons and strategies?
❏ choose appropriate strategies?
❏ argue logically?

B Summarize Findings

Analyze and summarize assessment data for each student. Determine which Assessment Follow-Up is appropriate for each student. Use the Student Assessment Record in **Assessment** or **eAssess** to update assessment records.

Assessment page T41

C Assessment Follow-Up ● DIFFERENTIATE INSTRUCTION

Based on your observations, use these teaching strategies for assessment follow-up.

INTERVENTION

Review student performance on **Intervention** Lesson 9.A to see if students have mastered prerequisite skills for this lesson.

ENGLISH LEARNER

Review

Use Lesson 9.6 in **English Learner Support Guide** to review lesson concepts and vocabulary.

ENRICH

If . . . students are proficient in the lesson concepts,

Then . . . encourage them to work on chapter projects or **Enrichment** Lesson 9.6.

PRACTICE

If . . . students would benefit from additional practice,

Then . . . assign **Practice** Lesson 9.6.

RETEACH

If . . . students are having difficulty understanding customary units of capacity,

Then . . . reteach the concept using **Reteach** Lesson 9.6.

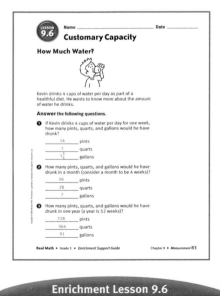

Enrichment Lesson 9.6

Practice Lesson 9.6

Reteach Lesson 9.6

Lesson Planner

OBJECTIVES
To provide practice with choosing the correct unit of measurement

NCTM STANDARDS
Measurement
Selecting and using benchmarks to estimate measurements

Problem Solving
Applying a variety of appropriate strategies to solve problems

MATERIALS
- *Response Wheels
- *Metric Unit Game Mat
- *Number Cubes

TECHNOLOGY
ⓔPresentation Lesson 9.7

TEST PREP
Cumulative Review
Mental Math reviews fractions of time (Lesson 8.4).

Choosing the Correct Unit

Context of the Lesson This lesson follows a series of six lessons in which students estimated and measured length, weight, and capacity in metric and customary units. Here students will use their knowledge of these units to choose the unit or units that are appropriate for measuring various objects.

See page 342B for Math Background for teachers for this lesson.

Planning for Learning ● DIFFERENTIATE INSTRUCTION

INTERVENTION

If . . . students lack the prerequisite skill of measuring in centimeters and inches,

Then . . . teach *Intervention* Lesson 9.A.

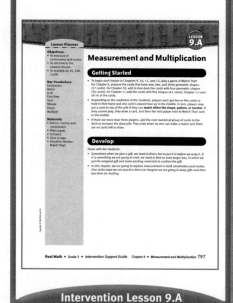

Intervention Lesson 9.A

ENGLISH LEARNER

Preview

If . . . students need language support,

Then . . . use Lesson 9.7 in *English Learner Support Guide* to preview lesson concepts and vocabulary.

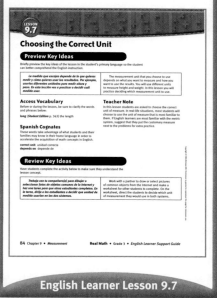

English Learner Lesson 9.7

ENRICH

If . . . students are proficient in the lesson concepts,

Then . . . emphasize the playing of the **Metric Unit Game.**

PRACTICE

If . . . students would benefit from additional practice,

Then . . . extend Skill Building before assigning the student pages.

RETEACH

If . . . students are having difficulty choosing the correct unit of measure,

Then . . . extend Guided Discussion before assigning the student pages.

Spanish Cognates
correct unit unidad correcta
depends on depende de

Mental Math   5

  Present exercises in which you ask students to tell how many minutes there are in a fraction of an hour. Have students show the number of minutes on their **Response Wheels.** Possible examples include the following:

a. $\frac{3}{4}$ of an hour 45 minutes   **b.** $\frac{1}{2}$ of an hour 30 minutes

c. $\frac{4}{4}$ of an hour 60 minutes   **d.** $\frac{2}{4}$ of an hour 30 minutes

e. $\frac{1}{3}$ of an hour 20 minutes   **f.** $\frac{2}{3}$ of an hour 40 minutes

1 Develop   30

Tell Students In Today's Lesson They Will

practice choosing the correct unit to measure the length, weight, and capacity of various objects.

Guided Discussion REASONING   Whole Group

1. Conduct a discussion in which you propose something that needs to be measured and students choose an appropriate measuring instrument and measuring unit. Have students explain the reasons for their choices. You might want to do this in two parts, one for metric units and one for customary units. Possible examples include the following:

Metric

weight of a fish tank scale; kilograms

length of a music CD case ruler; centimeters

capacity of a punch bowl measuring cylinder; liters

Customary

weight of a strawberry double-pan balance or scale; ounces

length of a blade of grass ruler; inches

capacity of a cereal bowl measuring cylinder; cups

2. Be prepared for answers that might appear to be wrong but for which a student might have a reasonable explanation. For example, although it is usually appropriate to measure the length of an automobile in feet, a student might suggest that inches are more appropriate if you are comparing the lengths of two automobiles that are close to the same length. Students might also reasonably suggest using different units to measure the same thing. For example, the length of a window could be measured in inches, feet, or yards depending on the type of window being measured.

Skill Practice REASONING   Whole Group

1. To review choosing the correct metric or customary unit, write one of the following numbered lists on the board: **Metric**—millimeter, centimeter, meter, kilometer, gram, kilogram, milliliter, liter; **Customary**—inch, foot, yard, mile, ounce, pound, fluid ounce, cup, pint, quart, gallon. Write the other list on the board after completing the exercises for the first list. Do not list both columns, metric and customary, on the board at the same time.

2. Present situations that call for a measurement, and using the Find, Hide, and Show procedure, have students respond by showing the number of the unit from the list on the board. Accept all reasonable answers. Possible examples include the following:

Metric

the distance from New York to Los Angeles kilometers (4)

the weight of a bag of apples kilograms (6)

the height of a large tree meters (3)

the capacity of a teacup milliliters (1)

Customary

the weight of a washing machine pounds (6)

the length of a highway miles (4)

the distance from first to second base on a baseball field yards (3)

the capacity of a large bucket gallons (11)

the capacity of a small bottle of medicine fluid ounces (7)

Skill and Strategy Building ENGAGING   Whole Group

 Metric Unit Game
Demonstrate how to play the **Metric Unit Game.** Divide the class into two teams to play a whole-class version of the game. This game provides practice with choosing appropriate metric units of weight and length for various objects. The rules for play can be found on the **Metric Unit Game Mat** in the back of this *Teacher's Edition.*

2 Assign Student Pages   20

Pages 360–361 APPLYING

Have students complete pages 360–361 independently.

As Students Finish

  Metric Unit Game

LESSON 9.7 Choosing the Correct Unit

Key Ideas

The measurement unit you choose depends on what you want to measure and how you want to use the results.

If you were measuring these people and things in real life, what metric units would you use? Write *kilometers*, *meters*, *centimeters*, *kilograms*, or *grams*. Work down the page.

1 About 2 ▪ tall meters
2 Weighs about 80 ▪ kilograms

7 About 130 ▪ tall centimeters
8 Weighs about 27 ▪ kilograms

3 About 2 ▪ across centimeters
4 Weighs about 3 ▪ grams

9 About 30 ▪ long centimeters
10 Weighs about 500 ▪ grams

5 About 18 ▪ long centimeters
6 Weighs about 6 ▪ grams

11 About 2 ▪ long meters
12 Weighs about 8 ▪ kilograms

360

Textbook This lesson is available in the *eTextbook*.

If you were measuring these people and things in real life, what customary units would you use? Write *inches*, *feet*, *yards*, *ounces*, or *pounds*.

13 About 18 ▪ long feet
14 Weighs about 3,500 ▪ pounds

19 About 1 ▪ long yard
20 Weighs about 24 ▪ ounces

15 About 6 ▪ tall feet
16 Weighs about 160 ▪ pounds

21 About 1 ▪ long foot
22 About 2 ▪ thick inches

17 About 100 ▪ long yards
18 About 50 ▪ wide yards

23 About 7 ▪ long inches
24 Weighs about 2 ▪ ounces

---

3 Reflect

5

Guided Discussion REASONING

Whole Group

Present, discuss, and possibly illustrate the following problems, all of which deal with aspects of indirect measurement:

- Grant wanted to weigh his dog Bowser, but each time he put Bowser on the scales, the dog would jump off. What could Grant do? Accept all reasonable answers, including the most likely one that he could carry Bowser as he stepped on the scale and note the combined weight. He could then weigh himself and subtract his weight from the combined weight to find out how much Bowser weighed.

- Analise wanted to know the distance around the classroom globe at the equator. The only measuring device she had was a meterstick. How could she do this? Accept all reasonable suggestions, including Analise wraps a string around the globe and then measures the string.

- Ben had two irregularly shaped rocks. He wanted to know which rock occupied more space. How could he find out? Accept all reasonable answers, including that he could fill a measuring cylinder to a known volume, place the rock in the cylinder, and note the new volume. Then he could subtract to find out how much water the rock displaced.

Cumulative Review: For cumulative review of previously learned skills, see page 367–368.

Family Involvement: Assign the *Practice, Reteach,* or *Enrichment* activities depending on the needs of your students.

Encourage students to practice choosing the correct unit to measure various objects with a friend or a relative.

Concept/Question Board: Encourage students to continue to post questions, answers, and examples on the Concept/Question Board.

Math Puzzler: Keith is unpacking books. Each book is 5 centimeters thick. Can he stack 8 books in a space that is 37 centimeters high? no; 5 × 8 = 40 and 40 > 37

Assess and Differentiate

 Assess Use **eAssess** to record and analyze evidence of student understanding.

A Gather Evidence

Use the Daily Class Assessment Records in **Assessment** or **eAssess** to record daily observations.

Informal Assessment
☑ **Guided Discussion**

Did the student **REASONING**
❑ provide a clear explanation?
❑ communicate reasons and strategies?
❑ choose appropriate strategies?
❑ argue logically?

Informal Assessment
☑ **Game**

Did the student **ENGAGING**
❑ pay attention to others' contributions?
❑ contribute information and ideas?
❑ improve on a strategy?
❑ reflect on and check the accuracy of his or her work?

B Summarize Findings

Analyze and summarize assessment data for each student. Determine which Assessment Follow-Up is appropriate for each student. Use the Student Assessment Record in **Assessment** or **eAssess** to update assessment records.

Assessment page T41

C Assessment Follow-Up ● DIFFERENTIATE INSTRUCTION

Based on your observations, use these teaching strategies for assessment follow-up.

INTERVENTION

Review student performance on **Intervention** Lesson 9.A to see if students have mastered prerequisite skills for this lesson.

ENGLISH LEARNER

Review

Use Lesson 9.7 in **English Learner Support Guide** to review lesson concepts and vocabulary.

ENRICH

If . . . students are proficient in the lesson concepts,

Then . . . encourage them to work on chapter projects or **Enrichment** Lesson 9.7.

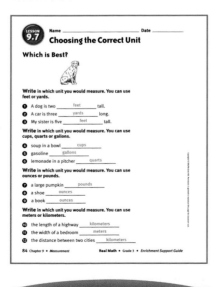

Enrichment Lesson 9.7

PRACTICE

If . . . students would benefit from additional practice,

Then . . . assign **Practice** Lesson 9.7.

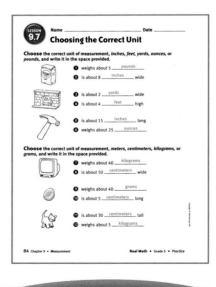

Practice Lesson 9.7

RETEACH

If . . . students struggle with choosing the correct unit,

Then . . . have them find a real example for each picture and measure it. Have students work in small groups to discuss possible answers. Students can also practice by making up their own examples for other students to answer.

Lesson Planner

OBJECTIVES
To provide practice with calculating elapsed time

NCTM STANDARDS
Measurement
Applying appropriate techniques, tools, and formulas to determine measurements

Communication
Communicating mathematical thinking to others

MATERIALS

- *Response Wheels
- *Harder Minutes Game Mat
- Demonstration clock

TECHNOLOGY
Presentation Lesson 9.8

TEST PREP
Cumulative Review
- Mental Math reviews telling time to the nearest minute (Lesson 3.1).
- Problem 13 reviews understanding A.M. and P.M. when telling time (Lesson 3.1).

Writing + Math
Journal

Measuring Elapsed Time

Context of the Lesson Telling time was reintroduced in Chapter 3, Lesson 1. This skill should have been reinforced throughout the year up to now by referring often to the classroom clock and asking students when routine activities start and end. In this lesson, we build on these skills by focusing on calculating elapsed time.

See page 342B for Math Background for teachers for this lesson.

Planning for Learning • DIFFERENTIATE INSTRUCTION

INTERVENTION
If . . . students lack the prerequisite skill of telling time to the nearest minute,

Then . . . teach *Intervention* Lesson 9.B.

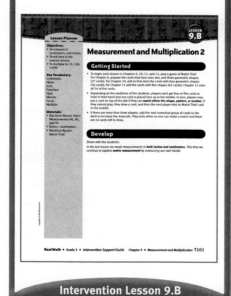

Intervention Lesson 9.B

ENGLISH LEARNER
Preview

If . . . students need language support,

Then . . . use Lesson 9.8 in *English Learner Support Guide* to preview lesson concepts and vocabulary.

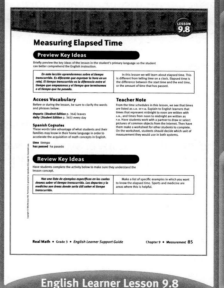

English Learner Lesson 9.8

ENRICH
If . . . students are proficient in the lesson concepts,

Then . . . emphasize the playing of the **Harder Minutes Game** after they finish the student pages.

PRACTICE
If . . . students would benefit from additional practice,

Then . . . extend Skill Practice before assigning the student pages.

RETEACH
If . . . students are having difficulty measuring elapsed time,

Then . . . extend Guided Discussion before assigning the student pages.

Vocabulary
elapsed\ilapst´\ n. the amount of time that has passed
hour\au(ə)r\ n. a measure of time equal to 60 minutes
minute\mi´nət\ n. a measure of time equal to 60 seconds

Access Vocabulary
daily every day
departs leaves

Spanish Cognates
time tiempo
has passed ha pasado

*Manipulative Kit Item

Mental Math
5

  Set the hands of the demonstration clock to various times, and have students use their **Response Wheels** to show the time to the nearest minute. Have students use their index fingers to represent the colon. Possible examples include the following:

a. 3:07   **b.** 5:46   **c.** 11:58
d. 1:12   **e.** 4:24   **f.** 8:33

1 Develop
25

Tell Students In Today's Lesson They Will
practice measuring elapsed time.

Guided Discussion UNDERSTANDING
Whole Group

1. Ask students questions such as the following about events that have occurred. Begin with events for which the elapsed time can be calculated in years or months. Then move to events that occurred today for which elapsed time can be calculated in hours. Possible questions include the following:

   ■ **About how many years has it been since you were born?**
   ■ **About how many years has it been since your third birthday?**
   ■ **About how many years has it been since your first day of kindergarten?**
   ■ **About how many months has it been since the beginning of this school year?**
   ■ **About how many hours has it been since you woke up this morning?**
   ■ **About how many hours has it been since you got to school?**

2. Explain that by answering the questions above, students were calculating elapsed time. Make sure students understand that *elapsed time* refers to the amount of time that has passed and that it is helpful to think of elapsed time as the difference between the start time and the end time.

3. Draw a table, such as the following, on the board or an overhead transparency. List start times, end times, and shortest possible elapsed times.

Start Time	End Time	Elapsed Time
12:30	1:30	1 hour
12:45	1:30	45 minutes
12:50	2:30	1 hour and 40 minutes

4. Discuss each of the time spans listed on the chart, making sure students understand how to find the elapsed time. For example, to find the elapsed time from 12:50 to 2:30, students could think the following:

   12:50 to 1:00 is 10 minutes

   1:00 to 2:30 is 1 hour and 30 minutes

   So, the elapsed time is 1 hour and 40 minutes.

Skill Practice UNDERSTANDING
Whole Group

 Write pairs of related start and end times on the board, one at a time, and have students use their **Response Wheels** to show the elapsed time in minutes. Use examples such as the following:

8:05 to 9:00 55	4:20 to 4:45 25	2:50 to 3:21 31
8:06 to 9:00 54	4:20 to 4:50 30	2:51 to 3:21 30
8:10 to 9:00 50	4:20 to 4:55 35	2:50 to 3:18 28

2 Assign Student Pages
25

Pages 362–363 APPLYING
Have students complete pages 362–363 independently.

Monitoring Student Progress

If . . . students have difficulty with any aspect of this lesson,

Then . . . rather than spending time with intensive remediation now, the best help is to refer often to elapsed time in relation to daily or weekly routine activities. This will help students see the usefulness of these skills and will provide the necessary practice.

As Students Finish

Game Harder Minutes Game

 RESEARCH IN ACTION

"For children's development of the logic necessary to understand the measurement of time, it is therefore desirable to encourage them to think hard not only about time but also about all kinds of objects, people, and events all day long. A good way to encourage thinking is to put children in situations that require debate, negotiations, and decision making."

Kamii, Constance and Kathy Long. "The Measurement of Time" in *Learning and Teaching Measurement: 2003 Yearbook.* Clements, Douglas H. and George Bright, eds. Reston, VA: National Council of Teachers of Mathematics, Inc. 2003, p. 179.

LESSON 9.8 Measuring Elapsed Time

Key Ideas

The time difference between the start of an event and the end of the event is called **elapsed time**. It is the amount of time that has passed.

Start Time	End Time	Elapsed Time
11:25	12:10	45 minutes

Think: The time from 11:25 to noon is 35 minutes. Noon to 12:10 is 10 minutes. So, the elapsed time is 45 minutes.

Copy and complete the table by filling in the elapsed times. The first one is done for you.

Daily Schedule for Art Camp

Activity	Time	Elapsed Time	
Campers Arrive	8:45–9:00 A.M.	**1** 15 minutes	
Morning Meeting	9:00–9:10 A.M.	**2** 10 minutes	
Puppetry	9:15–9:55 A.M.	**3** 40 minutes	
Dance Class	10:00–10:55 A.M.	**4** 55 minutes	
Making Your Own Movie	11:05–11:55 A.M.	**5** 50 minutes	
Lunch	12:00–12:30 P.M.	**6** 30 minutes	
Special Guest	12:35–1:50 P.M.	**7**	**7** 1 hr and 15 min or 75 minutes
World Music	1:55–2:35 P.M.	**8** 40 minutes	
Soccer	2:40–3:40 P.M.	**9** 1 hour	
Farewell Meeting	3:45–3:55 P.M.	**10** 10 minutes	
Campers Depart	4:00 P.M.		

362   ⬛ **Textbook** This lesson is available in the *eTextbook*.

Daily Bus Schedule from San Antonio, TX, to Dallas, TX

Bus	Departs	Arrives
A	1:45 A.M.	7:00 A.M.
B	5:00 A.M.	10:45 A.M.
C	7:00 A.M.	12:55 P.M.
D	9:15 A.M.	3:00 P.M.
E	12:45 P.M.	6:00 P.M.
F	3:15 P.M.	8:50 P.M.
G	4:30 P.M.	10:15 P.M.
H	6:00 P.M.	11:25 P.M.
I	8:00 P.M.	1:20 A.M.
J	10:05 P.M.	3:00 A.M.
K	10:45 P.M.	4:30 A.M.

Use the bus schedule to answer the questions.

11 Bus D arrived 15 minutes early. What time was that?   2:45 P.M.

12 Bus F arrived 10 minutes late. What time was that?   9:00 P.M.

 13 Which buses could you take if you need to depart from San Antonio before noon?   A, B, C, or D

14 What is the elapsed time between the time Bus E departs and the time the next bus departs?   2 hours and 30 minutes

15 If you take Bus K to Dallas, how many hours travel time will you have?   5 hours and 45 minutes

16 If you take Bus J to Dallas, how many hours travel time will you have?   4 hours and 55 minutes

Writing + Math ▶ Journal

Why do you think the number of hours of travel time is different depending on which bus you take?   See *Teacher's Edition* for answer.

③ Reflect   5 🕐

Guided Discussion [APPLYING]   Whole Group

Ask students to give examples of situations in which it is helpful or essential to measure or calculate elapsed time. Possible examples include the following:

- You need to know how long it takes to get ready for school.
- You need to know how long it takes to get to school.
- It is essential for sports such as track or swimming in which winning is based on having the fastest time from the starting line to the finish line.
- It is important for knowing when a game such as football will end. What, for example, does it mean when we say that there are 5 more minutes and each team has 2 time-outs? If we understand elapsed time, we can estimate how much more time the game will actually take.
- If you want to sleep for 7 hours, you need to know what time to set the alarm clock.
- It is helpful to know the elapsed time for the length of a movie so you can plan your day or evening.

Writing + Math ▶ Journal

Possible answers: The buses make different numbers of stops; there is more traffic at some times than at other times; the buses probably take different routes because they make different stops.

 Curriculum Connection: Have students investigate record-breaking times in sports.

 Cumulative Review: For cumulative review of previously learned skills, see page 367–368.

 Family Involvement: Assign the *Practice, Reteach,* or *Enrichment* activities depending on the needs of your students.

Encourage students to practice measuring elapsed time with a friend or a relative.

 Concept/Question Board: Have students attempt to answer any unanswered questions on the Concept/Question Board.

 Math Puzzler: The sum of two numbers is 18. The difference of the same two numbers is 6. What are the two numbers?   6 and 12

Assess and Differentiate

 Assess Use *eAssess* to record and analyze evidence of student understanding.

A Gather Evidence

Use the Daily Class Assessment Records in *Assessment* or *eAssess* to record daily observations.

Informal Assessment
☑ **Guided Discussion**

Did the student UNDERSTANDING
- ❏ make important observations?
- ❏ extend or generalize learning?
- ❏ provide insightful answers?
- ❏ pose insightful questions?

Informal Assessment
☑ **Student Pages**

Did the student APPLYING
- ❏ apply learning in new situations?
- ❏ contribute concepts?
- ❏ contribute answers?
- ❏ connect mathematics to real-world situations?

B Summarize Findings

Analyze and summarize assessment data for each student. Determine which Assessment Follow-Up is appropriate for each student. Use the Student Assessment Record in *Assessment* or *eAssess* to update assessment records.

Assessment page T41

C Assessment Follow-Up • DIFFERENTIATE INSTRUCTION

Based on your observations, use these teaching strategies for assessment follow-up.

INTERVENTION

Review student performance on *Intervention* Lesson 9.B to see if students have mastered prerequisite skills for this lesson.

ENGLISH LEARNER

Review

Use Lesson 9.8 in *English Learner Support Guide* to review lesson concepts and vocabulary.

ENRICH

If . . . students are proficient in the lesson concepts,

Then . . . encourage them to work on chapter projects or *Enrichment* Lesson 9.8.

PRACTICE

If . . . students would benefit from additional practice,

Then . . . assign *Practice* Lesson 9.8.

RETEACH

If . . . students struggle with determining elapsed time,

Then . . . have them use a demonstration clock and move the hands through the elapsed time to keep track of the minutes. They should be able to count by 5s. If they need to keep a tally, they may. They may need to review showing times on a clock with hands before completing this exercise.

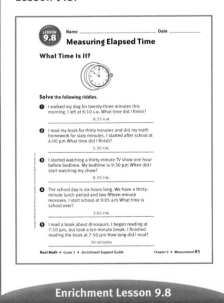

Enrichment Lesson 9.8

Practice Lesson 9.8

Lesson Planner

OBJECTIVES
- To present metric units of measure in the form of a table that helps students see the relationship between the units and that can be used for later reference
- To relate the metric system of measures to U.S. currency as a way of helping students understand and remember conversions within the system

NCTM STANDARDS

Measurement
- Becoming familiar with standard units in the metric system
- Carrying out unit conversions within a system of measurement

Connections
Understanding how mathematical ideas interconnect

MATERIALS
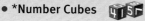
- *Response Wheels
- Metric Unit Game Mat
- *Number Cubes

TECHNOLOGY
ⓔPresentation Lesson 9.9

TEST PREP
Cumulative Review
Mental Math reviews measuring elapsed time (Lesson 9.8).

Extended Response
Problems 15 and 16

Looking Ahead
Lesson 10.1 will begin the formal study of decimals. In advance of that lesson, consider showing the students what a number written as a decimal looks like and ask them to try to find decimal numbers on package labels, in magazines, on road signs, and the like. Have them bring examples to class so you can use them as part of the lesson.

Understanding the Metric System

Context of the Lesson This lesson summarizes previous lessons that used metric measures and lays a foundation for work in later grades. The table on page 365 relates units of the metric system to U.S. currency, a context with which students are already familiar. This will prepare students to better understand conversions between units in the metric system. Such conversions require decimal notation, which is covered in the next chapter.

See page 342B for Math Background for teachers for this lesson.

Planning for Learning ● DIFFERENTIATE INSTRUCTION

INTERVENTION
If . . . students lack the prerequisite skill of multiplying by 10, 100, and 1,000,

Then . . . teach *Intervention* Lesson 9.C.

Intervention Lesson 9.C

ENGLISH LEARNER
Preview

If . . . students need language support,

Then . . . use Lesson 9.9 in *English Learner Support Guide* to preview lesson concepts and vocabulary.

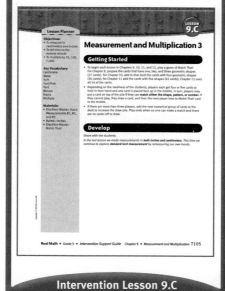

English Learner Lesson 9.9

ENRICH
If . . . students are proficient in the lesson concepts,

Then . . . emphasize chapter projects.

PRACTICE
If . . . students would benefit from additional practice,

Then . . . extend Guided Discussion before assigning the student pages.

RETEACH
If . . . students are having difficulty understanding the metric system,

Then . . . use play money and do the first few problems with students before assigning the student pages.

Access Vocabulary
currency money
dollar bill paper money

Spanish Cognates
metric system sistema métrico
to convert convertir

Mental Math 5

  Write pairs of related start and end times on the board, one at a time, and have students use their *Response Wheels* to show the elapsed time in minutes. Possible examples include the following:

a. 1:45 to 2:15 30 **b.** 1:45 to 2:17 32 **c.** 1:44 to 2:18 34

d. 7:10 to 8:00 50 **e.** 7:12 to 8:00 48 **f.** 7:12 to 8:02 50

g. 9:25 to 9:45 20 **h.** 9:25 to 9:50 25 **i.** 9:26 to 9:50 24

1 Develop 25

Tell Students In Today's Lesson They Will

- study a table that will help them understand the relationship between metric units of measure.
- relate the metric system of measures to U.S. currency.

Guided Discussion UNDERSTANDING   Whole Group

With the students' books open, discuss and explain the table on page 365. Before beginning, assure students that the table is just for reference and that they do not need to memorize it. Then through discussion establish the following:

- The basic units of the metric system—the meter, gram, and liter—can be compared with the U.S. dollar.
- To know how many centimeters are in 1 meter, we can think of how many cents are in $1.
- To know how many grams are in 1 kilogram (or meters in 1 kilometer or liters in 1 kiloliter), we can think of how many dollars are in $1,000.
- To know how many millimeters (or milligrams or milliliters) there are in 1 meter (or gram or liter), we can think of how many mills there are in $1. Tell students that although the mill has never been produced in coin form, it was invented by the United States government in 1786 to refer to the smallest subdivision of $1 and is used only for calculation purposes. Explain that there are 10 mills in 1 cent and 1,000 mills in $1. Students should notice that that relationship between the mill and the cent is the same as the relationship between the millimeter and the centimeter.
- The nine underlined metric units are commonly used and the units not underlined are used only in special situations.
- The symbols for metric units (cm, m, g, kg, L, kL, and so on) do not take periods.

2 Assign Student Pages 25

Pages 364–365 APPLYING

Have students complete pages 364–365 independently. Tell them to use the table on page 365 as they answer the questions on page 364.

As Students Finish

Game Metric Unit Game

LESSON 9.9 Understanding the Metric System

Key Ideas

Relating the metric system of measures to United States currency can help you remember how to convert metric units.

Use the table on the next page to answer these questions.

1. How many cents are in $1? **100**
2. How many centimeters are in 1 meter? **100**
3. How many dollars are in $1,000? **1,000**
4. How many grams are in 1 kilogram? **1,000**
5. How many liters are in 1 kiloliter? **1,000**
6. How many centiliters are in 1 liter? **100**
7. How many dimes are in $1? **10**
8. How many cents are in 1 dime? **10**
9. How many decimeters are in 1 meter? **10**
10. How many centigrams are in 1 decigram? **10**

The highway department in President County has decided to replace old signs. Look at the old signs to the right. Then help the highway department create the new sign by converting the units to kilometers. Use the table on the next page to help.

11. 2 kilometers
12. 5 kilometers
13. 3 kilometers
14. 7 kilometers

364

Textbook This lesson is available in the *eTextbook*.

This table shows how metric units can be related to United States currency.

Length Units	Weight Units	Capacity Units	U.S. Currency
millimeter (mm)	milligram (mg)	milliliter (mL)	mill
centimeter (cm)	centigram (cg)	centiliter (cL)	cent
decimeter (dm)	decigram (dg)	deciliter (dL)	dime
meter (m)	gram (g)	liter (L)	dollar bill ($1)
dekameter (dam)	dekagram (dag)	dekaliter (daL)	10-dollar bill
hectometer (hm)	hectogram (hg)	hectoliter (hL)	100-dollar bill
kilometer (km)	kilogram (kg)	kiloliter (kL)	1,000-dollar bill

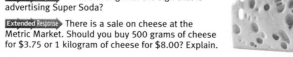

SUPER SODA 1-LITER BOTTLE $1.49
SUPER SODA 100 CENTILITER BOTTLE $1.29

15. **Extended Response** What's wrong with the sign that is advertising Super Soda?

16. **Extended Response** There is a sale on cheese at the Metric Market. Should you buy 500 grams of cheese for $3.75 or 1 kilogram of cheese for $8.00? Explain.

15. The bottles contain the same amount of soda, but the prices are different. A smart shopper would choose to buy the bottle for $1.29.

16. The price of 500 grams is less than half the price for 1 kilogram, so buying 500 grams is the better buy. In fact, you can buy two 500-gram packages for less than the cost of the 1 kilogram package.

Chapter 9 • Lesson 9

365

3 Reflect

5

Guided Discussion **APPLYING**

Whole Group

Explain that if you know how to convert units of length in the metric system, you also know how to convert units of weight and capacity, but the same is not true in the customary system. Ask questions such as the following:

■ **How many centimeters are in 1 meter?** 100
■ **How many inches are in 2 yards?** 72
■ **How many grams are in 1 kilogram?** 1,000
■ **How many ounces are in 1 pound?** 16

Then note that the metric system of measures is a base-ten system, but the customary system is not.

Review **Cumulative Review:** For cumulative review of previously learned skills, see page 367–368.

Family Involvement: Assign the *Practice, Reteach,* or *Enrichment* activities depending on the needs of your students.

Encourage students to practice converting metric units with a friend or a relative.

Concept/Question Board: Have students attempt to answer any unanswered questions on the Concept/Question Board.

Math Puzzler: The Central All Stars played 26 basketball games. They won 6 more games than they lost. How many games did they win? 16

Assess and Differentiate

@Assess Use **eAssess** to record and analyze evidence of student understanding.

A Gather Evidence

Use the Daily Class Assessment Records in **Assessment** or **eAssess** to record daily observations.

Informal Assessment

☑ **Guided Discussion**

Did the student **UNDERSTANDING**
- ❏ make important observations?
- ❏ extend or generalize learning?
- ❏ provide insightful answers?
- ❏ pose insightful questions?

Informal Assessment

☑ **Student Pages**

Did the student **APPLYING**
- ❏ apply learning in new situations?
- ❏ contribute concepts?
- ❏ contribute answers?
- ❏ connect mathematics to real-world situations?

B Summarize Findings

Analyze and summarize assessment data for each student. Determine which Assessment Follow-Up is appropriate for each student. Use the Student Assessment Record in **Assessment** or **eAssess** to update assessment records.

Assessment page T41

C Assessment Follow-Up ● DIFFERENTIATE INSTRUCTION

Based on your observations, use these teaching strategies for assessment follow-up.

INTERVENTION	ENRICH	PRACTICE	RETEACH
Review student performance on **Intervention** Lesson 9.C to see if students have mastered prerequisite skills for this lesson.	**If . . .** students are proficient in the lesson concepts, **Then . . .** encourage them to work on chapter projects or **Enrichment** Lesson 9.9.	**If . . .** students would benefit from additional practice, **Then . . .** assign **Practice** Lesson 9.9.	**If . . .** students struggle with the metric system, **Then . . .** have them find an example for each of the metric measurements listed in the table in the lesson. For example, for a liter, have them show a liter of juice. They can pull pictures from grocery ads, magazines, and newspapers.

ENGLISH LEARNER

Review

Use Lesson 9.9 in **English Learner Support Guide** to review lesson concepts and vocabulary.

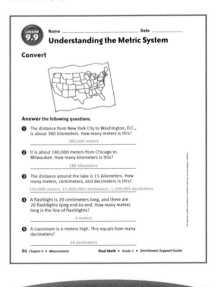

Enrichment Lesson 9.9

Practice Lesson 9.9

Problem Solving

Exploring Problem Solving

Objectives
- To solve a real-world problem involving customary measures and elapsed time
- To provide practice solving and presenting solutions to nonroutine problems
- To continue to provide practice using proportional reasoning and fractions

Materials
None

Context of the Lesson While continuing the theme of camping introduced in the Chapter Introduction, this lesson gives students an opportunity to apply what they have been learning about fractions, time, and measurement to a real-world, nonroutine problem.

1 Develop 5

Tell Students In Today's Lesson They Will
find out when three campers will finish an important job.

Guided Discussion

Remind students about previous activities in this chapter in which they helped design a campground. Tell students that today they are going to read and solve a problem about children on a camping trip.

Read and discuss the information on page 366 with the class. Make sure students understand the information in the opening paragraph and in the illustrations by asking questions such as the following:

- **What are the children doing?** filling a barrel with water
- **How are they doing that?** walking to the stream, filling containers, carrying them back, and emptying them into the barrel
- **How much water does it take to fill the barrel?** 30 gallons
- **How much water does each child carry back from the stream?** 6 quarts
- **Is 6 quarts more than a gallon? Is it 2 gallons?** yes; no
- **How long does it take the children to make one complete trip?** 10 minutes
- **What are you being asked to do?** find out when the children will fill the barrel
- **What are some ways you might try to solve this problem?** Allow students to suggest and explain methods without going through entire solutions. See Sample Solutions Strategies.

Exploring Problem Solving

On a camping trip with their group, three children are filling a water barrel. They walk to the stream to fill their containers. Then they carry them back and pour the water into the barrel. The pictures show their first trip.

❶ about 11:35, assuming they do not spill a lot; If they take 10 minutes for each trip, they can fill the barrel in 7 trips, or 70 minutes. See *Teacher's Edition* Sample Solutions Strategies for possible methods.

Work in groups to solve this problem. Show how you solved it.

❶ If the children keep working at this rate, when will the barrel be full?

❷ What will happen on the last trip?
Only two of the children need to make the last trip. Or all three of them go, but only one of them needs to carry two containers; the others can carry one container each.

366　　　📖 Textbook　This lesson is available in the *eTextbook*.

Using Student Pages

Have students work in pairs or small groups to solve the problem. Provide support as needed. If students seem to be having difficulty, encourage them to struggle with the problem for a while. When needed, ask guiding questions such as the following:

■ **How much water will the children bring back on the next trip? What time will it be then?**
■ **How can you keep track of the water they bring and of the time?**

Students who finish early may solve the extension problem below.

Extension

What if the children's containers could hold only 2 quarts instead of 3 quarts. When would the children have filled the barrel? 12:05 P.M.; Three children each carrying a gallon would need to make 10 trips, which would take 100 minutes, or 1 hour and 40 minutes.

3 Reflect 30

Problem Formulation, Planning, and Strategizing Ask
each group to share their solution and their strategies for solving the problem. Help students understand the following points:

● People sometimes use different strategies to find the same answer.
● Different people may prefer to use different units to solve the same problem. In this problem, for example, some people may prefer to change all capacity measures to quarts in order to work with only whole numbers. Others may prefer to convert to gallons in order to keep the numbers smaller.
● Because the problem is asking students to assume that the children continue at the same rate, they can extend the pattern of 18 quarts, or $4\frac{1}{2}$ gallons, every 10 minutes. But students should be aware that not all patterns continue. Certainly the children could not continue carrying water at that rate all day; they would get tired or hungry, would need to stop for a break, and so on.

Sample Solutions Strategies

Students might use one or more of the following strategies to help solve the problem.

Make a Diagram

Students might make a diagram by using clock faces to show that every 10 minutes the children put another 18 quarts, or $4\frac{1}{2}$ gallons, into the barrel.

Make a Table

Students might make a table similar to this one.

Time	Gallons of Water
10:35	$4\frac{1}{2}$
10:45	9
10:55	$13\frac{1}{2}$
11:05	18
11:15	$22\frac{1}{2}$
11:25	27
11:35	more than 30

Use Number Sense

After finding that the children need to make 7 trips, students might use the fact that every 10 minutes the children put another 18 quarts, or $4\frac{1}{2}$ gallons, into the barrel. Then, starting at 10:25, students might say what the time would be 10 minutes later, then 10 minutes later again, and so on, until they know what the time would be after seven 10-minute intervals.

Use Proportional Reasoning

Students might streamline their use of any strategy by thinking proportionally. Use the following example:

In 1 trip, the children carry 18 quarts.
In 10 trips, they can carry 180 quarts.
In 5 trips, they can carry 90 quarts (half of 180).
In 6 trips, they can carry 108 quarts (90 + 18).
In 7 trips, they can carry more than the 120 quarts needed (108 + 18 > 120).

Use a Physical Model

Students might use containers and counters to act out the problem. They might use a demonstration clock or any clock with a movable minute hand to keep track of time.

4 Assess 15

When evaluating student work, focus not only on the correctness of the answer, but also on whether students thought rationally about the problem. Questions to consider include the following:

● Did the student understand the problem?
● Did the student use measurement concepts and units in reasonable ways?
● Did the student explain his or her thinking clearly enough?
● Could the student figure out what happens when a rate is continued?
● Could the student understand other people's strategies?

Cumulative Review

Assign Pages 367–368

Use the Cumulative Review as a review of concepts and skills that students have previously learned.

Here are different ways that you can assign these problems to your students as they work through the chapter:

- With some of the lessons in the chapter, assign a set of cumulative review problems to be completed as practice or for homework.
  Lesson 9.5—Problems 1–6
  Lesson 9.6—Problems 7–10
  Lesson 9.7—Problems 11–15
  Lesson 9.8—Problems 16–21
  Lesson 9.9—Problems 22–32
- At any point during the chapter, assign part or all of the cumulative review problems to be completed as practice or for homework.

Cumulative Review

Problems 1–6 review multiplying three-digit numbers by one-digit numbers, Lesson 7.3.

Problems 7–10 review finding perimeter, Lesson 3.6.

Problems 11–15 review metric lengths, Lesson 9.1.

Problems 16–21 review fractions of time, Lesson 8.4.

Problems 22–32 review converting customary weights, Lesson 9.4.

Monitoring Student Progress

If . . . students miss more than one problem in a section,

Then . . . refer to the indicated lesson for remediation suggestions.

Cumulative Review

Multiplying Three-Digit Numbers by One-Digit Numbers Lesson 7.3
Multiply. You may draw pictures to help.

❶	523	❷	122	❸	801	❹	869	❺	374	❻	752
	× 4		× 5		× 7		× 0		× 6		× 9
	2,092		610		5,607		0		2,244		6,768

Perimeter Lesson 3.6
Find the perimeter for each figure.

❼ 2 cm, 2 cm, 2 cm, 2 cm
Perimeter: **8** centimeters

❾ 5 cm, 3 cm, 3 cm, 5 cm
Perimeter: **16** centimeters

❽ 4 cm, 3 cm, 3 cm, 4 cm
Perimeter: **14** centimeters

❿ 3 cm, 3 cm, 3 cm, 3 cm
Perimeter: **12** centimeters

Metric Length Lesson 9.1
Write the metric unit (millimeters, centimeters, meters, or kilometers) you would use to measure these lengths or distances.

⓫ the length of the Pacific Coast Highway **kilometers**

⓬ the length of an airplane **meters**

⓭ the distance from one state capital to the next state capital **kilometers**

⓮ the length of a shoelace **centimeters**

⓯ the thickness of a quarter **millimeters**

Chapter 9 • Cumulative Review   367

Cumulative Review

Fractions of Time Lesson 8.4
How many minutes?

⓰ $\frac{3}{4}$ of an hour = ▢ minutes **45**

⓱ $\frac{1}{2}$ of an hour = ▢ minutes **30**

⓲ 1 hour = ▢ minutes **60**

⓳ $\frac{1}{3}$ of an hour = ▢ minutes **20**

Customary Weight Lesson 9.4
Convert each measure from pounds to ounces or from ounces to pounds. Write the new measure. Then answer the questions.

Lillia is going camping in the mountains. She must take a plane to get to the mountains. The plane has a weight limit for each passenger. With all of her luggage, she cannot weigh more than 265 pounds.

⓴ food 240 ounces = **15** pounds

㉑ first aid kit 32 ounces = **2** pounds

㉒ sleeping bag 48 ounces = **3** pounds

㉓ tent 128 ounces = **8** pounds

㉔ ropes 32 ounces = **2** pounds

㉕ backpack 80 ounces = **5** pounds

㉖ Lillia 1,920 ounces = **120** pounds

㉗ shelter gear 80 ounces = **5** pounds

㉘ clothes 160 ounces = **10** pounds

㉙ cooking gear 80 ounces = **5** pounds

㉚ How many pounds does she have altogether? How many more pounds of equipment could she bring with her? **175 pounds; she could bring 90 pounds more.**

368   Textbook This lesson is available in the *eTextbook*.

Wrap-Up

1 Discuss 5

Concept/Question Board

Review the Concept/Question Board with students.

- Discuss students' contributions to the Concept side of the Board.
- Have students re-pose their questions, and lead a discussion to find satisfactory answers.

Chapter Projects APPLYING

Provide an opportunity for students who have worked on one or more of the projects outlined on page 343C to share their work with the class. Allow each student or student group five minutes to present or discuss their projects. For formal assessment, use the rubrics found in *Across the Curriculum Math Connections;* the rubric for **Evaluate Campfire Songs** is on page 97, and the rubric for **Plan a Family Camping Trip** is on page 101. For informal assessment, use the following rubric and questions.

	Exceeds Expectations	Meets Expectations	Minimally Meets Expectations
Applies mathematics in real-world situations:	❏	❏	❏
Demonstrates strong engagement in the activity:	❏	❏	❏

Evaluate Campfire Songs

- Why do you think people sing songs around campfires?
- What songs did you choose for your program? Why did you choose those songs?
- How long was your program? How did you measure the time?
- What criteria did you use to evaluate the program?
- How did you evaluate your program?
- What type of campfire song do you like best? Why?
- What changes would you make to your program? Why?

Plan a Family Camping Trip

- What park did you choose for your camping trip? Why did you choose that park?
- What information did you find about the park you chose?
- What unit did you use to measure the distance? Why did you choose that unit?
- How did you describe the park's environment?
- What other information did you include in your paragraph?
- What items did you include in your list? Why did you choose those items?

2 Assign Student Pages 25

Key Ideas Review UNDERSTANDING

Have students complete the Review questions independently or in small groups. Then discuss each question as a class.

Possible Answers

Problem ❶ This problem involves converting centimeters to meters. The answer is 20. Students should reason that because there are 100 centimeters in 1 meter, 10 tiles placed end to end will be 1 meter long because each square tile is 10 centimeters wide. Therefore, 20 tiles can be laid end to end in one row across the width of the floor.

Problem ❷ This problem involves converting feet to inches. The answer is 31 inches. John's bedroom is 8 feet, or 96 inches, long. Because the bed takes up 65 inches of wall space, there will be 31 inches left.

Problem ❸ This problem involves converting pints to cups. Students should determine that Ms. Maples does have enough milk to make the cookies because $\frac{1}{2}$ pint is equivalent to 1 cup.

Extended Response

Problem ❹ This problem involves converting yards to feet and determining an approximate answer. Students should convert 13 yards to 39 feet and 14 yards to 42 feet, and then explain that the length of the classroom could be between 39 feet and 42 feet, so a length of 40 feet is possible.

Extended Response

Problem ❺ This problem involves converting pounds to ounces and determining an approximate answer. Students should convert 5 pounds to 80 ounces, and then explain that because the bag weighed a bit more than 5 pounds, it could reasonably weigh 82 ounces.

CHAPTER 9 Key Ideas Review

In this chapter you learned about the customary and metric systems of measure.

You learned to estimate and measure length, weight, and capacity in these systems.

You learned how to convert from one measure to another within each system.

- -

Solve each problem.

❶ Sanjay is laying square tiles on his bathroom floor. Each tile is 10 centimeters wide, and the floor is 2 meters wide. If Sanjay lays the tiles across the width of the floor, about how many tiles can he lay end to end in each row? **20 tiles**

❷ The length of one of the walls in John's bedroom is 8 feet. The length of his bed is 65 inches. If he places the bed along the wall, how much space will be left along the wall for other things? **31 inches**

❸ Ms. Maples is making cookies. The recipe calls for 1 cup of milk, and she has $\frac{1}{2}$ pint of milk left. Does she have enough milk to make the cookies? **yes**

Extended Response **Provide** a detailed answer for the following exercises.

❹ Aileen measured the length of her classroom and reported that the length was a bit more than 13 yards but less than 14 yards. Could the length of the classroom be 40 feet? Why or why not? Explain your answer.

❺ Taylor weighed a bag of apples. It weighed a bit more than 5 pounds. Could its weight be 82 ounces? Why or why not? Explain your answer. See *Teacher's Edition* for answers.

Milk

Chapter 9 • Key Ideas Review 369

Chapter Review

Use the Chapter 9 Review to indicate areas in which each student is having difficulty or in which the class may need help. If students do well on the Chapter 9 Review, you may wish to skip directly to the Chapter Test; if not, you may want to spend a day or so helping students overcome their individual difficulties before taking the Practice Test.

Next to each set of problems is a list of the lessons in the chapter that covered those concepts. If they need help, students can refer to a specific lesson for additional instruction. You can also use this information to make additional assignments based on the previous lesson concepts.

Have students complete pages 370–371 on their own. For review purposes, you may want to do some of the word problems on page 371 as a class.

Monitoring Student Progress

Problems 1–18 Lessons 9.1–9.6

If . . . students have difficulty with these conversions,

Then . . . remind them to think about whether they are moving from a larger number to a smaller number or vice versa, then check their answers for reasonableness.

Problems 19–20 Lesson 9.7

If . . . students have difficulty solving these problems,

Then . . . have students practice estimating the length, weight, and capacity of various objects and then measuring to check their estimates.

Problems 21–22 Lesson 9.8

If . . . students have difficulty determining elapsed time,

Then . . . determine whether students have computational problems or problems telling time, and then provide individual tutoring as needed.

CHAPTER 9 · Chapter Review

Lessons 9.1–9.6 Convert.

1. ☐ centimeters = 5 meters   500
2. ☐ meters = 6 kilometers   6,000
3. 2 kilometers = ☐ meters   2,000
4. 300 centimeters = ☐ meters   3

5. ☐ inches = 5 feet   60
6. 10 yards = ☐ feet   30
7. 36 feet = ☐ yards   12
8. ☐ feet = 2 miles   10,560

9. 5,000 grams = ☐ kilograms   5
10. ☐ grams = 10 kilograms   10,000

11. ☐ ounces = 2 pounds   32
12. 6 pounds = ☐ ounces   96

13. ☐ milliliters = 3 liters   3,000
14. 16 liters = ☐ milliliters   16,000

15. ☐ cups = 3 pints   6
16. 4 pints = ☐ quarts   2
17. ☐ cups = 2 quarts   8
18. ☐ quarts = 10 gallons   40

370   📖 Textbook This lesson is available in the *eTextbook*.

Lesson 9.7

Solve each problem.

19. **Extended Response** Tricia wants to buy a fish tank that could fit on her desk. What customary measuring unit should she use to measure the fish tank and her desk? Explain your answer.
She should use feet. Inches are too small, and yards are too big.
If Tricia could measure the weight of her new goldfish, which customary measuring unit would she use? Why? Tricia would measure the goldfish's weight in ounces.

20. **Extended Response** A zookeeper needs to weigh a new baby elephant. What metric measuring unit should he use to weigh the baby elephant? Explain your answer.
He should use kilograms because grams are too small.
Would the zookeeper use the same measuring unit to measure the amount of water the baby elephant drinks every day? Why? No. He would use units of capacity to measure the amount of water.

Lesson 9.8

Measure the elapsed time.

21. Bob read a book from 7:50 to 9:15. How long did he spend reading?   1 hour and 25 minutes

22. Karl wanted to get a good night's sleep. He went to bed at 9:45 P.M. and woke up at 6:15 A.M. How long did he sleep?   8 hours and 30 minutes

3 **Chapter Tests** 40

Practice Test

Student Pages 372–375

- The Chapter 9 Practice Test on **Student Edition** pages 372–375 provides an opportunity to formally evaluate students' proficiency with concepts developed in this chapter.
- The content is similar to the Chapter 9 Review in standardized format.

Problem 30 Extended Response

Problem 30 involves measuring elapsed time. For Part b, students should note that the schedule does include 45 minutes for science and 45 minutes for social studies. For Part d, students should determine that reading and language arts is scheduled for 2 hours each day, which is 10 hours each week because $2 \times 5 = 10$.

CHAPTER 9 **Practice Test**

Answer each question.

1. Francis ran 1 kilometer. How many meters did he run? **1,000**

2. How many centimeters are in 1 meter? **100**

3. Bob counted 250 pennies. How can he write this amount of money in dollars and cents? **$2.50**

4. Marcus has a 2-liter bottle of sports drink. How many milliliters of sports drink does he have? **2,000**

5. Casey's mother is making fruit punch. She needs 3 quarts of lemonade. How many cups is this? **12**

6. What is the inverse function of $+7$? **-7**

7. What is an expression that has the same product as 9×7? **7×9**

8. Paul is 4 feet tall. How many inches tall is he? **48**

9. Karla's new football weighs 15 ounces. About how many pounds does it weigh? **1**

10. Rafael's piano lesson lasts 60 minutes. How many hours is that? **1**

11. Should you use a gram or a kilogram to measure the weight of a stamp? **gram**

12. Should you use inches or yards to measure the perimeter of your classroom? **yards**

13. Should you use cups or quarts to measure the amount of coffee in a coffee mug? **cups**

14. Should you use kilometers or meters to measure the length of the Potomac River. **kilometers**

372   Textbook This lesson is available in the *eTextbook*.

Student Page

Choose the unit that makes sense.

15. A deck of cards is about 1.6 ▢ thick.
    - Ⓐ kilometers
    - Ⓑ meters
    - Ⓒ centimeters
    - Ⓓ yards

16. A deck of cards weighs about 50 ▢.
    - Ⓐ grams
    - Ⓑ kilograms
    - Ⓒ kilometers
    - Ⓓ inches

17. A standard ruler is usually 12 ▢ long.
    - Ⓐ kilometers
    - Ⓑ meters
    - Ⓒ inches
    - Ⓓ yards

18. The distance from first base to second base in baseball is 90 ▢.
    - Ⓐ inches
    - Ⓑ feet
    - Ⓒ yards
    - Ⓓ kiloliters

19. A baseball weighs about 5 ▢.
    - Ⓐ pounds
    - Ⓑ ounces
    - Ⓒ inches
    - Ⓓ kilograms

20. A whale is about 8 ▢ long.
    - Ⓐ kilometers
    - Ⓑ meters
    - Ⓒ centimeters
    - Ⓓ inches

21. A whale can weigh up to 5,000 ▢.
    - Ⓐ kilograms
    - Ⓑ grams
    - Ⓒ ounces
    - Ⓓ milliliters

Chapter 9 • Practice Test   373

CHAPTER 9 Practice Test

Convert. Then choose the correct answer.

22. 1 gallon = ▮ pints
- Ⓐ 2
- Ⓑ 4
- Ⓒ 8
- Ⓓ 10

23. ▮ dimes = 3 dollars
- Ⓐ 10
- Ⓑ 30
- Ⓒ 50
- Ⓓ 60

24. 2 meters = ▮ centimeters
- Ⓐ 2
- Ⓑ 20
- Ⓒ 200
- Ⓓ 2,000

25. ▮ inches = 2 yards
- Ⓐ 72
- Ⓑ 60
- Ⓒ 48
- Ⓓ 36

26. ▮ kilograms = 7,000 grams
- Ⓐ 7,000
- Ⓑ 700
- Ⓒ 70
- Ⓓ 7

27. If 3 is the input, what is the output?

- Ⓐ 3
- Ⓑ 6
- Ⓒ 9
- Ⓓ 12

28. If 6 is the output, what is the input?

- Ⓐ 18
- Ⓑ 32
- Ⓒ 54
- Ⓓ 56

29. Which mixed number is equal to $\frac{17}{6}$?
- Ⓐ $3\frac{1}{6}$
- Ⓑ $2\frac{5}{6}$
- Ⓒ $2\frac{2}{6}$
- Ⓓ $2\frac{1}{6}$

374   📖 Textbook This lesson is available in the eTextbook.

Answer this question.

30. **Extended Response** Mr. Davis is deciding on a schedule for the new school year. The school day begins at 8:10 A.M. and ends at 2:35 P.M. Here is his proposed schedule:

Subject	Time
Reading and Language Arts	8:15–10:15
Math	10:15–11:30
Lunch and Recess	11:30–12:00
Specials	12:00–12:45
Science	12:45–1:30
Social Studies	1:30–2:15
Cleanup	2:15–2:30

a. How long is math class?   75 minutes

b. Mr. Davis wants to set aside at least 45 minutes for science and 45 minutes for social studies every day. Does his schedule show that? Explain.   Yes, science and social studies are each 45 minutes long.

c. Which subject does he plan to spend the most time on each day?   reading and language arts

d. Mr. Davis wants his students to study reading and language arts for at least 6 hours each school week. Does his schedule show that? Explain.
yes; See *Teacher's Edition* for explanation.

Chapter Test ✓ COMPUTING

For further evaluation instead of or in addition to this test, you might want to have students take the Chapter 9 Test provided in *Assessment*.

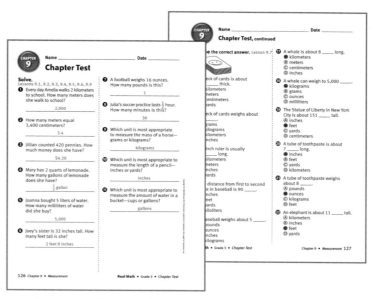

Assessment Pages 126–127

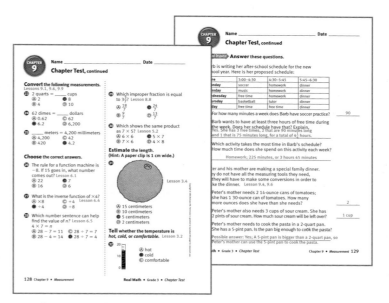

Assessment Pages 128–129

4 Assess and Differentiate

 Assess Use *eAssess* to record and analyze evidence of student understanding.

A Gather Evidence

Use the Daily Class Assessment Records in **Assessment** or **eAssess** to record Informal and Formal Assessments.

Informal Assessment

☑ **Key Ideas Review** `UNDERSTANDING`

Did the student
- ❑ make important observations?
- ❑ extend or generalize learning?
- ❑ provide insightful answers?
- ❑ pose insightful questions?

Informal Assessment

☑ **Project** `APPLYING`

Did the student
- ❑ meet the project objectives?
- ❑ communicate clearly?
- ❑ complete the project accurately?
- ❑ connect mathematics to real-world situations?

Formal Assessment

☑ **Chapter Test** `COMPUTING`

Score the test, and record the results.

B Summarize Findings

Analyze and summarize assessment data for each student. Determine which Chapter Follow-Up is appropriate for each student. Use the Student Assessment Record in **Assessment** or **eAssess** to update assessment records.

C Chapter Follow-Up ● DIFFERENTIATE INSTRUCTION

Based on your observations, use these teaching strategies for chapter follow-up.

ENRICH	PRACTICE	RETEACH	INTERVENTION
If . . . students demonstrate **secure understanding** of chapter concepts,	**If . . .** students demonstrate **competent understanding** of chapter concepts,	**If . . .** students demonstrate **emerging understanding** of chapter concepts,	**If . . .** students demonstrate **minimal understanding** of chapter concepts,
Then . . . move on to the next chapter.	**Then . . .** move on to the next chapter.	**Then . . .** move on to the next chapter, but continue to provide cumulative review.	**Then . . .** intensive intervention is still needed before they start the next chapter.

Mosquito Lake

Context of the Thinking Story Ferdie's family goes to Mosquito Lake, and Ferdie discovers that it is usually good to test things more than once.

Lesson Planner

OBJECTIVES
To develop logical thinking while integrating reading skills with mathematics

NCTM STANDARDS
Problem Solving
- Building new mathematical knowledge through problem solving
- Solving problems that arise in mathematics and in other contexts

Communication
- Communicating mathematical thinking coherently and clearly
- Analyzing and evaluating the mathematical thinking and strategies of others

READING STANDARDS
- Listening for details
- Drawing conclusions
- Making inferences
- Evaluating information

Using the Thinking Story

The Thinking Story may be used anytime throughout the chapter. Read the Thinking Story "Mosquito Lake" to your class as they follow along in the **Student Edition** on pages 380–383. As you read the story, give students time to think about each question, but not so much that they forget the point being made.

Thinking Story

Mosquito Lake

"Hooray!" shouted Ferdie. "We're going camping at Mosquito Lake."

"I wish we were going camping someplace else," said Portia. "It always rains at Mosquito Lake."

"How do you know that?" asked Ferdie.

"Because it has rained every time I've been there," she said.

"Oh," said Ferdie, "then I guess you're right."

Does Portia have a good reason for saying it rains all the time at Mosquito Lake? ❶

What do you need to know before you can decide if Portia has a good reason? ❷

"How many times have you been to Mosquito Lake?" their mother asked.

"Lots of times," said Portia. "Well, let me see … just twice, I guess."

376

Is that enough times to know how often it rains at Mosquito Lake? ❸

If Portia had been there 20 times and it had rained every time, would you be more willing to believe her? ❹

"I've been going to Mosquito Lake for years and years," their mother said, "and it hardly ever rains. It just happened to rain the two times you were along. According to the weather report, it isn't likely to rain this weekend."

"Good," said Ferdie. "Then we won't have to take along anything to protect us from the rain."

Can they be sure it isn't going to rain? ❺

Why or why not? ❻

"I think we'll take raincoats and a waterproof tent, just in case," their mother said. "It probably won't rain, but you can never be sure, and it's best to be prepared."

Saturday morning the three of them piled into a car and headed for Mosquito Lake. As soon as they arrived, Ferdie ran down to the water and put his foot in it. "This lake is cold," he complained.

"You can't be sure," said Portia. "You just tested one little part of it. Maybe the rest of the lake is warm."

Could Portia be right? ❼

Why or why not? ❽

"That's silly," Ferdie said. "If one part of the lake is cold, it's all cold." But the children ran down the beach anyway and tested the water in different places. Strangely enough, the rest of the lake water

was warmer. Ferdie and Portia investigated and found a spring of cold water bubbling up out of the ground where Ferdie had tested the first time. That was why the lake water was colder there.

As soon as the sun went down, the mosquitoes came out. Portia sprayed her arm to keep the mosquitoes off. "This stuff doesn't work," she said. "I sprayed my arm all over, and right away two mosquitoes came and landed on it."

Does Portia have a good reason for saying the spray doesn't work? ❾

Guided Discussion

As students answer the questions in the story, ask them to communicate how they decided on their answers. Allow students to debate the answers if necessary.

1 no

2 how many times she has been there

3 no

4 yes

5 no

6 Weather predictions are not always right.

7 yes

8 There may be a reason that part of the lake is cold and part of the lake is warm.

9 yes

10 no

11 In this case, if the spray does not work on Portia's arm, there is no reason to believe it will work on her legs or her other arm.

12 yes

13 She tried the shortest piece.

14 the shortest piece

15 no

16 yes

17 It is from the same container that Portia tried.

18 because the new carton has been kept cold

"You can't tell from that," Ferdie said. "You sprayed only one part of you. If you tried your other arm and your legs, you might find it worked there."

Do you agree with Ferdie's argument? **10**

Why or why not? **11**

Portia tried spraying herself all over, but still the mosquitoes kept landing and biting her. Her mother looked at the can and said, "Someone brought the wrong thing. This isn't mosquito spray; it's hairspray. No wonder it doesn't keep the mosquitoes off!"

Ferdie and Portia went off to gather wood for the outdoor fireplace. They found many long pieces of wood and brought back as many as they could carry. Their mother took the shortest one and tried to lay it in the fireplace. It wouldn't fit. "I'm afraid all the pieces of wood you brought are too long," she said.

Does their mother have a good reason for saying all the pieces of wood are too long? **12**

Why or why not? **13**

"You just tried one of them," Ferdie said. "Maybe the rest of them will fit."

Which piece of wood did their mother try? **14**

Could the other pieces fit if the shortest one didn't? **15**

"I tried the shortest one," their mother said. "If it's too long, then all the others must be even longer. Since we don't have an ax, I guess you'll have to go find shorter pieces of wood."

It was a hot night, but Ferdie and Portia slept with the tent closed to keep the mosquitoes away. In the morning Portia took the big jug of milk they had kept in the tent with them and poured herself a cupful to drink. "This milk is all sour!" she said.

378

"You can't tell for sure," Ferdie said. "You tried only one cupful. I'm going to pour myself some, and I'll bet it will be all right."

Do you think the milk Ferdie pours will be sour? **16**

Why or why not? **17**

The milk Ferdie poured was sour. He tried some more, and it was sour too. "We have no milk to drink," Ferdie complained. "It's all sour."

"Don't give up yet," said their mother. "There's another carton of milk in the cooler. Maybe it is still good."

"No, it isn't," Ferdie said. "I just found out that if some of the milk is sour, it's all sour."

Why could Ferdie be wrong about the carton of milk? **18**

They opened the new carton of milk and found that it was still good. "Milk keeps better when it stays cold," their mother said. "That's probably why this milk is still good."

"I'm confused," Ferdie said. "Sometimes everything is like the part you try, and sometimes it isn't. How can you tell?"

"You can't always tell," their mother said. "You have to think about whether the other parts could be different or whether they are probably the same. I think you have the right idea that it's usually good to test things more than once."

The End

Lesson Study

Reflect on each of the lessons you taught in this chapter. Rate each one on the following scale, and then consider ways to maintain or improve positive teaching experiences in the future.

Lessons	Very Effective	Effective	Less Effective	What Worked	Ways to Improve
9.1 Metric Length					
9.2 Customary Length					
9.3 Metric Weight					
9.4 Customary Weight					
9.5 Metric Capacity					
9.6 Customary Capacity					
9.7 Choosing the Correct Unit					
9.8 Measuring Elapsed Time					
9.9 Understanding the Metric System					

Lessons

Decimals

Teaching for Understanding

This chapter introduces students to decimals and their practical applications. Students will explore the relationship between decimals and fractions and learn how to add, subtract, multiply, and divide decimals in both strictly computational and problem-solving situations.

Prerequisite Skills and Concepts

- Comparing Fractions ● Multidigit Addition and Subtraction ● Multidigit Multiplication

Decimals Skills Trace

Before Grade 3	Grade 3	After Grade 3
Grades K–2 Students are informally and formally introduced to multidigit addition and subtraction	**Chapters 2, 7, and 8** formally introduced students to multidigit addition and subtraction, multidigit multiplication, and fractions, respectively. **This chapter** formally introduces students to decimals and their practical applications.	Explore the relationship among fractions, decimals, and percentages

Problem solving is in every lesson. This chapter includes the following:

CHAPTER INTRODUCTION Students use what they already know about tenths to estimate parts of a whole (pp. 380I–381C).

EXPLORING PROBLEM SOLVING The first lesson focuses on the Make a Physical Model and Guess, Check, and Revise strategies (pp. 394–395, 395A). The second lesson provides practice interpreting measurements on diagrams (pp. 408–408A).

THINKING STORY In "Muddle the Engineer" students help a character develop strategies for building bridges and buildings. (pp. 418–421)

Games

- **Harder Shopping Game** (Lesson 10.2)
- **Metric Unit Game** (Lesson 10.3)
- **Decimal Roll a Problem Game** (Lessons 10.5–10.8)
- **Store Game** (Lesson 10.9)
- **Harder Store Game** (Lesson 10.9)

Math Background

Decimals

About Decimals

Our decimal system lets us write numbers of all sizes, using a symbol called the decimal point. Because of money, our world revolves around decimals. Even the library uses the Dewey Decimal System. Food is packaged by weight and uses decimals. The metric system uses decimals since it is a base-ten system.

Most children through the age of 9 or 10 think of fractions and percents as operators. That is, you take a fraction of something or a percent of something. However, they think of decimals as numbers; for example, you do not take 0.73 of something. Lesson 10.4 is designed to help students begin to develop an intuitive feel for the relationship that adults see between fractions, decimals, and percents.

Key Concepts

- To help students understand the meaning of decimals by relating them to dollars and cents and to conversions within the metric system of measures
- To provide applications that make use of both decimals and fractions
- To solve problems that involve the addition, subtraction, multiplication, and division of decimals with two decimal places

Types of Problems

There are different types of problems that students use in learning decimals.

COMPUTATION PROBLEM

CONVERSION   37 dm = ? m and ? dm

MULTIPLE CHOICE $106 - 5.43 = ?$, a. 437, b. 51.7, c. 100.57

MULTIPLICATION 7.5×2

WORD PROBLEM

EVALUATIVE   Wei made curtains for one window. She used 2.68 yards of cloth. How many yards of cloth will she need to make curtains for four more windows the same size?

MULTI-STEP   Building laws in Shasta say that a house cannot be more than 6.5 meters from front to back. Ms. Soto measured her house. It was exactly 5.75 meters from front to back. But she forgot to measure the small front porch. The porch floor sticks out 7 decimeters from the house. The porch railing sticks out another 4 centimeters. Does the house follow the law? If so, how much extra room does Ms. Soto have? If not, how far over the limit is the house?

EXTENDED RESPONSE   If a bird flew directly between Cat Corners and Duck Crossing, about how far would it fly? Explain your answer.

Using Decimals

USING DECIMALS
Decimal and Metric Prefixes
1000 = thousand = kilo-
100 = hundred = hecto-
10 = ten = deca-
0.10 = tenth = deci-
0.01 = hundredth = centi-
0.001 = thousandth = milli-

What Research Says

About Decimal Numbers

How Children Learn Decimal Numbers

"Children need to learn that rational numbers are numbers in the same way that whole numbers are numbers. For children to use rational numbers to solve problems, they need to learn that the same rational number may be represented in different ways, as a fraction, a decimal, or a percent. Fraction concepts and representations need to be related to those of division, measurement, and ratio. Decimal and fractional representations need to be connected and understood. Building these connections takes extensive experience with rational numbers over a substantial period of time. Researchers have documented that difficulties in working with rational numbers can often be traced to weak conceptual understanding….Instructional sequences in which more time is spent at the outset on developing meaning for the various representations of rational numbers and the concept of unit have been shown to promote mathematical proficiency."

Kilpatrick, J., J. Swafford, and B. Findell, eds. *Adding It Up: Helping Children Learn Mathematics.* Washington, D.C.: National Research Council/ National Academy Press, 2001, pp. 415–416.

"Most students do not develop sufficient meanings for decimal symbols when they are introduced. Soon students are asked to learn rules for manipulating decimals. Because they do not know what the symbols mean, they have no way of figuring out why the rules work. They must memorize each rule and hope that they remember on which problems to use them, a method that works for the simplest routine problems that are practiced heavily but not for problems that are even a little different. Without knowing what the symbols mean, students are unable to judge whether their answers are reasonable or whether they are on the right track. Because decimals are the last number system with which many students work, the initial errors they make persist and are difficult to remediate."

Hiebert, James. "Decimal Fractions." *Arithmetic Teacher.* March 1987.

Research-Based Teaching Strategies

In third grade, students will use models and other strategies to represent and study decimal numbers. Students need to be exposed to a variety of activities to help them develop a rich understanding of decimal numbers and equivalence among the many representations of fractional parts of a whole. For example, calculator activities can help expose students to counting and place value patterns for decimal numbers as they count up to and then beyond 1.0. Similarly, involving students in an exploration of metric conversions while working with various metric units of measure provides the students with meaningful and practical contexts of common uses of decimal numbers in their world.

National Council of Teachers of Mathematics. *Principles and Standards for School Mathematics.* Reston, VA: NCTM, 2000, pp. 148–150.

 RESEARCH IN ACTION

Decimal Numbers Chapter 10 will reinforce the development of part-whole number concepts and the understanding of how decimal numbers represent fractional parts of a whole.

Metric Units of Measure In Chapter 10 students will develop awareness and appreciation of the role that 'ten' plays in metric units of measure and metric conversions.

Equivalence Chapter 10 will provide students with a variety of activities and contexts for thinking about part-whole relationships with numbers as represented by decimals, fractions, and percents.

Place Value The importance of place value is reinforced throughout Chapter 10, as students explore and compare decimal forms of fractional numbers.

Vocabulary

centimeter (Lesson 10.3) a unit of length in the metric system equal to one-hundredth of a meter

decimal point (Lesson 10.1) a dot used in separating the ones digit from the tenths digit

decimeter (Lesson 10.3) a unit of length in the metric system equal to one-tenth of a meter

hundredth (Lesson 10.1) one of a hundred equal parts; $\frac{1}{100}$

kilometer (Lesson 10.9) a unit of length in the metric system equal to 1,000 meters

tenth (Lesson 10.1) one of ten equal parts

English Learner

Cognates

For English learners, a quick way to acquire new English vocabulary is to build on what is known in the primary language.

English	Spanish
decimals	decimales
decimal point	punto decimal
dollars	dólares
cents	centavos
meters	metros
centimeter	centímetro
decimeter	decímetro
fraction	fracción
percent	por ciento
problems	problemas
blank	blanco
correct	correcto
exercise	ejercicio
multiplication	multiplicación
to multiply	multiplicar
division	división
to divide	dividir
application	aplicación
combination	combinación

Access Vocabulary

English learners may understand words in different contexts or not understand idioms. Review chapter vocabulary for this concern. For example:

laps	number of times one runs around a fixed track
price tag	a small label put on an item to tell how much it costs
exchange	to trade one thing for another thing that is worth the same amount
sell at a profit	the amount of money you have after paying for the cost of the item that you are selling
meterstick	a measuring stick that is one meter long
running errands	doing small tasks outside the home, such as shopping dropping things off, and picking things up
shortcuts	quicker ways of doing tasks

Chapter Planner

Lessons	Objectives	NCTM Standards	State Standards
10.1 **Where Do We See Decimals?** pages 382A–383A	To introduce students to decimals and their applications	Number and Operations	
10.2 **Decimals and Money** pages 384A–385A	To review the relationship between dollars and dimes	Number and Operations	
10.3 **Decimals and Metric Measures** pages 386A–387A	To develop students' understanding of how decimal numbers are used in the context of metric measurement	Measurement, Geometry, Problem Solving	
10.4 **Comparing Decimals and Fractions** pages 388A–389A	To explore the relationship between decimals and fractions	Number and Operations	
10.5 **Adding Decimals** pages 390A–393B	To introduce adding decimals with tenths and hundredths	Number and Operations, Data Analysis and Probability	
10.6 **Subtracting Decimals** pages 398A–401B	To introduce subtracting decimals with tenths and hundredths	Number and Operations, Problem Solving	
10.7 **Multiplying Decimals by Whole Numbers** pages 402A–403A	To introduce multiplying decimals by whole numbers	Number and Operations, Problem Solving	
10.8 **Dividing Decimals** pages 404A–405A	To explore division involving decimals	Number and Operations	
10.9 **Decimal Applications** pages 406A–407A	To explore practical applications of decimals	Problem Solving Representation	

Vocabulary	Manipulatives and Materials	Games to reinforce skills and concepts
decimal point tenth hundredth	• Response Wheels • Package labels or other real-world examples of the use of decimal notation (optional)	
	• Response Wheels • Play money ($100 bills, $50 bills, $20 bills, $10 bills, $5 bills, and $1 bills) • One 0–5 Number Cube	Harder Shopping Game
centimeter decimeter	• Response Wheels • Meterstick • Metric Unit Game Mat	Metric Unit Game
	Response Wheels	
	• Response Wheels • One 5–10 Number Cube • Meterstick • Play money	Decimal Roll a Problem Game
	• Response Wheels • One 5–10 Number Cube	Decimal Roll a Problem Game
	• Response Wheels • One 5–10 Number Cube	Decimal Roll a Problem Game
	• Response Wheels • Play money ($100 bills, $10 bills, $1 bills, dimes, and pennies)	Decimal Roll a Problem Game
kilometer	• Response Wheels • Store Game Mat	Store Game and Harder Store Game

Additional Resources

Differentiated Instruction

Intervention Support Guide Provides instruction for the following prerequisite skills:

- Lesson 10.A Comparing Fractions
- Lesson 10.B Multidigit Addition and Subtraction
- Lesson 10.C Multidigit Multiplication

Enrichment Support Guide Extends lesson concepts

Practice Reinforces lesson skills and concepts

Reteach Support Guide Provides alternate instruction for lesson concepts

English Learner Support Guide Previews and reviews lesson concepts and vocabulary for English learners

Technology

The following electronic resources are available:

Planner Lessons 10.1–10.9

Presentation Lessons 10.1–10.9

Textbook Lessons 10.1–10.9

Assess Lessons 10.1–10.9

MathTools *Coins and Money* Lesson 10.2
　　　　　　Estimating Proportion Lesson 10.4

Assessment

Informal Assessment rubrics at the end of each lesson provide daily evaluation of student math proficiency.

Chapter Planner, continued

Problem Solving	When to use	Objectives	NCTM Standards	Skills Covered
Chapter Introduction pp. 380I–381C 15–30 minutes	Use after the Chapter 10 Pretest.	To introduce chapter concepts in a problem-solving setting	Measurement, Communication	Using decimals
Exploring Problem Solving pp. 394–395, 395A 30–45 minutes	Use anytime during the chapter.	To explore methods of solving nonroutine problems	Measurement, Communication	Using decimals, Comparison, Computation
Exploring Problem Solving pp. 408–408A 45–60 minutes	Use anytime after the first Exploring Problem Solving.	To explore methods of solving nonroutine problems	Number and Operations, Reasoning and Proof	Using decimals, Computation
Thinking Story–Muddle the Engineer pp. 418–419, 420–421 20–30 minutes	Use anytime during the chapter.	To develop logical reasoning while integrating reading skills with mathematics	Problem Solving, Communication	Proportion, Reasoning, Measuring

Review	When to use	Objectives	NCTM Standards	Skills Covered
Cumulative Review p. 396–397 15–30 minutes	Use anytime after Lesson 10.5.	To review concepts and skills taught earlier in the year	Number and Operations, Measurement	Customary conversions; Problem solving with metric measures; Comparing, Adding, and Subtracting Decimals
Cumulative Review p. 409–410 15–30 minutes	Use anytime after Lesson 10.9.	To review concepts and skills taught earlier in the year	Number and Operations, Measurement	Adding and Subtracting, Fractions, Division, Measuring elapsed time
Chapter 10 Review pp. 412A, 412–413 30–45 minutes	Use after Lesson 10.9.	To review concepts and skills taught in the chapter	Number and Operations, Problem Solving	Adding, subtracting, multiplying, and dividing decimals; Comparing decimals and fractions; Problem solving with decimals

Assessment	When to use	Objectives	NCTM Standards	Skills Covered
Informal Assessment Rubrics pp. 383A–407A 5 minutes per student	Use at the end of the lesson.	To provide daily evaluation of math proficiency	Number and Operations	Computing, Understanding, Reasoning, Applying, Engaging
Pretest (*Assessment* pp. 131–132) 15–30 minutes	Use prior to Chapter 10.	To provide assessment of prerequisite and chapter topics	Number and Operations	Computation, Comparison
Individual Oral Assessment pp. 397A 5 minutes per student	Begin use after Lesson 10.5.	To provide alternate means of assessing students' progress	Number and Operations	Decimals and money, Comparing decimals and fractions
Mastery Checkpoint (*Assessment* pp. T72–T76) 5 minutes per student	Use after Lessons 10.2, 10.5, 10.7, and 10.8.	To provide assessment of mastery of key skills	Number and Operations	Computation, Comparison
Chapter 10 Practice Test pp. 414–415, 416–417 30–45 minutes	Use after or in place of the Chapter 10 Review.	To provide assessment or additional practice of the lesson concepts	Number and Operations, Measurement, Problem Solving	Decimals and money; Decimals and measurement; Adding, subtracting, multiplying, and dividing decimals; Decimals and fractions
Chapter 10 Test (*Assessment* pp. 138–141) 30–45 minutes	Use after or in place of the Chapter 10 Review.	To provide assessment of the chapter concepts	Number and Operations, Measurement, Problem Solving	Computation, Comparison

Technology Resources and Support

Visit SRAonline.com for online versions of the **Real Math** eSuite.

Technology for Teachers

e Presentation	Lessons 10.1–10.9 Use the **ePresentation** to interactively present chapter content.
e Planner	Use the Chapter and Lesson Planners to outline activities and time frames for Chapter 10.
e Assess	Students can take the following assessments in **eAssess**: • Chapter Pretest • Mastery Checkpoint **Lessons 10.2, 10.5, 10.7, and 10.8** • Chapter Test Teachers can record results and print reports for all assessments in this chapter.
e MathTools	**Coins and Money** Lesson 10.2 **Estimating Proportion** Lesson 10.4

Technology for Students

e Textbook	An electronic, interactive version of the **Student Edition** is available for all lessons in Chapter 10.
e MathTools	**Coins and Money** Lesson 10.2 **Estimating Proportion** Lesson 10.4
TECH KNOWLEDGE	**TechKnowledge** Level 3 provides lessons that specifically teach the Unit 10 Internet and Unit 2 Keyboarding applications that students can use in this chapter's projects.

Decimals

 Introduce Chapter 10 5

Chapter Objectives

Explain to students that in this chapter they will build on what they already know about decimals. They will

- use decimals with money and with measurements.
- explore the relationship between decimals and fractions.
- add, subtract, multiply, and divide decimals and solve problems that involve decimals.

Pretest COMPUTING

Administer the Pretest on **Assessment** pages 131–132.

The Pretest covers the following skills and topics from this chapter:

- Money and measurement conversion (Problems 1–5)
- Appropriate unit of measure (Problems 6–9)
- Elapsed time (Problems 10–12)
- Fractions, decimals, and percents (Problems 17–19)
- Operations with decimals (Problems 21–23)

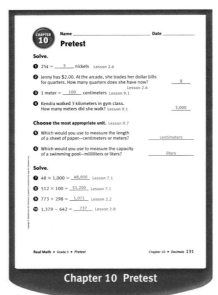

Chapter 10 Pretest

Access Prior Knowledge UNDERSTANDING

As students look at the photo on page 380, have them talk about what they see in the picture and what they know or think they know about totem poles.

You may wish to share the following information about totem poles:

- Totem poles are not religious structures; they are like signboards and libraries. They are a way to announce who lives on the land and a way to pass on stories from one generation to another.
- Many totem poles are carved from cedar logs because the wood is soft and resists rot and insects. A cedar totem pole can last more than a century.
- Centuries ago, carvers using stone tools would take a year to make a totem pole.
- It is common for one Northwest Coast American Indian tribe to invite an artist from another tribe to carve a pole for them.

 Exploring Problem Solving 30

Tell Students In Today's Lesson They Will

- see one of the tasks involved in making a totem pole.
- estimate how much of the task is done.

Materials

Paper and pencils

Using Student Pages

Have students look at the illustration at the top of page 381. Read the problem together. Then go over Problems 1 and 2, allowing time for students to think about, answer, and discuss each one before going on.

Help students as needed with guiding questions such as the following:

- **How can you tell that six-tenths of trunk A has already been stripped?** The trunk is divided into ten equal parts, so each part is a tenth, and six of the parts have been stripped.
- **For trunk B, is more than half of the job done?** yes
- **Why wouldn't three-tenths be a reasonable estimate for the work done on trunk B?** because three-tenths is less than five-tenths, or one-half, and we can see that more than half of the job has been done

Strategy Building

To check the estimates they made for Problem 1, students can use the following method to divide any length into ten equal parts.

- On a strip of paper, mark off the length of the tree trunk you want to divide.
- Place the strip of paper on a separate sheet of lined paper so that the length you marked starts at one line and ends ten lines below.

CHAPTER 10 Decimals

In This Chapter You Will Learn
- how to use decimals with money and with measurements.
- about the relationship between decimals and fractions.
- how to add, subtract, multiply, and divide decimals and to solve problems that involve decimals.

Problem Solving

A totem pole begins with a straight tree with few branches. Before figures can be carved, the tree must be cut, the branches removed, and the bark stripped.

The picture below shows six tree trunks that will become totem poles. For some of the trunks, the task of stripping the bark is further along than for others.

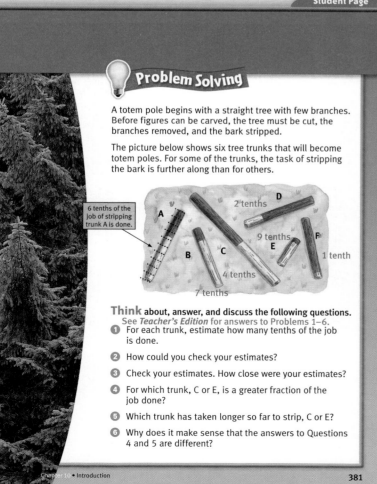

6 tenths of the job of stripping trunk A is done.

Think about, answer, and discuss the following questions.
See *Teacher's Edition* for answers to Problems 1–6.

1 For each trunk, estimate how many tenths of the job is done.

2 How could you check your estimates?

3 Check your estimates. How close were your estimates?

4 For which trunk, C or E, is a greater fraction of the job done?

5 Which trunk has taken longer so far to strip, C or E?

6 Why does it make sense that the answers to Questions 4 and 5 are different?

Chapter 10 • Introduction   381

- Make marks at the lines.

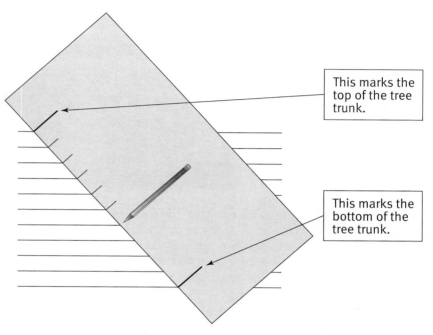

This marks the top of the tree trunk.

This marks the bottom of the tree trunk.

- The length is now divided into ten equal parts and can be used as a "tenths ruler" by placing it next to the illustration of the tree trunk.

Have students work in pairs or small groups on Problems 3–6. Explain to students that estimates do not have to be exact. If they are off by a tenth or so, that is all right. But before they measure to check their estimates, students should think about the estimates to make sure they are reasonable.

Answers to Problems 1–6

Problem 1
Estimates may vary but should be close to answers shown.

Problem 2
For example, divide each trunk into ten equal sections, and then count how many sections have been stripped.

Problem 3
Students' estimates should be reasonable; they may be off by a tenth or so.

Problem 4
E

Problem 5
C

Problem 6
Possible answer: students might argue this is true because trunk E is shorter or has a type of bark that is easier to remove.

Concept/Question Board **APPLYING**

Questions

Have students think of and write three questions they have about decimals and how they can be used. Then have them select one question to post on the Question side of the Board.

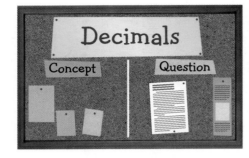

Concepts

As students work through the chapter, have them collect examples of how decimals are used in everyday situations. For each example, have them write a problem that relates to the item(s). Have them display their examples on the Concept side of the Board. Suggest the following:

- price tags
- bottles of juice or soda
- cans of cat food

Answers

Throughout the chapter, have students post answers to the questions and solutions to the problems on the Board.

3 Reflect
10

 Knowledge Age Skills

Effective Communication Have groups present their answers and results. In discussion, bring out the following points:

- Dividing things into tenths can be a useful way to compare parts of different things.
- When you use tenths, or any fraction, keep in mind what the fraction means and what whole it is part of. Four-tenths of a long tree trunk can be more tree than nine-tenths of a short tree trunk.

Home Connection

At this time, you may want to send home the letter on pages 38–41 of *Home Connection.* This letter describes what students will be learning and what activities they can do at home to support their work in school.

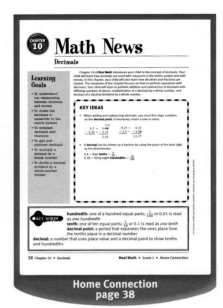

Home Connection page 38

Assess and Differentiate

 **Assess** Use **eAssess** to record and analyze evidence of student understanding.

Gather Evidence

Use the Daily Class Assessment Records in **Assessment** or **eAssess** to record Informal and Formal Assessments.

Informal Assessment

☑ **Access Prior Knowledge**

Did the student `UNDERSTANDING`
- ❏ make important observations?
- ❏ extend or generalize learning?
- ❏ provide insightful answers?
- ❏ pose insightful questions?

Informal Assessment

☑ **Concept/Question Board**

Did the student `APPLYING`
- ❏ apply learning in new situations?
- ❏ contribute concepts?
- ❏ contribute answers?
- ❏ connect mathematics to real-world situations?

Formal Assessment

☑ **Pretest** `COMPUTING`

Review student answers in each problem set.
- ❏ Money and measurement conversion (Problems 1–5)
- ❏ Appropriate unit of measure (Problems 6–9)
- ❏ Elapsed time (Problems 10–12)
- ❏ Fractions, decimals, and percents (Problems 17–19)
- ❏ Operations with decimals (Problems 21–23)

B Summarize Findings

Analyze and summarize assessment data for each student. Determine which Assessment Follow-Up is appropriate for each student. Use the Student Assessment Record in **Assessment** or **eAssess** to update assessment records.

C Assessment Follow-Up • DIFFERENTIATE INSTRUCTION

Based on your observations of each student, use these teaching strategies as a general approach to the chapter. Look for specific Differentiate Instruction and Monitoring Student Progress strategies in each lesson that relate specifically to lesson content.

ENRICH	PRACTICE	RETEACH	INTERVENTION	ENGLISH LEARNER
If . . . students demonstrate **secure understanding** of chapter concepts, **Then . . .** move quickly through the chapter or use **Enrichment** Lessons 10.1–10.9 as assessment follow-up to extend and apply understanding.	**If . . .** students grasp chapter concepts with **competent understanding,** **Then . . .** use **Practice** Lessons 10.1–10.9 as lesson follow-up to develop fluency.	**If . . .** students have prerequisite understanding but demonstrate emerging understanding of chapter concepts, **Then . . .** use **Reteach** Lessons 10.5 and 10.6 to reteach lesson concepts.	**If . . .** students are not competent with prerequisite skills, **Then . . .** use **Intervention** Lessons 10.A–10.C before each lesson to develop fluency with prerequisite skills.	Use **English Learner Support Guide** Lessons 10.1–10.9 for strategies to preteach lesson vocabulary and concepts.

Math Across the Curriculum

Preview the chapter projects with students. Assign projects to extend and enrich concepts in this chapter.

Research Monuments around the World

LANGUAGE ARTS

1–2 weeks

MATH OBJECTIVE
To reinforce studies of metric measure by researching measurements of monuments

LANGUAGE ARTS OBJECTIVE
To reinforce studies of note taking by taking notes about monuments around the world

TECHNOLOGY OBJECTIVE
To use electronic references to research monuments around the world

Have students use mathematics to research measurements of monuments and express them in meters and centimeters. To broaden the language arts concept, have students research monuments mentioned in works you are currently studying.

As part of the project, students should consider the following issues:

- how to use note cards to take notes
- monuments around the world
- organizing monuments by continent and height
- expressing measurements in meters and centimeters

For specific step-by-step instructions for this project, see *Across the Curriculum Math Connections* pages 102–105.

Problem Formulation, Planning, and Strategizing Students use note cards to organize monuments by various criteria.

Effective Communication Students clearly and convincingly communicate by using their note cards.

Write about Totem Poles   3 weeks

SOCIAL STUDIES WebQuest

MATH OBJECTIVE
To reinforce studies of tenths by creating a $\frac{1}{10}$ scale drawing

SOCIAL STUDIES OBJECTIVE
To reinforce studies of Native American cultures by writing about totem poles

TECHNOLOGY OBJECTIVE
To reinforce proper keyboarding techniques

Have students use technology to

- research information about totem poles.
- key information about their totem poles.

For this project, students use the Internet to investigate the following information:

- what a totem pole is and why totem poles are erected
- what the meanings of figures on totem poles are
- examples of what totem poles look like

For specific step-by-step instructions for this project, see *Across the Curriculum Math Connections* pages 106–111.

Problem Formulation, Planning, and Strategizing Students formulate plans for making their totem-pole drawings to scale.

Creative Work with Ideas Students create designs of totem poles with meaningful figures.

TECH KNOWLEDGE *TechKnowledge* Level 3 provides lessons that specifically teach the Unit 10 Internet and Unit 2 Keyboarding applications that students can use in this project.

OBJECTIVES
- To formally introduce the decimal point and decimal notation
- To familiarize students with common uses of decimals
- To help students understand the meaning of decimals by relating them to dollars and cents and to conversions within the metric system of measures

NCTM STANDARDS
Number and Operations
- Recognizing decimals
- Representing decimals

MATERIALS

- *Response Wheels
- Package labels or other real-world examples of the use of decimal notation (optional)

TECHNOLOGY
 Presentation Lesson 10.1

TEST PREP
Cumulative Review
Mental Math reviews two-digit addition and subtraction (Lessons 2.2 and 2.4).

Extended Response
Problem 8

Where Do We See Decimals?

Context of the Lesson This lesson develops the meaning of decimals and decimal notation. In previous grades and in Chapter 2 students were introduced to the decimal point as a way of expressing dollars and cents. The terms *decimal* or *decimal fraction* are used in this program for a numeral that is expressed with a decimal point.

See page 380B for Math Background for teachers for this lesson.

Planning for Learning ● DIFFERENTIATE INSTRUCTION

INTERVENTION
If . . . students lack the prerequisite skill of multidigit addition and subtraction,

Then . . . teach *Intervention* Lesson 10.B.

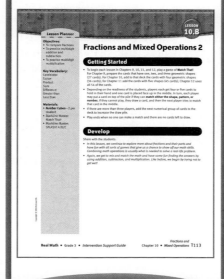

Intervention Lesson 10.B

ENGLISH LEARNER
Preview

If . . . students need language support,

Then . . . use Lesson 10.1 in *English Learner Support Guide* to preview lesson concepts and vocabulary.

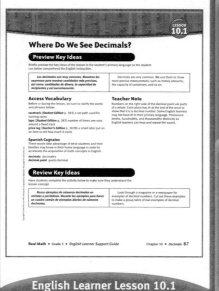

English Learner Lesson 10.1

ENRICH
If . . . students are proficient in the lesson concepts,

Then . . . emphasize additional game time with a game of their choice.

PRACTICE
If . . . students would benefit from additional practice,

Then . . . extend Skill Practice before assigning the student pages.

RETEACH
If . . . students are having difficulty understanding the meaning of decimals,

Then . . . extend the discussion of student page 382 before assigning the student pages.

Vocabulary
decimal point *n.* a dot used in separating the ones digit from the tenths digit
tenth \tenth\ *n.* one of ten equal parts
hundredth \hun'dridth\ *n.* one of a hundred equal parts; $\frac{1}{100}$

Access Vocabulary
race track a set path used for running races
laps number of times one runs around a fixed track
price tag a small label put on an item to tell how much it costs

Spanish Cognates
decimals decimales
decimal point punto decimal

Mental Math 5

  Present related multidigit addition and subtraction exercises. Write exercises such as the following on the board one at a time and one under the other so students can see the relationships. Have students show their answers with their **Response Wheels.**

a. 25 + 25 = 50
b. 24 + 26 = 50
c. 50 − 26 = 24
d. 51 − 26 = 25
e. 52 − 26 = 26

f. 22 + 40 = 62
g. 23 + 39 = 62
h. 24 + 38 = 62
i. 62 − 38 = 24
j. 62 − 37 = 25

1 Develop 25

Tell Students In Today's Lesson They Will

- look at examples of decimals used in everyday situations.
- understand the meaning of decimals.

Using Student Pages UNDERSTANDING Whole Group

1. Using the illustration on page 382 or having actual examples of decimal notation available, show students that such numbers are widely used and that in today's lesson they will learn about what these numbers mean.
2. Draw students' attention to the price tag on the bicycle in the illustration, and explain the value of each of the four digits.
3. Repeat for each of the four digits on the package of the catsup bottle.
4. Now write the decimal numbers for the bicycle and the catsup examples on the board. Line up the decimal points, as shown:

$$76.98$$
$$1.814$$

Point out that in both numbers the decimal point is to the right of the ones, or units, place. Tell students that this will always be true and that the other places are paired around the ones place, *not* around the point. That is, tenths and tens are one step to the right and to the left of the ones place. Hundredths and hundreds are two steps from the ones place, and so on.

Skill Practice   THUMBS UP UNDERSTANDING Whole Group

Do a brief response exercise in which you write a decimal quantity on the board, point to a digit, and make a statement about it. Have students show thumbs-up if the statement is true and thumbs-down if it is not true. Possible examples include the following:

71.42 meters
The 4 represents $\frac{4}{10}$ of 1 meter. up
The 7 represents 7 kilometers. down
The 2 represents 2 centimeters. up

$49.58
The 5 represents 5 dollars. down
The 8 represents 8 dollars. down
The 8 represents 8 cents. up
The 8 represents $\frac{8}{100}$ of 1 dollar. up

16.75 ounces
The 6 represents $\frac{6}{10}$ of an ounce. down
The 7 represents $\frac{7}{10}$ of an ounce. up
The 5 represents $\frac{5}{100}$ of an ounce. up

2 Assign Student Pages 25

Page 383 APPLYING

Have students answer the questions on page 383. Most students have not previously encountered this kind of problem, so you might want to do one or two with the class before allowing them to work independently.

As Students Finish

 Have students play a game of choice from those previously introduced, or assign games based on needed skill practice.

LESSON 10.1 Where Do We See Decimals?

Key Ideas

We see decimal numbers often.

What do decimal numbers mean? Let's consider the price tag on the bicycle.

The 7 represents 7 tens, or 70 dollars. It is in the tens place.

The 6 represents 6 ones, or 6 dollars. It is in the ones place.

$76.98

The **decimal point** separates ones and tenths.

The 9 represents $\frac{9}{10}$ of 1 dollar, or 90 cents. It is in the **tenths** place.

The 8 represents $\frac{8}{100}$ of 1 dollar, or 8 cents. It is in the **hundredths** place.

$$76.98 = 70 + 6 + 0.9 + 0.08$$

Let's look at another example, the number of kilograms of ketchup.

The 1 represents 1 kilogram. It is in the ones place.

 NET WT 64 OZ (4 LB)-1.814kg

The 8 represents $\frac{8}{10}$ of 1 kilogram, or 8 hectograms. It is in the tenths place.

The 1 represents $\frac{1}{100}$ of 1 kilogram, or 1 dekagram. It is in the hundredths place.

The 4 represents $\frac{4}{1,000}$ of 1 kilogram, or 4 grams. It is in the thousandths place.

$$1.814 = 1 + 0.8 + 0.01 + 0.004$$

382   Textbook This lesson is available in the *eTextbook*.

Student Page

Answer these questions.

1. One box of crayons costs 253¢. How much do 2 boxes cost? Write the answer using dollars and cents. $5.06

2. Bowser the dog eats about 750 grams of dog food each day. About how much does he eat in one week? Write your answer in kilograms. about 5.25 kilograms

3. Memorial Park is shaped like a triangle. Each side is 432 meters long. What is the perimeter of the park? Write your answer in kilometers. 1.296 kilometers

4. One box of crackers weighs 375 grams. How much do 5 boxes weigh? Write your answer in grams and in kilograms. 1,875 grams; 1.875 kilograms

5. The distance around a racetrack is 320 meters. How many kilometers is a race of 4 laps? 1.280 kilometers

6. If Nick saves 10¢ every day, how long will it take him to save $1.00? How long will it take him to save $2.00? 10 days; 20 days

7. Sugar the cat is 9 years old and weighs about 3 kilograms. She eats about 100 grams of cat food each day. How old will Sugar be next year? 10 years old

8. **Extended Response** Shelley is making punch for a party. She needs 5 liters of juice like the one shown in the picture. How many bottles must she buy? Explain your answer.

9. Raulito is about 173 centimeters tall. About how many meters is that? 1.73 meters

10. Juanita is 15 years old. She runs 2 laps around the track every morning. How many miles is that? can't tell; We don't know the length of the track.

Chapter 10 • Lesson 1 383

Where Do We See Decimals? **LESSON 10.1**

3 Reflect 5

Guided Discussion APPLYING Whole Group

1. Write an amount of money on the board, such as $15.45.

2. Ask if anyone knows how to multiply that amount by 10. Accept suggestions, but focus on the notion that the "short" way to do this is to simply move the decimal point one digit to the right, which has the effect of moving each digit to a place of ten times the value of its previous place. Then the new amount is $154.50.

3. Do two or three more examples, perhaps allowing students to do it the "long" way and the "short" way.

4. If time and interest allow, discuss how to multiply a decimal by 100.

Extended Response

Problem 8 The answer is 6 bottles. Students should point out that 0.9465 liters is less than 1 liter so 5 bottles will not be enough. A sixth bottle is needed to bring the total amount above 5 liters.

 Curriculum Connection: Have students look for package labels, such as bags of snacks, at home that include decimals.

 Cumulative Review: For cumulative review of previously learned skills, see page 396–397.

 Family Involvement: Assign the *Practice, Reteach,* or *Enrichment* activities depending on the needs of your students.

Encourage students to practice identifying digits in decimal numbers with a friend or a relative.

 Concept/Question Board: Have students look for additional ways to use decimals and post their ideas on the Concept/Question Board.

 Math Puzzler: Michelle is having a birthday party. There are 4 girls from her scout troop and 5 of her classmates coming. How should Michelle's mother cut the birthday cake so that Michelle and her guests each get an equal share? 10 equal slices: 1 + 4 + 5 = 10

Assess and Differentiate

e Assess Use *eAssess* to record and analyze evidence of student understanding.

A Gather Evidence

Use the Daily Class Assessment Records in *Assessment* or *eAssess* to record daily observations.

Informal Assessment
☑ **Skill Practice**

Did the student   **UNDERSTANDING**
- ❑ make important observations?
- ❑ extend or generalize learning?
- ❑ provide insightful answers?
- ❑ pose insightful questions?

Informal Assessment
☑ **Concept/Question Board**

Did the student   **APPLYING**
- ❑ apply learning in new situations?
- ❑ contribute concepts?
- ❑ contribute answers?
- ❑ connect mathematics to real-world situations?

B Summarize Findings

Analyze and summarize assessment data for each student. Determine which Assessment Follow-Up is appropriate for each student. Use the Student Assessment Record in *Assessment* or *eAssess* to update assessment records.

Assessment page T41

C Assessment Follow-Up ● DIFFERENTIATE INSTRUCTION

Based on your observations, use these teaching strategies for assessment follow-up.

INTERVENTION

Review student performance on *Intervention* Lesson 10.B to see if students have mastered prerequisite skills for this lesson.

ENGLISH LEARNER

Review

Use Lesson 10.1 in *English Learner Support Guide* to review lesson concepts and vocabulary.

ENRICH

If . . . students are proficient in the lesson concepts,

Then . . . encourage them to work on chapter projects or *Enrichment* Lesson 10.1.

Enrichment Lesson 10.1

PRACTICE

If . . . students would benefit from additional practice,

Then . . . assign *Practice* Lesson 10.1.

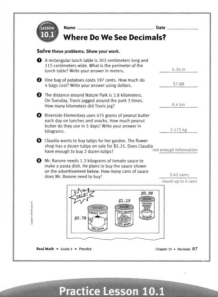

Practice Lesson 10.1

RETEACH

If . . . students struggle with working with decimal numbers,

Then . . . have them work in pairs to make up word problems using newspapers and magazines for real numbers. Then have pairs of students trade problems and solve them.

Lesson Planner

OBJECTIVES
- To review the relationship between dimes and dollars
- To develop the concept of tenths through the use of dollars and dimes

NCTM STANDARDS
Number and Operations
- Representing decimals
- Computing with decimals

Algebra
Using decimals to complete patterns

MATERIALS

- *Response Wheels
- *Play money ($100 bills, $50 bills, $20 bills, $10 bills, $5 bills, and $1 bills)
- Harder Shopping Game Mat
- One 0–5 *Number Cube*

TECHNOLOGY
- Presentation Lesson 10.2
- MathTools Coins and Money

TEST PREP
Cumulative Review
Mental Math reviews two-digit addition and subtraction (Lessons 2.2 and 2.4).

Multistep Problems
Problems 17 and 18

Extended Response
Problem 16

Decimals and Money

Context of the Lesson This is the second of nine lessons that develop the concept of decimals and decimal notation. In this lesson we develop the concept of tenths by considering the dime as one-tenth of one dollar. In the next lesson we develop the concept of tenths further by considering the decimeter as one-tenth of one meter. The concept of hundredth, although briefly included in this lesson, is considered more fully beginning in Lesson 10.4. This lesson contains a Mastery Checkpoint.

See page 380B for Math Background for teachers for this lesson.

Planning for Learning ● DIFFERENTIATE INSTRUCTION

INTERVENTION
If . . . students lack the prerequisite skill of multidigit addition and subtraction,

Then . . . teach *Intervention* Lesson 10.B.

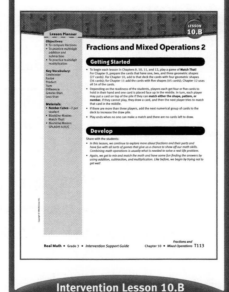

Intervention Lesson 10.B

ENGLISH LEARNER
Preview

If . . . students need language support,

Then . . . use Lesson 10.2 in *English Learner Support Guide* to preview lesson concepts and vocabulary.

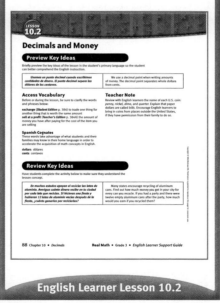

English Learner Lesson 10.2

ENRICH
If . . . students are proficient in the lesson concepts,

Then . . . emphasize using *eMath Tools: Coins and Money* to explore forming amounts of money.

PRACTICE
If . . . students would benefit from additional practice,

Then . . . extend Skill Building before assigning the student pages.

RETEACH
If . . . students are having difficulty understanding decimals and money,

Then . . . extend Guided Discussion before assigning the student pages.

Access Vocabulary
exchange to trade one thing for another thing that is worth the same amount

sell at a profit the amount of money you have after paying for the cost of the item that you are selling

Spanish Cognates
dollars dólares
cents centavos

Mental Math 5

  As in the previous lesson, give related multidigit addition and subtraction exercises. Write exercises such as the following on the board one at a time and one under the other so students can see the relationships. Have students show their answers with their *Response Wheels.*

a. 35 + 35 = 70
b. 35 + 36 = 71
c. 71 − 36 = 35
d. 72 − 36 = 36
e. 73 − 36 = 37

f. 42 + 30 = 72
g. 43 + 29 = 72
h. 44 + 28 = 72
i. 72 − 44 = 28
j. 72 − 45 = 27

1 Develop 30

Tell Students In Today's Lesson They Will
- review the relationship between dimes and dollars.
- understand what *tenths* means.

Guided Discussion UNDERSTANDING
Whole Group

1. Ask students how many dimes are in $1. 10 Then briefly elicit from students that $1 is worth the same as 10 dimes, so 1 dime is one-tenth of a dollar. Write $1 = 10 *dimes* on the board, and point out that the dollar symbol is placed before the number of dollars.

2. Continue asking similar questions, such as the following, and write the corresponding equalities on the board. Have students use play money or **eMathTools: Coins and Money** if necessary.

   ■ **How many dimes are in $5?** 50

   If students have difficulty finding the answer, have them set out 1 row of 10 dimes, determine how many rows they would need to equal $5, and then count the rows in 10s (10, 20, 30, 40, 50). Then write $5 = 50 *dimes* on the board.

   ■ **How many dimes are in $7?** 70 Write $7 = 70 *dimes* on the board.

   ■ **How many dimes are in $10?** 100 Write $10 = 100 *dimes* on the board.

3. Write statements such as the following on the board one at a time. Discuss each one with the class.

   20 dimes = _____ $2
   $7 and 8 dimes = _____ dimes 78
   $_____ and _____ dimes = 34 dimes 3; 4
   _____ dimes = $1 and 4 dimes 14
   25 dimes = $_____ and _____ dimes 2; 5

4. Explain that the last statement can have several correct answers (0 and 25, 1 and 15, 2 and 5) but that for statements such as this, students should make the number of dimes as small as possible; that is, the number of dimes should be less than 10.

5. Present two or three statements with dollar amounts greater than 9. Possible examples include the following:

   $10 and 7 dimes = _____ dimes 107
   $_____ and _____ = 127 dimes 12; 7

6. Write $10.7 on the board. Remind students that 1 dime is one-tenth of a dollar, so the money amount on the board stands for 10 dollars and seven-tenths of a dollar. Explain that a notation such as $10.7 is not commonly used for money amounts in this country, but a similar notation is often used for money amounts in other countries.

7. Now write 3.5 on the board without the dollar sign. Tell students that decimal numbers do not always show dollar amounts; often they have no units attached to them at all. Explain that this number is read *three point five* or *three and five tenths*. Continue using these terms interchangeably and in context in later lessons.

8. Finally, write $10.75 on the board, and ask if anybody can tell what the 5 stands for. Accept all answers that focus on the 5 as representing cents or hundredths of one dollar. If necessary, remind students that this is read as *ten dollars and seventy-five cents.*

Skill Building UNDERSTANDING
Whole Group

Write problems such as the following on the board one at a time. Ask volunteers to give the answers.

$4.7 = $_____ and _____ dimes 4; 7
$_____ = $3 and 9 dimes 3.9
$10 and 7 dimes = _____ dimes 107
$_____ = $12 and 8 dimes 12.8
$_____ and _____ dimes = 137 dimes 13; 7

2 Assign Student Pages 20

Pages 384–385 APPLYING
Have students complete pages 384 and 385 independently.

As Students Finish

 Harder Shopping Game

LESSON 10.2 Decimals and Money

Key Ideas

We use a decimal point when writing amounts of money.

$4.58

A dime is one-tenth of a dollar. A cent is one-hundredth of a dollar.

Solve these problems.

1. 3 dimes = ¢   30
2. 17 dimes = $ 1.70
3. 200 dimes = $ 20
4. $ = 80 dimes   8
5. $ = $8 and 7 dimes   8.70
6. $4.20 = dimes   42

7. If you have $8, how many dimes could you get for it at the bank?   80

8. If you have $7.60, how many dimes could you get?   76

9. If you take 253 dimes to the bank to exchange for $1 bills, how many $1 bills will you get? Will you have any dimes left over?   twenty-five $1 bills with 3 dimes left over

10. How many dimes could you get for 73¢? Would you have any cents left over?   7 dimes with 3 cents left over

Solve these problems. Make the least number of dimes and cents possible in each case.

11. $8.47 = $ and dimes and ¢   8; 4; 7
12. $ = $7 and 15 dimes and 8¢   8.58
13. $17.93 = $ and dimes and ¢   17; 9; 3
14. $ = $43 and 9 dimes and 10¢   44.00

384   **Textbook** This lesson is available in the *eTextbook*.

Student Page

15. Jean is thinking about her savings plan for the next year (which is not a leap year).

a. If she saves 1¢ each day, how much money is that? $3.65

b. If she saves 10¢ each day, how much money is that? $36.50

c. If she saves $1 each day, how much money is that? $365.00

d. If she saves $2 each day, how much money is that? $730.00

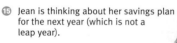

David buys umbrellas and sells them when it is raining. He sells the umbrellas at a profit. He pays $4.00 for each small umbrella and $6.00 for each large umbrella. He makes a profit of $1.50 on each small umbrella and a $2.00 profit for each large umbrella.

16. **Extended Response** Is it fair to make a greater profit on the large umbrellas? Why or why not?

17. *Multistep* If David sells 10 large umbrellas and 5 small umbrellas, how many dollars is that in sales? What is his profit? $107.50; $27.50

18. *Multistep* On one rainy day David's sales totaled $64.50. He knew he sold 3 small umbrellas but forgot how many large umbrellas did he sold. How many large umbrellas did he sell? What was his profit that day?   6; $16.50

Chapter 10 • Lesson 2   385

---

3 Reflect   5

Guided Discussion   REASONING

Whole Group

Ask what 78 cents plus 42 cents is. Have students use their calculators to add 0.78 + 0.42. Most calculators will show 1.2 (not 1.20). Explain that on some calculators we can set the number of decimal places, so if we set it for two places, the calculator would show 1.20 as the answer. Remind students that it is important to know what their calculators are going to do.

Extended Response

Problem 16 It depends. The amount of work is the same for buying and selling each umbrella, but he spends more of his own money to buy the large umbrellas and may have to wait a long time before he gets his money back. Students will likely have many other acceptable answers.

 Use Mastery Checkpoint 19 found in *Assessment* to evaluate student mastery of familiarity with money (coins and bills). By this time, students should be able to correctly answer eighty percent of the Mastery Checkpoint items.

Cumulative Review: For cumulative review of previously learned skills, see page 396–397.

Family Involvement: Assign the *Practice, Reteach,* or *Enrichment* activities depending on the needs of your students.

Encourage students to practice writing money amounts that include decimal points with a friend or a relative.

Concept/Question Board: Have students look for additional ways to use decimals and money and post their ideas on the Concept/Question Board.

 Math Puzzler: Pei found $1.35 in her pocket and bought 135 gumdrops. The next day she found $1.25 in her jacket pocket and bought 125 gumdrops. How much money did Pei find altogether? $2.60 How many gumdrops did she buy altogether? 260

Assess and Differentiate

 Assess Use *eAssess* to record and analyze evidence of student understanding.

A Gather Evidence

Use the Daily Class Assessment Records in *Assessment* or *eAssess* to record daily observations.

Formal Assessment

☑ **Mastery Checkpoint 19**

Did the student

❑ use correct procedures?
❑ respond with at least 80% accuracy?

Assessment Page T72

B Summarize Findings

Analyze and summarize assessment data for each student. Determine which Assessment Follow-Up is appropriate for each student. Use the Student Assessment Record in *Assessment* or *eAssess* to update assessment records.

Assessment Page T41

C Assessment Follow-Up ● DIFFERENTIATE INSTRUCTION

Based on your observations, use these teaching strategies for assessment follow-up.

INTERVENTION	ENRICH	PRACTICE	RETEACH
Review student performance on *Intervention* Lesson 10.B to see if students have mastered prerequisite skills for this lesson.	**If . . .** students are proficient in the lesson concepts, **Then . . .** encourage them to work on chapter projects or *Enrichment* Lesson 10.2.	**If . . .** students would benefit from additional practice, **Then . . .** assign *Practice* Lesson 10.2.	**If . . .** students struggle with understanding the coin values, **Then . . .** have them play "store" using toy money. Price items so that students will need to use a variety of coins. Encourage students to write down the prices and practice saying them. Make sure students always use two decimal places and do not try to shortcut by writing $5 or $3.

ENGLISH LEARNER

Review

Use Lesson 10.2 in *English Learner Support Guide* to review lesson concepts and vocabulary.

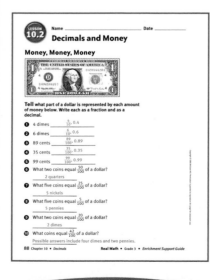

Enrichment Lesson 10.2

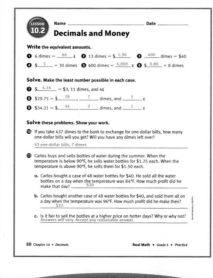

Practice Lesson 10.2

OBJECTIVES
- To introduce the decimeter as a standard unit of length
- To show the relationship between decimeters and meters
- To develop students' understanding of tenths

NCTM STANDARDS

Measurement
Converting metric units

Geometry
Finding perimeter

Problem Solving
Solving problems that arise in real-life contexts

MATERIALS
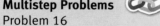
- *Response Wheels
- Meterstick
- *Metric Unit Game Mat

TECHNOLOGY
Presentation Lesson 10.3

TEST PREP

Cumulative Review
Mental Math reviews addition, subtraction, multiplication, and division facts (Chapters 1 and 5).

Multistep Problems
Problem 16

Extended Response
Problem 18

Decimals and Metric Measures

Context of the Lesson This is the third in a series of nine lessons that develop the arithmetic of decimal numbers. The previous lesson compared decimal numbers with United States currency (money). This parallel lesson compares decimal numbers with metric measures and builds on the metric measurement lessons in Chapter 9.

See page 380B for Math Background for teachers for this lesson.

Planning for Learning ● DIFFERENTIATE INSTRUCTION

INTERVENTION

If . . . students lack the prerequisite skill of multidigit multiplication,

Then . . . teach *Intervention* Lesson 10.C.

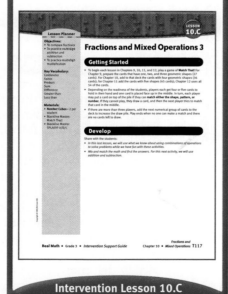

Intervention Lesson 10.C

ENGLISH LEARNER

Preview

If . . . students need language support,

Then . . . use Lesson 10.3 in *English Learner Support Guide* to preview lesson concepts and vocabulary.

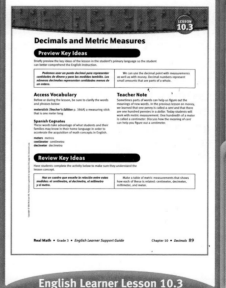

English Learner Lesson 10.3

ENRICH

If . . . students are proficient in the lesson concepts,

Then . . . emphasize chapter projects.

PRACTICE

If . . . students would benefit from additional practice,

Then . . . extend Guided Dicussion before assigning the student pages.

RETEACH

If . . . students are having difficulty understanding decimals and metric measures,

Then . . . dicuss Key Ideas on student page 386 before assigning the student pages.

Vocabulary
centimeter \sen′ ti mē′ tər\ *n.*
a unit of length in the metric system equal to one-hundredth of a meter

decimeter \des′ i mē′ tər\ *n.*
a unit of length in the metric system equal to one-tenth of a meter

Access Vocabulary
meterstick a measuring stick that is one meter long

Spanish Cognates
meters metros
centimeter centímetro
decimeter decímetro

Mental Math   5

  Do a fast-paced basic fact drill, presenting exercises in no particular order and focusing on speedy recall. Possible examples include the following:

a. $3 + 8 = 11$
b. $2 \times 7 = 14$
c. $8 \times 5 = 40$
d. $17 - 10 = 7$
e. $4 + 9 = 13$
f. $20 - 10 = 10$
g. $10 \div 5 = 2$
h. $16 \div 4 = 4$
i. $4 + 7 = 11$
j. $45 \div 5 = 9$

1 Develop   25

Tell Students In Today's Lesson They Will

- understand the relationship between a decimeter and a meter.
- use a decimal point with metric measures.

Guided Discussion UNDERSTANDING   Whole Group

1. Show the class how long a decimeter is. 10 centimeters; about the width of an adult's hand Ask if anyone knows or can guess how many decimeters there are in a meter. Show on a meterstick that there are 10 decimeters in a meter.

2. Explain that *deci* means "tenth" and that the number system we use is called the decimal system because it is based on the number *ten*. Point out that the root *deci* is used in the term *decimal point*.

3. Have students complete several statements like the ones below. Explain that *dm* is the symbol for decimeter. If students have difficulties with any statement, stop and discuss the statement; use a meterstick and a card or other object that is 1 decimeter long to confirm the correct answer. Possible examples include the following:

5 m = _____ dm 50
4 m and 5 dm = _____ dm 45
_____ m = 80 dm 8
_____ m and _____ dm = 53 dm 5; 3
35 dm = _____ m and 5 dm 3
40 dm = _____ m and _____ dm 4; 0
_____ dm = 8 m and 4 dm 84
_____ dm = 10 m and 8 dm 108

4. When students can complete these statements readily, ask a question such as the following:

■ **What does 3.5 m stand for?**

Correct answers include *three point five meters, three and five-tenths meters, three and a half meters, three meters and five decimeters,* and *thirty-five decimeters.*

5. Present statements involving decimal points, such as the following:

3.5 m = _____ dm 35
_____ m = 25 dm 2.5
4.8 m = _____ dm 48
57 dm = _____ m 5.7
_____ dm = 12.2 m 122
143 dm = _____ m 14.3

2 Assign Student Pages   20

Pages 386–387   APPLYING

Have students complete pages 386 and 387 independently. Tell students that although some problems may have more than one correct answer (such as Problem 8), they should use a number less than 10 for the number of decimeters (3 m and 7 dm, not 2 m and 17 dm).

As Students Finish

 Metric Unit Game (introduced in Lesson 9.9)

RESEARCH IN ACTION

"Most students do not develop sufficient meanings for decimal symbols when they are introduced. Soon students are asked to learn rules for manipulating decimals. Because they do not know what the symbols mean, they have no way of figuring out why the rules work. They must memorize each rule and hope that they remember on which problems to use them, a method that works for the simplest routine problems that are practiced heavily but not for problems that are even a little different. Without knowing what the symbols mean, students are unable to judge whether their answers are reasonable or whether they are on the right track. Because decimals are the last number system with which many students work, the initial errors they make persist and are difficult to remediate."

Hiebert, James. "Decimal Fractions" *Arithmetic Teacher* March 1987.

LESSON 10.3 Decimals and Metric Measures

Key Ideas

We can use the decimal point with measurements as well as with money.

With money, we could write $3.4 for 3 dollars and 4 dimes because a dime is one-tenth of a dollar.

With measurement, we write 3.4 meters for 3 meters and 4 decimeters because a **decimeter** is one-tenth of a meter. You can read 3.4 as *three and four-tenths* or *three point four.*

We write 3.46 for 3 meters, 4 decimeters, and 6 centimeters because a **centimeter** is one-hundredth of a meter. You can read 3.46 as *three and forty-six hundredths* or *three point four six.*

About 1.2 meters from the floor

About 120 centimeters from the floor

About 12 decimeters from the floor

Answer these questions.

1. How many decimeters are in 1 meter?   10
2. How many decimeters are in 2.5 meters?   25
3. How many meters are 15 decimeters?   1.5
4. How many decimeters are in 7.3 meters?   73
5. How many decimeters are in 73 meters?   730
6. How many meters are 125 decimeters?   12.5

386

Textbook This lesson is available in the *eTextbook*.

There are 10 decimeters in 1 meter.

10 dm = 1 m

There are 10 centimeters in 1 decimeter.

10 cm = 1 dm

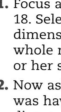

Write the equivalent measures.

7. 2 m = ☐ dm   20
8. 200 dm = ☐ m   20
9. 37 dm = ☐ m and ☐ dm   3; 7
10. ☐ m and ☐ dm = 9.2 m   9; 2
11. 4.5 m = ☐ dm   45
12. ☐ dm = 6.5 m   65
13. 2 m and 3 dm = ☐ m   2.3
14. ☐ m = 6 m and 1 dm   6.1

Mr. Thompson wants to buy fencing for his garden. The garden is shaped like a rectangle with one side 12 meters and another side 4 meters in length. Fencing is sold in lengths of 80 centimeters.

15. What is the perimeter of Mr. Thompson's garden?
    12 + 4 + 12 + 4 = 32; The perimeter is 32 meters.
16. **Multistep** How many lengths of fencing must Mr. Thompson buy?   40
17. If each length of fencing costs $20, how much will the fencing cost? $800
18. **Extended Response** Mr. Thompson was thinking of enlarging his garden. He needed to keep the width the same but could extend the length to between 17 and 22 meters. He decided to make the garden 20 meters long. Why might Mr. Thompson have chosen 20 meters rather than one of the other possible lengths?

387

---

3 Reflect   10

Guided Discussion   REASONING   Whole Group

1. Focus attention on and discuss students' answers to Problem 18. Select a student who appears to have noticed that the dimensions Mr. Thompson chose for his garden correspond to whole numbers of fencing lengths. Ask the student to explain his or her solution to the class.

2. Now ask the class how they would help another student who was having difficulty understanding the situation. Through discussion, help students focus on the use of labeled diagrams as an aid for solving this type of problem.

3. Conclude the lesson by drawing a diagram of the garden with marks on the sides that correspond to where each length of fencing will fit. Label the spaces between the marks as 80 cm. There will be 25 spaces on each long side.

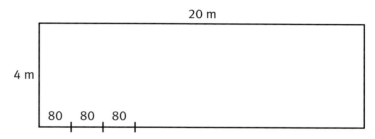

20 m

4 m

80   80   80

Extended Response

Problem 18 The fencing he planned to buy would fit along each side without having to be cut. Students may suggest other reasonable answers.

Cumulative Review: For cumulative review of previously learned skills, see page 396–397.

Family Involvement: Assign the **Practice, Reteach,** or **Enrichment** activities depending on the needs of your students.

Encourage students to practice writing metric measures that include decimal points with a friend or a relative.

Concept/Question Board: Have students look for additional ways to use decimals and metric measures and post their ideas on the Concept/Question Board.

Math Puzzler: Write the following symbols on the board, and have students find the value of ☐ and △. △ is 6, and ☐ is 5.

$$\triangle + \square = 11$$
$$\triangle - \square = 1$$

Assess and Differentiate

 **Assess** Use *eAssess* to record and analyze evidence of student understanding.

A Gather Evidence

Use the Daily Class Assessment Records in *Assessment* or *eAssess* to record daily observations.

Informal Assessment
✓ **Guided Discussion**

Did the student ╠UNDERSTANDING╣
- ❑ make important observations?
- ❑ extend or generalize learning?
- ❑ provide insightful answers?
- ❑ pose insightful questions?

Informal Assessment
✓ **Student Pages**

Did the student ╠APPLYING╣
- ❑ apply learning in new situations?
- ❑ contribute concepts?
- ❑ contribute answers?
- ❑ connect mathematics to real-world situations?

B Summarize Findings

Analyze and summarize assessment data for each student. Determine which Assessment Follow-Up is appropriate for each student. Use the Student Assessment Record in *Assessment* or *eAssess* to update assessment records.

Student Assessment Record

Assessment Page T41

C Assessment Follow-Up • DIFFERENTIATE INSTRUCTION

Based on your observations, use these teaching strategies for assessment follow-up.

INTERVENTION

Review student performance on *Intervention* Lesson 10.C to see if students have mastered prerequisite skills for this lesson.

ENGLISH LEARNER

Review

Use Lesson 10.3 in *English Learner Support Guide* to review lesson concepts and vocabulary.

ENRICH

If . . . students are proficient in the lesson concepts,

Then . . . encourage them to work on chapter projects or *Enrichment* Lesson 10.3.

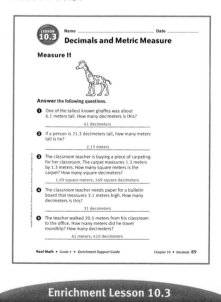

Enrichment Lesson 10.3

PRACTICE

If . . . students would benefit from additional practice,

Then . . . assign *Practice* Lesson 10.3.

Practice Lesson 10.3

RETEACH

If . . . students struggle with using metric measures with decimals,

Then . . . have them make metric measurements out of receipt tape. Have them make a number of 1-meter strips, 10-centimeter strips, and centimeter strips. When they measure an object, have them use the strips. For example, to make 1.2 meters, students would line up a 1-meter strip and two 10-centimeter strips. Thinking of the 10-centimeter strips as tenths places and the 1-centimeter strips as hundredths places will help them understand the decimal places.

Lesson Planner

OBJECTIVES
- To compare decimal and fraction notation
- To provide applications that make use of both decimals and fractions

NCTM STANDARDS
Number and Operations
- Recognizing and generating equivalent forms of commonly used fractions and decimals
- Comparing fractions and decimals

MATERIALS
*Response Wheels

TECHNOLOGY
Presentation Lesson 10.4
MathTools Estimating Proportion Tool

TEST PREP
Cumulative Review
Mental Math reviews addition, subtraction, multiplication, and division facts (Chapters 1 and 5).

Comparing Decimals and Fractions

Context of the Lesson In this lesson students will begin to explore the relationship between decimals and fractions to further develop their understanding of rational numbers. More work with relating fractions, decimals, and percents as equivalent forms is included in Grade 4. In the next four lessons, students will learn how to add, subtract, multiply, and divide decimal numbers.

See page 380B for Math Background for teachers for this lesson.

Planning for Learning ● DIFFERENTIATE INSTRUCTION

INTERVENTION	ENGLISH LEARNER	ENRICH
If . . . students lack the prerequisite skill of comparing fractions,	Preview	**If . . .** students are proficient in the lesson concepts,
Then . . . teach *Intervention* Lesson 10.A.	**If . . .** students need language support,	**Then . . .** emphasize exploring *eMathTools: Estimating Proportion Tool.*
	Then . . . use Lesson 10.4 in *English Learner Support Guide* to preview lesson concepts and vocabulary.	

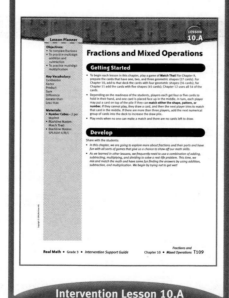

Intervention Lesson 10.A

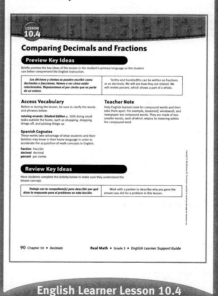

English Learner Lesson 10.4

PRACTICE

If . . . students would benefit from additional practice,

Then . . . extend Skill Practice before assigning the student pages.

RETEACH

If . . . students are having difficulty understanding how to relate decimals and fractions,

Then . . . extend Guided Discussion before assigning the student pages.

Access Vocabulary
running errands doing small tasks outside the home, such as shopping, dropping things off, and picking things up

Spanish Cognates
fraction fracción
decimal decimal
percent por ciento

Mental Math — 5

Continue doing a fast-paced basic fact drill, presenting exercises in no particular order and focusing on speedy recall. Possible examples include the following:

a. $2 + 7 = 9$ **b.** $2 \times 6 = 12$

c. $3 \times 7 = 21$ **d.** $19 - 10 = 9$

e. $5 + 9 = 14$ **f.** $18 - 8 = 10$

g. $12 \div 2 = 6$ **h.** $18 \div 6 = 3$

i. $5 + 6 = 11$ **j.** $35 \div 5 = 7$

1 Develop — 25

Tell Students In Today's Lesson They Will

learn how to relate decimals and fractions.

Guided Discussion UNDERSTANDING Whole Group

1. Draw illustrations similar to those on page 388 on the board, and have students tell you the fraction of each figure that is shaded. Allow students to come to the board and write the answer as a fraction and again as a decimal. Possible illustrations include the following:

   • Draw a square that is divided into 5 equal vertical columns, and shade 1 of the columns. Students should note that $\frac{1}{5}$ of the square is shaded.

   • Draw a circle that is divided into 4 equal parts, and shade 3 of the parts. Students should note that $\frac{3}{4}$ of the square is shaded.

2. After a few examples, draw two equal-sized squares side by side, one divided into 10 equal vertical columns and the other divided into 100 squares. Then shade the first three columns in both squares as shown:

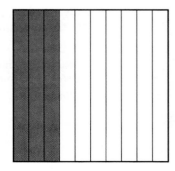 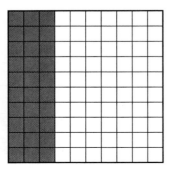

3. Ask the following question:

   ■ **Which square has the greater area shaded?**

   Allow students to discuss and conclude that if the squares were drawn the same size, then they both have the same area shaded. Help students understand that $\frac{3}{10}$ and $\frac{30}{100}$ are equal. Write the following on the board to represent this equality:

   $0.3 = 0.30$

   Note that when we report an answer as 0.30 we imply a greater degree of precision than 0.3. However, it is not necessary to raise this issue with students at this time.

Skill Practice UNDERSTANDING Whole Group

Write pairs of numbers on the board. Using the Find, Hide and Show procedure, have students show **THUMBS UP** thumbs-up if the number on the left is greater, thumbs-down if the number on the right is greater, and an open hand if both numbers are equal. Possible examples include the following:

a. 0.2 0.20 open hand **b.** 0.40 0.43 down

c. $\frac{1}{4}$ 0.5 down **d.** 0.50 $\frac{1}{4}$ up

e. 1.5 $1\frac{1}{2}$ open hand **f.** 4.5 $4\frac{3}{4}$ down

g. 0.37 0.40 down **h.** $4\frac{1}{2}$ 0.45 up

Monitoring Student Progress

If . . . students make consistent errors during the Skill-Practice exercise,

Then . . . plan to work with those students during the student book exercise while the rest of the class works independently. As students catch on, they too can work independently.

---

2 Assign Student Pages — 20

Pages 388–389 APPLYING

Review the text and illustrations on page 388. Then allow students to complete both pages independently.

As Students Finish

 MathTools *Estimating Proportion Tool* Use this tool to explore equivalent fractions and decimals.

 Game Have students play a game of choice from those previously introduced, or assign games based on needed skill practice.

LESSON 10.4   Comparing Decimals and Fractions

Key Ideas

Tenths and hundredths can be written as fractions or decimals.

Fraction	Decimal	Percent
$\frac{2}{10}$	0.2	20%

Fraction	Decimal	Percent
$\frac{20}{100}$	0.20	20%

Two-tenths of the square is shaded.

Twenty-hundredths of the square is shaded.

Notice that $\frac{20}{100}$ of the square and $\frac{2}{10}$ of the square is the same amount.

Fraction	Decimal	Percent
$1\frac{35}{100}$	1.35	135%

388   📖 **Textbook** This lesson is available in the *eTextbook*.

Write these fractions as decimals.

1 $\frac{3}{10}$ 0.3

2 $\frac{5}{10}$ 0.5

3 $1\frac{5}{10}$ 1.5

4 $\frac{6}{100}$ 0.06

5 $\frac{65}{100}$ 0.65

6 $4\frac{32}{100}$ 4.32

7 $\frac{20}{100}$ 0.20

8 $\frac{2}{10}$ 0.2

Write these decimals as fractions. Do not reduce the fraction.

9 0.10 $\frac{10}{100}$

10 0.25 $\frac{25}{100}$

11 0.5 $\frac{5}{10}$

12 0.05 $\frac{5}{100}$

13 0.67 $\frac{67}{100}$

14 0.60 $\frac{60}{100}$

15 0.04 $\frac{4}{100}$

16 1.25 $1\frac{25}{100}$

17 4.58 $4\frac{58}{100}$

18 5.01 $5\frac{1}{100}$

Solve these problems.

19 Mark earned $4\frac{1}{2}$ dollars running errands. His sister earned $4.50 delivering newspapers.

   a. Who earned more? neither; They earned the same amount.

   b. How much money did they earn together? $9; Students might, for example, add $4 + 4 + \frac{1}{2} + \frac{1}{2} = 9$.

20 Henry was paid $2.00 each hour he worked in his mother's garden. He worked for $3\frac{3}{4}$ hours.

   a. Did he earn more than $6.00? yes

   b. Did he earn less than $8.00? yes

   c. Did he earn more than $7.00? yes

   d. How much did he earn? $7.50

---

3 Reflect   10

Guided Discussion   ✓ REASONING   Small Group

Draw the following four figures on the board: a square, a circle, a rectangle, and an equilateral triangle. Have students copy the figures. Then challenge them to shade approximately $\frac{25}{100}$ of each figure. (You might want to assign each figure to a different group.) Allow students to work independently or in small groups, and then have volunteers report their solutions and how they arrived at their solutions to the class. One way to shade $\frac{1}{4}$ of the triangle is the following:

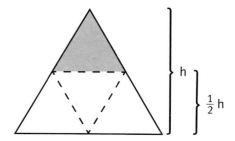

Curriculum Connection: Have students draw pictures of different shapes, divide them into 10 or 100 sections, shade some of the sections, and report the amount shaded in both decimals and fractions.

Cumulative Review: For cumulative review of previously learned skills, see page 396–397.

Family Involvement: Assign the *Practice, Reteach,* or *Enrichment* activities depending on the needs of your students.

Encourage students to practice comparing decimals and fractions with a friend or a relative.

Concept/Question Board: Have students look for additional ways to use decimals and fractions and post their ideas on the Concept/Question Board.

Math Puzzler: Fay called her friend Samir and asked him to meet her at the library. Fay lives 3.4 kilometers away from the library, and Samir lives 1.62 kilometers away. Who must travel farther to the library? Fay; $3.4 > 1.62$ How much farther? 1.78 km; $3.40 - 1.62 = 1.78$

4 Assess and Differentiate

e Assess Use **eAssess** to record and analyze evidence of student understanding.

A Gather Evidence

Use the Daily Class Assessment Records in **Assessment** or **eAssess** to record daily observations.

Informal Assessment
✓ Skill Practice

Did the student **UNDERSTANDING**
- ❏ make important observations?
- ❏ extend or generalize learning?
- ❏ provide insightful answers?
- ❏ pose insightful questions?

Informal Assessment
✓ Guided Discussion

Did the student **REASONING**
- ❏ provide a clear explanation?
- ❏ communicate reasons and strategies?
- ❏ choose appropriate strategies?
- ❏ argue logically?

B Summarize Findings

Analyze and summarize assessment data for each student. Determine which Assessment Follow-Up is appropriate for each student. Use the Student Assessment Record in **Assessment** or **eAssess** to update assessment records.

Assessment Page T41

C Assessment Follow-Up • DIFFERENTIATE INSTRUCTION

Based on your observations, use these teaching strategies for assessment follow-up.

INTERVENTION

Review student performance on **Intervention** Lesson 10.A to see if students have mastered prerequisite skills for this lesson.

ENGLISH LEARNER

Review

Use Lesson 10.4 in **English Learner Support Guide** to review lesson concepts and vocabulary.

ENRICH

If . . . students are proficient in the lesson concepts,

Then . . . encourage them to work on chapter projects or **Enrichment** Lesson 10.4.

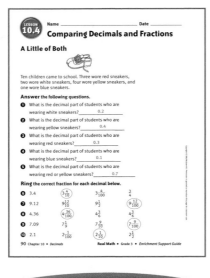

Enrichment Lesson 10.4

PRACTICE

If . . . students would benefit from additional practice,

Then . . . assign **Practice** Lesson 10.4.

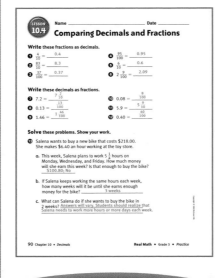

Practice Lesson 10.4

RETEACH

If . . . students struggle with converting between fractions and decimals,

Then . . . have them use 100-square grids for each of the problems to help them. Students should work in pairs to check their work.

OBJECTIVES
- To introduce adding decimal numbers with tenths and hundredths
- To approximate answers to decimal addition

NCTM STANDARDS

Number and Operations
Adding decimals

Data Analysis and Probability
Predicting the probability of outcomes

MATERIALS
- *Response Wheels
- *One 5–10 Number Cube
- Meterstick
- *Play money

TECHNOLOGY
e Presentation Lesson 10.5

TEST PREP
Cumulative Review
Mental Math reviews division facts (Lessons 5.7–5.9).

Multistep Problems
Problem 26

Adding Decimals

Context of the Lesson This is the fifth of nine lessons that develop the arithmetic of decimal numbers. The next three lessons cover subtraction, multiplication, and division of decimals in that order. This lesson contains a Mastery Checkpoint.

See page 380B for Math Background for teachers for this lesson.

Planning for Learning ● DIFFERENTIATE INSTRUCTION

INTERVENTION

If . . . students lack the prerequisite skill of multidigit addition and subtraction,

Then . . . teach *Intervention* Lesson 10.B.

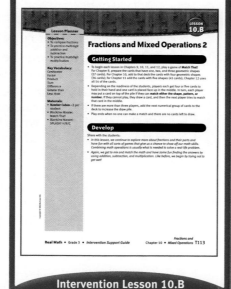

Intervention Lesson 10.B

ENGLISH LEARNER

Preview

If . . . students need language support,

Then . . . use Lesson 10.5 in *English Learner Support Guide* to preview lesson concepts and vocabulary.

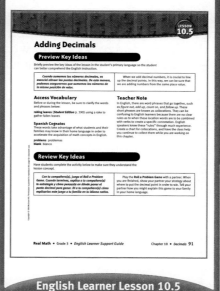

English Learner Lesson 10.5

ENRICH

If . . . students are proficient in the lesson concepts,

Then . . . emphasize thinking about game strategies for the **Decimal Roll a Problem Game.**

PRACTICE

If . . . students would benefit from additional practice,

Then . . . extend the playing of the **Decimal Roll a Problem Game** before assigning the student pages.

RETEACH

If . . . students are having difficulty understanding how to add decimals,

Then . . . extend Guided Discussion before assigning the student pages.

Access Vocabulary
raking leaves using a rake to gather fallen leaves

Spanish Cognates
problems problemas
blank blanco

Mental Math 5

  Do a fast-paced division fact drill. Possible examples include the following:

a. $12 \div 3 = 4$ b. $6 \div 6 = 1$ c. $18 \div 2 = 9$

d. $24 \div 4 = 6$ e. $15 \div 3 = 5$ f. $21 \div 3 = 7$

g. $36 \div 6 = 6$ h. $56 \div 8 = 7$ i. $48 \div 8 = 6$

j. $72 \div 9 = 8$ k. $25 \div 5 = 5$ l. $30 \div 6 = 5$

1 Develop 30

Tell Students In Today's Lesson They Will

- add numbers that have up to two decimal places.
- solve word problems that involve adding decimals.

Guided Discussion UNDERSTANDING Whole Group

1. Write $4.53 on the board, and ask what it means. 4 dollars and 53 cents Next write 4.53 m on the board and explain, or have a student explain, that it means 4 meters and 53 centimeters, or 4 and 53 hundredths meters, and it can also be read *four point five three meters*.

2. Present several similar examples, but give special attention to amounts that have no tenths. Have students explain what each example means. Possible examples include the following:

   $5.06 5 dollars and 6 cents

   5.06 m 5 meters and 6 centimeters, or 5 and 6 hundredths meters

   5.60 m 5 meters, 6 decimeters, and 0 centimeters

   5.6 m 5 meters, 6 decimeters

3. To introduce adding decimals, tell a story about someone who has $1.39 and earns $2.75. Ask how much money the person now has. Encourage students to work out the answer in whatever way they want, but have them explain their processes to the class. For example, 139 cents and 275 cents equals 414 cents, which equals $4.14. Some students may simply write the two amounts in the usual addition form and then put the decimal point in what seems to be the appropriate place. Encourage this. They should write their exercises in the following way:

$$\begin{array}{r} 1.39 \\ + 2.75 \\ \hline 4.14 \end{array}$$

4. Present several word problems, such as the following, that involve the addition of decimals:

   - One table is 2.45 meters long; another is 3.21 meters long. How long will they be if they are placed end to end? 5.66 m
   - Jo spent $5.46 and has $2.95 left. How much money did she start with? $8.41

5. Students should notice that as long as they are careful to line up the decimal points, they get the same results when adding numbers with decimal points as when adding numbers as though the decimal points were not there. To show how lining up the decimal points is important, ask students to add 4.5 and 3.25, and have them discuss how to do it. They should realize that because 5 tenths and 50 hundredths are equivalent, the problem may be written as follows:

$$\begin{array}{r} 4.50 \\ + 3.25 \end{array}$$

6. Use a meterstick or play money to demonstrate why $4.5 + 3.25$ is the same as $4.50 + 3.25$. Then give another similar problem, such as 2.7 m + 1.46 m = _____. 4.16 m

Skill and Strategy Building ENGAGING Whole Group

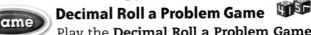

Game Decimal Roll a Problem Game

Play the **Decimal Roll a Problem Game** found on student page 393. The purpose of this game is to give students practice with adding decimals while also applying the principles of place value and probability. Although the game is best played as a whole-class activity so students benefit from others' analyses, students can also play the game in groups of two, three, or four. Follow these steps to play the whole-class version of the game:

1. Write the outline of a three-digit addition exercise on an overhead transparency, as in the following example:

   _____ _____ _____ + _____ _____ _____ = 100

2. Have each student copy the outline onto a piece of paper.

3. Turn off the light on the overhead projector so students cannot see what you write.

4. Roll a 5–10 **Number Cube.** Call out the number, and have each student write it in one of the six spaces on his or her outline. At the same time, write the number in one of the spaces on the transparency. (If a 10 is rolled, don't count it, and roll again.) Explain that once a number is written, it cannot be moved.

5. Repeat the procedure above until all six spaces have been filled in. Place a decimal point in each number so the sum is as close as possible to 100. Have students place decimal points in their numbers. Then turn on the overhead projector light so students can see the addition exercise you made.

6. Say that you would like students to approximate sums in this game *without doing the calculation*. Then ask students to raise their hands if, after approximating, they think they have a sum that is closer to 100 than yours.

7. Select a student whose hand is raised, and ask him or her to write the exercise on the board, again without doing the calculation. Have the student explain why his or her sum is closer to 100 than your sum.

8. In a similar manner, ask other students if they have a sum that is still closer to 100. If so, have them write their exercises on the board and explain why the sums are closer to 100. Continue until you have the sum closest to 100 and can declare a winner or winners.

2 Assign Student Pages 20

Pages 390–391 APPLYING

Review the two examples on page 390 with students. Then have students complete page 391 independently.

Monitoring Student Progress

If . . . students have difficulty reading decimals that have no tenths, such as $5.06,

Then . . . have them practice reading decimals that do have tenths first, such as $4.53 = 4 dollars, 5 dimes, and 3 cents. Then have them use the same procedure to read decimals that do not have tenths. For example, $5.06 could be read as *5 dollars, 0 dimes, and 6 cents* or simply *5 dollars and 6 cents.*

 **RESEARCH IN ACTION**

"Children need to learn that rational numbers are numbers in the same way that whole numbers are numbers. For children to use rational numbers to solve problems, they need to learn that the same rational number may be represented in different ways, as a fraction, a decimal, or a percent. Fraction concepts and representations need to be related to those of division, measurement, and ratio. Decimal and fractional representations need to be connected and understood. Building these connections take extensive experience with rational numbers over a substantial period of time. Researchers have documented that difficulties in working with rational numbers can often be traced to weak conceptual understanding….Instructional sequences in which more time is spent at the outset on developing meaning for the various representations of rational numbers and the concept of unit have been shown to promote mathematical proficiency."

Kilpatrick, J., J. Swafford and B. Findell, eds. *Adding It Up: Helping Children Learn Mathematics.* Washington, D.C.: National Research Council/ National Academy Press, 2001, pp. 415–416.

LESSON 10.5 Adding Decimals

Key Ideas

Before adding decimals, line up the decimal points.

If you had $3.86 and you earned $4.75 raking leaves, how much money would you have now? Add the two numbers to find out.

$3.86 + $4.75 = ?

$$\begin{array}{r} 3.86 \\ + 4.75 \\ \hline \end{array}$$ Line up the decimal points.

$$\begin{array}{r} ^{1\ 1}3.86 \\ + 4.75 \\ \hline 8.61 \end{array}$$ Add.

- - - - - - - - - - - - - - - - - - - -

$6.39 + 2.4 = ?$

$$\begin{array}{r} 6.39 \\ + 2.4 \\ \hline \end{array}$$ Line up the decimal points.

$$\begin{array}{r} 6.39 \\ + 2.40 \\ \hline \end{array}$$ If it helps, put in a 0 (because 2.4 and 2.40 have the same value), but be sure to add ones to ones, tenths to tenths, and so on.

$$\begin{array}{r} 6.39 \\ + 2.40 \\ \hline 8.79 \end{array}$$ Add.

390   **Textbook** This lesson is available in the *eTextbook.*

Add.

① $\begin{array}{r}3.27\\+2.48\\\hline 5.75\end{array}$	② $\begin{array}{r}7.63\\+1.54\\\hline 9.17\end{array}$	③ $\begin{array}{r}5.4\\+2.55\\\hline 7.95\end{array}$	④ $\begin{array}{r}8.31\\+4.24\\\hline 12.55\end{array}$
⑤ $\begin{array}{r}7.45\\+6.7\\\hline 14.15\end{array}$	⑥ $\begin{array}{r}1.30\\+2.74\\\hline 4.04\end{array}$	⑦ $\begin{array}{r}10.28\\+17.94\\\hline 28.22\end{array}$	⑧ $\begin{array}{r}12.34\\+19.8\\\hline 32.14\end{array}$
⑨ $\begin{array}{r}43.72\\+56.28\\\hline 100.00\end{array}$	⑩ $\begin{array}{r}2.4\\+1.65\\\hline 4.05\end{array}$	⑪ $\begin{array}{r}325.6\\+35.3\\\hline 360.9\end{array}$	⑫ $\begin{array}{r}98.6\\+98.6\\\hline 197.2\end{array}$

Add. Work down the page.

⑬ 4.3 + 1.5 =   5.8   ⑰ 25.6 + 30.2 =   55.8

⑭ 2.5 + 4 =   6.5   ⑱ 25.7 + 30.2 =   55.9

⑮ 25.6 + 30.2 =   55.8   ⑲ 257 + 302 =   559

⑯ 86.8 + 2.7 =   89.5   ⑳ 2.57 + 3.02 =   5.59

Solve.

㉑ Olga ran 100 meters in 14.3 seconds. Jenny ran the same distance, but 3.7 seconds slower. What was Jenny's time?   18.0 seconds

㉒ Bill wants to run 20 kilometers this week. Monday he ran 8.4 kilometers. Tuesday he ran 4.8 kilometers. How far has Bill run so far this week?   13.2 kilometers

Teaching Lesson 10.5

Assign Student Pages, continued

Pages 392–393 APPLYING

Have students complete pages 392–393 independently.

Monitoring Student Progress

If . . . students can add multidigit whole numbers but have trouble adding decimals,

Then . . . have those students model addition exercises using play money or other concrete objects. For example, to add 4.8 + 1.5, they should add 4 dollars and 8 dimes to 1 dollar and 5 dimes, or they might add a string that is 4.8 meters long to another string that is 1.5 meters long. Lead students to see that addition of decimals is identical to addition of whole numbers except that because the decimal points determine the place values, it is essential to line up the points.

As Students Finish

Game Decimal Roll a Problem Game

LESSON 10.5 · Adding Decimals

Solve these problems.

㉓ Serena worked for $3\frac{1}{2}$ hours. She needs to earn $14.25 to buy a present for her mother. Will she earn enough money?   can't tell; We don't know her hourly rate.

㉔ Grant is 67 centimeters tall. How many meters is that?   0.67 meter

㉕ Mr. Bourne drives to work and back each day. If he lives 76.54 kilometers from work, how far does he drive in a day?   153.08 km

Multistep ㉖ Building laws in Shasta say that a house cannot be more than 6.5 meters from front to back. Ms. Soto measured her house. It was exactly 5.75 meters from front to back. But she forgot to measure the small front porch. The porch floor sticks out 7 decimeters from the house. The porch railing sticks out another 4 centimeters. Does the house follow the law? If so, how much extra room does Ms. Soto have? If not, how far over the limit is the house?

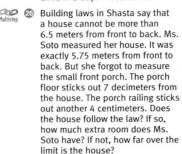

5.75m   7dm 4cm

㉗ Sonia can usually jump about 2.6 meters. She marked a spot 2.6 meters from the starting line. On her first jump, she landed 53 centimeters past that mark. How far did she jump?   3.13 meters

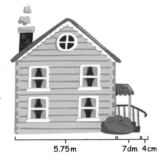

㉘ The next time Sonia jumped, she landed 53 centimeters short of the 2.6-meter mark. How far did she jump this time?   2.07 meters

㉖ The house is not over the limit; there is 1 centimeter of extra room.

392   📖 **Textbook** This lesson is available in the *eTextbook*.

Game

Addition and Strategies Practice

Roll a Problem (Decimals) Game

Players: Two or more

Materials: *Number Cube:* one 5–10

Object: To get the sum that is closest to 100

HOW TO PLAY

❶ Use blanks to outline an addition exercise on your paper, such as this:

___ ___ ___ + ___ ___ ___ = 100

❷ One player rolls the *Number Cube* six times.

❸ Each time the *Number Cube* is rolled, all players write that number in one of the blanks in their outlines. If a 10 is rolled, don't count it, and roll again. Once a number is placed, it cannot be moved.

❹ When all of the blanks have been filled in, place a decimal point in each number so that the sum is as close as possible to 100. The sum can be less than or more than 100.

❺ Determine the greatest sum. Do exact calculations only if you need to. The player with the sum closest to 100 is the winner.

SAMPLE GAME:

Numbers Rolled

8 6 7 8 8 7

Libby   87.6 + 8.78 = 96.38

Devin   88.7 + 8.67 = 97.37

Devin's sum is closer to 100. He is the winner.

Chapter 10 · Lesson 5   393

---

③ Reflect 5

Guided Discussion REASONING

Small Group

1. Present the following problem and wrong answer. Allow students to figure out what error was made and how they might help a student who made the error.

Henry saved $5.45, and his sister saved $7. How much have they saved together?

The wrong answer was $5.52.

2. Through discussion, have students explain the following points:

- The answer $5.52 is contrary to reason—the real answer must be considerably more because $5 + $7 is $12.

- The student who made this mistake added 7 cents rather than 7 dollars to $5.45, most likely because he or she did not think of 7 dollars as 7 dollars and zero cents, or $7.00.

- The student can best be helped by making sure that he or she lines up the decimal points before adding.

 Use Mastery Checkpoint 20 found in **Assessment** to evaluate student mastery of understanding decimal numbers. By this time, students should be able to correctly answer eighty percent of the Mastery Checkpoint items.

 Cumulative Review: For cumulative review of previously learned skills, see page 396–397.

 Family Involvement: Assign the *Practice, Reteach,* or *Enrichment* activities depending on the needs of your students.

Encourage students to practice adding decimals with a friend or a relative.

 Concept/Question Board: Encourage students to continue to post questions, answers, and examples on the Concept/Question Board.

 Math Puzzler: Write the following on the board, and have students fill in the missing numbers so that all sums across and down are correct.

$$137 \ + \underline{286} = 423$$
$$\underline{249} \ + 105 = \underline{354}$$
$$\underline{386} \ + \underline{391} = 777$$
$$\overline{772} \quad \overline{782}$$

Assess and Differentiate

 Assess Use **eAssess** to record and analyze evidence of student understanding.

A Gather Evidence

Use the Daily Class Assessment Records in **Assessment** or **eAssess** to record daily observations.

Formal Assessment
☑ **Mastery Checkpoint 20**

Did the student
- ❑ use correct procedures?
- ❑ respond with at least 80% accuracy?

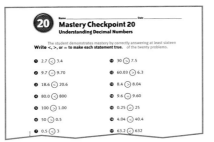

Assessment Page T73

B Summarize Findings

Analyze and summarize assessment data for each student. Determine which Assessment Follow-Up is appropriate for each student. Use the Student Assessment Record in **Assessment** or **eAssess** to update assessment records.

Assessment Page T41

C Assessment Follow-Up • DIFFERENTIATE INSTRUCTION

Based on your observations, use these teaching strategies for assessment follow-up.

INTERVENTION

Review student performance on **Intervention** Lesson 10.B to see if students have mastered prerequisite skills for this lesson.

ENGLISH LEARNER

Review

Use Lesson 10.5 in **English Learner Support Guide** to review lesson concepts and vocabulary.

ENRICH

If . . . students are proficient in the lesson concepts,

Then . . . encourage them to work on chapter projects or **Enrichment** Lesson 10.5.

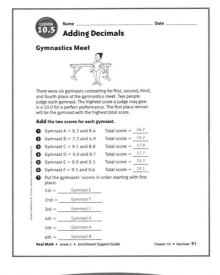

Enrichment Lesson 10.5

PRACTICE

If . . . students would benefit from additional practice,

Then . . . assign **Practice** Lesson 10.5.

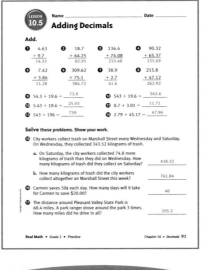

Practice Lesson 10.5

RETEACH

If . . . students are having difficulty understanding how to add decimals,

Then . . . reteach the concept using **Reteach** Lesson 10.5.

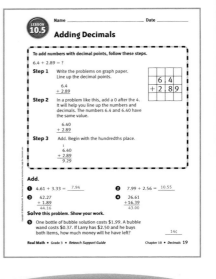

Reteach Lesson 10.5

10

Exploring Problem Solving

Objectives

- To explore the strategies Make a Physical Model and Guess, Check, and Revise
- To provide practice using decimals and metric units
- To provide practice in solving and presenting solutions to nonroutine, real-world problems

Materials

- Graph paper
- Tape or glue

Context of the Lesson Reasoning and problem solving are prevalent in every *Real Math* lesson. This lesson and other special problem-solving lessons allow more time for students to share and compare their strategies. While continuing the totem-pole theme introduced on page 380, this lesson provides students with a situation in which they can apply what they have been learning about decimals and metric measurement.

 Develop 5

Tell Students In Today's Lesson They Will

- read a problem about carving a totem pole.
- look at how two students are using two different strategies to solve the problem.
- solve the problem themselves and share how they did it.

Guided Discussion

Help students recall the problems they solved in the Chapter Opener about totem poles. Discuss other tasks involved in making a totem pole besides stripping the bark from a tree—tasks such as planning, carving, and perhaps painting. Explain to students that today they will solve a problem related to planning figures for a totem pole.

Exploring Problem Solving

Omak is carving a totem pole that is 17.0 meters tall. He wants to carve ten figures to fill the pole, and he wants them all to be the same height. How high should he make each figure?

Tracy is using guess, check, and revise to solve the problem.

Guess	Check	Result
1 meter	10 meters	Too short
2 meters		

Think about Tracy's strategy. Then answer and discuss these questions.

❶ Why did Tracy write *10 meters* when she checked her first guess? That is how long the totem pole would be if each figure were 1 meter tall.

❷ What do you think Tracy will write when she checks her second guess? 20 meters

❸ What do you think Tracy will guess next? Answers may vary but should be between 1 and 2 meters.

❹ How can Tracy check her next guess? See answer in *Teacher's Edition*.

❺ Do you think Tracy's strategy will work? Yes; if she uses the results of each guess, she can get closer until she finds a measurement that works.

394 ⬚ Textbook This lesson is available in the *eTextbook*.

Ross is using a physical model to solve the problem.

Think about Ross's strategy. Then answer and discuss the following questions.

❻ In Ross's model, what does each strip stand for? 1 meter of the totem pole

❼ What does each small square on a strip stand for? one-tenth of a meter or 1 decimeter

❽ How could Ross use his model to solve the problem?

❾ What do you think of Ross's strategy?

❿ Work with your group to solve the problem. Use any strategy you like. Each totem will be 1.7 meters high.

❽ He might divide the long strip into 10 equal parts, and then count how many squares long each part is.

❾ Answers may vary. Students should see that the strategy does involve a lot of time and effort, and that there may be a way to solve the problem more efficiently with some other method.

Chapter 10 • Exploring Problem Solving 395

---

2 Exploring Problem Solving 30

Using Student Pages

As students look at the illustration on page 394, read the problem together. Make sure they understand the problem by asking questions such as the following:

- **What is the problem asking?** how high each of the figures on the totem will be
- **How tall will the whole totem pole be?** 17.0 meters
- **What else do you know about the totem pole?** It will have 10 figures, and they will form the complete length of the pole.
- **How might you work to solve this problem?** Allow students to offer approaches.

Tell students they will have a chance to solve the problem, but first they will look at how two other students are trying to solve it.

Analyzing Sample Solution 1

Guide students through Tracy's strategy by discussing Problems 1–5.

Answer to Problem 4

Because students have not learned a procedure for multiplying a decimal, they will need to figure out a way to do this. Suppose the guess students want to check is 1.5. They might suggest using any of these methods:

- Keep adding 1.5 until they have found the sum of ten 1.5s.
- Add 1.5 five times, and then add that sum to itself.
- Think of 1.5 as 1 and 0.5, and then find ten 1s and ten 0.5s.
- Use play money to model the problem. Students could model 1.5 with 1 dollar and 5 dimes.

Analyzing Sample Solution 2

Guide students through Ross's strategy by discussing Problems 6–9.

Have students work on the problem individually or in pairs. They may use Tracy's strategy, Ross's strategy, or one of their own. Provide support as needed, remembering to suggest approaches rather than show students the answer. Commend students for persistence they show when they get stuck.

3 Reflect 10

Effective Communication Ask students to share their solutions and their strategies. In discussion, bring out the following points:

- When students need to do a computation for which they have not learned a standard procedure, they can use what they know about numbers and operations to figure out a way to find the answer.

- Different strategies can be used to solve the same problem.
- In real life, there is often more than one reasonable way to do a job, but some ways may be more efficient or more practical than others.

Sample Solutions Strategies

Use a Physical Model

Students may act out the problem by using play money, metric rulers, or any base-ten material.

Use a Physical Model/Look for a Pattern

Students might use the lined-paper method illustrated on page 380–381 of this **Teacher's Edition** to explore what happens when you divide a decimal by 10. They could use a centimeter ruler to draw lines of different lengths, divide them each into 10 equal parts, and then measure to find one-tenth of each length. In this way, they might discover the rule that you can divide a number by 10 simply by moving the decimal point one place to the left.

Use Simple Numbers/Make a Table

Students might also discover a rule for dividing by 10 by trying simple decimals, keeping track of what happens when they put 10 of the decimal lengths together. Use the following example:

Height of figure (cm)	Height of 10 of these figures (cm)
0.1	1
0.2	2
0.3	3
1.1	11
1.2	12

Use a Pattern

If students see that they can find 10 of any decimal simply by moving the decimal point, they can use that rule to check guesses quickly to find what number times 10 equals 17.0.

Work Backward

If students see that they can find 10 of any decimal simply by moving the decimal point one way, they might realize they can divide by 10 simply by moving the decimal point the other way.

4 Assess 15

When evaluating student work, focus not only on the correctness of the answer but also on whether the student thought rationally about the problem. Questions to consider include the following:

- Did the student understand the problem?
- Was the student able to think flexibly about ways to work with decimals?
- Did the student check to see that answers were reasonable?
- Was the student able to explain his or her strategy?

10

Cumulative Review

Assign Pages 396–397

Use the Cumulative Review as a review of concepts and skills that students have previously learned.

Here are different ways you can assign these problems to your students as they work through the chapter:

- With some of the lessons in the chapter, assign a set of Cumulative Review problems to be completed as practice or for homework.
  Lesson 10.1—Problems 1–6
  Lesson 10.2—Problems 7–12
  Lesson 10.3—Problems 13–15
  Lesson 10.4—Problems 16–19
  Lesson 10.5—Problems 20–23
- At any point during the chapter, assign part or all of the Cumulative Review problems to be completed as practice or for homework.

Cumulative Review

Problems 1–6 review customary measures of capacity, Lesson 9.6.

Problems 7–12 review applications with money, Lesson 2.6.

Problems 13–15 review the metric system and prices, Lesson 9.9.

Problems 16–19 review comparing fractions, Lesson 8.6.

Problems 20–23 review adding and subtracting fractions, Lesson 8.7.

Monitoring Student Progress

If . . . students miss more than one problem in a section, | **Then . . .** refer to the indicated lesson for remediation suggestions.

Cumulative Review

Customary Capacity Lesson 9.6

Convert each measure. Write the new measure.

1. 6 quarts = ☐ cups   24
2. 4 quarts = ☐ cups   16
3. 1 gallon = ☐ pints   8
4. 7 gallons = ☐ quarts   28
5. $\frac{1}{4}$ gallon = ☐ quart   1
6. 1 pint = ☐ quart $\frac{1}{2}$

Applications with Money Lesson 2.6

Match the dollar amounts to the money listed.

a. $32.38   b. $32.35   c. $4.80
d. $70.60   e. $44.05   f. $53.02

7. 4 one-dollar bills   c; $4.80
   2 quarters
   3 dimes

8. 5 five-dollar bills   a; $32.38
   4 one-dollar bills
   9 quarters
   2 dimes
   3 nickels
   78 pennies

9. 6 five-dollar bills   b; $32.35
   1 one-dollar bill
   5 quarters
   1 dime

10. 2 twenty-dollar bills   d; $70.60
    1 ten-dollar bill
    3 five-dollar bills
    4 one-dollar bills
    6 quarters
    2 nickels

11. 4 ten-dollar bills   f; $53.02
    2 five-dollar bills
    3 one-dollar bills
    2 pennies

12. 1 twenty-dollar bill   e; $44.05
    22 one-dollar bills
    6 quarters
    5 dimes
    1 nickel

☐ **Textbook** This lesson is available in the *eTextbook*.

Understanding the Metric System Lesson 9.9

Use the table on page 365 to answer the following questions.

13. **Extended Response** There is a sale on juice at the Metric Market. Should you buy 2,000 milliliters of juice for $4.35 or 1 liter of juice for $2.00? Explain your answer.

14. **Extended Response** There are two options for buying salt at the Metric Market. You can buy a 1-kilogram container of salt for $3.50, or you can buy a 500-gram container of salt for $1.75. Which container should you buy? Explain your answer.

15. **Extended Response** The Metric Market also sells rope. The green rope is sold by the meter. The black rope is sold by the centimeter. This week the price for the green rope is $3.80 per meter. The price of the black rope is $0.03 per centimeter. Which rope is more expensive? Explain your answer.

13. 1 liter; There are 1,000 milliliters in 1 liter, so you could buy 2 of the 1-liter containers for $4.00 and still save money.

14. either; It depends on how much salt you need. Two 500-gram containers cost the same as one 1-kilogram container.

15. green; Black rope is $3.00 per meter, and green rope is $3.80 per meter.

Comparing Fractions Lesson 8.6

Write <, >, or = to make each statement true.

16. $\frac{1}{3}$ ☐ $\frac{1}{2}$ <
17. $\frac{2}{5}$ ☐ $\frac{1}{2}$ <
18. $\frac{2}{6}$ ☐ $\frac{1}{3}$ =
19. $\frac{3}{4}$ ☐ $\frac{2}{3}$ >

Adding and Subtracting Fractions Lesson 8.7

Add or subtract.

20. $\frac{1}{2} + \frac{1}{2} =$ ☐ $\frac{2}{2}$ or 1
21. $\frac{1}{4} + \frac{1}{8} =$ ☐ $\frac{3}{8}$
22. $\frac{3}{4} - \frac{1}{4} =$ ☐ $\frac{2}{4}$ or $\frac{1}{2}$
23. $\frac{1}{5} - \frac{1}{10} =$ ☐ $\frac{1}{10}$

Individual Oral Assessment

Purpose of the Test

The Individual Oral Assessment is designed to measure students' growing knowledge of chapter concepts. It is administered individually to each student, and it requires oral responses from each student. The test takes about five minutes to complete. See *Assessment* for detailed instructions for administering and interpreting the test, and record students' answers on the Student Assessment Recording Sheet.

Assessment Page T36

Directions

Read each question to the student and record his or her oral response. If the student answers correctly, go to the next question. Stop when the student misses two questions at the same level. Students should not use scrap paper.

Materials

Questions

Level 1: Prerequisite

1. What is 10 + 10 + 10 + 10? 40
2. What is 6 × 10? 60
3. What is 10 × 10? 100
4. What is 250 ÷ 10? 25

Level 2: Basic

5. How many dimes are in $1.00? 10
6. How many dimes are in $2.50? 25
7. What is 25¢ + 25¢ + 50¢? $1.00
8. If you have 100 dimes, how many dollars do you have? $10.00

Level 3: At Level

9. What decimal is the same as $\frac{6}{10}$? 0.6
10. What fraction is the same as 1.35? $1\frac{35}{100}$
11. How many decimeters are in 7 meters? 70
12. How many meters are equal to 520 decimeters? 52

Level 4: Challenge Application

13. Harry spends 80¢ on a drink each day after school. How much does he spend on drinks each week? $4.00 also accept $5.60
14. How much does Harry spend on drinks each month? $16.00 also accept $22.40
15. What decimal and what percent are equal to $1\frac{4}{100}$ 1.04 and 104%
16. What fraction and what decimal are equal to 85%? $\frac{85}{100}$ and .85

Level 5: Content Beyond Mid-Chapter

17. Somya saved $5.50 one week and $6.25 the next week. Does he have enough money to buy a CD that costs $12.00? No.
18. How much more does Somya need to buy the $12.00 CD? 25¢
19. The ticket for an afternoon movie cost $5.25. How much does it cost for three children to go to the show? $15.75
20. Four children helped rake Mrs. Boldman's yard. She paid them $32.44. How much did each child receive? $8.11

Lesson Planner

OBJECTIVES
To introduce subtracting decimal numbers with tenths and hundredths

NCTM STANDARDS
Number and Operations
- Subtracting decimals
- Using strategies to estimate the results of computing

Problem Solving
Solving problems that arise in real-life contexts

MATERIALS
- *Response Wheels
- *One 5–10 Number Cube

TECHNOLOGY
Presentation Lesson 10.6

TEST PREP
Cumulative Review
Mental Math reviews adding decimals and multidigit numbers (Lessons 2.2, 2.7, and 10.5).

Subtracting Decimals

Context of the Lesson This is the sixth of nine lessons that develop the arithmetic of decimal numbers. The previous lesson covered addition of decimals; the next two lessons cover multiplication and division. The chapter concludes with a lesson that focuses on applications of decimal arithmetic.

See page 380B for Math Background for teachers for this lesson.

Planning for Learning ● DIFFERENTIATE INSTRUCTION

INTERVENTION

If . . . students lack the prerequisite skill of multidigit addition and subtraction,

Then . . . teach *Intervention* Lesson 10.B.

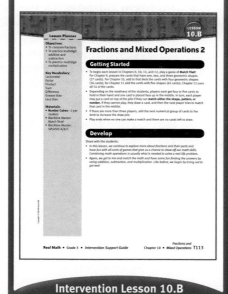

Intervention Lesson 10.B

ENGLISH LEARNER

Preview

If . . . students need language support,

Then . . . use Lesson 10.6 in *English Learner Support Guide* to preview lesson concepts and vocabulary.

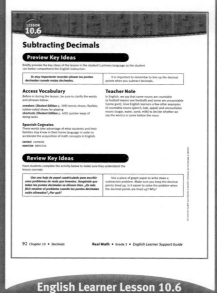

English Learner Lesson 10.6

ENRICH

If . . . students are proficient in the lesson concepts,

Then . . . emphasize thinking about game strategies for the subtraction version of the **Decimal Roll a Problem Game.**

PRACTICE

If . . . students would benefit from additional practice,

Then . . . extend the playing of the subtraction version of the **Decimal Roll a Problem Game** before assigning the student pages.

RETEACH

If . . . students are having difficulty understanding how to subtract decimals,

Then . . . extend Guided Discussion before assigning the student pages.

Access Vocabulary
sneakers tennis shoes; flexible, rubber-soled shoes for playing
shortcuts quicker ways of doing tasks

Spanish Cognates
correct correcto
exercise ejercicio

Mental Math 5

Write related addition exercises one at a time on the board. Write one under the other so students can see the relationships. Include some exercises with decimals. Have students show their answers with their **Response Wheels** by pointing over the top of the card toward the place where the decimal point should be. Possible examples include the following:

a. 12 + 42 = 54

b. 1.2 + 4.2 = 5.4

c. 0.12 + 0.42 = 0.54

d. 120 + 420 = 540

e. 1.6 + 9.3 = 10.9

f. 16 + 93 = 109

g. 0.16 + 0.93 = 1.09

h. 160 + 930 = 1,090

1 Develop 25

Tell Students In Today's Lesson They Will

- subtract numbers that have up to two decimal places.
- solve word problems that involve subtracting decimals.

Guided Discussion UNDERSTANDING   Whole Group

1. To introduce subtracting decimals, present problems such as the following, and each time have the student who got the correct answer go to the board to show how he or she got it. Praise nonstandard methods. For example, a student might answer the first question by saying, *$8.84 is $4.84 more than $4, so the answer must be 4¢ more than $4.84, or $4.88.*

   - **Tomás had $8.84, spent some of it, and now has $3.96. How much money did he spend?** $4.88
   - **Mr. López is 1.81 meters tall, and his daughter is 1.34 meters tall. What is the difference in their heights?** 0.47 m
   - **Isabel has $4.78 and wants to buy something for $6.00. How much more money does she need?** $1.22

2. Present four or five subtraction exercises without a story, such as the following:

   9.03 − 3.67 = _____ 5.36

   8.74 − 3.02 = _____ 5.72

   $6.00 − $3.47 = _____ $2.53

   7.50 − 4.28 = _____ 3.22

3. Next, present a story problem such as the following, and ask students to suggest ways to solve it:

   - **Rita is buying a sandwich that costs $3.34, and she gives the cashier a $5 bill. How much change should Rita get?**

   After a student suggests solving the problem by subtraction, write the following on the board:

   $5 − $3.34 = $_____

   Ask if anyone can do this subtraction. A student or you should explain that $5 can be written as $5.00, so the problem can be put into this form:

$$\begin{array}{r} \$5.00 \\ - \ \$3.34 \\ \hline \$1.66 \end{array}$$

4. Present a few more problems of the type just discussed, but do not include a story. Possible examples include the following:

   10 − 4.75 = _____ 5.25

   7 − 2.50 = _____ 4.50

   6.5 − 3.42 = _____ 3.08

   3.1 − 1.05 = _____ 2.05

Skill and Strategy Building ENGAGING   Whole Group

Game Decimal Roll a Problem Game

Play a subtraction version of the **Decimal Roll a Problem Game** with the whole class. The addition version of this game was introduced in Lesson 10.5. Although the game is best played as a whole-class activity so students benefit from others' analyses, students can also play the game in groups of two, three, or four. To play the game, roll a 5–10 **Number Cube** as before, but now try to get as close to 10 as possible. The answer cannot be a negative number. Use the following outline:

_____ _____ _____ − _____ _____ _____ = 10

2 Assign Student Pages 25

Pages 398–399 APPLYING

Review the two examples on page 398 with students. Then have students complete page 399 independently.

RESEARCH IN ACTION

"To use numbers effectively, to speak about them, or to manipulate them requires that they have names. Modern societies use decimal place-value notation in daily life and commerce… The decimal system is versatile and simple, although not necessarily obvious or easily learned. The decimal place-value system is one of the most significant intellectual constructs of humankind, and it has played a decisive role in the development of mathematics and science."

Kilpatrick, J., J. Swafford and B. Findell, eds. *Adding It Up: Helping Children Learn Mathematics*. Washington, D.C.: National Research Council/ National Academy Press, 2001, p. 280.

LESSON 10.6 Subtracting Decimals

Key Ideas

When you subtract decimals, remember to line up the decimal points.

If you had \$23.79 and you bought a book for \$10.82, how much money would you have left? Subtract to find out.

\$23.79 − \$10.82 = ?

$$\begin{array}{r} 23.79 \\ -\ 10.82 \\ \hline \end{array}$$ Line up the decimal points.

$$\begin{array}{r} {}^{2\ 17} \\ 23.79 \\ -\ 10.82 \\ \hline 12.97 \end{array}$$ Subtract.

4.6 − 3.25 = ?

$$\begin{array}{r} 4.6 \\ -\ 3.25 \\ \hline \end{array}$$ Line up the decimal points.

$$\begin{array}{r} 4.60 \\ -\ 3.25 \\ \hline \end{array}$$ If it helps, put in a 0 (because 4.6 and 4.60 have the same value).

$$\begin{array}{r} {}^{5\ 10} \\ 4.60 \\ -\ 3.25 \\ \hline 1.35 \end{array}$$ Subtract.

398 · Textbook This lesson is available in the *eTextbook*.

Subtract.

1 $\begin{array}{r} 12.73 \\ -\ 9.06 \\ \hline 3.67 \end{array}$ **2** $\begin{array}{r} 5.45 \\ -\ 2.9 \\ \hline 2.55 \end{array}$ **3** $\begin{array}{r} 10.00 \\ -\ 2.50 \\ \hline 7.50 \end{array}$ **4** $\begin{array}{r} 43.85 \\ -\ 27.8 \\ \hline 16.05 \end{array}$

5 $\begin{array}{r} 63.5 \\ -\ 18.55 \\ \hline 44.95 \end{array}$ **6** $\begin{array}{r} 2.05 \\ -\ 1.38 \\ \hline 0.67 \end{array}$ **7** $\begin{array}{r} 5.09 \\ -\ 4.92 \\ \hline 0.17 \end{array}$ **8** $\begin{array}{r} 6.43 \\ -\ 2.31 \\ \hline 4.12 \end{array}$

9 $\begin{array}{r} 4.7 \\ -\ 4 \\ \hline 0.7 \end{array}$ **10** $\begin{array}{r} 10.00 \\ -\ 0.03 \\ \hline 9.97 \end{array}$ **11** $\begin{array}{r} 17.4 \\ -\ 15.26 \\ \hline 2.14 \end{array}$ **12** $\begin{array}{r} 12.07 \\ -\ 9.38 \\ \hline 2.69 \end{array}$

13 7.0 − 3.5 = ▇ 3.5

14 8.30 − 4.17 = ▇ 4.13

15 11.7 − 2.9 = ▇ 8.8

16 4.2 − 1.75 = ▇ 2.45

17 80.3 − 41.7 = ▇ 38.6

18 80.4 − 41.7 = ▇ 38.7

19 804 − 417 = ▇ 387

20 8.04 − 4.17 = ▇ 3.87

21 12.2 − 6.6 = ▇ 5.6

22 5.06 − 1.43 = ▇ 3.63

23 0.42 − 0.39 = ▇ 0.03

24 0.03 − 0.03 = ▇ 0

Solve.

25 On Monday Nikki bought a pair of sneakers for \$42.99. On Tuesday the same sneakers went on sale for \$40.50. How much would Nikki have saved if she had waited a day to buy the sneakers? \$2.49

26 Agatha spent \$3.43 for milk and bread. The bread cost \$1.39. How much was the milk? \$2.04

Teaching Lesson 10.6

Assign Student Pages, continued

Pages 400–401 APPLYING

Have students complete pages 400–401 independently.

Monitoring Student Progress

If . . . students can subtract multidigit whole numbers but have trouble subtracting decimals,	**Then . . .** remind them to line up the points so ones are subtracted from ones, tenths are subtracted from tenths, and so on. Students should notice that subtracting decimals is identical to the subtraction of whole numbers except for the necessity of lining up the decimal points.

As Students Finish

 Game ✓ **Decimal Roll a Problem Game** Have students play the subtraction version of this game.

Student Page

LESSON 10.6 • Subtracting Decimals

There is only one correct answer to each exercise. Can you use shortcuts to find it?

27 4.35 − 2.1 = ▢
  a. 4.14
  b. 2.25
  c. 2.24

32 8.79 − 3.74 = ▢
  a. 5.05
  b. 4.95
  c. 4.05

28 106 − 5.43 = ▢
  a. 437
  b. 51.7
  c. 100.57

33 10.3 − 4.76 = ▢
  a. 3.73
  b. 5.54
  c. 15.06

29 3.7 + 4.65 = ▢
  a. 5.02
  b. 7.35
  c. 8.35

34 73.2 − 6.47 = ▢
  a. 8.5
  b. 67.73
  c. 66.73

30 3.74 + 8.79 = ▢
  a. 11.53
  b. 12.53
  c. 13.53

35 106 + 5.43 = ▢
  a. 111.43
  b. 160.3
  c. 649

31 10.3 + 4.76 = ▢
  a. 15.06
  b. 57.9
  c. 5.79

36 73.2 + 6.47 = ▢
  a. 79.67
  b. 13.79
  c. 137.9

📖 **Textbook** This lesson is available in the *eTextbook*.

Student Page

Solve these problems.

37 Helena is 9 years old. Last year she was 110 centimeters tall. How tall is she this year? can't tell

38 Sid is saving his money to buy a football. It costs $12. He has $5.65 in his bank. How much more money does he need? $6.35

39 Mr. Rice bought some gum for 55¢. He gave the cashier a $5 bill. How much change should the cashier give Mr. Rice? $4.45

40 Before today, Andrea had ridden her bicycle a total of 274.8 kilometers. Now she has ridden her bicycle a total of 275.4 kilometers. How far did Andrea ride today? 0.6 km

41 Jack earned $10.50 babysitting. Does he have enough money to buy the book he wants? can't tell; not enough information

42 Megan had $7.43. She bought a book. She had $1.48 left. How much did the book cost? $5.95

---

③ **Reflect** 5 ⊘

Guided Discussion REASONING

Small Group

Have students discuss the shortcuts they used to find the answers to the exercises on student page 400. For example, for Exercise 27 students might notice that the answer must have a 5 in the hundredths place, which eliminates two of the choices. Similarly, for Exercise 28 students might notice that the answer is less than 106 but more than 100.

 Cumulative Review: For cumulative review of previously learned skills, see page 409–410.

 Family Involvement: Assign the *Practice, Reteach,* or *Enrichment* activities depending on the needs of your students.

Encourage students to practice subtracting decimals with a friend or a relative.

 Concept/Question Board: Encourage students to continue to post questions, answers, and examples on the Concept/Question Board.

 Math Puzzler: Adam is 6 years older than Joe and 4 years younger than Elizabeth. Joe is 22. How old is Elizabeth? How old is Adam? 32; 28

Assess and Differentiate

 Assess Use *eAssess* to record and analyze evidence of student understanding.

A Gather Evidence

Use the Daily Class Assessment Records in *Assessment* or *eAssess* to record daily observations.

Informal Assessment
☑ **Mental Math**

Did the student **COMPUTING**
- ❑ respond accurately?
- ❑ respond quickly?
- ❑ respond with confidence?
- ❑ self-correct?

Performance Assessment
☑ **Game**

Did the student **ENGAGING**
- ❑ pay attention to others' contributions?
- ❑ contribute information and ideas?
- ❑ improve on a strategy?
- ❑ reflect on and check the accuracy of his or her work?

B Summarize Findings

Analyze and summarize assessment data for each student. Determine which Assessment Follow-Up is appropriate for each student. Use the Student Assessment Record in *Assessment* or *eAssess* to update assessment records.

Assessment Page T41

C Assessment Follow-Up • DIFFERENTIATE INSTRUCTION

Based on your observations, use these teaching strategies for assessment follow-up.

INTERVENTION	ENRICH	PRACTICE	RETEACH
Review student performance on *Intervention* Lesson 10.B to see if students have mastered prerequisite skills for this lesson.	**If . . .** students are proficient in the lesson concepts, **Then . . .** encourage them to work on chapter projects or *Enrichment* Lesson 10.6.	**If . . .** students would benefit from additional practice, **Then . . .** assign *Practice* Lesson 10.6.	**If . . .** students are having difficulty understanding how to subtract decimals, **Then . . .** reteach the concept using *Reteach* Lesson 10.6.

ENGLISH LEARNER

Review

Use Lesson 10.6 in *English Learner Support Guide* to review lesson concepts and vocabulary.

Enrichment Lesson 10.6

Practice Lesson 10.6

Reteach Lesson 10.6

Lesson Planner

OBJECTIVES
- To introduce multiplying decimals by whole numbers
- To solve problems that involve the multiplication of decimals (with two decimal places) by one-digit whole numbers

NCTM STANDARDS
Number and Operations
Multiplying decimals by whole numbers

Problem Solving
Solving problems that arise in real-life contexts

MATERIALS

- *Response Wheels
- *One 5–10 Number Cube

TECHNOLOGY
ePresentation Lesson 10.7

TEST PREP
Cumulative Review
Mental Math reviews adding and subtracting decimals and multidigit numbers (Lessons 2.2, 2.4, 2.7–2.8, 10.5, and 10.6).

Writing + Math
Journal

Multiplying Decimals by Whole Numbers

Context of the Lesson This is the seventh of nine lessons that develop the arithmetic of decimal numbers. The previous two lessons covered addition and subtraction of decimals; the next lesson covers division. The chapter concludes with a lesson that focuses on applications of decimal arithmetic. This lesson contains a Mastery Checkpoint.

See page 380B for Math Background for teachers for this lesson.

Planning for Learning • DIFFERENTIATE INSTRUCTION

INTERVENTION

If . . . students lack the prerequisite skill of multidigit multiplication,

Then . . . teach *Intervention* Lesson 10.C.

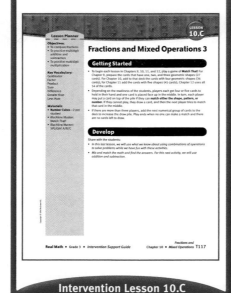

Intervention Lesson 10.C

ENGLISH LEARNER

Preview

If . . . students need language support,

Then . . . use Lesson 10.7 in *English Learner Support Guide* to preview lesson concepts and vocabulary.

English Learner Lesson 10.7

ENRICH

If . . . students are proficient in the lesson concepts,

Then . . . emphasize thinking about game strategies for the multiplication version of the **Decimal Roll a Problem Game.**

PRACTICE

If . . . students would benefit from additional practice,

Then . . . extend the playing of the multiplication version of the **Decimal Roll a Problem Game** before assigning the student pages.

RETEACH

If . . . students are having difficulty understanding how to multiply decimals by whole numbers,

Then . . . extend Guided Discussion before assigning the student pages.

Spanish Cognates
multiplication multiplicación
to multiply multiplicar

Mental Math 5

  Write related addition and subtraction exercises one at a time on the board. Write one under the other so students can see the relationships. Include some exercises with decimals. Have students show their answers with their **Response Wheels,** using a finger bent over between digits to indicate a decimal point when needed. Possible examples include the following:

a. 32 + 27 = 59

b. 3.2 + 2.7 = 5.9

c. 320 + 270 = 590

d. 0.32 + 0.27 = 0.59

e. 48 − 16 = 32

f. 0.48 − 0.16 = 0.32

g. 4.8 − 1.6 = 3.2

h. 480 − 160 = 320

1 Develop 25

Tell Students In Today's Lesson They Will

- learn how to multiply decimals by one-digit numbers.
- solve problems by multiplying decimals.

Guided Discussion UNDERSTANDING Whole Group

1. Present several word problems, one at a time, that require multiplication of decimals (with two decimal places) by one-digit whole numbers. For each problem, let students try to determine the answer, and then ask them to explain how they got it. Possible problems include the following:

   ■ **One bag of aquarium gravel costs $4.87. How much will 8 bags cost?**

   ■ **Andrew earns $2.85 for each hour he works. How much will he earn in 8 hours?**

   For the first problem, students should be able to estimate that the answer is less than 8 × 5, or $40, but more than 8 × 4, or $32. Therefore, any answer not between $32 and $40 can be ruled out immediately. One way to approach the problem is to think only in cents. One bag costs 487 cents; therefore, 8 bags cost 8 × 487, or 3,896 cents. This is the same as 3,800 cents and 96 cents. Because 1 dollar is the same as 100 cents, 3,800 cents is $38. So the answer is $38.96.

2. Point out that another way to find the answer to the first problem is by multiplying in this way:

   ```
     4.87
   ×    8
   ------
      .56
     6.40
    32.00
   ------
    38.96
   ```

   Emphasize that you have lined up the decimal points in partial products to make it easier to add them correctly.

3. Now present and discuss a few problems, such as the following, in which the decimal has only one decimal place.

   ■ **A bookcase is 3.7 meters long. If 5 bookcases are placed end to end, how long will the 5 bookcases be altogether?**

   First ask students to estimate the product. (The product must be between 15 and 20 meters.) This problem can be solved in these ways:

   ```
     3.7 (meters)          37 (decimeters)
   ×   5                 ×    5
   ------                ------
     3.5                    35
    15.0                   150
   ------                ------
    18.5 (meters)         185 (decimeters)
   ```

   Since 1 meter is the same as 10 decimeters, 180 decimeters is 18 meters, and 185 decimeters is the same as 18.5 meters.

Skill and Strategy Building ENGAGING   Whole Group

 Decimal Roll a Problem Game

Play a multiplication version of the **Decimal Roll a Problem Game** with the whole class. The addition version of this game was introduced in Lesson 10.5, and the subtraction version was played in Lesson 10.6. Although the game is best played as a whole-class activity so students benefit from others' analyses, students can also play the game in groups of two, three, or four. To play the game, roll a 5–10 **Number Cube** as before, but now try to get as close to 300 as possible. Use the following outline:

_____ _____ _____ × _____ _____ _____ = 300

2 Assign Student Pages 20

Pages 402–403 APPLYING

Have students complete pages 402 and 403 independently. Have students check their answers to the exercises on page 403 to see if they are reasonable. For example, for the exercise 4.5 × 6 (Exercise 18), an answer that is not between 24 (4 × 6) and 30 (5 × 6) is unreasonable.

Monitoring Student Progress

If . . . students have trouble solving multiplication problems involving decimals,	**Then . . .** have them estimate the answer, multiply the numbers without decimal points, and then place the point so that the answer is close to the estimate.

As Students Finish

 Decimal Roll a Problem Game

LESSON
10.7 Multiplying Decimals by Whole Numbers

Key Ideas

When you multiply a decimal by a whole number, remember to estimate first and to place the decimal point in the answer.

Solve.

1. One book costs 347¢. How many cents do 8 books cost? 2,776¢

2. One book costs $3.47. How much do 8 books cost? $27.76

3. Each table is 127 centimeters long. How many centimeters long are 6 tables placed end to end? 762

4. Each table is 1.27 meters long. How many meters long are 6 tables placed end to end? 7.62

5. One ticket to the movie costs $7.25. How much do 4 tickets cost? $29.00

6. One lap around the racetrack is 1.25 miles. How many miles is 6 laps? 7.5

402

Textbook This lesson is available in the *eTextbook*.

Multiply.

7. $7.5 \times 2 =$ ☐ 15
8. $7.5 \times 4 =$ ☐ 30
9. $7.50 \times 4 =$ ☐ 30
10. $75.0 \times 4 =$ ☐ 300
11. $7.5 \times 8 =$ ☐ 60

12. $2.43 \times 5 =$ ☐ 12.15
13. $3.02 \times 7 =$ ☐ 21.14
14. $4.25 \times 4 =$ ☐ 17.00
15. $1.75 \times 5 =$ ☐ 8.75
16. $4.42 \times 6 =$ ☐ 26.52

17. $6.33 \times 3 =$ ☐ 18.99
18. $4.5 \times 6 =$ ☐ 27.0
19. $3.7 \times 9 =$ ☐ 33.3
20. $7.5 \times 4 =$ ☐ 30.0
21. $2.43 \times 7 =$ ☐ 17.01

22. $3.00 \times 8 =$ ☐ 24.00
23. $2.5 \times 4 =$ ☐ 10.0
24. $1.25 \times 8 =$ ☐ 10.00
25. $3.2 \times 7 =$ ☐ 22.4
26. $8.1 \times 2 =$ ☐ 16.2

27. $13.61 \times 5 =$ ☐ 68.05
28. $8.12 \times 2 =$ ☐ 16.24
29. $7.33 \times 9 =$ ☐ 65.97
30. $5.8 \times 6 =$ ☐ 34.8
31. $1.48 \times 3 =$ ☐ 4.44
32. $3.1 \times 2 =$ ☐ 6.2

33. $9.9 \times 6 =$ ☐ 59.4
34. $1.3 \times 8 =$ ☐ 10.4
35. $2.04 \times 5 =$ ☐ 10.20
36. $1.01 \times 9 =$ ☐ 9.09
37. $2.29 \times 4 =$ ☐ 9.16
38. $3.47 \times 7 =$ ☐ 24.29

Writing + Math Journal

Cakes at the bakery cost $10.00 each, but people can buy portions that are $\frac{1}{4}$ of a whole cake. A $\frac{1}{4}$ section of a cake sells for $3.50. If 8 people want a $\frac{1}{4}$ portion of a cake, should they purchase 2 whole cakes and cut the cakes themselves, or should they purchase eight $\frac{1}{4}$ portions? Explain.

---

3 Reflect

10

Guided Discussion REASONING

Small Group

1. Pose the following problem, and discuss different solution strategies:

■ **The school football team needs to buy 8 footballs. Each football costs $25.50. How much did the footballs cost?**

Some students might use the standard algorithm and multiply 25.50 by 8. Others might notice that 8×25 dollars is $200 and $8 \times \$0.50$ is $4, so the footballs cost $204.00.

2. Discuss the two solution strategies. Ask students which method they think is better. Ask questions such as the following:

■ **Is the second method better because you can do the arithmetic in your head?**
■ **Is the first method better because you don't have to think as much and if you can do the multiplication quickly and correctly every time, you can be sure that your answer is correct?**

It is not necessary to reach a conclusion, but it will be useful for students to think about it and form their own opinions. Both solutions are equally useful, but in general, the more efficient a method is, the better.

Writing + Math Journal

Students should explain that the 8 people would save money if they purchased 2 whole cakes and cut the cakes themselves. The price of 2 whole cakes is $20, and the price of eight $\frac{1}{4}$ portions is $28.

✓ Use Mastery Checkpoint 21 found in *Assessment* to evaluate student mastery of addition and subtraction of decimal numbers. By this time, students should be able to correctly answer eighty percent of the Mastery Checkpoint items.

Cumulative Review: For cumulative review of previously learned skills, see page 409–410.

Family Involvement: Assign the *Practice, Reteach,* or *Enrichment* activities depending on the needs of your students.

Encourage students to practice multiplying decimals by whole numbers with a friend or a relative.

Concept/Question Board: Encourage students to continue to post questions, answers, and examples on the Concept/Question Board.

Math Puzzler: Dale wrote the numbers from 1 to 30. How many times did he write the number 6? 3

Assess and Differentiate

 Assess Use *eAssess* to record and analyze evidence of student understanding.

A Gather Evidence

Use the Daily Class Assessment Records in *Assessment* or *eAssess* to record daily observations.

Formal Assessment

☑ **Mastery Checkpoint 21**

Did the student
- ❏ use correct procedures?
- ❏ respond with at least 80% accuracy?

21 Name _____ Date _____
Mastery Checkpoint 21
Addition and Subtraction of Decimal Numbers

The student demonstrates mastery by correctly
Solve. Watch the signs. answering at least twelve of the fifteen problems.

❶ 4.37 + 5.63 10.00	❷ 9.3 − 5.5 3.8	❸ 27.32 + 4.1 31.42
❹ 8.8 − 6.22 2.58	❺ 4.73 + 2.62 7.35	❻ 5.54 + 4.73 10.27
❼ 3.43 − 2.62 .81	❽ 5.05 − 4.5 .55	❾ 4.6 + 2.4 7.0

Assessment Page T74

B Summarize Findings

Analyze and summarize assessment data for each student. Determine which Assessment Follow-Up is appropriate for each student. Use the Student Assessment Record in *Assessment* or *eAssess* to update assessment records.

Student Name _____
Student Assessment Record
Directions: Use this chart to record student performance on all chapter assessments.

Assessment Page T41

C Assessment Follow-Up • DIFFERENTIATE INSTRUCTION

Based on your observations, use these teaching strategies for assessment follow-up.

INTERVENTION

Review student performance on *Intervention* Lesson 10.C to see if students have mastered prerequisite skills for this lesson.

ENGLISH LEARNER

Review

Use Lesson 10.7 in *English Learner Support Guide* to review lesson concepts and vocabulary.

ENRICH

If . . . students are proficient in the lesson concepts,

Then . . . encourage them to work on chapter projects or *Enrichment* Lesson 10.7.

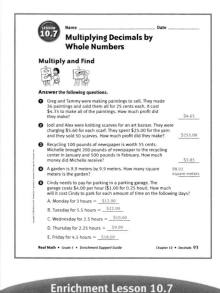

Enrichment Lesson 10.7

PRACTICE

If . . . students would benefit from additional practice,

Then . . . assign *Practice* Lesson 10.7.

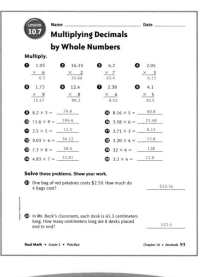

Practice Lesson 10.7

RETEACH

If . . . students struggle with multiplying with decimals,

Then . . . have them convert the decimal numbers to different units and then convert back to decimals after solving the whole-number problem. You might also have students use play money as an aid and repeat the multiplication problems.

Lesson Planner

OBJECTIVES
To develop a process for division involving decimals

NCTM STANDARDS
Number and Operations
Dividing decimals by whole numbers

MATERIALS

- *Response Wheels
- *Play money ($100 bills, $10 bills, $1 bills, dimes, and pennies)

TECHNOLOGY
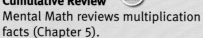 **e Presentation** Lesson 10.8

TEST PREP
Cumulative Review
Mental Math reviews multiplication facts (Chapter 5).

Extended Response
Problem 4

Dividing Decimals

Context of the Lesson This is the eighth of nine lessons that develop the arithmetic of decimal numbers. The previous three lessons covered addition, subtraction, and multiplication of decimals. The next lesson focuses on applications of decimal arithmetic. This lesson contains a Mastery Checkpoint.

See page 380B for Math Background for teachers for this lesson.

Planning for Learning ● DIFFERENTIATE INSTRUCTION

INTERVENTION

If . . . students lack the prerequisite skill of multidigit multiplication,

Then . . . teach *Intervention* Lesson 10.C.

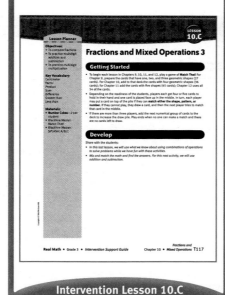

Intervention Lesson 10.C

ENGLISH LEARNER

Preview

If . . . students need language support,

Then . . . use Lesson 10.8 in *English Learner Support Guide* to preview lesson concepts and vocabulary.

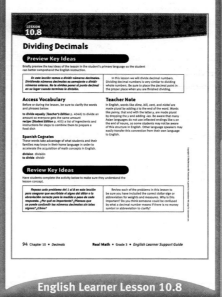

English Learner Lesson 10.8

ENRICH

If . . . students are proficient in the lesson concepts,

Then . . . emphasize chapter projects.

PRACTICE

If . . . students would benefit from additional practice,

Then . . . extend Guided Discussion before assigning the student pages.

RETEACH

If . . . students are having difficulty understanding how to divide decimals,

Then . . . review the division skills covered in Lesson 7.8 before assigning the student pages.

Access Vocabulary
to divide equally to divide an amount so that everyone gets the same amount

recipe a list of ingredients and steps to combine them to prepare a food dish

Spanish Cognates
division división
to divide dividir

Mental Math 5

  Do a fast-paced multiplication fact drill. Possible examples include the following:

a. $7 \times 7 = 49$ **b.** $6 \times 8 = 48$ **c.** $8 \times 8 = 64$ **d.** $9 \times 7 = 63$

e. $4 \times 4 = 16$ **f.** $5 \times 3 = 15$ **g.** $7 \times 4 = 28$ **h.** 3×7 21

i. $5 \times 8 = 40$ **j.** $4 \times 8 = 32$ **k.** $7 \times 8 = 56$ **l.** $7 \times 6 = 42$

m. $5 \times 9 = 45$ **n.** $5 \times 5 = 25$ **o.** $7 \times 5 = 35$ **p.** $7 \times 3 = 21$

1 Develop 30

Tell Students In Today's Lesson They Will
learn how to use decimals during division.

Guided Discussion UNDERSTANDING Whole Group

1. Using play money, have 7 students work with you as you show the whole class how to divide 720 by 7. Start with 7 hundred dollar bills and 2 tens, and ask the following question:

   ■ **What should we do first to divide the money among these 7 people?**

   Students should suggest giving 1 hundred dollar bill to each student, leaving 2 tens. Have each of the 7 students take 1 hundred dollar bill.

2. Next, ask a question such as the following about what to do with the 2 tens:

   ■ **How can we divide 2 tens among 7 people?**

   Students should suggest exchanging the 2 tens for 20 ones and giving each person 2 ones, leaving 6 ones. Have each of the 7 students take 2 ones. (Do not have $5 bills available.)

3. Ask students how to proceed with dividing the remaining money:

   ■ **How can we divide 6 ones among 7 people?**

   If students suggest exchanging the ones for quarters, tell them your bank doesn't have any quarters, but you do have dimes. Ask students to determine how many dimes they can get for 6 ones. 60 Then ask the following question:

   ■ **Now that we have 60 dimes, how many dimes should each of the 7 people get?**

   Each person should get 8 dimes. Students should explain how they determined the answer. One way is to find the ×7 multiplication fact that is closest to but not greater than 60 ($7 \times 8 = 56$).

4. After each person has taken 8 dimes and there are 4 dimes remaining, ask students how to divide up the remaining dimes. Students should suggest exchanging the dimes for 40 cents and giving each of the 7 people 5 cents, leaving 5 cents still to be distributed. Have each of the 7 students take 5 cents.

5. Tell students that you want to record the steps the class followed to divide up the money. Write the following on the board, and explain how it accurately shows what happened and provides an answer that is correct to cents. Make sure students understand that the decimal point separates dollars from dimes.

$$
\begin{array}{r}
102.85 \\
7\overline{)720.00} \\
\underline{7} \\
20. \\
\underline{14.} \\
6.0 \\
\underline{5.6} \\
.40 \\
\underline{.35} \\
.05
\end{array}
$$

6. Ask students what should be done with the remaining 5 cents. Accept all reasonable responses. Then have students check the answer by multiplying 7×102.85. When students get 719.95 as the answer, ask if that is the answer they expected. Students should explain that it is the answer they expected because there was 5 cents remaining.

7. If necessary, do one or two more problems that include dollars and cents to be distributed.

2 Assign Student Pages 20

Pages 404–405 APPLYING
Review the division example on page 404 with students. Then have students complete page 405 independently or in small groups.

As Students Finish

 Decimal Roll a Problem Game Have students play the addition, subtraction, or multiplication version of this game.

LESSON 10.8 **Dividing Decimals**

Key Ideas

Dividing decimal numbers is very similar to dividing whole numbers.

A group of 8 students earned $573.47 and decided to divide it equally among themselves. There were 5 hundred-dollar bills, 7 ten-dollar bills, 3 one-dollar bills, 4 dimes, and 7 pennies. How much should each get?

```
        7 1.___
    8 )5 7 3.4 7
      5 6
        1 3
         8
         5
```

Because the students could not share the 5 hundred-dollar bills, they exchanged them for 50 ten-dollar bills. Now they had a total of 57 ten-dollar bills. Each student took 7 tens. That left 1 ten-dollar bill. Then they exchanged the remaining ten-dollar bill for 10 one-dollar bills.

The students now had 13 one-dollar bills. Each one took 1 one-dollar bill, leaving 5 one-dollar bills. Does the record at the right show what has happened so far?

Because the students could not share the 5 one-dollar bills, they exchanged them for 50 dimes. Now they had a total of 54 dimes. Each student took 6 of the 54 dimes. That used up 48 dimes, and they had 6 dimes left. They exchanged the 6 dimes for 60 cents, so they had 67 cents to be distributed. Each student got 8 cents.

```
        7 1.6 8_
    8 )5 7 3.4 7
      5 6
        1 3.
         8.
         5.4
         4.8
          .67
          .64
          .03
```

How many cents did they have left to be distributed? What would you do with the 3 cents if you were one of the 8 students?

404   Textbook This lesson is available in the *eTextbook.*

Solve.

1. A recipe for 6 people calls for 1.2 kilograms of flour. Mitchell is making the recipe for one person. How many kilograms of flour should she use? How many grams is that?   0.2; 200

2. There are 5 students who will share a 1-liter bottle of apple juice. How much is each person's share?   0.2 liter, or 200 ml

3. The 9 members of the history club were preparing for a trip to Washington, D.C. They estimated that the trip would cost $500. About what is each person's share?   about $60, perhaps a bit more to be sure that all expenses are covered

4. **Extended Response** Raulito is a member of the history club that is going to visit Washington, D.C. He reported that his share of the $500 would be $55.56. Is Raulito correct? Why or why not?

5. There are 9 classrooms and about 200 students in Northview School. How many of the students walk to school?   can't tell

6. A wooden board measures 5.75 meters in length. If the board is cut into 5 equal-sized pieces, how long will each piece be? How many centimeters is that?   1.15 meters; 115

7. Suzie read that if you jog around the perimeter of Seward Park, you will have jogged about 2.5 miles. The park is shaped like a square. What is the length of each side of the park?   0.625 miles

8. Tammy, Brandt, and Sally want to share equally the cost of a new bicycle. If the full price of the bicycle is $375.96, what is each person's share? $125.32

4. Students should answer that Raulito is *and* isn't correct. If the trip actually costs $500, he is correct. However, $500 is only an estimate, so an exact calculation is not warranted.

Chapter 10 • Lesson 8   405

---

3 Reflect   5

Guided Discussion   REASONING   Small Group

Ask whether students think the division process for 720 divided by 7 will end with a 0 remainder after some number of steps, and if so, how many steps will be required before they get to 0. The answer is *no*. The process will go on forever, but after a while a pattern will become obvious as remainders begin to repeat. You need not give this answer to students—let them discuss what they think and continue thinking about it.

✓ Use Mastery Checkpoint 22 found in **Assessment** to evaluate student mastery of converting metric units of length. By this time, students should be able to correctly answer eighty percent of the Mastery Checkpoint items.

 Cumulative Review: For cumulative review of previously learned skills, see page 409–410.

 Family Involvement: Assign the **Practice, Reteach,** or **Enrichment** activities depending on the needs of your students.

Encourage students to practice dividing decimals with a friend or a relative.

 Concept/Question Board: Have students attempt to answer any unanswered questions on the Concept/Question Board.

 Math Puzzler: Salvio had 24 baseballs, Mark had 8 baseballs, and Tony had 16. Salvio gave Mark some of his baseballs. Now they all have the same number of baseballs. How many does each have? 16

4 Assess and Differentiate

e Assess Use *eAssess* to record and analyze evidence of student understanding.

A Gather Evidence

Use the Daily Class Assessment Records in **Assessment** or **eAssess** to record daily observations.

Formal Assessment
☑ **Mastery Checkpoint 22**

Did the student
☐ use correct procedures?
☐ respond with at least 80% accuracy?

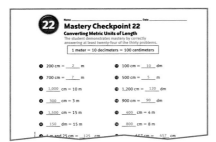

Assessment Page T75

B Summarize Findings

Analyze and summarize assessment data for each student. Determine which Assessment Follow-Up is appropriate for each student. Use the Student Assessment Record in **Assessment** or **eAssess** to update assessment records.

Assessment Page T41

C Assessment Follow-Up ● DIFFERENTIATE INSTRUCTION

Based on your observations, use these teaching strategies for assessment follow-up.

INTERVENTION

Review student performance on **Intervention** Lesson 10.C to see if students have mastered prerequisite skills for this lesson.

ENGLISH LEARNER

Review

Use Lesson 10.8 in **English Learner Support Guide** to review lesson concepts and vocabulary.

ENRICH

If . . . students are proficient in the lesson concepts,

Then . . . encourage them to work on chapter projects or **Enrichment** Lesson 10.8.

Enrichment Lesson 10.8

PRACTICE

If . . . students would benefit from additional practice,

Then . . . assign **Practice** Lesson 10.8.

Practice Lesson 10.8

RETEACH

If . . . students struggle with dividing decimals,

Then . . . have them divide as if the decimal wasn't there. Then show them how to apply the decimal to the answer. Because they are not dividing by a decimal, the answer should line up with the original decimal when placed in long division format.

Lesson Planner

OBJECTIVES
- To provide applications of decimal arithmetic
- To solve routine and nonroutine map problems

NCTM STANDARDS
Problem Solving
Applying a variety of appropriate strategies to solve problems

Representation
Representing distances and locations using a map

MATERIALS

- *Response Wheels
- Store Game Mat

TECHNOLOGY
⒠Presentation Lesson 10.9

TEST PREP
Cumulative Review
Mental Math reviews multiplication facts (Chapter 5).

Extended Response
Problems 13–14

Decimal Applications

Context of the Lesson This is the last of a nine-lesson sequence on decimal arithmetic. In this lesson, students apply their knowledge to solving problems. Decimals will continue to be used, in context, throughout the rest of the **Real Math** program.

See page 380B for Math Background for teachers for this lesson.

Planning for Learning ● DIFFERENTIATE INSTRUCTION

INTERVENTION

If . . . students lack the prerequisite skill of multidigit addition and subtraction,

Then . . . teach **Intervention** Lesson 10.B.

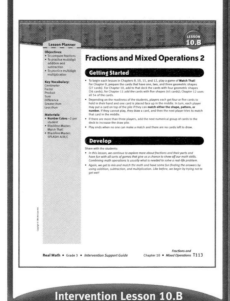

Intervention Lesson 10.B

ENGLISH LEARNER

Preview

If . . . students need language support,

Then . . . use Lesson 10.9 in **English Learner Support Guide** to preview lesson concepts and vocabulary.

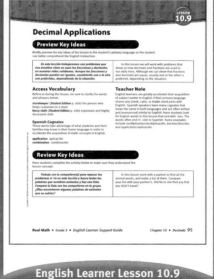

English Learner Lesson 10.9

ENRICH

If . . . students are proficient in the lesson concepts,

Then . . . emphasize chapter projects.

PRACTICE

If . . . students would benefit from additional practice,

Then . . . extend Strategy Building before assigning the student pages.

RETEACH

If . . . students are having difficulty understanding decimal applications,

Then . . . extend Guided Discussion before assigning the student pages.

Vocabulary
kilometer \ki lom′ i tər, kil′ ə mē′ tər\ *n.* a unit of length in the metric system equal to 1,000 meters

Spanish Cognates
application aplicación
combination combinación

Mental Math 5

  Do a fast-paced multiplication fact drill. Possible examples include the following:

a. $7 \times 7 = 49$ **b.** $6 \times 8 = 48$ **c.** $8 \times 8 = 64$ **d.** $9 \times 7 = 63$

e. $4 \times 4 = 16$ **f.** $5 \times 3 = 15$ **g.** $7 \times 4 = 28$ **h.** $3 \times 7 = 21$

i. $5 \times 8 = 40$ **j.** $4 \times 8 = 32$ **k.** $7 \times 8 = 56$ **l.** $7 \times 6 = 42$

m. $5 \times 9 = 45$ **n.** $5 \times 5 = 25$ **o.** $7 \times 5 = 35$ **p.** $7 \times 3 = 21$

1 Develop 30

Tell Students In Today's Lesson They Will

learn to apply what they have learned about decimals to solve problems.

Guided Discussion UNDERSTANDING   Whole Group

1. Conduct a brief discussion that allows students to tell about where they have seen decimal numbers outside the classroom and how they might have used them for solving problems. Probably most applications they have encountered deal with money and measurement.

2. Briefly review how to use a map to find distances between places. You might do this with a real map of your local area or with a partially made-up map drawn on the board, using the map on student page 407 as a guide. Ask a few routine questions about the map. Then ask a question that is not directly readable from the map, but which can be inferred from it. For example, if you show 5 local communities or places on the map, ask where a known place that is not on the map might be located.

Strategy Building ENGAGING   Small Group

Have students work in small groups to sketch the outline of a local map with four or five places and label the approximate distances. To begin, select two places that should be on the map, and give the distance between them using a decimal number; for example, the distance between our school and the local library is about 1.4 kilometers. Although the maps will be imperfect, have students try to draw the maps to scale.

2 Assign Student Pages 20

Pages 406–407 APPLYING

Allow students to do pages 406 and 407 independently.

Monitoring Student Progress

| **If . . .** students are having difficulty with the problems on either student page, | **Then . . .** work individually or in small groups with those students as you think aloud and act out similar problems using play money or a local map, as appropriate. |

As Students Finish

- **Store Game**
- **Harder Store Game**

LESSON 10.9 Decimal Applications

Key Ideas
You can use what you have learned about decimals to solve problems. Problems dealing with money and measurement often involve decimals.

Solve these problems.

1. Wei made curtains for one window. She used 2.68 yards of cloth. How many yards of cloth will she need to make curtains for 4 more windows the same size? **10.72 yards**

2. Wei is buying 10.8 yards of cloth. The piece at the store is 14.5 yards long. What length of cloth will be left? **3.7 yards**

3. The cloth costs $35.26. Wei gave the storekeeper two $20 bills. How much change should Wei get? **$4.74**

4. Wei decided to buy 2 yards of fancy cloth to make a pillowcase. The fancy cloth costs $8.99 per yard. How much did Wei spend? **$17.98**

5. How much would she spend if she bought 3 yards of the fancy cloth? **$26.97**

406

📖 **Textbook** This lesson is available in the **eTextbook**.

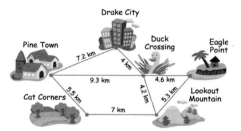

Solve.

6. How far is it from Pine Town to Duck Crossing? **9.3 km**

7. How far is it from Pine Town to Eagle Point? **13.9 km**

8. How far is it from Pine Town to Lookout Mountain if you go through Duck Crossing? **13.5 km**

9. How far is it from Pine Town to Lookout Mountain if you go through Cat Corners? **12.5 km**

10. Suppose you are going from Duck Crossing to Pine Town. How much farther would it be to go through Drake City? **1.9 km**

11. What is the shortest route from Eagle Point to Cat Corners? **Eagle Point to Lookout Mountain to Cat Corners**

12. How many kilometers is that route? **12.3 km**

13. **Extended Response** New City is located about 10 kilometers from Cat Corners and 10 kilometers from Pine Town.

    a. Is New City closer to Duck Crossing or Eagle Point?

    b. What other information do you need to know to locate New City?

14. **Extended Response** If a bird flew directly between Cat Corners and Duck Crossing, about how far would it fly? Explain.
    7 kilometers; see Teacher's Edition for explanation.

Chapter 10 • Lesson 9

407

Decimal Applications — LESSON 10.9

3 Reflect
5 ⏱

Guided Discussion   REASONING
Small Group

Draw a sketch of the map at the top of page 407 on the board. Then have student volunteers present their answers and their reasoning for the last two problems on that page. Discussion should focus on the following points:

- estimating distances
- the use of scale
- the detection of obviously wrong answers
- asking questions to get necessary information

Extended Response

Problem 13 For Part a, students should explain that with the information given, there are two possible locations: one east of Cat Corners and one west of Cat Corners. For Part b, students should explain that to locate New City, you need to know its distance from a third place. For example, if we knew that New City was located 17 kilometers from Lookout Mountain, we would know that New City was located west of Cat Corners.

Problem 14 Students should notice that the distance from Cat Corners to Lookout Mountain is about the same as the distance from Cat Corners to Duck Crossing. They can confirm this by marking the endpoints from Cat Corners to Lookout Mountain on a piece of paper and then lining up the marks with the endpoints from Cat Corners to Duck Crossing.

 Curriculum Connection: Have students research the distances from their home towns to several neighboring towns and then draw a map showing those distances in kilometers (similar to student page 407).

 Cumulative Review: For cumulative review of previously learned skills, see page 409–410.

 Family Involvement: Assign the **Practice, Reteach,** or **Enrichment** activities depending on the needs of your students.

Encourage students to practice solving real-world problems with decimals with a friend or a relative.

 Concept/Question Board: Have students attempt to answer any unanswered questions on the Concept/Question Board.

 Math Puzzler: I am thinking of a number. If you subtract 12 from the number, you get 9. What is the number? **21**

Assess and Differentiate

A Gather Evidence

Use the Daily Class Assessment Records in *Assessment* or *eAssess* to record daily observations.

Informal Assessment

☑ **Guided Discussion**

Did the student **UNDERSTANDING**

- ❑ make important observations?
- ❑ extend or generalize learning?
- ❑ provide insightful answers?
- ❑ pose insightful questions?

Informal Assessment

☑ **Guided Discussion**

Did the student **REASONING**

- ❑ provide a clear explanation?
- ❑ communicate reasons and strategies?
- ❑ choose appropriate strategies?
- ❑ argue logically?

B Summarize Findings

Analyze and summarize assessment data for each student. Determine which Assessment Follow-Up is appropriate for each student. Use the Student Assessment Record in *Assessment* or *eAssess* to update assessment records.

Assessment Page T41

C Assessment Follow-Up • DIFFERENTIATE INSTRUCTION

Based on your observations, use these teaching strategies for assessment follow-up.

INTERVENTION	ENRICH	PRACTICE	RETEACH
Review student performance on *Intervention* Lesson 10.B to see if students have mastered prerequisite skills for this lesson.	**If . . .** students are proficient in the lesson concepts, **Then . . .** encourage them to work on chapter projects or *Enrichment* Lesson 10.9.	**If . . .** students would benefit from additional practice, **Then . . .** assign *Practice* Lesson 10.9.	**If . . .** students struggle with adding and subtracting decimals, **Then . . .** have them work with concrete base-10 materials. Have them check over each problem, using play money as a model. When helping students do problems this way, focus on showing them the relationship between the model and the numbers written in decimal form. From the physical model, lead students to see that adding or subtracting decimals is identical to addition or subtraction of whole numbers because the decimal points determine the place values. Remind them to line up the points.

ENGLISH LEARNER

Review

Use Lesson 10.9 in *English Learner Support Guide* to review lesson concepts and vocabulary.

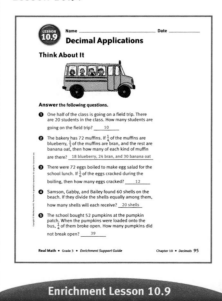

Enrichment Lesson 10.9

Practice Lesson 10.9

Exploring Problem Solving

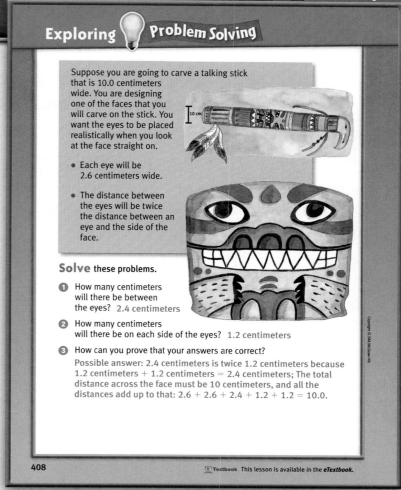

Exploring Problem Solving

Suppose you are going to carve a talking stick that is 10.0 centimeters wide. You are designing one of the faces that you will carve on the stick. You want the eyes to be placed realistically when you look at the face straight on.

- Each eye will be 2.6 centimeters wide.

- The distance between the eyes will be twice the distance between an eye and the side of the face.

Solve these problems.

1. How many centimeters will there be between the eyes? 2.4 centimeters

2. How many centimeters will there be on each side of the eyes? 1.2 centimeters

3. How can you prove that your answers are correct?
   Possible answer: 2.4 centimeters is twice 1.2 centimeters because 1.2 centimeters + 1.2 centimeters = 2.4 centimeters; The total distance across the face must be 10 centimeters, and all the distances add up to that: 2.6 + 2.6 + 2.4 + 1.2 + 1.2 = 10.0.

408   Textbook This lesson is available in the *eTextbook*.

Objectives
- To provide practice using decimals and metric measurements
- To provide practice interpreting measurements on diagrams
- To provide practice solving and justifying solutions to nonroutine, real-world problems

Materials
- Graph paper
- Rulers

Context of the Lesson Continuing the totem-pole theme begun on page 380, this lesson provides an opportunity for students to apply some of the skills they have been working on in this chapter to solve a challenging measurement problem involving decimals. The problem is similar to the one students solved earlier (Chapter 2, page 41) where they centered a window in a tree house. Here, they use decimals and center a pair of objects instead of a single object.

1 Develop   5

Tell Students In Today's Lesson They Will
figure out where to place the eyes on a totem figure.

Guided Discussion
Remind students of the problems about totem poles they have already solved on pages 394 and 395. Explain that today they will be designing a face for a talking stick, which may look like a miniature totem pole.

2 Exploring Problem Solving 30

Using Student Pages

Read the information at the top of page 408 together. Help students recall a similar problem they solved back in Chapter 2 on page 41 in which they centered a window in a tree house.

To make sure students understand the information, ask questions such as the following:

- **How wide will each eye be?** 2.6 centimeters
- **Show me with your fingers about how wide that is.** Students should indicate about an inch.
- **How wide is the face?** 10 centimeters
- **What must be true about the distance between the eyes compared to the distance to the side of the eyes?** The distance between the eyes must be twice the distance on the side of each eye.

Have students work Problems 1–3 in pairs or small groups. Tell them that when they present their solutions, they will need to explain not only the placement of the eyes but how they solved the problems and how they know their placement is correct.

Have graph paper available. Circulate around the room, and provide support as needed. Be sure to allow students time to struggle with the problem before offering suggestions. If students seem to be unable to make progress, ask questions such as the following:

- How might you use the graph paper to help you get started?
- Can you make a model or a diagram of the face?
- How does knowing that the face is 10 centimeters wide and the eyes are each 2.6 centimeters wide help you?
- How much of the 10-centimeter width of the face is taken up by the two eyes?

Sample Solutions Strategies

Students might use one or more of the following strategies to solve the problem.

Make a Diagram

Students might tape together enough graph paper to make a scale model of the face, for example, letting each grid unit stand for a tenth of a centimeter.

Make a Physical Model/Solve a Simpler Problem

Students might draw, cut out, and fold the face in half along a vertical line of symmetry. Then they can center one eye in the middle of one-half of the face.

Write Equations

Students might write equations to show the relationships among the distances.

width of eyes + space between eyes + space on left + space on right = width of face

space on left = space on right

space between eyes = 2 × space on left (or 2 × space on right)

Guess, Check, and Revise

Students might first find that the total amount of width not used by the eyes is 4.8 centimeters. Then they can try a different distance for the space on the side of the eyes until they find numbers that give a total of 4.8. The following illustrates this process:

	Guess	Check	
Space on sides	Space between eyes	Total empty space	Result
1 cm each	2 cm	1 + 1 + 2 = 4	4 < 4.8 too small

3 Reflect 10

Problem Formulation, Planning, and Strategizing Have groups present their answers and methods.

In discussion, bring out the following points:

- Different people may use different ways to solve the same problem. There is no right or wrong way—you can use any way that works for you.
- You can use what you know about numbers and shapes to help you solve problems that you have not come across before.
- Sometimes it is useful to find the sum of two numbers. Sometimes it is useful to find the difference of two numbers. In some situations, you may need to do both.

4 Assess 15

When evaluating student work, think not only about whether the answer was correct, but consider whether the student thought rationally about the problem. Questions to consider include the following:

- Did the student understand the problem?
- Did the student approach the problem in a reasonable way?
- If the student needed to add or subtract, was an appropriate method used?
- Did the student check to see that the answer was reasonable?
- Did the student use any particularly sophisticated reasoning to solve the problem?

Cumulative Review

Assign Pages 409–410

Use the Cumulative Review as a review of concepts and skills that students have previously learned.

Here are different ways you can assign these problems to your students as they work through the chapter:

- With some of the lessons in the chapter, assign a set of Cumulative Review problems to be completed as practice or for homework.
  Lesson 10.6—Problems 1–3
  Lesson 10.7—Problems 4–5
  Lesson 10.8—Problems 6–13
  Lesson 10.9—Problems 14–22
- At any point during the chapter, assign part or all of the Cumulative Review problems to be completed as practice or for homework.

Cumulative Review

Problems 1–3 review adding and subtracting large numbers, Lesson 2.12.

Problems 4–5 review fractions greater than a whole, Lesson 8.8.

Problems 6–13 review division with remainders, Lesson 7.5.

Problems 14–22 review measuring elapsed time, Lesson 9.8.

Monitoring Student Progress

If . . . students miss more than one problem in a section,   **Then . . .** refer to the indicated lesson for remediation suggestions.

Cumulative Review

Adding and Subtracting Very Large Numbers Lesson 2.12

Add or Subtract.

① 627534373
+ 322447972
949,982,345

② 726419397
+ 453627428
1,180,046,825

③ 770361529
− 524643011
245,718,518

Fractions Greater Than a Whole Lesson 8.8

Name the fraction represented by the shaded sections. Give the name in at least two ways.

④ $1\frac{1}{2}$, $\frac{3}{2}$

⑤ $1\frac{2}{4}$, $1\frac{1}{2}$, $\frac{6}{4}$, or $\frac{3}{2}$

Division with Remainders Lesson 7.5

Solve. If it is not possible to solve the problem, tell why.

⑥ $5)\overline{37}$ → 7 R2
⑦ $8)\overline{61}$ → 7 R5
⑧ $3)\overline{88}$ → 29 R1
⑨ $9)\overline{59}$ → 6 R5
⑩ $6)\overline{77}$ → 12 R5
⑪ $4)\overline{47}$ → 11 R3

Nia's class has been assigned group projects. Each group has 4 students and must tell about 37 different monuments.

⑫ If the group members are splitting the task equally, how many monuments should each of the 4 students research? How many monuments will still need to be researched? 9; 1

⑬ **Extended Response** How should the students in the group deal with the remainder?
Accept any logical answer. Possible answer: Three students can begin to compile the information while the fourth student researches the last monument.

Cumulative Review

Measuring Elapsed Time Lesson 9.8

Copy and complete the table by filling in the elapsed time.

Schedule for Monument Day

Activity	Time	Elapsed Time
Students Arrive	8:45 A.M.–9:00 A.M.	⑭ 15 minutes
Discuss Day's Events and Safety	9:00 A.M.–9:15 A.M.	⑮ 15 minutes
Inside Tour of Monument	9:15 A.M.–10:30 A.M.	⑯ 1 hour and 15 minutes
Guest Speaker	10:30 A.M.–11:45 A.M.	⑰ 1 hour and 15 minutes
Lunch	11:45 A.M.–12:30 P.M.	⑱ 45 minutes
Outside Tour of Monument	12:30 P.M.–1:40 P.M.	⑲ 1 hour and 10 minutes
Making Monumental Crafts	1:40 P.M.–3:05 P.M.	⑳ 1 hour and 25 minutes
Gift Shop Visit	3:05 P.M.–3:15 P.M.	㉑ 10 minutes
Students Depart	3:15 P.M.	

㉒ What is the total amount of elapsed time from the time the students arrive to the time they finish their lunches? Write your answer in hours and minutes (not just minutes).
3 hours and 45 minutes

Wrap-Up

1 Discuss 5

Concept/Question Board

Review the Concept/Question Board with students.

- Discuss students' contributions to the Concept side of the Board.
- Have students re-pose their questions, and lead a discussion to find satisfactory answers.

Chapter Projects APPLYING

Provide an opportunity for students who have worked on one or more of the projects outlined on page 381C to share their work with the class. Allow each student or student group five minutes to present or discuss their projects. For formal assessment, use the rubrics found in **Across the Curriculum Math Connections;** the rubric for **Research Monuments around the World** is on page 105, and the rubric for **Write about Totem Poles** is on page 111. For informal assessment, use the following rubric and questions.

	Exceeds Expectations	Meets Expectations	Minimally Meets Expectations
Applies mathematics in real-world situations:	❑	❑	❑
Demonstrates strong engagement in the activity:	❑	❑	❑

Research Monuments around the World

- What monuments did you research? Why did you choose those monuments?
- What notes did you take about the monuments?
- What were the measurements of the monuments that you researched?
- How did you express the measurements that you found?
- How did you organize your note cards?
- Are note cards a good way to record information? Why or why not?

Write about Totem Poles

- What are totem poles? What do they symbolize?
- What do the figures on totem poles mean?
- What size was your totem pole?
- What images or figures did you include on your totem pole design? Why did you choose those figures?
- What did you include in your word processing file about your totem pole design?
- How did you describe each of the symbols on your totem pole?
- Where would you put your totem pole if you could put it anywhere?

2 Assign Students Pages 25

Key Ideas Review UNDERSTANDING

Have students complete the Review questions independently or in small groups. Then discuss each question as a class.

Possible Answers

Problem ❶ Problem 1 involves using decimal points with measurement and adding decimals. The answer is that it will be possible to hang the two pictures on the wall with the space between them. Students should determine that 30 centimeters is equal to 0.3 meter and 10 centimeters is equal to 0.1 meter. Students' diagrams should show that the two pictures and the space between the pictures are 0.7 meter long because 0.3 + 0.1 + 0.3 = 0.7.

Extended Response

Problem ❷ This problem allows students to explain how to correctly add decimals. Students should answer that their friend added 3 to eight-tenths instead of adding 3 to 7. Then they should suggest that he line up the decimal points this way: 7.8 + 3.0 = 10.8.

Extended Response

Problem ❸ Students should explain that 4 tickets will cost more than $32 because 8 × 4 = 32, and 8.75 is greater than 8.

Extended Response

Problem ❹ This problem involves dividing decimals. The answer is no. Each person would have to contribute $2.25 for the cost to be shared equally.

CHAPTER 10 Key Ideas Review

In this chapter you explored decimals and some of their uses.

You learned how to use decimals with money and with measurements.

You learned how tenths and hundredths can be written as fractions or decimals.

You learned how to add, subtract, multiply, and divide decimals.

Solve each problem.

❶ Marsha wants to hang 2 pictures on a wall that is 1.2 meters wide. Each picture frame is 30 centimeters wide, and Marsha would like to have 10 centimeters of space between each picture. Will that be possible? Draw a diagram to show why or why not.

❶ yes; Students' diagrams should show that the length of the 2 pictures and the space between them is 0.7 meters.

Extended Response **Provide a detailed answer for the following exercises.**

❷ Suppose your friend added 7.8 and 3 and got an answer of 8.1. Explain the error your friend made, and tell how you might be able to help him get the right answer.

❸ Each ticket to the zoo costs $8.75. Will 4 tickets cost more than $32?

❹ Sam and two of his friends want to buy a collection of old postage stamps to share equally. The stamps cost $6.75. If Sam has $2, will the cost of the stamps be shared equally among he and his friends?
See Teacher's Edition for the answers to Problems 2–4.

Chapter 10 • Key Ideas Review   411

Chapter Review

Use the Chapter 10 Review to indicate areas in which each student is having difficulty or in which the class may need help. If students do well on the Chapter 10 Review, you may wish to skip directly to the Chapter Test; if not, you may want to spend a day or so helping students overcome their individual difficulties before taking the Practice Test.

Next to each set of problems is a list of the lessons in the chapter that covered those concepts. If they need help, students can refer to a specific lesson for additional instruction. You can also use this information to make additional assignments based on the previous lesson concepts.

Have students complete pages 412–413 on their own. For review purposes, you may want to do some of the word problems on page 413 as a class.

Monitoring Student Progress

Problems 1–4 Lessons 10.2–10.3

If . . . students have difficulty with these conversions,

Then . . . review the Key Ideas presented on student page 386 to make sure students understand the relationship between dollars and dimes, as well as meters and decimeters.

Problems 5–14 Lesson 10.4

If . . . students miss one or more of these exercises,

Then . . . review the Key Ideas presented on student page 388 to help students understand the relationship between fractions and decimals.

Problems 15–18 Lesson 10.5

If . . . students have difficulty with these addition exercises but can add multidigit whole numbers,

Then . . . have them model addition exercises using play money or other concrete objects. For example, to add 3.5 + 8.1, they should add 3 dollars and 5 dimes to 8 dollars and 1 dime, or they might add a string that is 3.5 meters long to another string that is 8.1 meters long.

Problems 19–22 Lesson 10.6

If . . . students have difficulty with these subtraction exercises,

Then . . . have them model subtraction exercises using play money or other concrete objects just as they did for adding decimals.

Problems 23–26 Lesson 10.7

If . . . students have difficulty with these multiplication exercises,

Then . . . encourage them to convert the numbers to different units to avoid multiplying with decimals. For example, to find the answer to 8.35×6, they can multiply 835 cents (instead of $8.35) by 6 and then convert back to dollars and cents.

Problems 27–28 Lesson 10.8

If . . . students have difficulty solving these problems,

Then . . . work individually or in small groups with them as you think aloud and act out similar problems using play money or other manipulatives, as appropriate.

Problems 29–30 Lesson 10.9

If . . . students have difficulty solving these problems,

Then . . . show them how to use play money to solve each problem.

10 CHAPTER Chapter Review

Lessons 10.2–10.3 Answer each question.

1. How many dimes are in $7.00? **70**

2. How many dimes are in $3.80? **38**

3. How many decimeters are in 3 meters? **30**

4. How many decimeters are in 3.5 meters? **35**

Lesson 10.4 Write true or false.

5. $0.5 = \frac{5}{100}$ **false**

6. $0.02 = \frac{2}{100}$ **true**

7. $0.78 = \frac{78}{100}$ **true**

8. $0.67 = \frac{67}{10}$ **false**

Write each fraction as a decimal or each decimal as a fraction.

9. $3\frac{25}{100}$ **3.25**

10. 0.08 **$\frac{8}{100}$**

11. $\frac{6}{10}$ **0.6**

12. 0.80 **$\frac{80}{100}$**

13. $\frac{40}{100}$ **0.40**

14. 0.9 **$\frac{9}{10}$**

Lesson 10.5 Add.

15. $\begin{array}{r} 3.67 \\ +\ 7.5 \\ \hline 11.17 \end{array}$

16. $\begin{array}{r} 4.43 \\ +\ 7.58 \\ \hline 12.01 \end{array}$

17. $\begin{array}{r} 60.3 \\ +\ 2.24 \\ \hline 62.54 \end{array}$

18. $\begin{array}{r} 198.5 \\ +\ 98.5 \\ \hline 297 \end{array}$

Lesson 10.6 Subtract.

19. $\begin{array}{r} 2.2 \\ -\ 0.06 \\ \hline 2.14 \end{array}$

20. $\begin{array}{r} 39.87 \\ -\ 17.5 \\ \hline 22.37 \end{array}$

21. $\begin{array}{r} 3.2 \\ -\ 0.3 \\ \hline 2.9 \end{array}$

22. $\begin{array}{r} 74.6 \\ -\ 29.06 \\ \hline 45.54 \end{array}$

Textbook This lesson is available in the *eTextbook*.

Lesson 10.7

Multiply.

23. $\begin{array}{r} 6.8 \\ \times\ 4 \\ \hline 27.2 \end{array}$

24. $\begin{array}{r} 14.52 \\ \times\ 3 \\ \hline 43.56 \end{array}$

25. $\begin{array}{r} 4.03 \\ \times\ 8 \\ \hline 32.24 \end{array}$

26. $\begin{array}{r} 2.9 \\ \times\ 9 \\ \hline 26.1 \end{array}$

Lesson 10.8

Solve.

27. A wooden board measures 3.65 meters in length. If the board is cut into 5 equal-sized pieces, how long will each piece be? How many centimeters is that?
0.73 meter; 73 centimeters

28. A. J., Micah, and Brandi want to share equally the cost of a new stereo. If the full price of the stereo is $214.98, what is each person's share? **$71.66**

Lesson 10.9

Solve each problem.

29. Mr. Morales spent $45.18 at the grocery store. Then he spent $25.87 at the gasoline station. He had $100 before going to the grocery store and the gasoline station. How much of the $100 did he have left after going to both places? **$28.95**

30. The 11 members of the art club were preparing for a trip to New York City to see an art exhibit. They estimated that the trip would cost $800. Miles reported that his share of the $800 would be about $70. Is he correct? Why or why not? **yes; The exact amount of each student's share is $72.73, which is about $70.**

10

3 Chapter Tests 40

Practice Test

Student Pages 414–417

- The Chapter 10 Practice Test on **Student Edition** pages 414–417 provides an opportunity to formally evaluate students' proficiency with concepts developed in this chapter.
- The content is similar to the Chapter 10 Review, in standardized format.

CHAPTER
10 Practice Test

Answer each question.

1. How many decimeters are in 1 meter?   10 dm
2. How many decimeters are in 58 meters?   580 dm
3. How many meters are in 42 decimeters?   4.2 m
4. Paula had $14.00 in dimes. How many dimes did she have?   140 dimes
5. Carol has 83 dimes. She wants to trade in her dimes for dollar bills. How many dollar bills can she get for her dimes? How many dimes will she still have?   8 dollar bills; 3 dimes
6. There are 50 dimes in 1 roll of dimes. There are 40 nickels in 1 roll of nickels.
   a. How much money is 1 roll of dimes worth? $5.00
   b. How much money is 1 roll of nickels worth? $2.00
   c. Mason wants to exchange 5 rolls of dimes and 3 rolls of nickels for dollar bills. How much money is that? $31

Convert.

7. ▢ meters = 80 decimeters   8
8. 2.7 meters = ▢ decimeters   27
9. $5.30 = ▢ dimes   53
10. 100 dimes = ▢¢   1,000
11. 65 dimes = $▢ $6.50

414   ⧉Textbook This lesson is available in the **eTextbook.**

Choose the correct answer.

12. Which fraction is equivalent to 3.38?
    Ⓐ $38\frac{3}{100}$ Ⓑ $3\frac{38}{100}$
    Ⓒ $\frac{38}{100}$ Ⓓ $\frac{338}{100}$

13. Which fraction is equivalent to 0.06?
    Ⓐ $\frac{6}{1000}$ Ⓑ $\frac{6}{100}$
    Ⓒ $\frac{1}{6}$ Ⓓ $\frac{6}{10}$

14. Which decimal is equivalent to $5\frac{2}{10}$?
    Ⓐ 520   Ⓑ 52
    Ⓒ 5.2   Ⓓ 0.52

15. Which decimal is equivalent to $\frac{64}{100}$?
    Ⓐ 64.4   Ⓑ 6.4
    Ⓒ 0.64   Ⓓ 0.064

16. Find the product. $8 \times 7 = ?$
    Ⓐ 15   Ⓑ 16
    Ⓒ 56   Ⓓ 65

17. Ali has a box of books that weighs 9.1 pounds. He adds to the box another book that weighs 1.4 pounds. How much does the box weigh now?
    Ⓐ 7.7 pounds
    Ⓑ 9.5 pounds
    Ⓒ 10.5 pounds
    Ⓓ 13.1 pounds

18. Caroline has 5.76 centimeters of ribbon. She uses 0.65 centimeter of ribbon for a project. How much ribbon does Caroline have left?
    Ⓐ 6.41 centimeters
    Ⓑ 5.41 centimeters
    Ⓒ 5.31 centimeters
    Ⓓ 5.11 centimeters

CHAPTER 10 Practice Test

Choose the correct answer.

19. Find the product. $8.2 \times 7 = ?$
- Ⓐ 15.2
- Ⓑ 56.4
- Ⓒ 57.4
- Ⓓ 87.2

20. Polly has 6 boxes of fruit juice. Each box holds 2.4 ounces. How many ounces of juice does Polly have in all?
- Ⓐ 24.2
- Ⓑ 14.4
- Ⓒ 8.4
- Ⓓ 3.6

21. Find the quotient. $10.25 \div 5 = ?$
- Ⓐ 2.05
- Ⓑ 2.5
- Ⓒ 5.25
- Ⓓ 15.30

22. Find the difference. $3.53 - 1.80 = ?$
- Ⓐ 1.33
- Ⓑ 1.73
- Ⓒ 2.73
- Ⓓ 5.33

23. How many inches are in 5 feet?
- Ⓐ 17
- Ⓑ 36
- Ⓒ 48
- Ⓓ 60

24. How many kilograms equal 4,600 grams?
- Ⓐ 4.6
- Ⓑ 46
- Ⓒ 460
- Ⓓ 4,600

25. Which mixed number is equal to $\frac{19}{5}$?
- Ⓐ $2\frac{1}{5}$
- Ⓑ $2\frac{4}{5}$
- Ⓒ $3\frac{1}{5}$
- Ⓓ $3\frac{4}{5}$

26. Which symbol makes this sentence true?
$5\frac{2}{5} \, \square \, 5\frac{1}{3}$
- Ⓐ $=$
- Ⓑ $<$
- Ⓒ $>$

🔲 Textbook This lesson is available in the *eTextbook*.

Solve.

27. Brendan lives 0.85 kilometer from his school. He lives 0.45 kilometer from the park.

   a. Brendan walks to and from school every day. How far does he walk to school each week? **8.5 kilometers**

   b. Two school days each week, Brendan has soccer practice at the park. He walks from his house to the park and back. How far does he walk each week for soccer practice? **1.8 kilometers**

   c. On average, how far does Brendan walk each school day? Round to the nearest tenth. **2.1 kilometers**

28. Nancy works at the library for 4 hours on Saturdays. She earns \$6.25 an hour. She wants to buy a new bike that costs \$187.00.

   a. How many Saturdays will she have to work before she has enough money to buy the bike? **8 Saturdays**

   b. How much money will Nancy have left after she buys the bike? **\$13.00**

Chapter Test COMPUTING

For further evaluation instead of or in addition to this test, you might want to have students take the Chapter 10 Test provided in ***Assessment***.

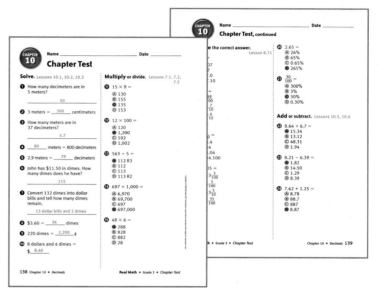

Assessment Pages 138–139

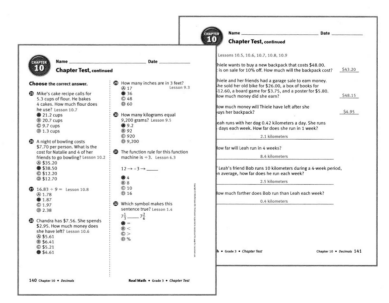

Assessment Pages 140–141

4 Assess and Differentiate

 Assess Use **eAssess** to record and analyze evidence of student understanding.

A Gather Evidence

Use the Daily Class Assessment Records in **Assessment** or **eAssess** to record Informal and Formal Assessments.

Informal Assessment
✓ **Key Ideas Review** `UNDERSTANDING`

Did the student
- ❑ make important observations?
- ❑ extend or generalize learning?
- ❑ provide insightful answers?
- ❑ pose insightful questions?

Informal Assessment
✓ **Project** `APPLYING`

Did the student
- ❑ meet the project objectives?
- ❑ communicate clearly?
- ❑ complete the project accurately?
- ❑ connect mathematics to real-world situations?

Formal Assessment
✓ **Chapter Test** `COMPUTING`

Score the test, and record the results.

B Summarize Findings

Analyze and summarize assessment data for each student. Determine which Chapter Follow-Up is appropriate for each student. Use the Student Assessment Record in **Assessment** or **eAssess** to update assessment records.

C Chapter Follow-Up • DIFFERENTIATE INSTRUCTION

Based on your observations, use these teaching strategies for chapter follow-up.

ENRICH	PRACTICE	RETEACH	INTERVENTION
If . . . students demonstrate **secure understanding** of chapter concepts,	**If . . .** students demonstrate **competent understanding** of chapter concepts,	**If . . .** students demonstrate **emerging understanding** of chapter concepts,	**If . . .** students demonstrate **minimal understanding** of chapter concepts,
Then . . . move on to the next chapter.	**Then . . .** move on to the next chapter.	**Then . . .** move on to the next chapter, but continue to provide cumulative review.	**Then . . .** intensive intervention is still needed before they start the next chapter.

Muddle the Engineer

Context of the Thinking Story Mr. Muddle takes a job as an engineer and uses math to solve problems.

Lesson Planner

OBJECTIVES
To develop logical thinking while integrating reading skills with mathematics

NCTM STANDARDS
Problem Solving
- Building new mathematical knowledge through problem solving
- Solving problems that arise in mathematics and in other contexts

Communication
- Communicating mathematical thinking coherently and clearly
- Analyzing and evaluating the mathematical thinking and strategies of others

READING STANDARDS
- Characterization
- Listening for details
- Predicting what will happen in a story
- Drawing conclusions
- Making inferences

Using the Thinking Story

The Thinking Story may be used anytime throughout the chapter. Read the Thinking Story "Muddle the Engineer" to your class as they follow along in the **Student Edition** on pages 418–421. As you read the story, give students time to think about each question, but not so much that they forget the point being made.

Muddle the Engineer

Mr. Muddle went to many different places looking for a job, but no one hired him. They would ask him a few questions, then say "Thank you" and send him away. But one day the president of a large engineering company called him in and offered him a job as chief engineer. The president of the company said, "We're very happy to hire a famous engineer like you, Mr. Nuddle, to help us build bridges and skyscrapers."

Mr. Muddle wondered why the president called him "Mr. Nuddle," but Mr. Muddle was too polite to correct the president. He also wondered why the president called him a famous engineer, because Mr. Muddle couldn't remember ever having built any bridges or large buildings.

What do you think has happened? ❶

The president gave Mr. Muddle a large office and introduced him to the engineers who would be taking directions from him. The first engineer brought in a small model bridge made out of toothpicks. "This is the bridge we are going to build across Roaring River," said the young engineer.

"It's very nice," said Mr. Muddle, holding it in his hands, "but don't you think it's a little small to reach across such a big river?"

What is it that Mr. Muddle doesn't understand? ❷

418

"This is just a model," said the engineer. "The real bridge will be 500 times as big."

"I see," said Mr. Muddle. "This is a kind of toy bridge, and we're going to make a real one just like it, only 500 times as big."

"If you approve," said the engineer.

"I certainly do," said Mr. Muddle. "I think it's a very clever idea. Now to get down to business. How many toothpicks did you use to make this little bridge?"

"About a thousand."

"Then if the real bridge is going to be 500 times as big, we'll need 500 times as many toothpicks. That will be about 500,000. Right?" said Mr. Muddle.

Is Mr. Muddle right? ❸

"I thought we would make the bridge out of steel," said the engineer.

"Another clever idea," said Mr. Muddle. "Steel toothpicks—they

should be much stronger than wooden ones."

How would you describe the pieces of steel that bridges are usually made of? ❹

The engineer looked a little puzzled, but she explained that the bridge was going to be made of large pieces of steel, like most other bridges. Then she and Mr. Muddle went down to the river to look at the place where the bridge was supposed to be built.

"Do you see any problems with building the bridge here?" the young engineer asked.

"Just one," said Mr. Muddle. "The river is full of water. People will get all wet trying to build a bridge here. We'll have to get rid of the water. Send a thousand people down with buckets, and have them empty all the water out of the river."

Would that work? ❺

Why or why not? ❻

Guided Discussion

As students answer the questions in the story, ask them to communicate how they decided on their answers. Allow students to debate the answers if necessary.

❶ The president has mixed up Mr. Muddle with someone else.

❷ It is only a model.

❸ No, the bridge will not be made of toothpicks.

❹ very large

❺ no

❻ The river would keep filling with water if they tried to empty it.

❼ Mr. Muddle does not seem to understand what the engineer is talking about.

❽ no

❾ The rooms will not be tall enough.

❿ about 1 meter

⓫ so that people can walk around

⓬ He thinks a bridge will be made of toothpicks, a hotel will have rooms 1 meter high, and a river can be emptied with buckets.

⓭ Every part cannot be the same and different at the same time.

⓮ He has given the parts different names.

The engineer thought Mr. Muddle was joking and didn't bother to explain that the river would keep filling up with water if they tried to empty it. Instead they went back to the office. Another engineer came in and showed Mr. Muddle the plans for a hotel they were building.

"We want the hotel to have as many rooms as possible," he said, "but the building itself isn't very large."

"I see," said Mr. Muddle. "You want a building that is big on the inside but small on the outside."

The engineer gave Mr. Muddle a strange look.

What do you think is bothering the engineer? ❼

"The building can be only about 100 meters high," said the engineer. "So how many stories do you think it can have?"

"That's simple," said Mr. Muddle. "It can be 100 stories high."

Is that right? ❽

Why or why not? ❾

How high would the rooms be? ❿

"One meter ought to be high enough," said Mr. Muddle. "After all, people use hotels to sleep in, so everyone will be lying down."

Why do the rooms really have to be more than 1 meter high? ⓫

"According to the law," said the engineer, "the rooms have to be at least $2\frac{1}{2}$ meters high so that people can walk around." The engineer left the room and went to talk to the other engineer. Together they went to see the president of the company. "We don't think Mr. Nuddle knows anything about engineering," they told him.

What things has Mr. Muddle said that show he doesn't know how to do his job? ⓬

"Something will have to be done about this," said the president, after he heard of all the strange things Mr. Muddle had said. "I'll give him an impossible problem, and then when he can't solve it we'll have an excuse to ask him to leave."

The president brought Mr. Muddle a model of a skyscraper his company had built. "We built a skyscraper like this several years ago," the president said, "and now someone wants us to build another one. The new one is supposed to be exactly like the old one in every

420

---

way, but every part of the new one must be different from the same part of the old one. Can you design such a skyscraper for us?"

"The whole skyscraper exactly the same but every part different?" asked Mr. Muddle. "That sounds pretty hard, but I'll try to have it worked out for you by tomorrow."

What is impossible about the problem? ⓭

Mr. Muddle worked hard all night. The next morning he showed the president the model he had made.

"This skyscraper is exactly like the other one!" the president said.

"That's what you wanted, isn't it?" said Mr. Muddle.

"Yes," he said, "but every part is supposed to be different, and I don't see anything different. Look, your roof is just the same as this other roof."

"Pardon me," said Mr. Muddle, "but that's not the roof of my skyscraper. That's the front door."

"Furthermore," the president went on, "the front of your

skyscraper is exactly the same as the front of the other skyscraper."

"Pardon me," said Mr. Muddle, "but that's not the front of my skyscraper. That's the roof."

"And I suppose the back wall of your skyscraper is really the floor!"

"Now you're getting the idea," Mr. Muddle said.

What has Mr. Muddle done to make every part of his skyscraper different? ⓮

"This is ridiculous," said the president. "All you've done is call every part something else. But you can't do that. The roof can't be on the front of the skyscraper. It has to be on the top."

"That's simple," said Mr. Muddle, turning the model over on its side. "Now the roof is on the top, just the way you want it. And the door, which I admit looks very much like a roof, is on the front where it should be. You see, the two skyscrapers are exactly alike, but every part is different."

The End

Chapter 10 • Thinking Story
421

Lesson Study

Reflect on each of the lessons you taught in this chapter. Rate each one on the following scale, and then consider ways to maintain or improve positive teaching experiences in the future.

Lessons	Very Effective	Effective	Less Effective	What Worked	Ways to Improve
10.1 Where Do We See Decimals?					
10.2 Decimals and Money					
10.3 Decimals and Metric Measures					
10.4 Comparing Decimals and Fractions					
10.5 Adding Decimals					
10.6 Subtracting Decimals					
10.7 Multiplying Decimals by Whole Numbers					
10.8 Dividing Decimals					
10.9 Decimal Applications					

Lessons

 11.1 Points and Lines

 11.2 Angles

 11.3 Triangles

 11.4 Quadrilaterals

 11.5 Polygons

 11.6 Congruence

 11.7 Slides, Flips, and Turns

 11.8 Symmetry

 11.9 Circles I

 11.10 Circles II

 11.11 Space Figures

 11.12 Nets and Surface Area

11.13 Volume

Geometry

Teaching for Understanding
This chapter formally introduces students to concepts in geometry. Students will be introduced to terminology in geometry. Students will also learn to compute surface area and volume.

Prerequisite Skills and Concepts
- Identifying Shapes • Describing Figures • Area of Rectangles

Geometry Skills Trace

Before Grade 3	Grade 3	After Grade 3
Grades K–2 Informally and formally introduced to geometry	**This chapter** formally introduces students to geometry.	Students will further develop concepts in geometry.

 **Problem Solving** Problem solving is in every lesson. This chapter includes the following:

CHAPTER INTRODUCTION Students will learn the definitions of geometric terms (pp. 422I–423C).

EXPLORING PROBLEM SOLVING The first lesson focuses on the Use Simple Numbers, Look for a Pattern, Make a Table, and Make a Physical Model strategies (pp. 444–445, 445A). The second lesson explores how shape affects volume and surface area (pp. 466–466A).

THINKING STORY In "A Paneful Story" students help a character develop strategies for designing windows (pp. 474–477).

Math Background

Geometry

What is Geometry?

Geometry is a branch of mathematics that includes properties and relationships of points, lines, angles, surfaces, and solid figures. The importance of geometry is not in the vocabulary of names of figures and other geometric terms. Rather, geometry is important because we live in a world of objects and need some spatial sense to interact with our world. Geometry also provides an opportunity to notice patterns and form conjectures in more concrete way than in other mathematical strands.

Geometry can be used to understand and to represent the objects, directions, and locations in our world, and the relationships between them. Geometric shapes can be described, analyzed, transformed and composed and decomposed into other shapes.

Clements, Douglas and Sarama, J. eds. *Engaging Young Children in Mathematics: Standards for Early Childhood Mathematics Education.* Mahwah, New Jersey: Lawrence Erlbaum Associates, Publishers, 2004. p. 39.)

Plane and Space Figures

- A plane is a geometric concept that cannot be created in our three-dimensional world. In geometry, a plane is a flat surface that extends indefinitely in every direction. A plane has no thickness, nor do geometric figures that lie in a plane.

- People often use the word 'solid' to refer to figures in space, such as a cube or sphere. However, in mathematics we generally think of such figures as only the empty shell. (This is why we can represent a space figure using a net that lies in a plane until it is "folded" to create a figure.) Therefore, in **Real Math** we refer to figures in a plane as plane figures and those that can not be placed in a plane as space figures.

- Note also that a square and a circle are one-dimensional objects in a plane (because they are composed of line segments, which have only the dimension of length) and a cube and sphere are two-dimensional objects in space (because their surfaces have length and width but not depth).

Polygons

- A closed figure separates the plane into 2 non-connected parts.
  This is a closed figure:

  This is not a closed figure:

- A polygon is a closed figure with straight (not curved) sides.
- A regular polygon has sides that are all the same length and angles that all have the same measure. A regular polygon may have any number of sides.

Types of Angles

Although angle measurement is not formally defined in this chapter, students should have an intuitive sense of how angles compare to right angles.

- The measure of an angle can be thought of as the amount of turning required to move from one side of the angle to the other side.

- A right angle represents one-fourth of a complete turn. The corners of pages and pieces of paper are often right angles, so paper can be used to check how angles compare to right angles.

- An obtuse angle represents more of a turn than a right angle. If a right angle is held against an angle so that one side of each angle coincides, and the other side of the unknown angle is visible, the unknown angle is obtuse

- An acute angle represents less of a turn than a right angle. If a right angle is held against an angle so that one side of each angle coincides, and the other side of the unknown angle is not visible because it is under the right angle, then the unknown angle is acute.

What Research Says

About Geometry

How Children Learn to Work with Geometric Figures

Children typically follow an observable developmental progression in learning about shapes with recognizable stages or levels. This developmental path can be described as part of a learning trajectory. Key steps in the learning trajectory for geometry from the first grade range are described below. For the complete trajectory, see Appendix B.

Level Name	Description
Shape Decomposer with Imagery	A significant sign of development is when a child is able to decompose shapes flexibly using independently generated imagery. For example, given pentagons, the child can break it apart to make shapes such as these. 
Shape Composer—Units of Units	Children demonstrate further understanding when they are able to build and apply units of units (shapes make from other shapes). For example, in constructing spatial patterns, the child can extend patterning activity to create a tiling with a new unit shape—a unit of unit shapes that he or she recognizes and consciously constructs.
Congruence Determiner	A sign of development is when a child determines congruence by comparing all attributes and all spatial relationships. For example, a child at this level says that two shapes are the same shape and the same size after comparing every one of their sides and angles.
Pattern Unit Recognizer	At this level, a child can identify the smallest unit of a pattern. For example, given objects in a row with one missing, ABBAB_ABB, identifies and fills in the missing element.

Clements, D. H., & J. Sarama, (in press). "Early Childhood Mathematics Learning." In F. K. Lester, Jr. ed., *Second Handbook of Research on Mathematics Teaching and Learning*. New York: Information Age Publishing.

Research-Based Teaching Techniques

"Overall research indicates that all types of geometric ideas appear to develop over time, becoming increasingly integrated and synthesized….Children's ideas about shapes do not come from passive looking. Instead, they come as children's bodies, hands, eyes, and minds engage in active construction. In addition, children need to explore shapes extensively to fully understand them; merely seeing and naming pictures is insufficient. Finally, they have to explore the parts and attributes of shapes."

Clements, Douglas and J. Sarama, eds. *Engaging Young Children in Mathematics: Standards for Early Childhood Mathematics Education*. Mahwah, New Jersey: Lawrence Erlbaum Associates, Publishers, 2004, p. 289.

"As with 2-D figures, children need more and richer experiences with solids. Research indicates that construction activities involving nets (foldout shapes of solids) may help student learn to discriminate between 2-D and 3-D figures."

Clements, Douglas H. "Teaching and Learning Geometry" in Kilpatrick, Jeremy, W. Gary Martin, and Deborah Schifter, eds. *A Research Companion to Principles and Standards for School Mathematics*. Reston, VA: National Council of Teachers of Mathematics, Inc. 2003. p.152.

RESEARCH IN ACTION

Geometric Figures Chapter 11 provides students with opportunities to explore, compare, describe, and classify geometric shapes and figures that include points, lines, angles, circles, triangles, polygons, and platonic solids.

Attributes In Chapter 11 students will work with various shapes and figures in order to classify, compare, and describe the attributes of those figures.

Language Development In Chapter 11 students will gain greater fluency and awareness of the language of geometry. Students will use the language of geometry to compare, classify, and describe geometric figures.

Congruence and Similarity Chapter 11 will support students in exploring the methods used to determine similarity and congruence among shapes and figures.

Vocabulary

angle (Lesson 11.2) the figure formed by two rays extending from the same point

center (Lesson 11.10) a point within a circle that is an equal distance from every point on the circle

congruent (Lesson 11.6) figures that are the same size and same shape; that is, they fit perfectly when placed on top of one another

diameter (Lesson 11.10) a line segment passing through the center of a circle or sphere from one side to the other

edge (Lesson 11.11) the line segment where two faces of a space figure meet

equilateral (Lesson 11.3) having all sides equal in length

face (Lesson 11.11) a plane figure that serves as one side of a space figure

intersecting lines (Lesson 11.1) lines that meet and cross each other at a point

isosceles (Lesson 11.3) having two equal sides

line (Lesson 11.1) a straight path that extends infinitely in opposite directions; thought of as having length but not thickness

line of symmetry (Lesson 11.8) a line on which a figure can be folded into two congruent parts

line segment (Lesson 11.1) a part of a line with two endpoints

net (Lesson 11.12) a pattern used to create a space figure

parallel lines (Lesson 11.1) lines that are the same distance apart, go in the same direction, and never meet

parallelogram (Lesson 11.4) a quadrilateral that has two pairs of parallel sides

perpendicular lines (Lesson 11.2) lines that intersect at right angles

point (Lesson 11.1) something having position but no length, width, or height

polygon (Lesson 11.5) a closed plane figure with three or more line segments as sides

quadrilateral (Lesson 11.4) a polygon with four sides

radius (Lesson 11.10) a line segment going from the center to the outside of a circle or sphere

ray (Lesson 11.2) a set of points that has one endpoint and extends forever in one direction

reflection (Lesson 11.7) a change in the location of a figure when it is flipped over a line

rhombus (Lesson 11.4) a parallelogram whose sides are all the same length

rotation (Lesson 11.7) a change in the location of a figure when it is turned in a circle around a point

surface area (Lesson 11.12) the sum of the areas of the faces of a space figure

symmetry (Lesson 11.8) having the same size and shape across a dividing line

translation (Lesson 11.7) a change in the location of a figure when it slides without being turned

trapezoid (Lesson 11.4) a quadrilateral with exactly one pair of parallel sides

vertex (Lesson 11.2) 1. the point of intersection of two rays. 2. the point of intersection of three edges of a space figure

volume (Lesson 11.13) the amount of space an object can hold

English Learner

Cognates

For English learners, a quick way to acquire new English vocabulary is to build on what is known in the primary language.

English	Spanish
point	punto
line	línea
segment	segmento
triangles	triángulos

Access Vocabulary

English learners may understand words in different contexts or not understand idioms. Review chapter vocabulary for this concern. For example:

plane	a flat surface
flip	turn over
the score	the number of points each player earned in the game

Chapter Planner

Lessons	Objectives	NCTM Standards	State Standards
11.1 Points and Lines pages 424A–427B	To introduce students to basic points and lines	Geometry, Connections	
11.2 Angles pages 428A–431B	To introduce students to the properties of angles	Geometry, Communication	
11.3 Triangles pages 432A–433A	To introduce students to triangles	Geometry, Communication	
11.4 Quadrilaterals pages 434A–437B	To introduce students to properties of four-sided figures	Geometry, Communication, Connections	
11.5 Polygons pages 438A–441B	To explore different polygons	Geometry, Connections	
11.6 Congruence pages 442A–443A	To introduce the concept of congruency	Geometry, Connections	
11.7 Slides, Flips, and Turns pages 448A–449A	To explore the concepts of translations, reflections, and rotations	Geometry, Communication	
11.8 Symmetry pages 450A–453B	To introduce the concepts of symmetry and line of symmetry	Geometry, Communication	
11.9 Circles I pages 454A–455A	To introduce students to properties of circles	Geometry, Connections	
11.10 Circles II pages 456A–457A	To develop concepts involving circles	Geometry, Measurement	
11.11 Space Figures pages 458A–459A	To familiarize students with solid objects	Geometry, Connections	
11.12 Nets and Surface Area pages 460A–461A	To introduce students to nets and surface area	Geometry, Measurement	
11.13 Volume pages 462A–465B	To develop concept of volume given in cubic units	Geometry, Measurement	

Vocabulary	Manipulatives and Materials	Games to reinforce skills and concepts
point line line segment intersecting lines parallel lines	• Response Wheels • Prepared leaves such as maple, corn, palm, and petunia	
ray angle vertex right angle perpendicular lines	Response Wheels	
equilateral isosceles right triangle	• Ruler • Scissors • 3 different coloring pencils, crayons, or markers per student	
quadrilateral parallelogram rhombus trapezoid	• Ruler • Scissors	
polygon pentagon hexagon octagon	Response Wheels	
congruent	• Response Wheels • Template of polygons, circles, and semicircles of various sizes • Pattern blocks (optional) • Student scissors • Multiple colors of construction paper • Square or rectangular unlined paper of various sizes	
translation reflection rotation	Response Wheels	
symmetry line of symmetry	• Response Wheels • Tracing paper • Small mirrors	
	• Response Wheels • Centimeters rulers	
center diameter radius	• Response Wheels • Unlined paper, 1 sheet for each student • Student scissors • Various circular traceable objects • Metric rulers	
face edge	• Platonic solids • Real models of space figures (optional)	
net surface area	• Response Wheels • Platonic solids	
volume cubic units	Interlocking cubes or base-ten blocks	

Additional Resources

Differentiated Instruction

Intervention Support Guide Provides instruction for the following prerequisite skills:

- Lesson 11.A Identifying Shapes
- Lesson 11.B Describing Figures
- Lesson 11.C Area of Rectangles

Enrichment Support Guide Extends lesson concepts

Practice Reinforces lesson skills and concepts

Reteach Support Guide Provides alternate instruction for lesson concepts

English Learner Support Guide Previews and reviews lesson concepts and vocabulary for English learners

Technology

The following electronic resources are available:

Planner Lessons 11.1–11.13

Presentation Lessons 11.1–11.13

Textbook Lessons 11.1–11.13

Assess Lessons 11.1–11.13

MathTools *Geometry Sketch Tool* Lessons 11.1, 11.3, 11.4, 11.5, 11.6, 11.7, 11.8, 11.10; *Shape Tool* Lessons 11.3, 11.4, 11.5, 11.7, 11.8; *Net Tool* Lessons 11.11, 11.12

Building Blocks *Geometry Snapshots 3* Lessons 11.1, 11.2, 11.7; *Shape Parts 1* Lesson 11.3; *Shape Parts 2* Lesson 11.4; *Shape Parts 3* Lesson 11.5; *Shape Parts 5* Lessons 11.6, 11.8; *Piece Puzzler 10* Lesson 11.9; *Geometry Snapshot 8* Lesson 11.11; *Create a Scene* Lesson 11.12; *Shape Parts 9* Lesson 11.13

Assessment

Informal Assessment rubrics at the end of each lesson provide daily evaluation of student math proficiency.

CHAPTER 11 · Overview

Chapter Planner, continued

Problem Solving	When to Use	Objectives	NCTM Standards	Skills Covered
Chapter Introduction pp. 422I–423C 15–30 minutes	Use after the Chapter 11 Pretest.	To introduce chapter concepts in a problem-solving setting	Geometry	Geometry
Exploring Problem Solving pp. 444–445, 445A 30–45 minutes	Use anytime during the chapter.	To explore methods of solving nonroutine problems	Geometry and Communication	Geometry, Measurement, Computation
Exploring Problem Solving pp. 466–466A 45–60 minutes	Use anytime during the chapter.	To explore methods of solving nonroutine problems	Geometry and Connections	Geometry, Measurement, Computation
Thinking Story— A Paneful Story pp. 476–477, 478–479 20–30 minutes	Use anytime during the chapter.	To develop logical reasoning while integrating reading skills with mathematics	Geometry, Problem Solving	Subdividing, combining, and transforming shapes, Drawing geometric objects

Review	When to Use	Objectives	NCTM Standards	Skills Covered
Cumulative Review pp. 446–447 15–30 minutes	Use anytime after Lesson 11.6.	To review concepts and skills taught earlier in the year	Geometry and Connections	Measurement, Computation, Fractions
Cumulative Review pp. 467–468 15–30 minutes	Use anytime after Lesson 11.13.	To review concepts and skills taught earlier in the year	Geometry, Connections, and Communication	Algebra, Computation, Fractions
Chapter 11 Review pp. 470A, 470–471 30–45 minutes	Use after Lesson 11.13.	To review concepts and skills taught in the chapter	Geometry, Connections, and Measurement	Geometry

Assessment	When to Use	Objectives	NCTM Standards	Skills Covered
Informal Assessment Rubrics pp. 427B–465B 5 minutes per student	Use at the end of each lesson.	To provide daily evaluation of math proficiency	Geometry, Connections, and Measurement	Geometry, Measurement, Computation
Pretest *Assessment* pp. 143–144 15–30 minutes	Use prior to Chapter 11.	To provide assessment of prerequisite and chapter topics	Geometry	Geometry
Individual Oral Assessment p. 447A 5 minutes per student	Begin use after Lesson 11.6.	To provide alternate means of assessing students' progress	Geometry and Connections	Geometry, Shape recognition
Mastery Checkpoint *Assessment* p. T77 5 minutes per student	Use after Lesson 12.7.	To provide assessment of mastery of key skills	Geometry	Geometry, Transformations
Chapter 11 Practice Test pp. 472–473, 474–475 30–45 minutes	Use after or in place of the Chapter 11 Review.	To provide assessment or additional practice of the lesson concepts	Geometry, Connections, and Measurement	Geometry, Shape recognition, Transformations
Chapter 11 Test *Assessment* pp. 152–155 30–45 minutes	Use after or in place of the Chapter 11 Review.	To provide assessment of the chapter concepts	Geometry, Connections, and Measurement	Geometry, Shape recognition, Computation

Technology Resources and Support

Visit SRAonline.com for online versions of the **Real Math** eSuite.

Technology for Teachers

e Presentation	Lessons 11.1–11.13 Use the *ePresentation* to interactively present chapter content.
e Planner	Use the Chapter and Lesson Planners to outline activities and time frames for Chapter 11.
e Assess	Students can take the following assessments in *eAssess:* • Chapter Pretest • Mastery Checkpoint **Lesson 12.7** • Chapter Test Teacher can record results and print reports for all assessments in this chapter.
e MathTools	*Geometry Sketch Tool* Lessons 11.1, 11.3, 11.4, 11.5, 11.6, 11.7, 11.8, 11.10; *Shape Tool* Lessons 11.3, 11.4, 11.5, 11.7, 11.8; *Net Tool* Lessons 11.11, 11.12

Technology for Students

e Textbook	An electronic, interactive version of the **Student Edition** is available for all lessons in Chapter 11.
e MathTools	*Geometry Sketch Tool* Lessons 11.1, 11.3, 11.4, 11.5, 11.6, 11.7, 11.8, 11.10; *Shape Tool* Lessons 11.3, 11.4, 11.5, 11.7, 11.8; *Net Tool* Lessons 11.11, 11.12
TECH KNOWLEDGE	**TechKnowledge** Level 3 provides lessons that specifically teach the Unit 10 Internet and Unit 6 Presentation applications that students can use in this chapter's projects.
Building Blocks	*Geometry Snapshots 3* Lessons 11.1, 11.2, 11.7; *Shape Parts 1* Lesson 11.3; *Shape Parts 2* Lesson 11.4; *Shape Parts 3* Lesson 11.5; *Shape Parts 5* Lessons 11.6, 11.8; *Piece Puzzler 10* Lesson 11.9; *Geometry Snapshot 8* Lesson 11.11; *Create a Scene* Lesson 11.12; *Shape Parts 9* Lesson 11.13

Geometry

1 Introduce Chapter 11 5

Chapter Objectives

Explain to students that in this chapter they will build on what they already know about geometry. They will

- identify points, lines, and angles.
- describe triangles, quadrilaterals, and other polygons.
- determine congruence and symmetry in geometric figures.
- name and describe circles and parts of circles.

Pretest COMPUTING

Administer the Pretest on **Assessment** pages 143 and 144.

The Pretest covers the following skills and topics from the chapter:

- Area and perimeter (Problems 1–3)
- Telling time (Problems 4 and 5)
- Identifying and comparing fractions and decimals (Problems 6–8)
- Properties of polygons (Problems 9–13)
- Symmetry (Problems 14 and 15)
- Congruence (Problems 16 and 17)
- Transformations (Problems 18–20)
- Volume (Problems 21 and 22)

Chapter 11 Pretest

Access Prior Knowledge UNDERSTANDING

Have students share what they like about their room or their home. Also have them talk about how they would make it different. Ask if they would change the shape and size if they could.

2 Exploring Problem Solving 30

Tell Students In Today's Lesson They Will

- design a house or room in which they would like to live.
- describe their design in words to see if someone else can draw it.

Materials

Graph paper

Using Student Pages

Discuss with the class the photo on page 422. To initiate discussion about shape, ask questions such as the following:

■ **What shapes do you see in the photo?**
■ **How would you describe the shapes visible on the house?**

Read the information on page 423 together, and go over the steps of the activity. Make sure students understand these points:

- Partners must not look at each other's design until the end.
- The design should be a floor plan—an outline of what you would see if you were looking down from overhead. You might wish to make a simple outline to show students what such a floor plan of the classroom would look like.
- When students write instructions for re-creating their design, they may use words and numbers but not pictures.

Encourage students to be imaginative, drawing a shape other than a single rectangle.

Have students work in pairs to do the activity. Have students discuss with their partner the parts of the instructions that were confusing. Discuss and answer the following questions together.

■ **Problem 1. How closely did your drawings match each other's original design?**
■ **Problem 2. What words were most useful in writing and reading instructions?**
■ **Problem 3. What words were most confusing in writing and reading instructions?** See Reflect.

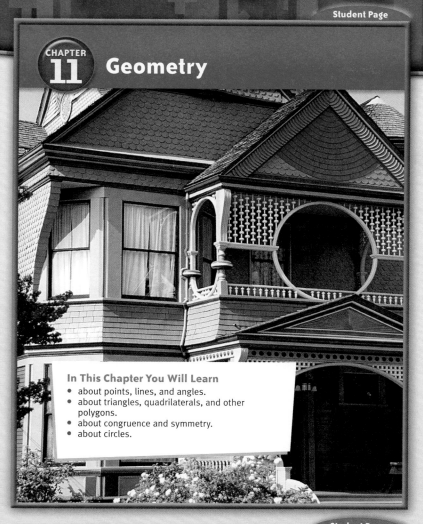

CHAPTER 11 Geometry

In This Chapter You Will Learn
- about points, lines, and angles.
- about triangles, quadrilaterals, and other polygons.
- about congruence and symmetry.
- about circles.

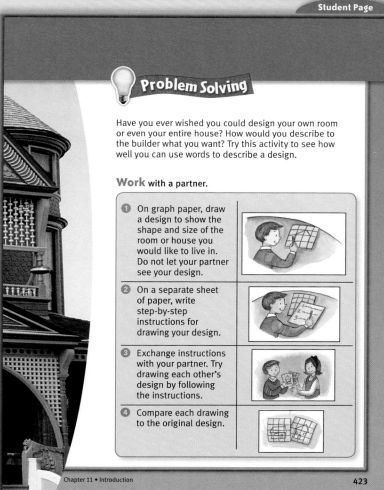

Problem Solving

Have you ever wished you could design your own room or even your entire house? How would you describe to the builder what you want? Try this activity to see how well you can use words to describe a design.

Work with a partner.

1. On graph paper, draw a design to show the shape and size of the room or house you would like to live in. Do not let your partner see your design.

2. On a separate sheet of paper, write step-by-step instructions for drawing your design.

3. Exchange instructions with your partner. Try drawing each other's design by following the instructions.

4. Compare each drawing to the original design.

Concept/Question Board ☑ APPLYING

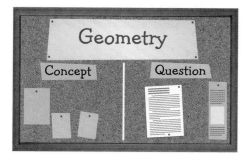

Questions

Have students think of and write three questions they have about geometry and how it can be used. Then have them select one question to post on the Question side of the Board.

Concepts

As students work through the chapter, have them collect examples of how geometry is used in everyday situations. For each example, write a problem that relates to the item(s). Have them display their examples on the Concept side of the Board.

Suggest the following:
- landscaping
- playgrounds
- quilts

Answers

Throughout the chapter, have students post answers to the questions and solutions to the problems on the Board.

Reflect

10

Effective Communication Have groups share their experiences doing the activity. Ask them what they learned from it. Discuss Problems 1–3.

For Problem 2, students may say that even a geometric term like *triangle* was not clear enough when they wanted someone to draw a triangle of a particular size.

Use Problem 3 to help students see the usefulness of precise language. This will help them see why subsequent lessons pay so much attention to definitions of geometric terms.

Home Connection

At this time, you may want to send home the letter on pages 42–45 of *Home Connection.* This letter describes what students will be learning and what activities they can do at home to support their work in school.

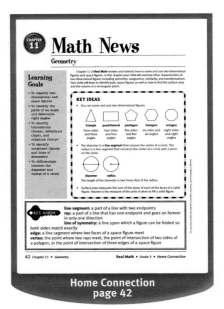

Home Connection
page 42

Assess and Differentiate

 **Assess** Use **eAssess** to record and analyze evidence of student understanding.

Gather Evidence

Use the Daily Class Assessment Records in **Assessment** or **eAssess** to record Informal and Formal Assessments.

Informal Assessment

✓ **Access Prior Knowledge**
Did the student **UNDERSTANDING**
- ❑ make important observations?
- ❑ extend or generalize learning?
- ❑ provide insightful answers?
- ❑ pose insightful questions?

Informal Assessment

✓ **Concept/Question Board**
Did the student **APPLYING**
- ❑ apply learning in new situations?
- ❑ contribute concepts?
- ❑ contribute answers?
- ❑ connect mathematics to real-world situations?

Formal Assessment

✓ **Pretest** **COMPUTING**
Review student answers in each problem set.
- ❑ Area and perimeter (Problems 1–3)
- ❑ Telling time (Problems 4 and 5)
- ❑ Identifying and comparing fractions and decimals (Problems 6–8)
- ❑ Properties of polygons (Problems 9–13)
- ❑ Symmetry (Problems 14 and 15)
- ❑ Congruence (Problems 16 and 17)
- ❑ Transformations (Problems 18–20)
- ❑ Volume (Problems 21 and 22)

 Summarize Findings

Analyze and summarize assessment data for each student. Determine which Assessment Follow-Up is appropriate for each student. Use the Student Assessment Record in **Assessment** or **eAssess** to update assessment records.

Assessment Follow-Up • DIFFERENTIATE INSTRUCTION

Based on your observations of each student, use these teaching strategies for a general approach to the chapter. Look for specific Differentiate Instruction and Monitoring Student Progress strategies in each lesson that relate specifically to the lesson content.

ENRICH	PRACTICE	RETEACH	INTERVENTION	ENGLISH LEARNER
If . . . students demonstrate **secure understanding** of chapter concepts, **Then . . .** move quickly through the chapter or use **Enrichment** Lessons 11.1–11.13 as assessment follow-up to extend and apply understanding.	**If . . .** students grasp chapter concepts with **competent understanding,** **Then . . .** Use **Practice** Lessons 11.1–11.13 as lesson follow-up to develop fluency.	**If . . .** students have prerequisite understanding but demonstrate **emerging understanding** of chapter concepts, **Then . . .** use **Reteach** Lessons 11.1 and 11.10 to reteach lesson concepts.	**If . . .** students are not competent with prerequisite skills, **Then . . .** use **Intervention** Lessons 11.A–11.C before each lesson to develop fluency with prerequisite skills.	Use **English Learner Support Guide** Lessons 11.1–11.13 for strategies to preteach lesson vocabulary and concepts.

Math Across the Curriculum

Preview the chapter projects with students. Assign projects or have students choose from the projects to extend and enrich concepts in this chapter.

Create a Map of Your Neighborhood

3–4 weeks

MATH OBJECTIVE
To reinforce studies of polygons by using polygons in a map design

FINE ARTS OBJECTIVE
To reinforce studies of the principle of balance by using balance in a map design

TECHNOLOGY OBJECTIVE
To use a drawing and graphics program to create a map of a neighborhood

• •

Have students use mathematics to create maps of their neighborhoods. To broaden the fine arts concept, have students incorporate techniques related to aspects of balance you are currently studying.

As part of the project, students should consider the following issues:

• map elements and the use of a compass
• types of polygons
• drawing and graphics tools

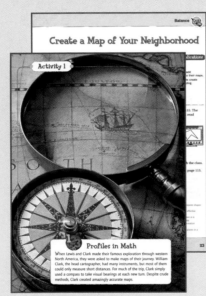

For specific step-by-step instructions for this project, see *Across the Curriculum Math Connections* pages 112–115.

Effective Communication Students create maps that effectively show interesting and important locations in their neighborhoods.

Self-Monitoring Students use tools such as compasses to complete work according to an established schedule.

Create a Presentation about Houses

3–4 weeks

LANGUAGE ARTS WebQuest

MATH OBJECTIVE
To reinforce studies of slides, flips, and turns by describing slides, flips, and turns in architecture

LANGUAGE ARTS OBJECTIVE
To reinforce studies of descriptive writing by describing houses around the world

TECHNOLOGY OBJECTIVE
To use a presentation program to create a presentation about houses around the world

• •

Have students use technology to

• research architecture and types of houses around the world.
• find and save pictures for their presentations.
• create presentations about houses around the world.

For this project, students use the Internet to investigate the following information:

• architectural styles, structures, and ornamentation
• building materials
• houses and architecture around the world

For specific step-by-step instructions for this project, see *Across the Curriculum Math Connections* pages 116–121.

Problem Formulation, Planning, and Strategizing Students plan presentations for their "clients" and use math to describe architecture.

Effective Communication Students clearly and convincingly communicate their ideas within their presentations.

TechKnowledge Level 3 provides lessons that specifically teach the Unit 10 Internet and Unit 6 Presentation applications that students can use in this project.

Lesson Planner

OBJECTIVES
To explore the relationships between the basic properties of points and lines

NCTM STANDARDS
Geometry
Analyzing characteristics and properties of two- and three-dimensional geometric shapes and developing mathematical arguments about geometric relationships

Connections
Recognizing and applying mathematics in contexts outside of mathematics

MATERIALS
- *Response Wheels
- Prepared leaves such as maple, corn, palm, and petunia

TECHNOLOGY
Presentation Lesson 11.1
Building Blocks Geometry Snapshots 3
MathTools Geometry Tools (Line Tool)

TEST PREP
Cumulative Review
Mental Math reviews adding decimals (Lesson 10.5).

Extended Response
Problems 11–16

Writing + Math
Journal

Points and Lines

Context of the Lesson In this introductory lesson on geometric concepts, students will review *points* and *lines* from Grade 2 and extend those explorations into types of lines and their formal names. These same concepts will be developed further in Grade 4.

See page 422B for Math Background for teachers for this lesson.

Planning for Learning ● DIFFERENTIATE INSTRUCTION

INTERVENTION
If . . . students lack the prerequisite skill of describing figures,

Then . . . teach *Intervention* Lesson 11.B.

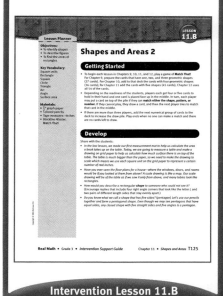

Intervention Lesson 11.B

ENGLISH LEARNER
Preview

If . . . students need language support,

Then . . . use Lesson 11.1 in *English Learner Support Guide* to preview lesson concepts and vocabulary.

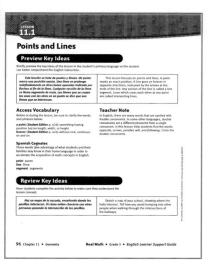

English Learner Lesson 11.1

ENRICH
If . . . students are proficient in the lesson concepts,

Then . . . emphasize the student pages.

PRACTICE
If . . . students would benefit from additional practice,

Then . . . extend Guided Discussion before assigning the student pages.

RETEACH
If . . . students are having difficulty understanding points and lines,

Then . . . extend Guided Discussion Pages before assigning the student pages.

Vocabulary
point \point\ *n.* something having position but no length, width, or height

line \līn\ *n.* a straight path that extends infinitely in opposite directions; thought of as having length but no thickness

line segment *n.* a part of a line with two endpoints

intersecting lines *n.* lines that meet and cross each other at a point

parallel lines *n.* lines that stay the same distance apart, go in the same direction, and never meet

Spanish Cognates
point punto
line línea
segment segmento

*Manipulative Kit Item

Mental Math

  Present students with addition problems involving decimals. Have students represent the decimal point using their finger on the *Response Wheel*. Use examples such as the following:

a. 0.2 + 0.5 0.7

b. 0.8 + 0.2 1.0 or 1

c. 1.4 + 1.5 2.9

d. 2.2 + 2.0 4.2

e. 0.4 + 0.4 0.8

f. 1.2 + 1.2 2.4

g. 2.3 + 3.2 5.5

h. 2.8 + 0.2 3.0 or 3

1 Develop 25

Tell Students In Today's Lesson They Will

develop a better understanding of the basic properties of points and lines.

Guided Discussion UNDERSTANDING Whole Group

Most students will be familiar with the words *point* and *line* from previous grades and from conversations outside school. Review with questions such as the following:

■ **What is a real-life example of a point?** Possible answers include a dot, a small hole, a pencil point, a speck, or any other small spot.

■ **How do we often represent a point?** by putting a dot there; If students do not know the answer to this question, show them the representation.

■ **What is an example of a line?** Possible answers include a street, a highway, or the intersection of a wall and the ceiling.

■ **How do we often represent a line?** a line with arrows at both ends; If students do not know the answer to this question, show them the representation.

Explain to students that a line segment is a part of a line with definite endpoints and that we can never actually see or draw a whole line. To indicate that a line goes on forever in both directions we draw an arrow at both ends. All of the examples students have used will most likely have been line segments. If a laser beam is assumed to go on forever, then it is an example of a ray. A ray is a part of a line that goes on forever in one direction. This will be discussed more thoroughly in Lesson 11.2.

Do the following activity with students to develop an understanding of the words *parallel* and *intersecting* before introducing the words:

1. Using a straightedge, draw two nonparallel lines on the board, and ask two or three student volunteers to come to the board and make a "point" where they think the lines will meet.

2. Using a yardstick, continue the lines to see where they meet and how close students were to estimating where that point is.

3. Repeat, but now draw two lines that are perpendicular to each other but do not meet. Have two or three volunteers come to the board and make points where they estimate the lines will meet. Then continue the lines to see how close the students were.

4. Repeat, but now draw two lines that are parallel to each other. Have two or three volunteers come to the board and make points where they estimate the lines will meet. Many students will recognize immediately that these two lines will never meet.

Ask students questions such as the following:

■ **In which examples did the lines meet?** the first two

Label the first two examples *intersecting*. Ask students to create a definition for *intersecting*. For example, any time two or more lines meet, or will meet if extended, the lines are intersecting.

Label the third example *parallel*. Have students create a definition for *parallel*. For example, any time two or more lines are in the same plane and will never meet, the lines are parallel.

Ask questions such as the following:

■ **What are examples of intersecting lines?** Possible answers include roads, paths, the edges of a desk, or calendar grids.

■ **What are examples of parallel lines?** Possible answers include sidewalks on both sides of a road, double yellow lines in the road, the opposite sides of a piece of paper, or railroad tracks.

2 Assign Student Pages   20 🕐

Pages 424–425 ☑️ APPLYING

Have students finish the exercises on pages 424 and 425 independently.

LESSON 11.1 Points and Lines

Key Ideas

A point marks an exact position. We represent a point with a dot, similar to a period: .

A straight path that goes on forever in opposite directions is called a line. We indicate infinite length by the arrows at the end of the line. This represents a line: ⟷

Any section of the line is called a line segment. A line segment always has two endpoints. This is a line segment: •—•

Label each of the following as *point, line,* or *line segment.*

1. • point

2. •——• line segment

3. ⟷ line

4. •——• line segment

5. • point

6. ↕ line

424   Textbook This lesson is available in the *eTextbook.*

Lines that cross each other at one point are called intersecting lines. These are intersecting lines: ⤬

Parallel lines are lines in the same plane that will never cross each other. These are two parallel lines: ⇉

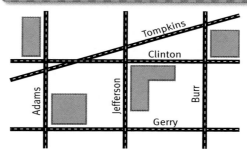

Tompkins · Clinton · Adams · Jefferson · Burr · Gerry

Answer these questions by studying the map.

7. Name one set of streets that are parallel to each other. Adams, Jefferson, and Burr

8. Name another set of streets that are parallel to each other. Clinton and Gerry

9. Name the streets that intersect Burr Street. Tompkins, Clinton, and Gerry

10. Name the streets that are intersected by four streets. Tompkins and Clinton

Teaching Lesson 11.1

Assign Student Pages, continued

Pages 426–427 [APPLYING]

Small Group

Have students complete the exercises on pages 426 and 427 independently.

Monitoring Student Progress

If . . . students have difficulty finding the meeting point of the pair of lines,

Then . . . have them trace the lines on a piece of paper and continue the lines using a straightedge.

As Students Finish

Building Blocks *Geometry Snapshots 3*

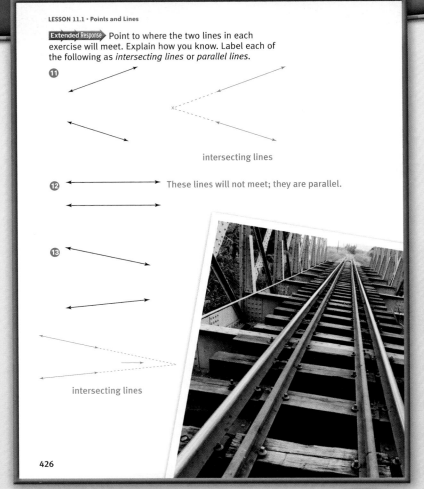

LESSON 11.1 · Points and Lines

Extended Response Point to where the two lines in each exercise will meet. Explain how you know. Label each of the following as *intersecting lines* or *parallel lines*.

11

intersecting lines

12 These lines will not meet; they are parallel.

13

intersecting lines

426

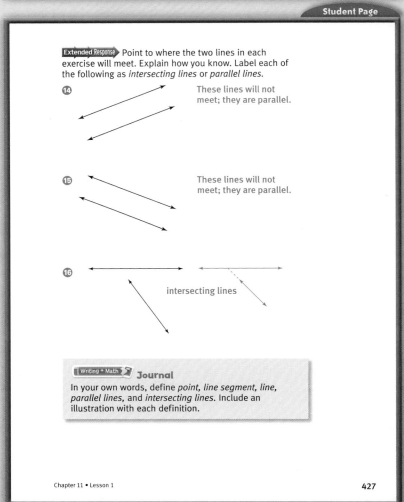

Extended Response Point to where the two lines in each exercise will meet. Explain how you know. Label each of the following as *intersecting lines* or *parallel lines*.

14 These lines will not meet; they are parallel.

15 These lines will not meet; they are parallel.

16 intersecting lines

Writing + Math Journal

In your own words, define *point, line segment, line, parallel lines,* and *intersecting lines*. Include an illustration with each definition.

Chapter 11 · Lesson 1

427

 Reflect 10

Guided Discussion UNDERSTANDING

Whole Group

Tell students that parallel and intersecting lines are found in nature. On the board, draw one leaf with intersecting veins and one leaf with parallel veins. Label each leaf *intersecting* or *parallel*.

Show students a leaf that has intersecting veins, such as a maple or petunia leaf (or a leaf from another dicotyledonous plant with intersecting veins), and a leaf that has almost parallel veins, such as a corn or palm leaf (or a leaf from another monocotyledonous plant with parallel veins). Have students classify the leaves, or pictures of leaves, into *parallel* or *intersecting* categories. Ask questions such as the following:

■ **What other real-world examples are there of intersecting and parallel lines?** Some possible answers are railroad tracks, streets, and edges of ceiling tiles.

 **Extended Response**

Most of the explanations will consist of showing their understanding of the difference between *parallel lines* and *intersecting lines*.

Writing + Math **Journal**

Accept any reasonable definition and illustration of *point, line segment, line, parallel lines,* and *intersecting lines.*

 Curriculum Connection: Students might be interested in looking at other patterns made by the leaves of many plants not mentioned in this lesson.

 Cumulative Review: For cumulative review of previously learned skills, see page 446–447.

 Family Involvement: Assign the **Practice, Reteach,** or **Enrichment** activities depending on the needs of your students.
Encourage students to find other real-world examples of parallel and intersecting lines with a friend or a relative.

 Concept/Question Board: Have students look for additional examples using geometry and post them on the Concept/Question Board.

 Math Puzzler: What are the 3 greatest numbers that can be created from the digits 7, 2, 6, and 3 if each digit is used only once? 7632, 7623, 7362

4 Assess and Differentiate

 e Assess Use **eAssess** to record and analyze evidence of student understanding.

A Gather Evidence

Use the Daily Class Assessment Records in **Assessment** or **eAssess** to record daily observations.

Informal Assessment
☑ **Guided Discussion**

Did the student **UNDERSTANDING**
- ❑ make important observations?
- ❑ extend or generalize learning?
- ❑ provide insightful answers?
- ❑ pose insightful questions?

Informal Assessment
☑ **Student Pages**

Did the student **APPLYING**
- ❑ apply learning in new situations?
- ❑ contribute concepts?
- ❑ contribute answers?
- ❑ connect mathematics to real-world situations?

B Summarize Findings

Analyze and summarize assessment data for each student. Determine which Assessment Follow-Up is appropriate for each student. Use the Student Assessment Record in **Assessment** or **eAssess** to update assessment records.

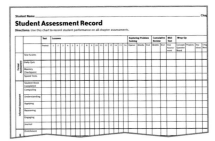

Assessment Page T41

C Assessment Follow-Up • DIFFERENTIATE INSTRUCTION

Based on your observations, use these teaching strategies for assessment follow-up.

INTERVENTION	ENRICH	PRACTICE	RETEACH
Review student performance on **Intervention** Lesson 11.B to see if students have mastered prerequisite skills for this lesson.	**If . . .** students are proficient in the lesson concepts, **Then . . .** encourage them to work on chapter projects or **Enrichment** Lesson 11.1.	**If . . .** students would benefit from additional practice, **Then . . .** assign **Practice** Lesson 11.1.	**If . . .** students are having difficulty understanding basic properties of points and lines, **Then . . .** reteach the concept using **Reteach** Lesson 11.1.

ENGLISH LEARNER

Review

Use Lesson 11.1 in **English Learner Support Guide** to review lesson concepts and vocabulary.

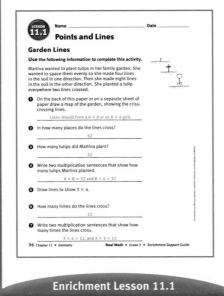

Enrichment Lesson 11.1

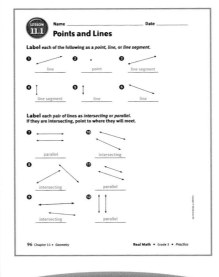

Practice Lesson 11.1

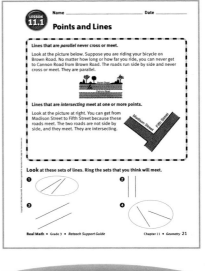

Reteach Lesson 11.1

OBJECTIVES
- To introduce students to the properties of angles
- To focus special attention on the properties of right angles and have students learn to distinguish among those angles with measures that are greater than right angles, those with measures that are less than right angles, and those that are right angles

NCTM STANDARDS
Geometry
Analyzing characteristics and properties of two- and three-dimensional geometric shapes and developing mathematical arguments about geometric relationships

Communication
Using the language of mathematics to express mathematical ideas precisely

MATERIALS
*Response Wheels

TECHNOLOGY
🖥 **Presentation** Lesson 11.2
Building Blocks Geometry Snapshots 3

TEST PREP
Cumulative Review
Mental Math reviews adding and comparing decimals (Lesson 10.5). Problems 19–26 review telling time (Lesson 3.1).

Writing + Math
Journal

Angles

Context of the Lesson In Lesson 11.1, students explored various types of lines and properties of lines. In this lesson, students will explore the concept of *angles*, which result from the intersection of two or more lines or rays. Students will also use comparisons to determine if angles are greater than or less than a right angle. In Grade 4 these properties of angles will be explored and defined further.

See page 422B for Math Background for teachers for this lesson.

Planning for Learning ● DIFFERENTIATE INSTRUCTION

INTERVENTION	ENGLISH LEARNER	ENRICH
If . . . students lack the prerequisite skill of describing figures, **Then . . .** teach *Intervention* Lesson 11.B.	Preview **If . . .** students need language support, **Then . . .** use Lesson 11.2 in *English Learner Support Guide* to preview lesson concepts and vocabulary.	**If . . .** students are proficient in the lesson concepts, **Then . . .** emphasize the student pages.

PRACTICE
If . . . students would benefit from additional practice,
Then . . . extend Skill Building before assigning the student pages.

RETEACH
If . . . students are having difficulty understanding angles,
Then . . . extend Guided Discussion before assigning the student pages.

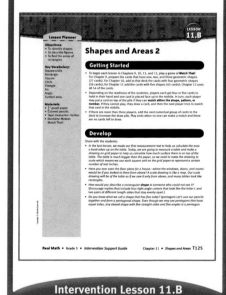

Intervention Lesson 11.B

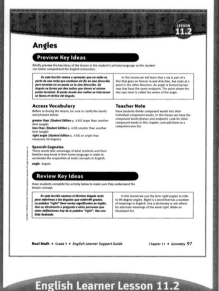

English Learner Lesson 11.2

Vocabulary
ray \rā\ *n.* a set of points that has one endpoint and extends forever in one direction
angle \ang´ gəl\ *n.* the figure formed by two rays extending from the same point
vertex \ver´ teks\ *n.* 1. the point of intersection of two rays

2. the point of intersection of three edges of a space figure
right angle *n.* an angle measuring 90°
perpendicular lines *n.* lines that intersect at right angles

Access Vocabulary
greater than larger than another item (angle)
less than smaller than another item (angle)
right angle an angle that measures 90°

Mental Math

10

Present students with addition exercises with decimals involving greater than, less than, or equal to. Have students give a thumbs-up signal if the number on the left is greater than the number on the right, thumbs-down if the number on the left is less than the number on the right, or open hand if both numbers are equal. Use examples such as the following:

a. 0.2 + 0.5 ▢ 7.0 down **e.** 0.4 + 0.4 ▢ 0.8 open

b. 0.8 + 0.2 ▢ 0.8 up **f.** 1.2 + 1.2 ▢ 2.4 open

c. 1.4 + 1.5 ▢ 6.9 down **g.** 2.3 + 3.2 ▢ 1.5 up

d. 2.2 + 2.0 ▢ 0.4 up **h.** 2.8 + 0.2 ▢ 3.0 open

1 Develop

25

Guided Discussion UNDERSTANDING

Whole Group

Draw a *line* on the board with arrows on both ends. Mark an obvious point on the line, and then erase everything past the point in one direction (thus creating a ray). Discuss with students some properties of this ray, such as the following:

- It is part of a line.
- It has one endpoint.
- It goes on forever in one direction.

Identify this geometric term as a *ray*.

Draw a point on the board. Label the point A, and call it *Point A*. From *Point A*, draw two rays, forming approximately a 45–60° angle.

Tell the class this is an angle, which we will call angle A. It consists of two rays starting at the same point. In addition, point out that many times the rays will not be drawn with arrows at the ends, but they are still thought of as rays that can be extended if we wish. Therefore, the size of the angle is not determined by how long we draw the side but rather by how far we would have to turn from facing along one ray in order to be facing along the other ray.

Draw another angle, a right angle, and label the common point B. Call this *Angle B,* labeling and introducing the term *vertex*. Have students describe the parts of this angle. Encourage use of the terminology to familiarize students with the vocabulary. After discussing *Angle B,* hold a corner of a piece of paper up to the angle. Ask questions such as the following:

- **What do you notice about Angle B and this corner?** They are the same; the paper fits into the angle.
- **Does it matter which corner is used?** no **Demonstrate this.**
- **Do you suppose the same thing is possible with Angle A?** No, *Angle A* should be less than the corner of the paper. **Demonstrate this.**

Draw a third angle, exaggerating the angle so that it is obviously larger than a right angle. Label this *Angle C.* Ask students to describe the parts of this angle and if they believe it to be larger or smaller than the corner of the paper. Continue this pattern with three or four more angles as needed. Explain to students that an angle is larger than another if it represents more of a turn going from one ray to another. For example, angle A is smaller than a right angle because if you hold a right angle at its vertex, overlapping one side, you can not see the other side. Angle C is larger than a right angle because if you hold a right angle up to it, you can see the other side. The lengths of the rays do not determine if an angle is larger or smaller than a right angle. This can best be demonstrated by drawing an angle, then lengthening the sides and asking whether the angle has changed size.

Skill Building UNDERSTANDING

Small Group

Have students do the following either individually or in small groups. Have them compare the results.

Take a piece of paper, and fold it once. Then without unfolding the paper, but using the crease as a guide, fold the paper once more as in the following diagram. Unfold the paper. The result of the folding is that you have made four right angles. Have students label as many recognized parts as possible.

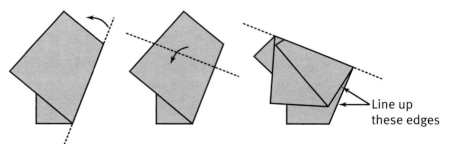

Line up these edges

While students are looking at their angles, point out the fact that the folds can also represent lines. These particular lines are *perpendicular lines* because when these lines intersect, they create four right angles.

2 Assign Student Pages 20

Pages 428–429

Have students complete the exercises on pages 428 and 429 independently.

LESSON 11.2 Angles

Key Ideas

A **ray** is part of a line that goes on forever in one direction but ends at a point in the other direction.

This represents a ray:

An **angle** is formed by two rays that have the same endpoint. The point where the two rays meet is called the **vertex** of the angle. This is an angle with its vertex labeled *Q*.

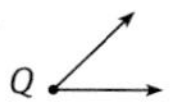

Q

This is an angle with the vertex labeled *S*.

S

Label the following as *ray, line,* or *angle*.

① ray

② line

③ angle

④ ray

⑤ angle

⑥ line

428   📖 **Textbook** This lesson is available in the *eTextbook*.

Two intersecting lines form four angles.

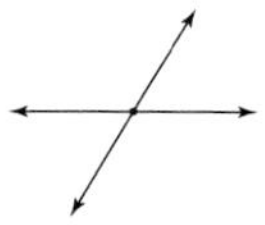

When two intersecting lines form four *identical* angles, the lines are **perpendicular**. The angles formed in this way are called **right angles**.

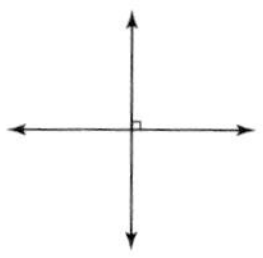

All of these are right angles.

None of these are right angles.

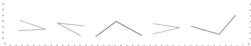

⑦ Which of the following are right angles?

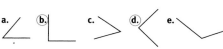

a.   (b.)   c.   (d.)   e.

Teaching Lesson 11.2

Assign Student Pages, continued

Pages 430–431

Have students complete the exercises on pages 430 and 431 independently. In problems 19–26, students will need to tell the time as well as what type of angle is represented.

Monitoring Student Progress

If . . . students have difficulty distinguishing between right, obtuse, and acute angles,

Then . . . provide brief individual or small-group tutoring. Extensive extra teaching is not necessary at this time as more practice is included in the next few lessons.

As Students Finish

 Have students play a game previously introduced in the book.

Building **B**locks *Geometry Snapshot 3*

LESSON 11.2 · Angles

Create a two-column chart. In one column, list the angles that are greater than a right angle. In the second column, list the angles that are smaller than a right angle. The remaining angles will be right angles. Estimate first, but use the corner of a book or page to check.

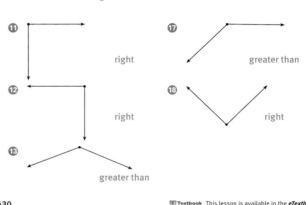

8   smaller than

9   smaller than

10   greater than

11   right

12   right

13   greater than

14   right

15   smaller than

16   smaller than

17   greater than

18   right

430   Textbook This lesson is available in the *eTextbook*.

An angle that is smaller than a right angle is called an *acute angle*. An angle that is greater than a right angle is called an *obtuse angle*.

Review   Write the correct time for each clock face. Then tell if the measure of the angle of the clock hands is a right angle, an acute angle, or an obtuse angle.

19   4:00; obtuse

23   9:00; right

20   3:00; right

24    6:10; obtuse

21   2:00; acute

25   4:15; acute

22   1:00; acute

26   12:05; acute

Writing + Math **Journal**
Describe the measure of the angle of the clock hands when it is 6:00.

Chapter 11 • Lesson 2   431

430–431   Chapter 11 • Lesson 2

 **Reflect** 5 ◔

Guided Discussion

Initiate a discussion in which students tell about angles they see in everyday life. Have students identify these angles as acute, right, or obtuse. Some examples include the following:

- the branches of trees
- the angles on a street or city map
- the edges on furniture

 **Journal** ☑ **REASONING**

Although students have not been introduced to the term *straight angle,* they have reviewed the term *line* in Lesson 11.1.

They may say there is no angle or that it is equal to two right angles. Some students may suggest it is a straight angle. Any of these suggestions could be considered correct. We will call this angle a *straight angle.*

 Curriculum Connection: Students might be interested in seeing how angles are used in everyday life, such as in architecture, science, and art.

 Cumulative Review: For cumulative review of previously learned skills, see page 446–447.

 Family Involvement: Assign the *Practice, Reteach,* or *Enrichment* activities depending on the needs of your students.

Encourage students to find real-world examples of angles with a friend or a relative.

 Concept/Question Board: Have students look for additional examples using geometry and post them on the Concept/Question Board.

 Math Puzzler: Write the following number pattern on the board; have students copy and complete it: 1, 2, 4, 5, 7, 8, 10, 11, ▨ , ▨ . 13; 14; The pattern is +1, +2, +1, +2, and so on.

Assess and Differentiate

 Assess Use *eAssess* to record and analyze evidence of student understanding.

A Gather Evidence

Use the Daily Class Assessment Records in **Assessment** or **eAssess** to record daily observations.

Informal Assessment

☑ **Guided Discussion**

Did the student UNDERSTANDING
- ❏ make important observations?
- ❏ extend or generalize learning?
- ❏ provide insightful answers?
- ❏ pose insightful questions?

Portfolio Assessment

☑ **Journal**

Did the student REASONING
- ❏ provide a clear explanation?
- ❏ communicate reasons and strategies?
- ❏ choose appropriate strategies?
- ❏ argue logically?

B Summarize Findings

Analyze and summarize assessment data for each student. Determine which Assessment Follow-Up is appropriate for each student. Use the Student Assessment Record in **Assessment** or **eAssess** to update assessment records.

Assessment Page T41

C Assessment Follow-Up • DIFFERENTIATE INSTRUCTION

Based on your observations, use these teaching strategies for assessment follow-up.

INTERVENTION	ENRICH	PRACTICE	RETEACH
Review student performance on **Intervention** Lesson 11.B to see if students have mastered prerequisite skills for this lesson.	**If . . .** students are proficient in the lesson concepts, **Then . . .** encourage them to work on chapter projects or **Enrichment** Lesson 11.2.	**If . . .** students would benefit from additional practice, **Then . . .** assign **Practice** Lesson 11.2.	**If . . .** students struggle with acute, obtuse, and right angles, **Then . . .** have them look up the definitions for each of the words. Discuss non-mathematical meanings for acute and obtuse to help students remember these types of angles.

ENGLISH LEARNER

Review

Use Lesson 11.2 in **English Learner Support Guide** to review lesson concepts and vocabulary.

Enrichment Lesson 11.2

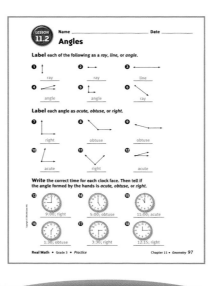

Practice Lesson 11.2

OBJECTIVES
To explore the properties of triangles

NCTM STANDARDS
Geometry
Classifying two- and three-dimensional shapes according to their properties and developing definitions of classes of shapes such as triangles and pyramids

Communication
Using the language of mathematics to express mathematical ideas precisely

MATERIALS
- Ruler
- Scissors
- 3 different coloring pencils, crayons, or markers

TECHNOLOGY
⊞ **Presentation** Lesson 11.3
Building Blocks Shapes Part 1
⊞ **MathTools** Shape Tools or
   Geometry Sketch Tools
   (Triangle Tool)

TEST PREP
Cumulative Review
- Mental Math reviews percents (Lesson 8.11).
- Problems 4–6 review perimeter (Lessons 3.6 and 3.7).

Writing + Math
Journal

Triangles

Context of the Lesson Students have been working with triangles since Kindergarten. In Grade 2, students explored basic properties of triangles. In this lesson, formal names for triangles, according to their sides and angles, will be introduced. These same names and other properties will continue to be explored in Grade 4.

See page 422B for Math Background for teachers for this lesson.

Planning for Learning ● DIFFERENTIATE INSTRUCTION

INTERVENTION

If . . . students lack the prerequisite skill of identifying shapes,

Then . . . teach *Intervention* Lesson 11.A.

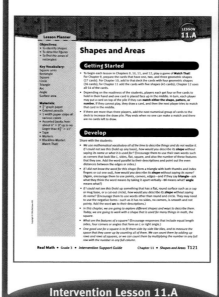

Intervention Lesson 11.A

ENGLISH LEARNER

Preview

If . . . students need language support,

Then . . . use Lesson 11.3 in *English Learner Support Guide* to preview lesson concepts and vocabulary.

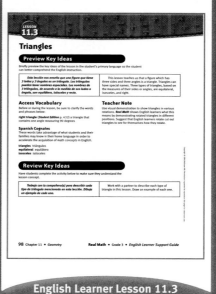

English Learner Lesson 11.3

ENRICH

If . . . students are proficient in the lesson concepts,

Then . . . emphasize the student pages.

PRACTICE

If . . . students would benefit from additional practice,

Then . . . extend Strategy Building before assigning the student pages.

RETEACH

If . . . students are having difficulty understanding properties of triangles,

Then . . . extend Strategy Building before assigning the student pages.

Vocabulary
Review from Grade 2: **triangle**
equilateral \ē´ kwə lat´ər əl\ *adj.* having all sides equal in length
isosceles \ī säs´ lēz\ *adj.* having two equal sides
right triangle *n.* a triangle with one right angle

Access Vocabulary
right triangle a triangle that contains one angle measuring 90°

Spanish Cognates
triangles triángulos
equilateral equilátero
isosceles isósceles

Mental Math 10

  Have students use their percent slider to show the percent. Use examples such as the following: check students' answers

a. 90%   **e.** 24%

b. 48%   **f.** 71%

c. 12%   **g.** 89%

d. 17%   **h.** 52%

1 Develop 20

Tell Students In Today's Lesson They Will

explore some properties of triangles.

Strategy Building UNDERSTANDING   Small Group

This activity is best done in small groups with students sharing materials.

1. Have each student draw a triangle on a clean sheet of paper using a straightedge. Have students cut out their triangles. Tell students there should be a variety of sizes and shapes among the triangles of each group. When all students are finished, have them show their triangles to the rest of the class, stressing the fact that there are large triangles and small triangles, but they are all triangles.

2. Have students color the three corners of the triangles with three different colors. Then have students tear off the angles. (It is important to tear rather than cut so that the sides of the original angles are recognizable along with the color.)

3. Have students put the three angles from their triangles together with the vertices at the same spot and the edges touching.

■ **What do you notice about these angles?** The three angles form a straight angle or line.

■ **Does it matter what kind of triangle we started with?** No, all triangles will form a straight angle or line when placed together like this.

2 Assign Student Pages 20

Pages 432–433   APPLYING

Have students complete the exercises on pages 432 and 433 independently.

Monitoring Student Progress

If . . . students have a hard time remembering the names of different types of triangles,

Then . . . they may be helped by making flash cards with the name on one side and a drawing of the triangle on the other side.

As Students Finish

 *Shapes Part 1*

LESSON 11.3 Triangles

Key Ideas

A figure that has three sides and three angles is a triangle. Triangles, like angles, can have special names. Three names of triangles, based on the lengths of their sides, or the size of their angles are *equilateral*, *isosceles*, and *right*.

All of these are equilateral triangles.

None of these are equilateral triangles.

1 Which of the following are equilateral triangles?

a.   b.   c.   d.   e.

All of these are isosceles triangles.

None of these are isosceles triangles.

2 Which of the following are isosceles triangles?

a.   b.   c.   d.   e.

432   Textbook This lesson is available in the *eTextbook*.

All of these are right triangles.

None of these are right triangles.

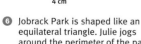

3 Which of the following are right triangles?

a.   b.   c.   d.   e.

Review ➜ Find the perimeters of these triangles. Then identify the type of triangle.

4 3 cm, 3 cm, 3 cm   9 cm; equilateral

5 3 cm, 5 cm, 4 cm   12 cm; right

6 Jobrack Park is shaped like an equilateral triangle. Julie jogs around the perimeter of the park every day. About how far does she jog in 3 days?

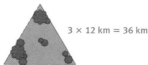
4 km

$3 \times 12 \text{ km} = 36 \text{ km}$

Writing + Math Journal

In your own words, define *triangle*, *equilateral triangle*, *isosceles triangle*, and *right triangle*. Include an illustration with each definition.

---

3 Reflect   10

Guided Discussion ✓ UNDERSTANDING   Whole Group

Have five or six volunteers come to the board and each draw one triangle. Present the following definitions, one at a time, to the class. Try to match up a triangle with each term. If there are no examples, have a volunteer come to the board and draw one. This can also be demonstrated using the *eMathTool: Shape Tools* or *Geometry Sketch Tool*.

Triangle: a three-sided polygon
Scalene Triangle: a triangle having three sides of unequal length
Isosceles Triangle: a triangle that has two equal sides
Equilateral Triangle: a triangle composed of three equal sides
Right Triangle: a triangle that has a right angle

Ask students to give examples of the shapes found in the classroom, home, or school.

Writing + Math Journal

Accept any reasonable and correct definition and illustration for *triangle*, *equilateral triangle*, *isosceles triangle*, and *right triangle*.

REAL WORLD — Curriculum Connection: Students might be interested in seeing how triangles are used in everyday life, such as in art, science, and architecture.

Review — Cumulative Review: For cumulative review of previously learned skills, see page 446–447.

Family Involvement: Assign the *Practice, Reteach,* or *Enrichment* activities depending on the needs of your students.

Encourage students to find real-world examples of triangles with a friend or a relative.

Concept/Question Board: Have students look for additional examples using geometry and post them on the Concept/Question Board.

Math Puzzler: Six students in Mrs. Nomura's class got the following scores on their math test: 82, 89, 82, 98, 79, and 90. List the scores in ascending order: 79, 82, 82, 89, 90, 98

4 Assess and Differentiate

 Assess Use **eAssess** to record and analyze evidence of student understanding.

A Gather Evidence

Use the Daily Class Assessment Records in **Assessment** or **eAssess** to record daily observations.

Informal Assessment
☑ **Student Pages**

Did the student **APPLYING**

❑ apply learning in new situations?
❑ contribute concepts?
❑ contribute answers?
❑ connect mathematics to real-world situations?

Informal Assessment
☑ **Guided Discussion**

Did the student **UNDERSTANDING**

❑ make important observations?
❑ extend or generalize learning?
❑ provide insightful answers?
❑ pose insightful questions?

B Summarize Findings

Analyze and summarize assessment data for each student. Determine which Assessment Follow-Up is appropriate for each student. Use the Student Assessment Record in **Assessment** or **eAssess** to update assessment records.

Assessment Page T41

C Assessment Follow-Up • DIFFERENTIATE INSTRUCTION

Based on your observations, use these teaching strategies for assessment follow-up.

INTERVENTION

Review student performance on **Intervention** Lesson 11.A to see if students have mastered prerequisite skills for this lesson.

ENGLISH LEARNER

Review

Use Lesson 11.3 in **English Learner Support Guide** to review lesson concepts and vocabulary.

ENRICH

If . . . students are proficient in the lesson concepts,

Then . . . encourage them to work on chapter projects or **Enrichment** Lesson 11.3.

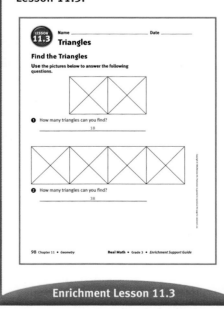

Enrichment Lesson 11.3

PRACTICE

If . . . students would benefit from additional practice,

Then . . . assign **Practice** Lesson 11.3.

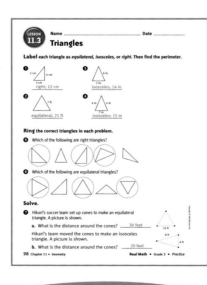

Practice Lesson 11.3

RETEACH

If . . . students struggle with types of triangles,

Then . . . have them construct examples of triangles using craft sticks and modeling clay. They can break the sticks in half to make differing sizes. Have students make examples of different types of angles and triangles.

Lesson Planner

OBJECTIVES
- To explore some of the properties of four-sided figures
- To learn or review the names and properties of some common quadrilaterals: squares, rectangles, parallelograms, rhombuses (rhombi), and trapezoids

NCTM STANDARDS

Geometry
- Identifying, comparing, and analyzing attributes of two- and three-dimensional shapes and developing vocabulary to describe the attributes
- Classifying two- and three-dimensional shapes according to their properties

Communication
Using the language of mathematics to express mathematical ideas precisely

Connections
Recognizing and using connections among mathematical ideas

MATERIALS
- Ruler
- Scissors

TECHNOLOGY
📧 Presentation Lesson 11.4
Building Blocks Shapes Part 2
📧 MathTools Shape Tools or Geometry Sketch Tools (Quadrilateral Tool)

TEST PREP

Cumulative Review
- Mental Math reviews lines, angles, and triangles (Lessons 11.1–11.3).
- Problems 13 and 14 review perimeter (Lessons 3.6 and 3.7).

Extended Response
Problems 8–13

Writing + Math
Journal

Quadrilaterals

Context of the Lesson Students are already familiar with quadrilaterals through study in previous grades and from earlier lessons in Grade 3. In this lesson students will explore the definitions of *quadrilaterals* and their properties. Although these topics are an important part of developing mathematical knowledge, and often motivate students to study mathematics, mastery of this material is not expected in third grade. In Grade 4 students will start classifying quadrilaterals along with other polygons.

See page 422B for Math Background for teachers for this lesson.

Planning for Learning • DIFFERENTIATE INSTRUCTION

INTERVENTION

If . . . students lack the prerequisite skill of identifying shapes,

Then . . . teach *Intervention* Lesson 11.A.

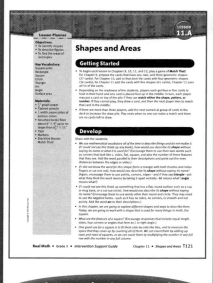

Intervention Lesson 11.A

ENGLISH LEARNER

Preview

If . . . students need language support,

Then . . . use Lesson 11.4 in *English Learner Support Guide* to preview lesson concepts and vocabulary.

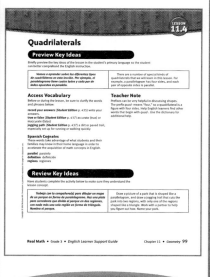

English Learner Lesson 11.4

ENRICH

If . . . students are proficient in the lesson concepts,

Then . . . emphasize the student pages.

PRACTICE

If . . . students would benefit from additional practice,

Then . . . extend Guided Discussion before assigning the student pages.

RETEACH

If . . . students are having difficulty understanding properties of quadrilaterals,

Then . . . extend Strategy Building before assigning the student pages.

Vocabulary
Review from Grade 2: **rectangle**
Review from Grade 2: **square**
quadrilateral \kwod rə lat′ ər əl\ *n.* a polygon with four sides
parallelogram \par ə lel′ ə gram\ *n.* a quadrilateral that has two pairs of parallel sides

rhombus \rom′ bəs\ *n.* a parallelogram whose sides are all the same length
trapezoid \trap′ ə zoid\ *n.* a quadrilateral with exactly one pair of parallel sides

Spanish Cognates
parallel paralelo
defintion definición
regions regiones

Mental Math 5

  Make true and false statements about lines, angles, and triangles. Have students show thumbs-up if the statement is true and thumbs-down if the statement is false. Use statements such as the following:

a. A line goes on forever in two directions. up

b. A triangle has three sides. up

c. A triangle with a right angle is called an equilateral triangle. down

d. A triangle with three sides of equal length is called a right triangle. down

e. Parallel lines will cross each other if you draw them long enough. down

f. Line segments are parts of lines. up

1 Develop 25

Tell Students In Today's Lesson They Will
explore the properties and names of four-sided figures.

Strategy Building UNDERSTANDING
Small Group

This activity is similar to the activity in the Teacher's Edition in Lesson 11.3. The difference is this time students will be drawing a quadrilateral instead of a triangle. If possible, students should work in groups of two or three.

Have students draw a quadrilateral on a piece of paper using a straightedge. Have students cut out their quadrilaterals. Emphasize that each group should have quadrilaterals of a variety of shapes and sizes. Next, have students perform the following steps in order:

1. Students color the angles of their quadrilaterals using four different colors.

2. They tear off, not cut, the angles in such a way that the separated angles show the color and the white space above them.

3. Students place the vertices of their angles together. The four angles should come together in a way that shows the sum of the angles is 360° (a full circle). Walk around the room, and ensure the angles are placed together correctly. You might need to allow students to use transparent tape to tape the angles together on a separate piece of paper in order to make the angles line up correctly.

4. Have students compare their completed projects and discuss the results.

Using Student Pages APPLYING
Small Group

Have students open their books to pages 434–436. Without referring to technical definitions, have students work individually or in pairs to complete pages 434–436. When the majority of the class has completed page 436, continue to *Guided Discussion* to have students become familiar with actual definitions for the terms in the pages they have completed.

Guided Discussion UNDERSTANDING
Whole Group

Ask students to name some four-sided figures. Some answers might include such figures as a square, a rectangle, or a diamond. Introduce the word *quadrilateral* as a word that is used to name all four-sided closed figures. Explain that this word is made of two words in another language. *Quad* is the Latin word for "four," and *lateral* means "sides or lines" in Latin. Explain that this is how we get the word *quadrilateral,* meaning "four-sided figure" in English.

Tell the class you are going to go over some definitions for some common quadrilaterals. Explain that all four-sided figures, no matter their shape, are called quadrilaterals. Draw an example of each figure on the board as you present the following definitions to the class. This can be done using the *eMathTools: Shape Tools* or *Geometry Sketch Tool.*

Parallelogram: a quadrilateral with opposite sides parallel and equal

Trapezoid: a quadrilateral having only two sides parallel

Square: a quadrilateral that has four equal sides and four right angles

Rectangle: a parallelogram having four right angles

Rhombus: a parallelogram with four equal sides

Each one of these figures is a special kind of quadrilateral. Ask students if they can think of any other shapes to go in this category.

Ask students if some common shapes are quadrilaterals. Have them explain their answers. Ask questions such as the following:

■ **Can a triangle be a quadrilateral?** no
■ **Can a circle be called a quadrilateral?** no
■ **Can we call a square a quadrilateral?** yes
■ **Can an octagon be a quadrilateral?** no

Draw an example of each shape on the board as you ask the questions. This visual representation will help students become familiar with the characteristics of quadrilaterals and other figures.

2 Assign Student Pages 20 🌙

Pages 434–435 ✓ **APPLYING**

Small Group

Have students correct any mistakes on pages 434 and 435 independently.

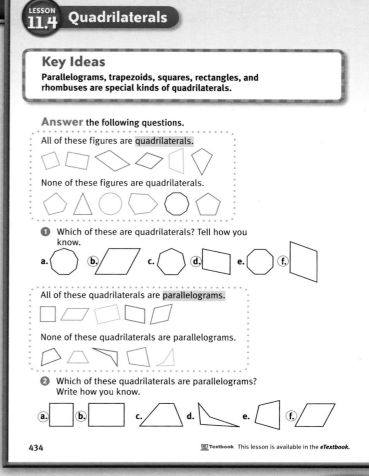

Teaching Lesson 11.4

Assign Student Pages, continued

Pages 436–437 `APPLYING` — Small Group

Have students correct any mistakes on pages 436 and 437 independently.

Monitoring Student Progress

If . . . students have difficulty remembering the names of the different kinds of quadrilaterals,

Then . . . they might be helped by making flash cards with the names of the shapes on one side and a drawing of the quadrilateral on the other.

As Students Finish

Building Blocks *Shapes Part 2*

LESSON 11.4 • Quadrilaterals

Answer the following question. Use a separate sheet of paper to record your answers.

All of these quadrilaterals are trapezoids.

None of these quadrilaterals are trapezoids.

⑤ Which of these quadrilaterals are trapezoids? How do you know?   They are trapezoids because they have only two parallel sides.

a.   b.   c.

d.   e.   f.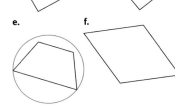

436   📖 Textbook This lesson is available in the *eTextbook*.

Extended Response ▶ **Label** each of the following as *true* or *false*. How do you know?

⑥ All rectangles are parallelograms. true, because they all have two sets of parallel lines

⑦ All parallelograms are rectangles. false, because parallelograms may not have right angles

⑧ All trapezoids are quadrilaterals. True. They all have four sides.

⑨ All squares are also rhombuses and parallelograms.

⑩ All quadrilaterals are parallelograms. False. Quadrilaterals do not need to have opposite sides parallel.

(Review) ⑪ **Extended Response** Sayeski Park is shaped like a rectangle. Its perimeter is 12 kilometers. Melissa jogs along the longer side of the park each day and then takes the bus home. About how far does Melissa jog each day?
about 4 km because 2 + 4 + 2 + 4 = 12

2 km

(Review) ⑫ Moss Park is shaped like a square. Its perimeter is 28 kilometers. What is the measurement of the sides? 7 km

⑬ **Extended Response** Moss Park has a jogging path that runs from one corner of the park to the corner at the opposite end. Notice that the jogging path divides the park into two regions that are shaped like triangles. What kind of triangles are they? How do you know? Isosceles triangles, because the sides of the square are congruent.

> **Writing + Math** **Journal**
>
> In your own words, define *quadrilateral, parallelogram, trapezoid, square, rectangle,* and *rhombus*. Include an illustration with each definition.

⑨ True. They are parallelograms because they have two sets of parallel sides and they are rhombuses because all four sides are equal in length.

Chapter 11 • Lesson 4   437

 **Reflect** 10

Guided Discussion UNDERSTANDING

Whole Group

Discuss the true and false questions at the top of page 437. Call on a few students to explain their answers.

Tell students there is another quadrilateral called an *isosceles trapezoid*. Review with students the definitions of *isosceles* and *trapezoid*. Ask them to come up with a definition and drawing of an isosceles trapezoid. (Possible answer: a trapezoid with two opposite sides the same length) Have students individually draw an example of an isosceles trapezoid. Students' examples will vary.

Relate the isosceles trapezoid to the isosceles triangle. For example, the isosceles triangle has two equal sides; an isosceles trapezoid cannot have two sets of equal parallel sides because if it did, it would be called a parallelogram. This discussion should lead the class to come up with a definition and an example of an isosceles trapezoid, such as the following:

Isosceles Trapezoid: a trapezoid having two nonparallel sides that are equal in length

 **Journal** REASONING

Accept reasonable definitions and illustrations of *quadrilateral, parallelogram, trapezoid, square, rectangle,* and *rhombus.*

 Curriculum Connection: Students might be interested in studying the etymology of other math-related words.

 Cumulative Review: For cumulative review of previously learned skills, see page 446–447.

 Family Involvement: Assign the *Practice, Reteach,* or *Enrichment* activities depending on the needs of your students.

Encourage students to find various real-world examples of quadrilaterals with a friend or a relative.

 Concept/Question Board: Have students look for additional examples involving geometry and post them on the Concept/Question Board.

 Math Puzzler: Michael figured out that he will be 18 years old when he graduates from high school. He also figured that he will be 3 times as old as he was in the first grade. How old was Michael when he was in the first grade?

6 years old; $18 \div 3 = 6$

4 Assess and Differentiate

 Assess Use **eAssess** to record and analyze evidence of student understanding.

A Gather Evidence

Use the Daily Class Assessment Records in **Assessment** or **eAssess** to record daily observations.

Informal Assessment

☑ **Student Pages**

Did the student **APPLYING**
- ❑ apply learning in new situations?
- ❑ contribute concepts?
- ❑ contribute answers?
- ❑ connect mathematics to real-world situations?

Portfolio Assessment

☑ **Journal**

Did the student **REASONING**
- ❑ provide a clear explanation?
- ❑ communicate reasons and strategies?
- ❑ choose appropriate strategies?
- ❑ argue logically?

B Summarize Findings

Analyze and summarize assessment data for each student. Determine which Assessment Follow-Up is appropriate for each student. Use the Student Assessment Record in **Assessment** or **eAssess** to update assessment records.

Assessment Page T41

C Assessment Follow-Up • DIFFERENTIATE INSTRUCTION

Based on your observations, use these teaching strategies for assessment follow-up.

INTERVENTION

Review student performance on **Intervention** Lesson 11.A to see if students have mastered prerequisite skills for this lesson.

ENGLISH LEARNER

Review

Use Lesson 11.4 in **English Learner Support Guide** to review lesson concepts and vocabulary.

ENRICH

If . . . students are proficient in the lesson concepts,

Then . . . encourage them to work on chapter projects or **Enrichment** Lesson 11.4.

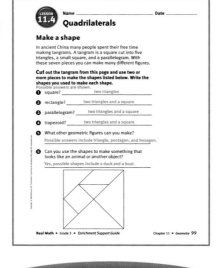

Enrichment Lesson 11.4

PRACTICE

If . . . students would benefit from additional practice,

Then . . . assign **Practice** Lesson 11.4.

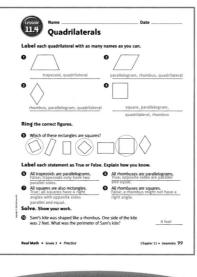

Practice Lesson 11.4

RETEACH

If . . . students struggle with the different types of quadrilaterals,

Then . . . have them work in small groups to draw a quadrilateral and name it. Have each student take turns explaining their reasoning.

Lesson Planner

OBJECTIVES
To provide further experiences in describing, classifying, and identifying polygons not previously covered

NCTM STANDARDS
Geometry
Analyzing characteristics and properties of two- and three-dimensional geometric shapes and developing mathematical arguments about geometric relationships

Connections
Recognizing and using connections among mathematical ideas

MATERIALS
*Response Wheels

TECHNOLOGY
ⓔ **Presentation** Lesson 11.5
Building Blocks **Shapes Part 3**
ⓔ **MathTools** **Shape Tools** or **Geometry Sketch Tools** (Perfect Polygon and Free Polygon)

TEST PREP
Cumulative Review
- Mental Math reviews quadrilaterals (Lesson 11.4).
- Problems 1–5, 12–15, and 20–22 review quadrilaterals (Lesson 11.4).
- Problems 6 and 16 review triangles (Lesson 11.3).

Writing + Math
Journal

Looking Ahead
Durable templates of polygons, circles, and semicircles of various sizes, to be used in Lesson 11.6

Polygons

Context of the Lesson In this lesson, students will explore the umbrella term *polygon*. Many polygons and their properties have been introduced previously in Grade 3, but students will now begin to define shapes according to the number of sides. In Grade 4 students will extend this concept to assist in understanding area, surface area, and space figures.

See page 422B for Math Background for teachers for this lesson.

Planning for Learning ● DIFFERENTIATE INSTRUCTION

INTERVENTION
If . . . students lack the prerequisite skill of identifying shapes,

Then . . . teach **Intervention** Lesson 11.A.

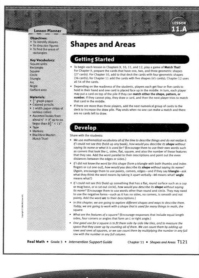

Intervention Lesson 11.A

ENGLISH LEARNER
Preview
If . . . students need language support,

Then . . . use Lesson 11.5 in **English Learner Support Guide** to preview lesson concepts and vocabulary.

English Learner Lesson 11.5

ENRICH
If . . . students are proficient in the lesson concepts,

Then . . . emphasize the Student Pages.

PRACTICE
If . . . students would benefit from additional practice,

Then . . . extend Using Student Pages before assigning the student pages.

RETEACH
If . . . students are having difficulty understanding properties of polygons,

Then . . . extend the use of the **eMathTools: Shape Tools** and **Geometry Sketch Tools** before assigning the student pages.

Vocabulary
polygon \pä´ lē gän´\ *n.* a closed plane figure with three or more line segments as sides
pentagon \pen´ tə gon\ *n.* a polygon with five line segments as sides

hexagon \hek´ sə gon\ *n.* a polygon with six line segments as sides
octagon \ok´ tə gon\ *n.* a polygon with eight line segments as sides

Access Vocabulary
plane a flat surface
octagon an 8-sided figure; the prefix *oct* means *8*

Spanish Cognates
polygon polígono
decagon decágono

Mental Math   5

Determine if the following shapes are quadrilaterals. If they are quadrilaterals, give the thumbs-up signal; if they are not quadrilaterals, give the thumbs-down signal. Use shapes such as the following:

a. triangle down

b. rectangle up

c. trapezoid up

d. square up

e. circle down

f. parallelogram up

1 Develop   25

Tell Students In Today's Lesson They Will

explore further how to describe, classify, and identify polygons not discussed previously.

Guided Discussion   UNDERSTANDING   Whole Group

Students will already be familiar with the polygons covered in previous lessons, such as triangles and quadrilaterals. Draw at least three different figures, and have students identify the figures. These also can be drawn by using the **eMathTools: Shape Tools** or **Geometry Sketch Tool.** Use examples such as the following:

- right triangle
- square
- rectangle
- isosceles triangle
- parallelogram

Have students talk about some of the properties unique to each figure and in common with other figures. (For example, they are made of line segments and angles; triangles have only three line segments; quadrilaterals have four line segments; squares have four right angles.) Introduce to students the phrase *closed plane figure* to describe polygons that have no openings and no overlapping. This phrase appears in the **Student Edition** to describe polygons.

On the board or by using **eMathTools: Shape Tools** and **Geometry Sketch Tool,** draw a *pentagon,* a *hexagon,* and an *octagon.* Have students identify properties for each of the figures and come up with definitions they believe would accurately define the figures.

If you think it is appropriate, show students how these names are derived from the Greek or Latin.

The Greek *Gonia* means "angles."

The Latin *Angulus* means "angle."

Tri is the Latin prefix for "three."

Quad is the Latin prefix for "four."

Penta is the Greek prefix for "five."

Hexa is the Greek prefix for "six."

Hepta is the Greek prefix for "seven."

Octa is the Greek prefix for "eight."

Using Student Pages

Page 438   UNDERSTANDING   Whole Group

Have students open their books to page 438. Go through the definition of *polygon* with students. Have students discuss the pictures and name each of the figures.

Assign Student Pages

20

Page 439 APPLYING

Have students complete the exercises on page 439 independently.

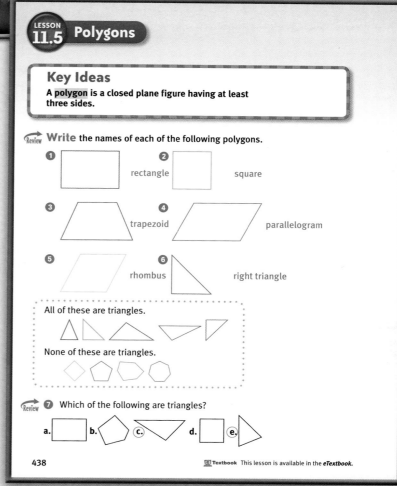

Teaching Lesson 11.5

Assign Student Pages, continued

Pages 440–441 APPLYING

Have students complete the exercises on pages 440 and 441 independently.

> **Monitoring Student Progress**
>
> **If . . .** students have difficulty remembering the names of each of the figures,
>
> **Then . . .** have them make and use flash cards with the word on the front and the definition or picture on the back.

As Students Finish

Building Blocks *Shapes Part 3*

LESSON 11.5 · Polygons

All of these are octagons.

None of these are octagons.

10 Which of the following are octagons?

a.   b.   c.   d.

Predict which shape comes next. Include a drawing and the name of the polygon in your answer.

11 △ ○ □ △ ○ □   ■ triangle

12 △ ⬡ ⬠ ⬡ ⬡   ■ octagon

Review How many of the following polygons can you find in this picture?

13 Squares ■ 6

14 Non-square Rectangles ■ 11

15 Non-rectangular Parallelograms ■ 3

16 Trapezoids ■ 7

17 Triangles ■ 6

440   📖 **Textbook** This lesson is available in the *eTextbook*.

Use the pictures to find the number.

18 Number of sides   5
19 Number of angles   5
20 Name of shape pentagon

21 Number of sides   4
22 Number of angles   4
23 Name of shape   trapezoid

24 Number of sides   6
25 Number of angles   6
26 Name of shape hexagon

27 Number of sides   8
28 Number of angles   8
29 Name of shape octagon

> **Writing + Math** **Journal**
>
> A polygon with ten sides is called a *decagon*. Draw three decagons in your journal that are not all alike.

Chapter 11 • Lesson 5   441

③ **Reflect** 10 ○

Guided Discussion UNDERSTANDING Whole Group

Ask students to think of words they know that use the same prefixes we use to name the polygons (for example, tricycle, triplicate, triple, triplets, quadrangle, quadrant, quad runner, quadruplets, the Pentagon, Pentathalon, Decathalon, and so on). To find other words with which students probably are not familiar, invite students to browse through a good dictionary or go online, noting the many words with the prefixes and their meanings.

 **Journal** REASONING

Accept all drawings of polygons with ten sides.

 Curriculum Connection: Students might be interested in researching other words or creating a list of words with the same prefixes discussed in the Guided Discussion.

 Cumulative Review: For cumulative review of previously learned skills, see page 446–447.

 Family Involvement: Assign the *Practice, Reteach,* or *Enrichment* activities depending on the needs of your students.

Encourage students to find real-world examples of polygons with a friend or a relative.

 Concept/Question Board: Encourage students to continue to post questions, answers, and examples on the Concept/Question Board.

 Math Puzzler: Use the numbers 0–8 to complete this magic square. The sum of each row, column, and diagonal is 12.

7	0	5
2	4	6
3	8	1

4 Assess and Differentiate

 **Assess** Use *eAssess* to record and analyze evidence of student understanding.

A Gather Evidence

Use the Daily Class Assessment Records in *Assessment* or *eAssess* to record daily observations.

Informal Assessment
☑ **Student Pages**

Did the student **APPLYING**
- ☐ apply learning in new situations?
- ☐ contribute concepts?
- ☐ contribute answers?
- ☐ connect mathematics to real-world situations?

Portfolio Assessment
☑ **Journal**

Did the student **REASONING**
- ☐ provide a clear explanation?
- ☐ communicate reasons and strategies?
- ☐ choose appropriate strategies?
- ☐ argue logically?

B Summarize Findings

Analyze and summarize assessment data for each student. Determine which Assessment Follow-Up is appropriate for each student. Use the Student Assessment Record in *Assessment* or *eAssess* to update assessment records.

Student Assessment Record

Assessment Page T41

C Assessment Follow-Up • DIFFERENTIATE INSTRUCTION

Based on your observations, use these teaching strategies for assessment follow-up.

INTERVENTION

Review student performance on *Intervention* Lesson 11.A to see if students have mastered prerequisite skills for this lesson.

ENGLISH LEARNER

Review

Use Lesson 11.5 in *English Learner Support Guide* to review lesson concepts and vocabulary.

ENRICH

If . . . students are proficient in the lesson concepts,

Then . . . encourage them to work on chapter projects or *Enrichment* Lesson 11.5.

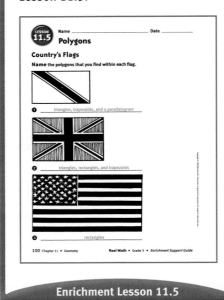

Enrichment Lesson 11.5

PRACTICE

If . . . students would benefit from additional practice,

Then . . . assign *Practice* Lesson 11.5.

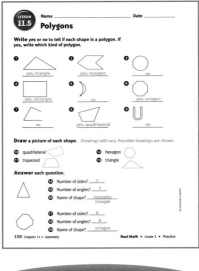

Practice Lesson 11.5

RETEACH

If . . . students struggle with recognizing shapes,

Then . . . have them go around the room and label different polygons that they recognize. Encourage them to find shapes with more than three or four sides. Students can also find examples of polygons outside the classroom and bring in drawings.

Lesson Planner

OBJECTIVES
- To introduce the concept of congruency
- To provide practice in determining whether two figures are congruent

NCTM STANDARDS

Geometry
- Exploring congruence and similarity
- Recognizing geometric ideas and relationships and applying them to other disciplines and to problems that arise in the classroom or everyday life

Connections
Recognizing and using connections among mathematical ideas

MATERIALS
- *Response Wheels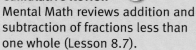
- Template of polygons, circles, and semicircles of various sizes
- *Pattern Blocks (optional)
- Student scissors
- Multiple colors of construction paper
- Square or rectangular unlined paper of various sizes

TECHNOLOGY
- **Presentation** Lesson 11.6
- **Building Blocks** Shapes Part 5
- **MathTools** Geometry Sketch Tools

TEST PREP

Cumulative Review
Mental Math reviews addition and subtraction of fractions less than one whole (Lesson 8.7).

Congruence

Context of the Lesson Congruence and similarity were introduced informally in Grade 2. In this lesson students will explore real-world applications and preview *slides, flips,* and *turns.* In Grade 4 students will continue to use the properties of congruency.

See page 422B for Math Background for teachers for this lesson.

Planning for Learning ● DIFFERENTIATE INSTRUCTION

INTERVENTION

If . . . students lack the prerequisite skill of describing figures,

Then . . . teach *Intervention* Lesson 11.B.

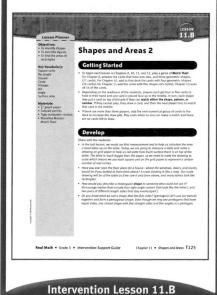

Intervention Lesson 11.B

ENGLISH LEARNER

Preview

If . . . students need language support,

Then . . . use Lesson 11.6 in *English Learner Support Guide* to preview lesson concepts and vocabulary.

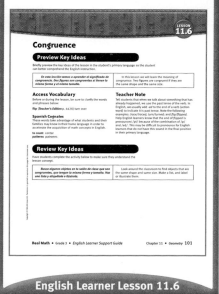

English Learner Lesson 11.6

ENRICH

If . . . students are proficient in the lesson concepts,

Then . . . emphasize the student pages.

PRACTICE

If . . . students would benefit from additional practice,

Then . . . extend Strategy and Skill Building before assigning the student pages.

RETEACH

If . . . students are having difficulty understanding congruence,

Then . . . extend Guided Discussion before assigning the student pages.

Vocabulary
congruent \kən grü´ ənt\ *adj.* figures that are the same size and same shape; that is, they fit perfectly when one is placed on top of the other

Access Vocabulary
flip turn over

Spanish Cognates
to count contar
patterns patrones

Mental Math 10

  Review basic addition and subtraction of fractions less than one whole with like denominators. Have students represent the fraction bar with their finger. The answers do not have to be in lowest terms. Use examples such as the following:

a. $\frac{1}{2} + \frac{1}{2}$ $\frac{2}{2}$ or 1

b. $\frac{1}{4} + \frac{2}{4}$ $\frac{3}{4}$

c. $\frac{3}{8} - \frac{3}{8}$ 0

d. $\frac{5}{10} - \frac{3}{10}$ $\frac{2}{10}$ or $\frac{1}{5}$

e. $\frac{1}{6} + \frac{1}{6}$ $\frac{2}{6}$ or $\frac{1}{3}$

f. $\frac{2}{3} - \frac{1}{3}$ $\frac{1}{3}$

g. $\frac{4}{9} + \frac{3}{9}$ $\frac{7}{9}$

h. $\frac{5}{12} + \frac{6}{12}$ $\frac{11}{12}$

1 Develop 25

Tell Students In Today's Lesson They Will

explore congruency and practice determining whether two figures are congruent.

Guided Discussion UNDERSTANDING

Whole Group

On the board or overhead projector, or using the *eMathTools: Geometry Sketch Tools,* draw two circles of the same size, two triangles of the same size and shape, and two rectangles of the same size and shape. Have the triangles and rectangles be rotations or flips of each other. Point to both circles, and state that the circles are *congruent*. Point to the triangles and the rectangles, and identify both sets as *congruent*. Have students provide a definition of *congruent*.

After students demonstrate a working understanding of congruence, draw on the board or overhead projector a polygon, circle, or a semicircle of any size. Have students come up and draw a congruent shape, creating as many variations as possible. Note that any way a circle is transformed, it results in a congruent circle. Although the terms are not introduced at this time, it might be a good time to introduce that some of the shapes have been flipped, slid, or turned to make a congruent shape. Transformations will be discussed in Lesson 11.7.

Strategy and Skill Building   APPLYING

Small Group

Prepare in advance durable templates of polygons, circles, and semicircles of various sizes. It might be helpful to use pattern blocks to get variety in sizes. These templates are to assist students in creating collages of "congruent" faces, bodies, animals, and so on. Students should trace and cut out pairs of congruent shapes from colored construction paper and attach them on another sheet of construction paper. For example, a face can be made with two circles for the eyes, two semicircles for the ears, a triangle for the nose, and a congruent triangle for the beard. Bodies can be made in a similar fashion, using triangles, circles, rectangles, and other shapes for torsos, arms, legs, and so on. A butterfly could be made using two large congruent semicircles for the top wings, two smaller semicircles for the bottom wings, two triangles for the antennae, and congruent small circles or other shapes for the designs on the wings.

2 Assign Student Pages 15

Pages 442–443 APPLYING

Have students complete the exercises on pages 442 and 443 independently.

As Students Finish

Building Blocks *Shapes Part 5*

 **Congruence**

Key Ideas

Two figures are congruent if they are the same shape and the same size.

You can check to see if two figures are congruent by tracing one figure and seeing if the tracing fits on top of the other figure. Flip the tracing paper to see that these two right triangles are congruent.

Look at the figures. Use tracing paper if needed to help you see which are congruent. List each pair of congruent figures. *b* and *e* are congruent; *c* and *f* are congruent

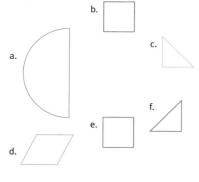

442   Textbook This lesson is available in the *eTextbook*.

List each pair of congruent figures. *c* and *h* are congruent; *a* and *d* are congruent; *b* and *e* are congruent

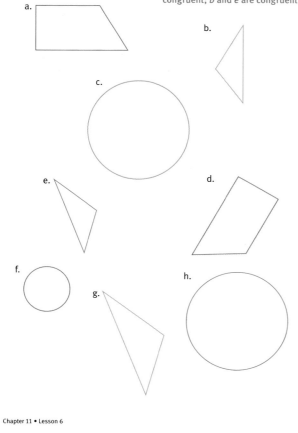

---

3 Reflect   10

Guided Discussion UNDERSTANDING   Small Group

Have students point to and identify congruent figures that are found in everyday life. Some examples would be packaged foods, tires of the same size on a vehicle, bricks in a wall, and so on. After these items have been identified, ask students why it would be important to have congruent objects. otherwise the car would wobble, boxes wouldn't stack, and so on

Curriculum Connection: Students might be interested in researching how M. C. Escher used congruent shapes to create his tessellation art.

Cumulative Review: For cumulative review of previously learned skills, see page 446–447.

Family Involvement: Assign the *Practice, Reteach,* or *Enrichment* activities depending on the needs of your students.

Encourage students to find various real-world examples of congruent shapes with a friend or a relative.

Concept/Question Board: Encourage students to continue to post questions, answers, and examples on the Concept/Question Board.

Math Puzzler: Luke is arranging his bottle collection. When he puts the bottles in groups of 8, he has 3 left over. When he puts them in groups of 5, he has 2 left over. When he puts them in groups of 3, he has none left over. He has fewer than 30 bottles. How many bottles does he have? 27

4 Assess and Differentiate

 Assess Use **eAssess** to record and analyze evidence of student understanding.

A Gather Evidence

Use the Daily Class Assessment Records in **Assessment** or **eAssess** to record daily observations.

Informal Assessment

✔ **Strategy and Skill Building**

Did the student **APPLYING**
- ❑ apply learning in new situations?
- ❑ contribute concepts?
- ❑ contribute answers?
- ❑ connect mathematics to real-world situations?

Informal Assessment

✔ **Guided Discussion**

Did the student **UNDERSTANDING**
- ❑ make important observations?
- ❑ extend or generalize learning?
- ❑ provide insightful answers?
- ❑ pose insightful questions?

B Summarize Findings

Analyze and summarize assessment data for each student. Determine which Assessment Follow-Up is appropriate for each student. Use the Student Assessment Record in **Assessment** or **eAssess** to update assessment records.

Assessment Page T41

C Assessment Follow-Up • DIFFERENTIATE INSTRUCTION

Based on your observations, use these teaching strategies for assessment follow-up.

INTERVENTION	ENRICH	PRACTICE	RETEACH
Review student performance on **Intervention** Lesson 11.B to see if students have mastered prerequisite skills for this lesson.	**If . . .** students are proficient in the lesson concepts, **Then . . .** encourage them to work on chapter projects or **Enrichment** Lesson 11.6.	**If . . .** students would benefit from additional practice, **Then . . .** assign **Practice** Lesson 11.6.	**If . . .** students struggle with determining if figures are congruent, **Then . . .** have them work in small groups and use pegboards with bands or dot paper to make figures. Have the other students make a figure congruent to the original.

ENGLISH LEARNER

Review

Use Lesson 11.6 in **English Learner Support Guide** to review lesson concepts and vocabulary.

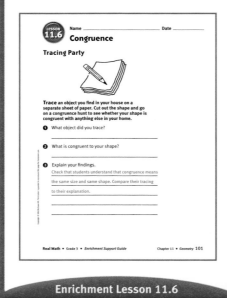

Enrichment Lesson 11.6

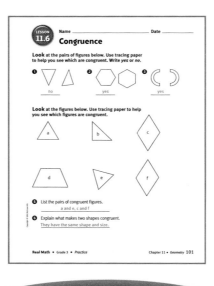

Practice Lesson 11.6

CHAPTER 11 Problem Solving

Exploring Problem Solving

Objectives
- To analyze the problem-solving strategies Use Simple Numbers, Look for a Pattern, Make a Table, and Make a Physical Model
- To provide experience solving a nonroutine problem involving patterns of geometric figures
- To provide additional opportunities to connect arithmetic and geometry

Materials
Triangle tiles or triangle dot paper, if available

Context of the Lesson This lesson builds on previous problem-solving lessons by providing more opportunity for students to spend extended time solving nonroutine problems and sharing their solution methods. This lesson also continues the theme of homes introduced in the Chapter Introduction.

1 Develop 5

Tell Students In Today's Lesson They Will
- read a problem about decorating their wall with triangle tiles.
- look at how two students are trying two different ways to solve the problem.
- solve the problem themselves and share how they solved it.

2 Exploring Problem Solving 30

Using Student Pages
Read the problem on page 444 with the class. To make sure students understand it, ask questions such as the following:

- **What is going on in the problem?** We are planning a wall design made from triangle tiles.
- **What are you supposed to find out?** how high the design will be
- **Can the design be any shape?** No, it must be in the triangle pattern shown.
- **Do you have to use every tile?** no, but we want to make the design as tall as possible
- **How many tiles will be in the top row?** 1
- **How many tiles will be in the row under that?** 3
- **How would you try to solve the problem?** Encourage students to suggest different methods.

Exploring Problem Solving

Do you remember designing your own room or house on page 423? Now you are going to decorate one of the walls. You will use triangle tiles in a pattern like the one shown at the right. You have 10 boxes of tiles with 25 tiles in each box. Each tile is 3 inches high. How high can you make your tile design?

3 inches

Jasmine started to solve the problem by making a physical model.

My Plan
1. Cut out 250 triangle pieces.
2. Build a design like the one in the picture, only bigger.

Think about Jasmine's strategy. Answer the following questions.

1 Why did Jasmine decide to make 250 triangles?
That's how many tiles there are; $10 \times 25 = 250$.
2 Do Jasmine's triangles have to be 3 inches high? Explain.

3 Would you use Jasmine's strategy to solve the problem? Explain.
Students should see that Jasmine's strategy would take a long time to carry out.

2 no; As long as they are all about the same size, she can use them to determine how many rows high the design can be.

444   Textbook This lesson is available in the eTextbook.

Javier used simple numbers, made a table, and looked for a pattern to solve the problem.

My Plan
1. Draw the design with just a few tiles. Record the results in a table.
2. Look for a pattern.
3. Use the pattern to find how big the design can be with 250 tiles.

Design	Number of Rows in the Design	Number of Tiles Used
	1	1
	2	1+3=4
	3	

Think about Javier's strategy. Answer the following questions.

4 What equation do you think Javier is about to write? $1 + 3 + 5 = 9$
5 How many tiles will be in the design if it has 4 rows? 16
6 How many complete rows can be made with 15 tiles? 3
7 What pattern do you see in the number of tiles in each row?
Ways of expressing the pattern will vary. For example, each row has 2 more tiles than the row above it.

Chapter 11 • Exploring Problem Solving   445

Analyzing Sample Solution 1

Guide students through Jasmine's strategy by discussing Problems 1–3. In discussion, bring out the following points:

- Making a physical model can be a useful way to understand and visualize what is going on.
- Jasmine's plan to cut out 250 tiles is a very tedious way to solve the problem even though it can eventually lead to the correct answer.

Analyzing Sample Solution 2

Guide students through Javier's strategy by discussing Problems 4–7. In discussion, bring out these points:

- Because the sides of the design are straight lines, it makes sense that the length of the rows keeps changing by the same amount from one row to the next. It is logical to look for and use a simple pattern.
- Strategies such as Use Simple Numbers, Draw a Diagram, Make a Physical Model, Make a Table, and Look for a Pattern are often very useful when combined to suit the particular problem being worked on. In this problem, Javier's diagrams helped him visualize the designs and count tiles; the table helped him keep track of the numbers and see the pattern; and the pattern helped him find out how many rows he could make.

Have students work in pairs or small groups to solve the problem using any strategies they like. Provide help as needed. Commend students who persist when they are stuck. Students should determine that there are enough tiles to make 15 rows, which would form a design 45 inches high.

Effective Communication Have each group present its answers and methods. In discussion, bring out the following points:

- Patterns can be useful in solving problems, but students should be careful that if they extend a pattern, it makes sense to do so. As an example, consider 3 people in line at a movie theater. The first is 8 years old, the second is 9 years old, and the third is 10 years old. That does not mean that the next person getting in line will be 11 years old.
- It is important to check not only that a solution makes sense, but that it answers the question asked. In this problem, even though students will likely spend most of their time finding the number of rows, they also need to report the total height of the design.
- If a strategy such as Jasmine's seems particularly tedious, it is worth taking a little time to try to come up with a plan that is easier to carry out.

Sample Solutions Strategies

Students might use the following strategies instead of or in combination with the strategies presented on pages 444 and 445.

Make a Diagram

Some students might use a more efficient version of Jasmine's strategy by drawing the entire design instead of trying to build it.

Find a (Different) Pattern

An alert and advanced student might recognize the "square number" pattern that develops in Javier's table as it is continued: 1, 4, 9, 16, and so on. They may see that the number of tiles in a design is equal to the number of rows times itself. Then they might guess and check to find what number times itself would be close to but not greater than 250.

When evaluating student work, focus on whether students thought rationally about the problem. Questions to consider include the following:

- Did the student understand the problem?
- Did the student understand the Sample Solutions Strategies and see how to continue using them?
- Could the student explain his or her strategy?

Cumulative Review

Assign Pages 446–447

Use the Cumulative Review as a review of concepts and skills that students have previously learned.

Here are different ways you can assign these problems to your students as they work through the chapter:

- With some of the lessons in the chapter, assign a set of Cumulative Review problems to be completed as practice or for homework.
  Lesson 11.1—Problems 1–3
  Lesson 11.2—Problems 4–9
  Lesson 11.3—Problems 10–11
  Lesson 11.4—Problems 12–16
  Lesson 11.5—Problems 17–21
  Lesson 11.6—Problems 22–25
- At any point during the chapter, assign part or all of the Cumulative Review problems to be completed as practice or for homework.

Cumulative Review

Problems 1–3 review conversions of customary length, Lesson 9.2.

Problems 4–9 review percents and hundredths, Lesson 8.11.

Problems 10–11 review multiplying three-digit numbers by one-digit numbers, Lesson 7.3.

Problems 12–16 review finding the perimeter, Lesson 3.6.

Problems 17–21 review decimals and metric measures, Lesson 10.3.

Problems 22–25 review equivalent fractions, Lesson 8.5.

Monitoring Student Progress

If . . . students miss more than one problem in a section,

Then . . . refer to the indicated lesson for remediation suggestions.

Cumulative Review

Customary Length Lesson 9.2

Answer the following questions.

1 Mrs. Jiménez has a window that is 64 inches wide. How many feet is that? $5\frac{1}{3}$ feet

2 She wants to make 9-foot-long curtains for the window. How many yards is that? 3 yards

3 Hannah is making beanbag chairs with 12 yards of fabric. How many feet is that? 36 feet

Percents and Hundredths Lesson 8.11

Write the fraction for each percent.

4 53% $\frac{53}{100}$ **7** 88% $\frac{88}{100}$

5 18% $\frac{18}{100}$ **8** 100% $\frac{100}{100}$, or 1

6 22% $\frac{22}{100}$ **9** 79% $\frac{79}{100}$

Multiplying Three-Digit Numbers by One-Digit Numbers Lesson 7.3

Solve. Be sure to label your answers correctly.

10 In one week's time, Alejandra and her 4 sisters each planted 235 tulip bulbs. How many tulip bulbs did the girls plant altogether? 1,175 tulip bulbs

11 Mr. Norman is an ornithologist. He loves to study birds. He studied 187 bird species each week for 4 weeks. How many bird species did he study altogether? 748 bird species

Textbook This lesson is available in the *eTextbook*.

Perimeter Lesson 3.6

Find the perimeter of each figure.

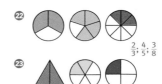

12 Perimeter: ▨ centimeters 22

13 Perimeter: ▨ centimeters 12

14 Perimeter: ▨ centimeters 8

15 Perimeter: ▨ centimeters 6

16 Perimeter: ▨ centimeters 12

Decimals and Metric Measures Lesson 10.3

Answer these questions.

17 How many decimeters are in 4 meters? 40

18 How many decimeters are in 3.5 meters? 35

19 How many meters are in 65 decimeters? 6.5

20 How many decimeters are in 5.7 meters? 57

21 How many decimeters are in 21 meters? 210

Equivalent Fractions Lesson 8.5

What fraction of each figure is shaded?

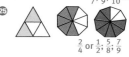

22 $\frac{2}{3}$; $\frac{4}{5}$; $\frac{3}{8}$

23 $\frac{2}{2}$ or 1; $\frac{2}{6}$ or $\frac{1}{3}$; $\frac{1}{4}$

24 $\frac{3}{7}$; $\frac{1}{9}$; $\frac{5}{10}$ or $\frac{1}{2}$

25 $\frac{2}{4}$ or $\frac{1}{2}$; $\frac{5}{8}$; $\frac{7}{9}$

Individual Oral Assessment

Purpose of the Test

The Individual Oral Assessment is designed to measure students' growing knowledge of chapter concepts. It is administered individually to each student, and it requires oral responses from each student. The test takes about five minutes to complete. See *Assessment* for detailed instructions for administering and interpreting the test, and record students' answers on the Student Assessment Recording Sheet.

Assessment Page T37

Directions

Read each question to the student, and record his or her oral response. If the student answers correctly, go to the next question. Stop when the student misses two questions at the same level. Students may use paper and pencil to solve the starred items.

Materials

None

Questions

Level 1: Prerequisite

1. How many sides does a square have? 4
2. How many sides does a triangle have? 3
3. How many sides does a rectangle have? 4
4. How many angles does a triangle have? 3

Level 2: Basic

5. (Show a ray.) What is the name of this figure? ray
*6. Draw two parallel lines. Check that the student's lines are an equal distance apart.
*7. Draw two lines that are not parallel. Check that the student's lines will meet at some point.
8. (Show perpendicular lines.) What kind of lines are these? perpendicular

Level 3: At Level

9. (Show a triangle, a rectangle, a circle, and a square.) Which of these shapes are quadrilaterals? rectangle and square
10. (Show an equilateral triangle.) What kind of triangle is this? equilateral
11. (Show a pentagon.) What is the name of this shape? pentagon
12. How many sides does a hexagon have? 6

Level 4: Challenge Application

13. How many sides does an octagon have? 8
14. What is a parallelogram? a four-sided figure with opposite sides that are parallel
*15. Draw an acute angle. Accept any angle less than 90°.
*16. Draw an obtuse angle. Accept any angle more than 90°.

Level 5: Content Beyond Mid-Chapter

17. What is the measure of a straight angle? 180°
18. What does *congruent* mean? the same as
*19. Draw two congruent squares. Squares should be the same size.
20. What is the straight line that cuts a circle into two equal pieces called? diameter

Lesson Planner

OBJECTIVES
- To explore slides, flips, and turns
- To introduce the words translations, reflections, and rotations

NCTM STANDARDS
Geometry
Predicting and describing the results of sliding, flipping, and turning two-dimensional shapes

Communication
Using the language of mathematics to express mathematical ideas precisely

MATERIALS
*Response Wheels

TECHNOLOGY
⒠Presentation Lesson 11.7
Building Blocks Geometry Snapshots 3
⒠MathTools Geometry Sketch Tools
(Rotate Tool) and **Shape Tools**

TEST PREP
Cumulative Review
Mental Math reviews multiplication facts (Chapter 5).

Multistep Problems
Problems 5–8

Writing + Math
Journal

*Manipulative Kit Item

Slides, Flips, and Turns

Context of the Lesson *Slides, flips,* and *turns* were introduced informally in Grade 2 and in Grade 3, Lesson 11.6. Students will explore the formal vocabulary of transformations in this lesson. In Grade 4 students will apply the concept of transformations to objects on a coordinate grid.

See page 422B for Math Background for teachers for this lesson.

Planning for Learning ● DIFFERENTIATE INSTRUCTION

INTERVENTION
If . . . students lack the prerequisite skill of describing figures,

Then . . . teach *Intervention* Lesson 11.B.

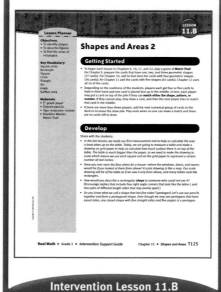

Intervention Lesson 11.B

ENGLISH LEARNER
Preview
If . . . students need language support,

Then . . . use Lesson 11.7 in *English Learner Support Guide* to preview lesson concepts and vocabulary.

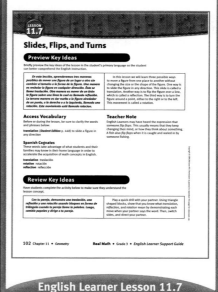

English Learner Lesson 11.7

ENRICH
If . . . students are proficient in the lesson concepts,

Then . . . emphasize the student pages.

PRACTICE
If . . . students would benefit from additional practice,

Then . . . extend Guided Discussion before assigning the student pages.

RETEACH
If . . . students are having difficulty understanding slides, flips, and turns,

Then . . . extend Guided Discussion before assigning the student pages.

Vocabulary
translation \tranz la′ shən\ *n.* a change in the location of a figure when it slides without being turned
reflection \ri flek′ shən\ *n.* a change in the location of a figure when it is flipped over a line

rotation \rō tā′ shən\ *n.* a change in the location of a figure when it is turned in a circle path around a point

Access Vocabulary
translation to slide a figure in any direction

Spanish Cognates
translation traslación
rotation rotación
reflection reflección

Mental Math 5

  Have students review basic multiplication facts. Use examples such as the following:

a. 5 × 5 = 25   **e.** 0 × 0 = 0
b. 3 × 8 = 24   **f.** 10 × 10 = 100
c. 9 × 4 = 36   **g.** 7 × 5 = 35
d. 11 × 0 = 0   **h.** 1 × 9 = 9

1 Develop 25

Tell Students In Today's Lesson They Will

explore slides, flips, and turns and be introduced to the formal names for those transformations.

Guided Discussion UNDERSTANDING   Whole Group

On the board or overhead projector, or by using *eMathTools: Geometry Sketch Tools,* draw a non-isosceles trapezoid of good size. Have students identify the shape and any properties of the trapezoid. To the right of this shape, draw a congruent trapezoid. Ask students questions about the two trapezoids such as the following:

- **Are these two trapezoids congruent?** yes
- **Is the second trapezoid facing a different direction?** no
- **What is different between the two trapezoids?** The second one has been slid over.

If students do not suggest it, mention that the second trapezoid has slid away from the first. Introduce the word *translation.* Draw another shape of any kind, and have a student come up and draw the same shape but slid up. Have another student draw a translation to the left and a fourth student draw a translation down. Have students show translations that are not horizontal or vertical.

On the board or overhead projector, or by using *eMathTools: Geometry Sketch Tools,* draw a trapezoid of good size, but the left side of the trapezoid should be a perpendicular side to the base. To the right of this shape draw another trapezoid, but reflect it over an invisible vertical line.

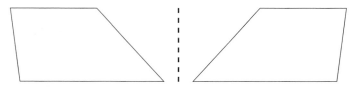

Ask students questions about the two trapezoids such as the following:

- **Are these two trapezoids congruent?** yes
- **Is the second trapezoid facing a different direction?** yes
- **What is different between the two trapezoids?** The second one has been flipped or reflected.

If students do not suggest it, mention that the second trapezoid has been reflected, like a mirror image, over an invisible line. It might help to draw in the *line* of symmetry with a dotted line to help with clarity and visualization. Introduce the word *reflection.* Draw another shape of any kind, and have a student come up and draw the same shape but reflect it up. Have another student draw a reflection to the left and a fourth student draw a reflection down.

On the board or overhead projector, or by using *eMathTools: Geometry Sketch Tools,* draw a trapezoid of good size, but the left side of the trapezoid should be a perpendicular side to the base. Then draw the figure as it would appear if rotated 90° clockwise around the lower left vertex (or corner).

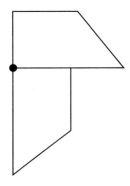

Ask students questions about the two trapezoids such as the following:

- **Are these two trapezoids congruent?** yes
- **Is the second trapezoid facing a different direction?** yes
- **What is different between the two trapezoids?** The second one has been rotated or turned.

If students do not suggest it, mention that the second trapezoid has been rotated like turning a doorknob or like the hands on a clock. Introduce the word *rotation.* Draw another shape of any kind, and have a student come up and draw the same shape but rotate it 180° (half a full turn). Have another student draw a rotation 90° counterclockwise (one quarter of a full turn). Ask students if there can be a rotation completely around the main point. If they answer yes, have them draw it. The rotated figure should look identical to the original figure. It is important to note with students that in a rotation, the shape rotates around one main point, often a vertex on the shape.

2 Assign Student Pages 20

Pages 448–449 APPLYING

Have students complete the exercises on pages 448 and 449 independently.

As Students Finish

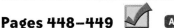 *Geometry Snapshots 3*

Student Page

LESSON 11.7 Slides, Flips, and Turns

Key Ideas

There are three ways to move a figure from one place to another without changing the size or the shape of the figure.

One way is to *slide* the figure in any direction. Another name for a slide is translation.

A second way is to *flip* the figure over a line. Another name for a flip is reflection.

A third way is to *turn* the figure around a point, either to the right or to the left. Another name for a turn is rotation.

Translations, reflections, and rotations are also called transformations. These transformations can also be combined.

448   📖 Textbook This lesson is available in the *eTextbook*.

Student Page

Look closely at each change. Determine if the change was due to a *translation,* a *reflection,* or a *rotation.*

❶
rotation

❸
translation

❷

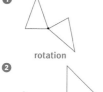
translation

❹
reflection

📎 **Describe** the change from one position to the other for the figure.
Multistep

❺
one possible answer: reflection and translation

❼
translation and rotation

❻
one possible answer: rotation and translation

❽
reflection and translation

Writing + Math ➤ Journal
Trace this triangle. Then draw a picture of this triangle after it is reflected and then rotated any amount.

---

3 Reflect   10 🕐

Guided Discussion UNDERSTANDING   Whole Group

Have students come to the board or overhead projector to draw their solutions to the journal exercise. Discuss the differences and similarities between the answers. Will they be able to rotate it enough to look exactly like the first triangle? If they answer yes, then have them come up and demonstrate.

If time allows, compare the results of reflecting then rotating to rotating *then* reflecting.

🔗 Problems 7–10

Writing + Math ➤ Journal ✔️ REASONING

📎 **Cumulative Review:** For cumulative review of previously learned skills, see page 467–468.

🎒 **Family Involvement:** Assign the **Practice, Reteach,** or **Enrichment** activities depending on the needs of your students.

Encourage students to find real-world examples of transformations with a friend or a relative.

📋 **Concept/Question Board:** Encourage students to continue to post questions, answers, and examples on the Concept/Question Board.

🧩 **Math Puzzler:** Sam goes to pottery class every other day. Ms. Watson goes every third day. They are both at the class on June 5th. What other days in June will they be in class together?
June 11, 17, 23, and 29

Assess and Differentiate

 Assess Use *eAssess* to record and analyze evidence of student understanding.

A Gather Evidence

Use the Daily Class Assessment Records in *Assessment* or *eAssess* to record daily observations.

Informal Assessment
✓ **Student Pages**

Did the student **APPLYING**
- ❏ apply learning in new situations?
- ❏ contribute concepts?
- ❏ contribute answers?
- ❏ connect mathematics to real-world situations?

Portfolio Assessment
✓ **Journal**

Did the student **REASONING**
- ❏ provide a clear explanation?
- ❏ communicate reasons and strategies?
- ❏ choose appropriate strategies?
- ❏ argue logically?

B Summarize Findings

Analyze and summarize assessment data for each student. Determine which Assessment Follow-Up is appropriate for each student. Use the Student Assessment Record in *Assessment* or *eAssess* to update assessment records.

Assessment Page T41

C Assessment Follow-Up ● DIFFERENTIATE INSTRUCTION

Based on your observations, use these teaching strategies for assessment follow-up.

INTERVENTION
Review student performance on *Intervention* Lesson 11.B to see if students have mastered prerequisite skills for this lesson.

ENGLISH LEARNER
Review

Use Lesson 11.7 in *English Learner Support Guide* to review lesson concepts and vocabulary.

ENRICH
If . . . students are proficient in the lesson concepts,

Then . . . encourage them to work on chapter projects or *Enrichment* Lesson 11.7.

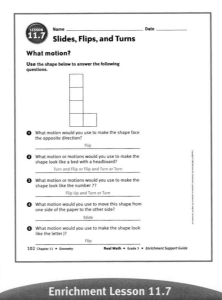

Enrichment Lesson 11.7

PRACTICE
If . . . students would benefit from additional practice,

Then . . . assign *Practice* Lesson 11.7.

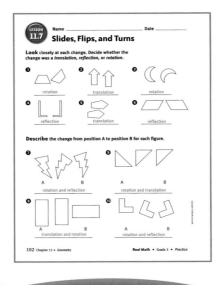

Practice Lesson 11.7

RETEACH
If . . . students struggle with recognizing slips, slides, and turns,

Then . . . have them trace each figure and cut it out. Then have them perform each of the transformations and trace and label the result. Have students test each other on which transformation was applied.

Lesson Planner

OBJECTIVES
- To introduce the concepts of symmetry and line of symmetry
- To provide practice with drawing lines of symmetry

NCTM STANDARDS
Geometry
Identifying and describing line symmetry in two-dimensional shapes and designs

Communication
Using the language of mathematics to express mathematical ideas precisely

MATERIALS
- *Response Wheels
- Tracing paper
- Small mirrors

TECHNOLOGY
- **Presentation** Lesson 11.8
- **Building Blocks** Shapes Part 5
- **MathTools** Geometry Tools or Shape Tools

TEST PREP
Cumulative Review
Mental Math reviews metric measurements (Chapter 10).

Writing + Math
Journal

Symmetry

Context of the Lesson Students have been informally introduced to symmetry in Grade 2 when exploring reflections. In this lesson students will take their intuitive understanding of symmetry and apply it in real-world and geometric situations. *Symmetry* is a concept that will be introduced in this lesson and further explored in Grade 4.

Se pages 422B for Math Background for teachers for this lesson.

Planning for Learning ● DIFFERENTIATE INSTRUCTION

INTERVENTION
If . . . students lack the prerequisite skill of identifying shapes,

Then . . . teach *Intervention* Lesson 11.A.

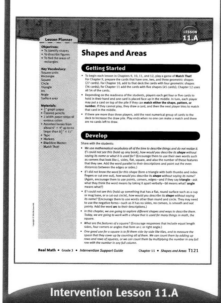

Intervention Lesson 11.A

ENGLISH LEARNER
Preview

If . . . students need language support,

Then . . . use Lesson 11.8 in *English Learner Support Guide* to preview lesson concepts and vocabulary.

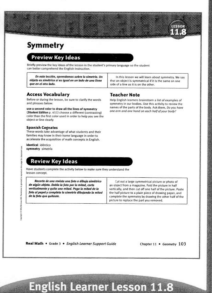

English Learner Lesson 11.8

ENRICH
If . . . students are proficient in the lesson concepts,

Then . . . emphasize the student pages.

PRACTICE
If . . . students would benefit from additional practice,

Then . . . extend Using Student Pages before assigning the student pages.

RETEACH
If . . . students are having difficulty understanding symmetry,

Then . . . extend Guided Discussion before assigning the student pages.

Vocabulary
symmetry \sim' i trē\ *n.* having the same size and shape across a dividing line
line of symmetry *n.* a line on which a figure can be folded into two congruent parts

Spanish Cognates
identical idéntico
symmetry simetría

Mental Math 10

Have students determine if the statements involving metric measurements are true or false. Show thumbs-up if the statement is true and thumbs-down if the statement is false. Use statements such as the following:

a. 100 cm = 1 meter up

b. 100 cm = 1 kilometer down

c. 100 meters = 1 kilometer down

d. 1 cm > 1 meter down

e. 1 meter < 1 km up

f. 1 meter = 1 km down

g. 1,000 meters = 1 km up

1 Develop 25

Tell Students In Today's Lesson They Will
explore symmetry and lines of symmetry.

Guided Discussion

On the board, draw a basic picture of a butterfly with two large top wings, two small bottom wings, and two antennae. Have students identify the butterfly and describe it. Next, draw a basic face with two eyes, one nose, one mouth, and two ears. Then have students identify the picture and describe it. Last, draw an asymmetric tree of any kind with various leaves or fruits on it. Have students identify the picture and describe it. Write on the board the word *symmetric*. Point out to students that two of the pictures on the board are symmetric and one is not. Tell them you are going to draw two more symmetric pictures on the board. Use examples such as the following:

- a T-shirt
- hearts
- stars
- a pine tree

Go back to the original butterfly, and draw a line down the middle of the butterfly. Refer to this line as the *line of symmetry,* and point out that the butterfly has only one line of symmetry. Have volunteers come to the board to draw the lines of symmetry for the rest of the symmetric items. Discuss with students why the asymmetric tree will *not* have a line of symmetry.

Using Student Pages APPLYING Whole Group

Have students open their books to page 450. Go over the definition of *symmetrical* for clarification. Have students explain why each of the figures in Problems 1 and 2 has a line of symmetry but the figure in Problem 3 does not.

2 Assign Student Pages 20

Pages 450–451 APPLYING

Have students complete the exercises on page 451. If mirrors are not available, begin by having students trace the figure on one side of the line of symmetry. Then have them flip the tracing paper over and match up the lines of symmetry. The figures should fit together.

Monitoring Student Progress

If . . . students have difficulty finding the lines of symmetry,

Then . . . have them trace the figure and fold the shape on the line of symmetry or use mirrors. The sides should match if the shape is symmetric.

LESSON 11.8 Symmetry

Key Ideas

An object is symmetric if it looks the same on one side of a line as it does on the other.

If you can trace the part of a figure on one side of a line and flip the tracing so it fits on the other half of the figure, the figure is symmetric about that line.

The flip line is the line of symmetry.

All lines of symmetry have been drawn in the following figures. Notice there is no line of symmetry for the third figure.

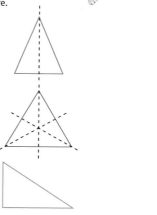

450   Textbook This lesson is available in the *eTextbook*.

Copy the figures on your paper. Use a second color to draw all the lines of symmetry.

❶

❷ no line of symmetry

❸

❹

❺

❻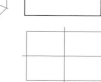

Assign Student Pages, continued

Pages 452–453 **APPLYING**

Have students complete the exercises on pages 452 and 453 independently.

As Students Finish

Building Blocks *Shapes Part 5*

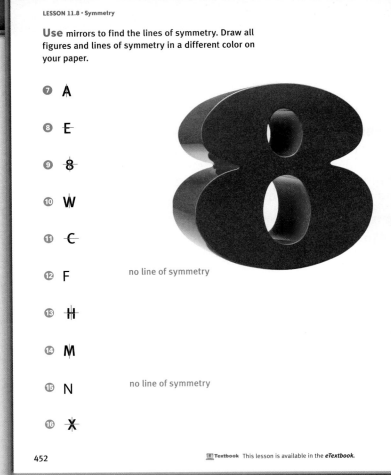

LESSON 11.8 • Symmetry

Use mirrors to find the lines of symmetry. Draw all figures and lines of symmetry in a different color on your paper.

7. A

8. E

9. 8

10. W

11. C

12. F

13. H

14. M

15. N — no line of symmetry

16. X

no line of symmetry

452   Textbook This lesson is available in the *eTextbook*.

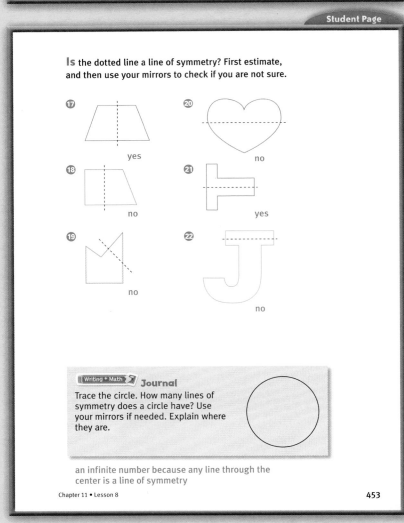

Is the dotted line a line of symmetry? First estimate, and then use your mirrors to check if you are not sure.

17. yes

20. no

18. no

21. yes

19. no

22. no

Writing + Math Journal

Trace the circle. How many lines of symmetry does a circle have? Use your mirrors if needed. Explain where they are.

an infinite number because any line through the center is a line of symmetry

Chapter 11 • Lesson 8   453

Reflect 5

Guided Discussion **UNDERSTANDING** Whole Group

Challenge students to identify where in real life they are likely to run into examples of symmetry or near symmetry; for example, in architecture, in nature (leaves and plants), in English words (such as MOM, BOB, OHIO, HOOD, and WOW), and so on. It should be noted that MOM and WOW have vertical symmetry and BOB, OHIO, and HOOD have horizontal symmetry.

 **Journal** **REASONING**

A circle has an infinite number of lines of symmetry all through the center of the circle.

 Curriculum Connection: Students might be interested in researching how nature uses symmetry, such as butterflies, snowflakes, our bodies, and so on.

 Cumulative Review: For cumulative review of previously learned skills, see page 467–468.

 Family Involvement: Assign the *Practice, Reteach,* or *Enrichment* activities depending on the needs of your students.

Encourage students to find various real-world examples of symmetry with a friend or a relative.

 Concept/Question Board: Encourage students to continue to post questions, answers, and examples on the Concept/Question Board.

 Math Puzzler: Print your name. How many letters in your name have a line of symmetry? Answers will vary depending on students' names. For example, in the word *MATT*, all four letters have symmetry, but only the *I* in *LIZ* has symmetry.

4 Assess and Differentiate

e Assess Use **eAssess** to record and analyze evidence of student understanding.

A Gather Evidence

Use the Daily Class Assessment Records in **Assessment** or **eAssess** to record daily observations.

Informal Assessment

☑ **Guided Discussion**

Did the student `UNDERSTANDING`

- ☐ make important observations?
- ☐ extend or generalize learning?
- ☐ provide insightful answers?
- ☐ pose insightful questions?

Portfolio Assessment

☑ **Journal**

Did the student `REASONING`

- ☐ provide a clear explanation?
- ☐ communicate reasons and strategies?
- ☐ choose appropriate strategies?
- ☐ argue logically?

B Summarize Findings

Analyze and summarize assessment data for each student. Determine which Assessment Follow-Up is appropriate for each student. Use the Student Assessment Record in **Assessment** or **eAssess** to update assessment records.

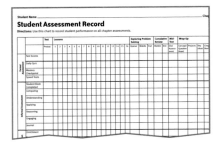

Assessment Page T41

C Assessment Follow-Up ● DIFFERENTIATE INSTRUCTION

Based on your observations, use these teaching strategies for assessment follow-up.

INTERVENTION

Review student performance on **Intervention** Lesson 11.A to see if students have mastered prerequisite skills for this lesson.

ENGLISH LEARNER

Review

Use Lesson 11.8 in **English Learner Support Guide** to review lesson concepts and vocabulary.

ENRICH

If . . . students are proficient in the lesson concepts,

Then . . . encourage them to work on chapter projects or **Enrichment** Lesson 11.8.

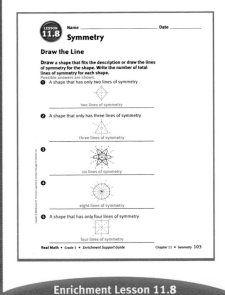

Enrichment Lesson 11.8

PRACTICE

If . . . students would benefit from additional practice,

Then . . . assign **Practice** Lesson 11.8.

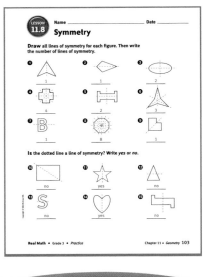

Practice Lesson 11.8

RETEACH

If . . . students struggle with lines of symmetry,

Then . . . have them use a mirror. Have them place the mirror where they think the line of symmetry is. If the parts of the figure on each side of the mirror match, then the mirror is on a line of symmetry.

Lesson Planner

Lesson Planner

OBJECTIVES
To develop an understanding about the points on a circle and their distance from the center

NCTM STANDARDS

Geometry
Identifying, comparing, and analyzing attributes of two- and three-dimensional shapes

Connections
Recognizing and using connections among mathematical ideas

MATERIALS

- *Response Wheels
- centimeter rulers

TECHNOLOGY
Presentation Lesson 11.9
Building Blocks Piece Puzzler 5

TEST PREP
Cumulative Review
Mental Math reviews percents (Lesson 8.11).

Extended Response
Problems 2, 3, 5, and 6

Circles I

Context of the Lesson This is the first of two lessons on the properties of circles. In this lesson students will explore points on a circle and learn how they relate to the center of the circle. In Lesson 11.9 students will be introduced to formal vocabulary for some of the properties of circles.

See page 422B for Math Background for teachers for this lesson.

Planning for Learning • DIFFERENTIATE INSTRUCTION

INTERVENTION

If . . . students lack the prerequisite skill of identifying shapes,

Then . . . teach *Intervention* Lesson 11.A.

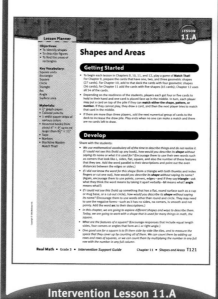

Intervention Lesson 11.A

ENGLISH LEARNER

Preview

If . . . students need language support,

Then . . . use Lesson 11.9 in *English Learner Support Guide* to preview lesson concepts and vocabulary.

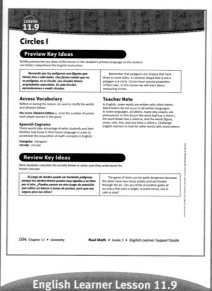

English Learner Lesson 11.9

ENRICH

If . . . students are proficient in the lesson concepts,

Then . . . emphasize the student pages.

PRACTICE

If . . . students would benefit from additional practice,

Then . . . extend Guided Discussion before assigning the student pages.

RETEACH

If . . . students are having difficulty understanding circles,

Then . . . extend Strategy Building before assigning the student pages.

Review Vocabulary
Review from Grade 2: **circle**

Access Vocabulary
the score the number of points each player earned in the game

Spanish Cognates
triangular triangular
circular circular

Teaching Lesson 11.9

Mental Math 5

 Review  Have students show percents with their percent slider. Use examples such as the following: check students' responses

a. 45%   **e.** 90%
b. 10%   **f.** 29%
c. 80%   **g.** 17%
d. 88%   **h.** 87%

1 Develop 25

Tell Students In Today's Lesson They Will

explore the points on a circle and their relationship to the center.

Strategy Building [UNDERSTANDING]   Whole Group

Create either ahead of time or with the class a target game made from a large sheet of cardboard or paper. The target should have concentric squares, and each region should be marked with a score (similar to the markings on a dartboard.) This target should look like a square dartboard. Label the center 100, the next ring out 75, the next ring out 50, and the last ring out 25. *An object to be tossed* (such as a key chain or some other nonhazardous object that will not roll, bounce, or float) is needed.

Demonstrate the target game by having teams of two students each play in the front of the class. Give each team three or four tosses; the goal is to toss the object so that it lands on the section of the target with the highest points. The team with the highest total score wins. Play a few more rounds, choosing new teams each round. Before each round, ask students if it is possible to predict who will get the highest total.

Guided Discussion [UNDERSTANDING]   Whole Group

After the games have finished, ask students questions such as the following:

- Did you like the game?
- What did you like about the game?
- What didn't you like about the game?
- What do you think about the shape of the target?
- What would you do differently next time or what would you change?

During the discussion elicit the comment that your toss can be farther from the center of the target than someone else's toss and you can still score more points.

Strategy Building [ENGAGING]   Small Group

Have students work in groups to make and then play target games of their own design, similar to the one in the earlier demonstration. For a functional and nonhazardous tossing object, students might experiment with different snakelike shapes made from aluminum foil or perhaps a coin or small disk.

2 Assign Student Pages 20

Pages 454–455

Have students complete the exercises on pages 454 and 455 independently. Have them copy the charts and fill in the blanks. Do the first few examples with the class.

As Students Finish

Building Blocks *Piece Puzzler 5*

LESSON 11.9 Circles I

Key Ideas

Polygons are closed plane figures that have three or more sides. A common shape that is not a polygon is a circle. Circles have special properties of their own.

Carmen and Dee each made a dartboard. Study both boards and decide which board gives a fairer score.

Dee's board

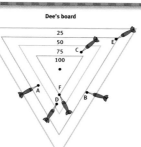

Find the score for each dart. Measure the distance from each dart to the center.

Carmen

Dart	Score	Distance from Center
A	50	cm 1.5
B	25	cm 2
C	75	cm 1.5
Total	150	cm 5

Dee

Dart	Score	Distance from Center
D	75	cm 2
E	50	cm 3.5
F	100	cm 1.5
Total	225	cm 7

① Who had the greater score? Dee

② **Extended Response** Which player do you think had more skill? Explain your answer.
See explanation in Reflect section of *Teacher's Edition*

③ **Extended Response** What is a fairer way to design a dartboard? Circles are more fair because each part on a circle circumference is an equal distance from the center of the circle.

454   Textbook This lesson is available in the *eTextbook*.

Find the score for each dart. Measure the distance from each dart to the center.

Carmen's board

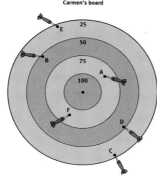

Carmen

Dart	Score	Distance from Center
A	75	cm 1.5
B	50	cm 3
C	25	cm 4
Total	150	cm 8.5

Dee

Dart	Score	Distance from Center
D	50	cm 3
E	25	cm 4
F	75	cm 1.5
Total	150	cm 8.5

④ Who had the greater score? They had the same score.

⑤ **Extended Response** Which player do you think had more skill? Explain your answer.   Both are about the same.

⑥ **Extended Response** To you, does the triangular dartboard or the circular dartboard seem more fair?
The circular dartboard is more fair.

LESSON 11.9

3 Reflect   10

Guided Discussion REASONING   Whole Group

Have students look at their answers to Problems 2 and 3 on page 454 and Problems 5 and 6 on page 455. Discuss any difference of opinions and the reasons behind the students' decisions regarding who had more skill. Ask questions such as the following:

- **Do you believe Carmen's skill changed between games?**
- **Do you believe Dee's skill changed between games?**
- **Looking at both targets, who do you believe had more skill overall?**
- **What explanations can you offer as to why you think there was a difference between scores (between the two targets)?**

Discuss the advantages and disadvantages of target games of different designs. From the discussion, lead into the idea that all points on a circle are the same distance from its center but that a player need not be aiming at the center of the target.

Extended Response

Problems 2 Some students might decide that Carmen had more skill because she was closer to the center. Some might decide that Dee had more skill because her score was higher.

Problems 3, 5, and **6** Accept all reasonable answers.

Cumulative Review: For cumulative review of previously learned skills, see page 467–468.

Family Involvement: Assign the *Practice, Reteach,* or *Enrichment* activities depending on the needs of your students.

Encourage students to find various real-world examples of circles with a friend or a relative.

Concept/Question Board: Have students attempt to answer any unanswered questions on the Concept/Question Board.

Math Puzzler: Oscar was supposed to get $4 in change after buying baseball cards at the hobby shop. As he left, he realized the clerk had mistakenly given him $103 in change. As a reward for returning the overpayment, the store's owner gave Oscar 5 times the amount of change that Oscar originally was owed. How much was the reward? $20; 4 × 5 = 20

4 Assess and Differentiate

 Assess Use **eAssess** to record and analyze evidence of student understanding.

A Gather Evidence

Use the Daily Class Assessment Records in **Assessment** or **eAssess** to record daily observations.

Informal Assessment
☑ **Guided Discussion**

Did the student **UNDERSTANDING**
- ❑ make important observations?
- ❑ extend or generalize learning?
- ❑ provide insightful answers?
- ❑ pose insightful questions?

Informal Assessment
☑ **Guided Discussion**

Did the student **REASONING**
- ❑ provide a clear explanation?
- ❑ communicate reasons and strategies?
- ❑ choose appropriate strategies?
- ❑ argue logically?

B Summarize Findings

Analyze and summarize assessment data for each student. Determine which Assessment Follow-Up is appropriate for each student. Use the Student Assessment Record in **Assessment** or **eAssess** to update assessment records.

Assessment Page T41

C Assessment Follow-Up ● DIFFERENTIATE INSTRUCTION

Based on your observations, use these teaching strategies for assessment follow-up.

INTERVENTION

Review student performance on **Intervention** Lesson 11.A to see if they have mastered prerequisite skills for this lesson.

ENGLISH LEARNER

Review

Use Lesson 11.9 in **English Learner Support Guide** to review lesson concepts and vocabulary.

ENRICH

If . . . students are proficient in the lesson concepts,

Then . . . encourage them to work on chapter projects or **Enrichment** Lesson 11.9.

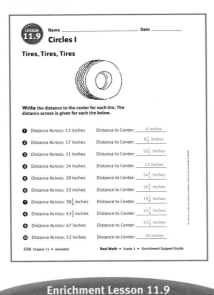

Enrichment Lesson 11.9

PRACTICE

If . . . students would benefit from additional practice,

Then . . . assign **Practice** Lesson 11.9.

Practice Lesson 11.9

RETEACH

If . . . students struggle with what a circle is,

Then . . . have them discuss what they know about circles. Summarize important points on the chalkboard. Then have students look up the definition of a circle. Compare it to the defintion of a polygon. Discuss why a circle is not a polygon.

OBJECTIVES
- To introduce the properties of the diameter, radius, and center of a circle
- To provide experiences that develop understanding of the relationship between the diameter and the radius of a circle
- To review the concept of symmetry
- To provide practice in measuring length

NCTM STANDARDS
Geometry
- Identifying, comparing, and analyzing attributes of two- and three-dimensional shapes and developing vocabulary to describe the attributes
- Identifying and describing line symmetry in two-dimensional shapes and designs

Measurement
Selecting and applying appropriate standard units and tools to measure length

MATERIALS
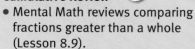
- *Response Wheels
- Unlined paper, one sheet for each student
- Student scissors
- Various circular traceable objects
- Metric rulers

TECHNOLOGY
- Presentation Lesson 11.10
- MathTools Geometry Sketch Tools (Circle)

TEST PREP
Cumulative Review
- Mental Math reviews comparing fractions greater than a whole (Lesson 8.9).
- Problems 1–4 review metric measurement (Lesson 9.1).

Circles II

Context of the Lesson This is the second of two lessons about the properties of circles. In Lesson 11.9, students explored informally how the points on a circle relate to the center. In Grade 4 these properties will be extended to include *chord* and finding the *circumference* of circles. See page 422B for Math Background for teachers for this lesson.

Planning for Learning ● DIFFERENTIATE INSTRUCTION

INTERVENTION
If . . . students lack the prerequisite skill of describing figures,

Then . . . teach **Intervention** Lesson 11.B.

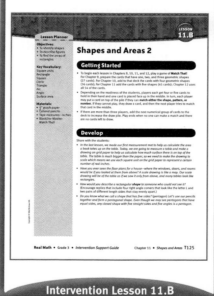

Intervention Lesson 11.B

ENGLISH LEARNER
Preview
If . . . students need language support,

Then . . . use Lesson 11.10 in *English Learner Support Guide* to preview lesson concepts and vocabulary.

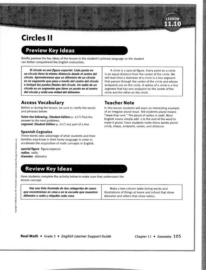

English Learner Lesson 11.10

ENRICH
If . . . students are proficient in the lesson concepts,

Then . . . emphasize the student pages.

PRACTICE
If . . . students would benefit from additional practice,

Then . . . extend Strategy Building before assigning the student pages.

RETEACH
If . . . students are having difficulty understanding the properties of circles,

Then . . . extend Guided Discussion before assigning the student pages.

Vocabulary
center \sen′ tər\ *n.* the point within a circle that is an equal distance from every point on the circle

diameter \dī am′ i tər\ *n.* a line segment passing through the center of a circle or sphere, from one side to the other

radius \rā′ dē əs\ *n.* a line segment going from the center to the outside of a circle or sphere

Spanish Cognates
special figure figura especial
radius radio
diameter diámetro

*Manipulative Kit Item

Mental Math 5

Review comparing fractions greater than a whole. Have students respond with thumbs-up if the left number is greater than the right number, thumbs-down if the left number is less than the right number, or open hand if both are equal. Use examples such as the following:

a. $1\frac{1}{2}$ ___ $1\frac{1}{3}$ up

b. $2\frac{2}{3}$ ___ $4\frac{1}{3}$ down

c. $9\frac{1}{10}$ ___ $10\frac{1}{10}$ down

d. $2\frac{1}{3}$ ___ $1\frac{1}{3}$ up

e. $2\frac{1}{4}$ ___ $\frac{9}{4}$ open

f. $5\frac{1}{5}$ ___ $\frac{26}{5}$ open

1 Develop 25

Tell Students In Today's Lesson They Will

explore some properties of circles.

Guided Discussion UNDERSTANDING Whole Group

Draw on the board a very large circle. This also can be demonstrated using the **eMathTools: Geometry Sketch Tools.** Ask students the name of this shape and what properties they know. Accept any answers that are correct descriptions of circles. Mark a point in the center of the circle. Mark the point with the letter P. Identify point P as the *center*.

Then, start at one point on the circle, and draw a line from that point, through the center, to the other side of the circle. Introduce the word *diameter*, and have students define it. Label one endpoint of the diameter point A and the other point as point B. Identify the diameter as *diameter AB*. Draw several other diameters, with labeling, to show that a diameter can go in any direction, as long as it goes through the center and its endpoints are on the circle.

Starting from the center P, draw a radius to any point on the circle. Introduce the word *radius* to the class, and have students define it. Label the second point Q. Identify the radius as *radius PQ*. Draw several other radii, with labeling, to demonstrate that the radius extends from the center to a point on the circle.

Strategy Building   APPLYING Small Group

Pass out unlined paper and a pair of scissors to each student. Make available various sizes of circular objects that are traceable. Have students use a circular object to draw a circle on a piece of paper. Then have students cut out the circle and fold it in halves and then in halves again. The intersection of the 2 folds will be the center. Unfold the circle and label its *center* with a point and the letter O. Next, have students draw and label several radii and diameters. They can create more diameters and radii by folding the circle in halves in another direction. After students have drawn several diameters and radii, measure them to the nearest millimeter, and record their measurements in a two-column chart. Keep this chart for discussion later in Reflect.

Review with students the terms *symmetry* and *line of symmetry*, and see if they can use the terms to describe any properties of their circle. (For example, if you fold the circle along a diameter, you get a line of symmetry and two symmetric parts.)

2 Assign Student Pages 20

Pages 456–457 APPLYING

Have students complete the exercises on pages 456 and 457 independently.

Monitoring Student Progress

If . . . students have difficulty measuring with a centimeter ruler,

Then . . . have them work with students who are proficient in measuring length. Give students practice measuring in real situations whenever possible.

As Students Finish

 Have students play a previously introduced game in the book.

LESSON 11.10 Circles II

Key Ideas

A **circle** is a special figure that has every point an equal distance from the **center**. The center point of this circle is point *P*.

A **diameter** of a circle is a line segment that passes through the center of the circle and whose endpoints are on the circle. One diameter of the circle above is *CD*. Another is *AB*.

A **radius** of a circle is a line segment that has one endpoint on the center of the circle and the other on the circle. The plural of *radius* is *radii*.

 Use Circle *P* to measure.

❶ Diameter *AB* is ☐ centimeters long.   5

❷ Diameter *CD* is ☐ centimeters long.   5

❸ Radius *PE* is ☐ centimeters long.   2.5

❹ Radius *PB* is ☐ centimeters long.   2.5

456   Textbook *This lesson is available in the eTextbook.*

Use the picture to name the following.

❺ Name a diameter.   line segment *AN* or *LK*

❻ Name a radius. line segment *DP*, *RP*, *KP*, *AP*, *NP*, or *LP*

❼ Name a line segment that is not a diameter or radius.   line segment *BC*

❽ Create one circle with the following attributes:
- Center labeled point *R*
- Diameters labeled *NS* and *QL*
- Radii labeled *FR*, *RD*, and *SR*
- A line segment (neither a diameter nor a radius) labeled *YZ*   check to see that students' circles have the correct attributes

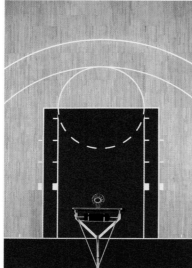

Chapter 11 • Lesson 10   457

Circles II   LESSON 11.10

 Reflect   10

Guided Discussion ☑ UNDERSTANDING   Whole Group

After students have finished measuring, engage them in discussion with questions such as the following:

■ **What did you notice about the measurements of the diameters of your circles?** They are all the same length within each circle.

■ **What did you notice about the radii?** They are all the same length within each circle.

■ **Are the diameters the same length for every circle in the classroom?** only if the circles are the same size

■ **What do you notice, if anything, about the diameter and the radii measurements within your circle?** Any radius is one-half the length of a diameter.

 Curriculum Connection: Students might be interested in researching how sports in America and abroad, use circles, diameters, radii, and other properties of circles

 Cumulative Review: For cumulative review of previously learned skills, see page 467–468.

 Family Involvement: Assign the *Practice, Reteach,* or *Enrichment* activities depending on the needs of your students.

Encourage students to find various real-world examples of circles with a friend or a relative.

 Concept/Question Board: Have students attempt to answer any unanswered questions on the Concept/Question Board.

 Math Puzzler: Write the numbers 0–4 once each so that the sum of the numbers along each line is 7.

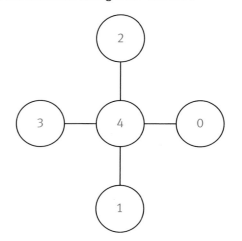

4 Assess and Differentiate

 Assess Use **eAssess** to record and analyze evidence of student understanding.

A Gather Evidence

Use the Daily Class Assessment Records in **Assessment** or **eAssess** to record daily observations.

Informal Assessment
☑ **Strategy Building**

Did the student **APPLYING**
- ❑ apply learning in new situations?
- ❑ contribute concepts?
- ❑ contribute answers?
- ❑ connect mathematics to real-world situations?

Informal Assessment
☑ **Guided Discussion**

Did the student **UNDERSTANDING**
- ❑ make important observations?
- ❑ extend or generalize learning?
- ❑ provide insightful answers?
- ❑ pose insightful questions?

B Summarize Findings

Analyze and summarize assessment data for each student. Determine which Assessment Follow-Up is appropriate for each student. Use the Student Assessment Record in **Assessment** or **eAssess** to update assessment records.

Assessment Page T41

C Assessment Follow-Up • DIFFERENTIATE INSTRUCTION

Based on your observations, use these teaching strategies for assessment follow-up.

INTERVENTION

Review student performance on **Intervention** Lesson 11.B to see if students have mastered prerequisite skills for this lesson.

ENGLISH LEARNER

Review

Use Lesson 11.10 in **English Learner Support Guide** to review lesson concepts and vocabulary.

ENRICH

If . . . students are proficient in the lesson concepts,

Then . . . encourage them to work on chapter projects or **Enrichment** Lesson 11.10.

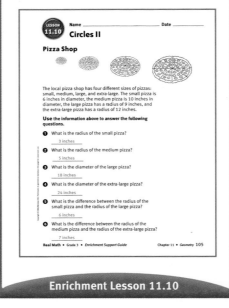

Enrichment Lesson 11.10

PRACTICE

If . . . students would benefit from additional practice,

Then . . . assign **Practice** Lesson 11.10.

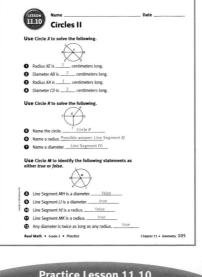

Practice Lesson 11.10

RETEACH

If . . . students are having difficulty understanding some properties of circles,

Then . . . reteach the concept using **Reteach** Lesson 11.10.

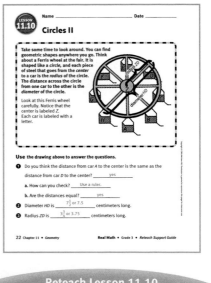

Reteach Lesson 11.10

Lesson Planner

OBJECTIVES
- To familiarize students with various space figures and their names
- To familiarize students with the terms *vertex* (plural *vertices*), *edges,* and *face* as they relate to space figures

NCTM STANDARDS
Geometry
Identifying, comparing, and analyzing attributes of two- and three-dimensional shapes and developing vocabulary to describe the attributes

Connections
Recognizing and using connections among mathematical ideas

MATERIALS
- *Platonic solids
- Real models of space figures (optional)

TECHNOLOGY
- e Presentation Lesson 11.11
- Building Blocks Geometry Snapshots 8
- e MathTools Net Tools (optional)

TEST PREP
Cumulative Review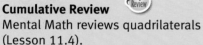
Mental Math reviews quadrilaterals (Lesson 11.4).

Space Figures

Context of the Lesson This is the first of three lessons on space figures and their properties. Students have been informally introduced to space figures in previous grades. In this lesson they will review formal names of some of those space figures and connect them with real-world examples. In Lesson 11.12, students will explore the nets and surface area of space figures. In Lesson 11.13 volume of space figures will be explored. In Grade 4 students will further explore space figures and their properties, such as surface area and volume.

See page 422B for Math Background for teachers for this lesson.

Planning for Learning ● DIFFERENTIATE INSTRUCTION

INTERVENTION

If . . . students lack the prerequisite skill of identifying shapes,

Then . . . teach *Intervention* Lesson 11.A.

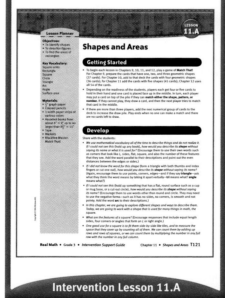

Intervention Lesson 11.A

ENGLISH LEARNER

Preview

If . . . students need language support,

Then . . . use Lesson 11.11 in *English Learner Support Guide* to preview lesson concepts and vocabulary.

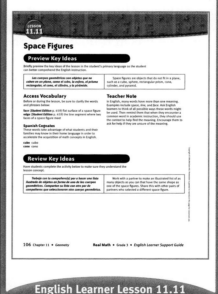

English Learner Lesson 11.11

ENRICH

If . . . students are proficient in the lesson concepts,

Then . . . emphasize the student pages.

PRACTICE

If . . . students would benefit from additional practice,

Then . . . extend Guided Discussion before assigning the student pages.

RETEACH

If . . . students are having difficulty understanding properties of space figures,

Then . . . extend Using Student Pages before assigning the student pages.

Vocabulary
face \fās\ *n.* a plane figure that serves as one side of a space figure
edge the line segment where two faces of a space figure meet

vertex \ver′ teks\ *n.* 1. the point where two rays meet. 2. the point of intersection of two sides of a polygon. 3. the point of intersection of three edges of a space figure.

Access Vocabulary
face flat surface of a space figure
edge the line segment where 2 faces of a space figure meet

Mental Math 5

  Determine if the following figures are quadrilaterals. If they are, give the thumbs-up **THUMBS UP** signal; if they are not quadrilaterals, give the thumbs-down signal. Use shapes such as the following:

a. parallelogram up

d. rectangle up

b. square up

e. circle down

c. triangle down

f. trapezoid up

1 Develop 25

Tell Students In Today's Lesson They Will

explore various space objects and their names, and the terms to describe parts of those space objects.

Guided Discussion UNDERSTANDING Whole Group

Place the set of space figures in front of students, or pass them around the classroom. Have students describe the figures, including what plane shapes they see and how many of each plane shape they see. Ask for a few comparisons of these space figures to real-life items, such as *the sphere looks like a tennis ball.*

Using the cube space figure, place your hand flat on one side and introduce the term *face.* Have students find one face of the classroom (for example, a wall, the ceiling, or the floor). Ask students how many faces the cube has and how many the classroom has. six

Using the same cube space figure, point to an *edge,* and introduce the term *edge.* Have students find an edge in the classroom (for example, where the ceiling meets the wall or where two walls meet). Ask students how many edges the cube has and how many edges the classroom has. twelve

Again using the cube space figure, point to a vertex, and introduce the term *vertex.* Have students find a vertex in the room (for example, any corner point where at least three edges meet). Introduce the plural of vertex as *vertices.* Ask students how many vertices the cube has and how many vertices the classroom has. eight

Using Student Pages APPLYING Small Group

Have students open their books to page 458. In their groups have them discuss with their groups the names for the solid figures and as many real-life items as possible. As a class discuss the names and the real-life items. It might be helpful to create a table to keep posted in the classroom as students finish this chapter and the year.

2 Assign Student Pages 20

Pages 458–459 APPLYING

Have students complete the exercises on pages 458 and 459 independently.

As Students Finish

Building Blocks *Geometry Snapshots 8*

LESSON 11.11 Space Figures

Key Ideas

Space figures are figures that cannot fit in a plane.

Look at the following pictures of space figures. How many do you recognize? List some things that look like each object.

 cube; Possible answers include a block or a die.

 cylinder; Possible answers include a soda pop or juice can or a rolling pin.

 rectangular prism; Possible answers include a box, an eraser for the board, or a brick.

 square pyramid; Possible answers include a mountain or the Egyptian pyramids.

 sphere; Possible answers include a baseball or any other kind of ball or a globe.

 cone; Possible answers include an ice-cream cone, an orange construction cone, or a party hat.

458   Textbook This lesson is available in the *eTextbook*.

A flat surface of a space figure is called a **face**. Faces are usually polygons. A line segment where two faces meet is called an **edge**. The point where three or more edges meet is called a **vertex**.

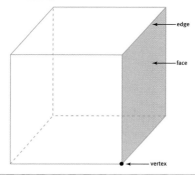

← edge

← face

← vertex

Answer the following questions. Use models of the figures if needed.

1. How many faces does a cube have? 6
2. How many edges does a cube have? 12
3. How many vertices does a cube have? 8
4. How many faces does a rectangular prism have? 6
5. How many edges does a rectangular prism have? 12
6. How many vertices does a rectangular prism have? 8
7. How many faces does a square pyramid have? 5
8. How many edges does a square pyramid have? 8
9. How many vertices does a square pyramid have? 5
10. How many faces does a triangular pyramid have? 4
11. How many edges does a triangular pyramid have? 6
12. How many vertices does a triangular pyramid have? 4

---

3 Reflect   10

Guided Discussion UNDERSTANDING   Whole Group

Ask if students noticed any interesting patterns in their answers on page 459. It might help to create a table to record their answers as a class. Give students time to talk about this and to perhaps study the table together. The pattern is $e + 2 = f + v$ where e is the number of edges, f is the number of faces, and v is the number of vertices. Have students discuss this pattern and use it to check their answers to page 459 of their text.

 Cumulative Review: For cumulative review of previously learned skills, see page 467–468.

 Family Involvement: Assign the *Practice, Reteach,* or *Enrichment* activities depending on the needs of your students.

Encourage students to find various real-world examples of space figures with a friend or a relative.

 Concept/Question Board: Have students attempt to answer any unanswered questions on the Concept/Question Board.

 Math Puzzler: Use the digits 4, 3, 7, 9, and 1 to complete this number sentence, using each digit only once to the left of the equal sign: ▢▢▢ − ▢▢ = ▢. What are the greatest and least differences that can be created?
greatest: 974 − 13 = 961; least: 134 − 97 = 37

Assess and Differentiate

 Assess Use *eAssess* to record and analyze evidence of student understanding.

A Gather Evidence

Use the Daily Class Assessment Records in *Assessment* or *eAssess* to record daily observations.

Informal Assessment
☑ **Mental Math**

Did the student **COMPUTING**
☐ respond accurately?
☐ respond quickly?
☐ respond with confidence?
☐ self-correct?

Informal Assessment
☑ **Student Pages**

Did the student **APPLYING**
☐ apply learning in new situations?
☐ contribute concepts?
☐ contribute answers?
☐ connect mathematics to real-world situations?

B Summarize Findings

Analyze and summarize assessment data for each student. Determine which Assessment Follow-Up is appropriate for each student. Use the Student Assessment Record in *Assessment* or *eAssess* to update assessment records.

Assessment Page T41

C Assessment Follow-Up • DIFFERENTIATE INSTRUCTION

Based on your observations, use these teaching strategies for assessment follow-up.

INTERVENTION	ENRICH	PRACTICE	RETEACH
Review student performance on *Intervention* Lesson 11.A to see if students have mastered prerequisite skills for this lesson.	**If . . .** students are proficient in the lesson concepts, **Then . . .** encourage them to work on chapter projects or *Enrichment* Lesson 11.11.	**If . . .** students would benefit from additional practice, **Then . . .** assign *Practice* Lesson 11.11.	**If . . .** students struggle with three-dimensional figures, **Then . . .** have them make a chart headed with Space Figure and Example. Then have them find examples for each of the space figures discussed in the lesson. Encourage them to find examples in school, outside, and at home.

ENGLISH LEARNER

Review

Use Lesson 11.11 in *English Learner Support Guide* to review lesson concepts and vocabulary.

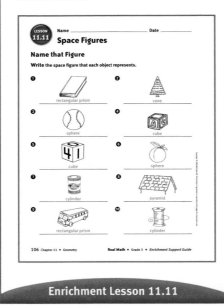

Enrichment Lesson 11.11

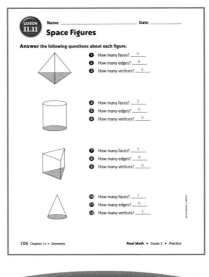

Practice Lesson 11.11

Lesson Planner

OBJECTIVES
- To decompose a solid figure to its net
- To identify the figures making up a net and find their area
- To find the surface area of a space figure

NCTM STANDARDS
Geometry
- Identifying and building a three-dimensional object from two-dimensional representations of that object
- Identifying and building a two-dimensional representation of a three-dimensional object

Measurement
- Developing, understanding, and using formulas to find the area of rectangles and related triangles and parallelograms
- Developing strategies to determine the surface area and volume of rectangular solids

MATERIALS

- *Response Wheels
- *Platonic solids

TECHNOLOGY
- **Presentation** Lesson 11.12
- **Building Blocks** Create a Scene
- **MathTools** Net Tools

TEST PREP
Cumulative Review
- Mental Math reviews subtracting decimals (Lesson 10.6).
- Problem 2 reviews quadrilaterals (Lesson 11.4).
- Problem 3 reviews area (Lesson 3.7).

Extended Response
Problem 4

Nets and Surface Area

Context of the Lesson This is the second of three lessons on space figures and their properties. In Lesson 11.11, students reviewed the names of these space figures and some real-world representations of these figures. Students will explore the concept of decomposition and nets of space figures to determine surface area. In Grade 4 students will review area and further explore composition and decomposition of nets and the surface area of space figures.

See page 422B for Math Background for teachers for this lesson.

Planning for Learning ● DIFFERENTIATE INSTRUCTION

INTERVENTION
If . . . students lack the prerequisite skill of finding area of rectangles,

Then . . . teach **Intervention** Lesson 11.C.

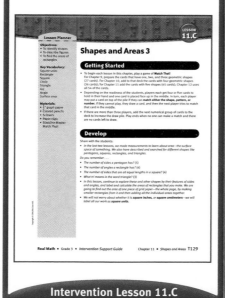

Intervention Lesson 11.C

ENGLISH LEARNER
Preview

If . . . students need language support,

Then . . . use Lesson 11.12 in **English Learner Support Guide** to preview lesson concepts and vocabulary.

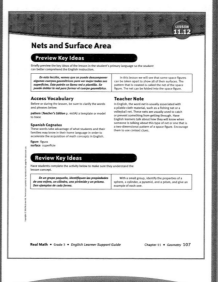

English Learner Lesson 11.12

ENRICH
If . . . students are proficient in the lesson concepts,

Then . . . emphasize the student pages.

PRACTICE
If . . . students would benefit from additional practice,

Then . . . extend the Guided Discussion before assigning the student pages.

RETEACH
If . . . students are having difficulty understanding nets and surface area

Then . . . extend the Guided Discussion before assigning the student pages.

Vocabulary
net \net\ n. a pattern used to create a space figure

surface area n. the sum of the areas of the faces of a space figure

Access Vocabulary
pattern a template or model to trade around

Spanish Cognates
figure figura

surface superficie

Mental Math 5

Present students with subtraction exercises with decimals. Use examples such as the following:

a. 0.5 − 0.3 0.2
b. 0.8 − 0.2 0.6
c. 1.5 − 1.4 0.1
d. 2.5 − 2.0 0.5

e. 0.4 − 0.1 0.3
f. 1.2 − 1.2 0.0
g. 3.3 − 3.1 0.2
h. 2.8 − 0.2 2.6

1 Develop 30

Tell Students In Today's Lesson They Will

break apart space figures into their individual faces, find the area of those faces, and in turn find the surface area of the space figure.

Guided Discussion UNDERSTANDING Whole Group

Using the **eMathTools: Net Tools** or a net drawn on a piece of paper, create a cube with dimensions of 5 inches on all sides. Have students identify this solid figure and discuss any properties they recall about the cube. Remind students of the terms *faces, edges,* and *vertices.* Verify with students that the cube has six faces, perhaps showing students a *Number Cube.* Have students identify the shapes of the faces (squares). Review area and how to find area. In this case, since 5 × 5 = 25, the area of each face is 25 square inches.

Draw or display another rectangular prism. Have students identify the number of faces and what shape each face is. Review area of each face. Have students add all of the areas to arrive at the *surface area* of the figure.

Strategy Building APPLYING Small Group

Have students look at the net of this space figure. Identify with students the faces, vertices, and edges. Talk about what space figure they predict this net will make. Then, have students trace the following net on a piece of unlined paper. Cut along the solid lines *only* and fold along the dotted lines. Use glue or another adhesive to connect the folding tabs. See if students can identify what space figure this is. triangular pyramid

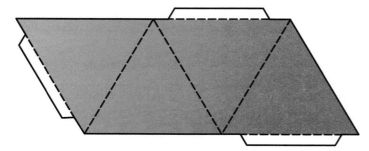

2 Assign Student Pages 20

Pages 460–461 APPLYING

Have students complete the exercises on pages 460 and 461 independently.

As Students Finish

Building Blocks *Create a Scene*

LESSON 11.12 Nets and Surface Area

Key Ideas

Any space figure can be taken apart to show all of its surfaces. The pattern that is created is called the net of the space figure. Likewise, the two-dimensional drawing, or net, can be folded into the three-dimensional space figure.

Look at the following net:

When this net is folded, it creates a triangular pyramid.

Trace the following net on a piece of unlined paper. Cut along the solid lines, and fold along the dotted lines.

① What space figure does it make? cube

460

Textbook This lesson is available in the *eTextbook*.

In previous lessons, we learned that the area of a rectangle is the length times the width. For example, the area of this rectangle would be 24 square units because
6 × 4 = 24.

The same idea applies to a square. For example, the area of this square would be 16 square units because 4 × 4 = 16.

Look at the net of a cube. Use the net to answer the following questions:

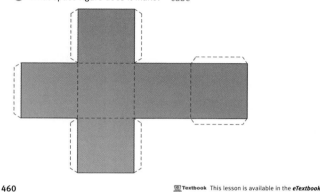

② What shape are all of the polygons in this net? squares

③ What is the area of one polygon in the net? ▨ square centimeters 9

④ **Extended Response** Another name for the total area of a cube is surface area. Describe how you would find the total area, or surface area, of the cube. What is the surface area for the cube?

④ Find the area of each square, and multiply the answer by 6; 54 square centimeters.

---

3 Reflect 5

Guided Discussion ✓ UNDERSTANDING Whole Group

Discuss with students what space figures they may have seen in a supermarket or grocery. If possible, have students make a list the next time they are in a supermarket or grocery. Have students discuss the space figures they found as a class.

Extended Response

Problem 4 If students are uncertain of finding surface area, break the net into the individual sections, and find the area of each section.

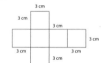 **Cumulative Review:** For cumulative review of previously learned skills, see page 467–468.

 Family Involvement: Assign the **Practice, Reteach,** or **Enrichment** activities depending on the needs of your students.

Encourage students to find the area of various rectangles with a friend or a relative.

 Concept/Question Board: Have students attempt to answer any unanswered questions on the Concept/Question Board.

 Math Puzzler: Hiroshi is making 3 beaded necklaces. Each necklace will be exactly the same. He has 96 red beads, 108 green beads, 84 yellow beads, and 27 black beads. How many beads will each necklace have? 105

Assess and Differentiate

 Assess Use **eAssess** to record and analyze evidence of student understanding.

A Gather Evidence

Use the Daily Class Assessment Records in **Assessment** or **eAssess** to record daily observations.

Informal Assessment
☑ **Student Pages**

Did the student **APPLYING**
- ❑ apply learning in new situations?
- ❑ contribute concepts?
- ❑ contribute answers?
- ❑ connect mathematics to real-world situations?

Informal Assessment
☑ **Guided Discussion**

Did the student **UNDERSTANDING**
- ❑ make important observations?
- ❑ extend or generalize learning?
- ❑ provide insightful answers?
- ❑ pose insightful questions?

B Summarize Findings

Analyze and summarize assessment data for each student. Determine which Assessment Follow-Up is appropriate for each student. Use the Student Assessment Record in **Assessment** or **eAssess** to update assessment records.

Assessment Page T41

C Assessment Follow-Up ● DIFFERENTIATE INSTRUCTION

Based on your observations, use these teaching strategies for assessment follow-up.

INTERVENTION

Review student performance on **Intervention** Lesson 11.C to see if students have mastered prerequisite skills for this lesson.

ENGLISH LEARNER

Review

Use Lesson 11.12 in **English Learner Support Guide** to review lesson concepts and vocabulary.

ENRICH

If . . . students are proficient in the lesson concepts,

Then . . . encourage them to work on chapter projects or **Enrichment** Lesson 11.12.

Enrichment Lesson 11.12

PRACTICE

If . . . students would benefit from additional practice,

Then . . . assign **Practice** Lesson 11.12.

Practice Lesson 11.12

RETEACH

If . . . students struggle with identifying the faces of a space figure,

Then . . . have them trace the shape onto a piece of paper. Encourage students to make their own nets by using graph paper and estimating or tracing the shape to form the sides.

Lesson Planner

OBJECTIVES
To introduce the concept of volume as a given number in cubic units

NCTM STANDARDS
Geometry
Using geometric models to solve problems in other areas of mathematics, such as number and measurement

Measurement
Developing strategies to determine the surface areas and volumes of rectangular solids

MATERIALS
- *Interlocking cubes or
- *Base-ten blocks

TECHNOLOGY
ⓔ **Presentation** Lesson 11.13
Building Blocks Shapes Part 7

TEST PREP
Cumulative Review
Mental Math reviews equivalent fractions (Lesson 8.5).

Multistep Problems
Problems 22–25

Volume

Context of the Lesson This is the third of three lessons on space figures. In this lesson, students will begin exploration of volume, which is a concept further developed in Grade 4. For Grade 3, students will determine volume merely by counting the cubic units. No formal formula is applied.

See page 422B for Math Background for teachers for this lesson.

Planning for Learning ● DIFFERENTIATE INSTRUCTION

INTERVENTION	ENGLISH LEARNER	ENRICH
If . . . students lack the prerequisite skill of identifying shapes, **Then . . .** teach **Intervention** Lesson 11.A.	**Preview** **If . . .** students need language support, **Then . . .** use Lesson 11.13 in **English Learner Support Guide** to preview lesson concepts and vocabulary.	**If . . .** students are proficient in the lesson concepts, **Then . . .** emphasize the student pages.

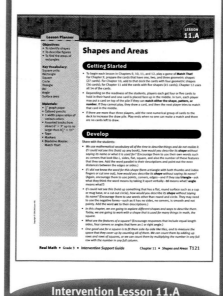
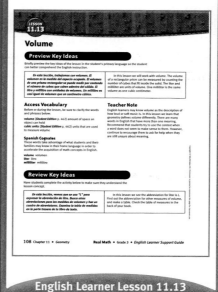

Intervention Lesson 11.A

English Learner Lesson 11.13

PRACTICE
If . . . students would benefit from additional practice,

Then . . . extend Strategy Building before assigning the student pages.

RETEACH
If . . . students are having difficulty understanding volume,

Then . . . extend Guided Discussion before assigning the student pages.

Vocabulary
volume \vol´ ūm\ *n.* the amount of space anything fills
cubic units *n.* units that are used to measure volume

Access Vocabulary
volume amount of space an object can hold
cubic units units that are used to measure volume

Spanish Cognates
volume volumen
liter litro
milliliter mililitro

---

*Manipulative Kit Item

Mental Math 5

  Review equivalent fractions using thumbs-up if the fractions are equivalent or thumbs-down **THUMBS UP** if the fractions are not equivalent. Based on your class, determine if the fractions could be greater than a whole. Use examples such as the following:

a. $\frac{1}{2}$ ▢ $\frac{5}{10}$ up

b. $\frac{4}{8}$ ▢ $\frac{5}{8}$ down

c. $\frac{4}{8}$ ▢ $\frac{3}{6}$ up

d. $\frac{1}{2}$ ▢ $\frac{3}{6}$ up

e. $\frac{4}{8}$ ▢ $\frac{1}{2}$ up

f. $\frac{4}{8}$ ▢ $\frac{2}{8}$ down

1 Develop 30

Tell Students In Today's Lesson They Will

explore the concept of volume as a given number of cubic units.

Guided Discussion   UNDERSTANDING   Whole Group

Use the cubes to build a rectangular prism that is 5 cubes long, 3 cubes wide, and 2 cubes high in this manner: Place 5 cubes in a row, then place 2 identical rows behind the first, and then repeat the procedure on top of the first layer.

Give the three dimensions of the space figures (5 cubes by 3 cubes by 2 cubes), and ask students how many cubes there are altogether.

Have students explain their answers without moving any of the cubes. Then count the cubes in a systematic manner. (For example, pick up and count each row of 5 cubes, one at a time, or count each 2-by-3 array, or count each 2-by-5 array.) Allow students to develop their own systematic way of counting the cubes in the space figures. For example, count one layer, and then use repeated addition or multiplication to find the total number of cubes, use multiplication to find the number of cubes in one layer, then use multiplication to find total cubes, and so on.

In a similar way, build several other space figures of different dimensions, for example, 3 by 3 by 3, 4 by 4 by 3, and 2 by 3 by 6. In each case, stack the cubes, and give the dimensions before asking, *How many cubes?* (NOTE: Mastery of a formula is not intended. Volume is to be obtained by counting cubes physically and then through pictures. However, if some students realize they can find the volume by multiplying length by width by height, commend them and encourage them to use whatever procedure they wish.)

Strategy Building UNDERSTANDING   Whole Group

Divide the class into small groups, and give a set of base-ten blocks or interlocking blocks to build solids with the given dimensions. Before building each new solid, write the dimensions (length, width, and height) on the board. Ask students to predict the total number of cubes that will be needed to build the specified solid. Have them build the solid in their group to check their estimation. Discuss students' results.

2 Assign Student Pages 20

Pages 462–463 APPLYING

Have students complete the exercises on pages 462 and 463 independently.

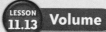

LESSON 11.13 Volume

Key Ideas

The volume of a rectangular prism can be measured by counting the number of cubes that will fit inside the solid. We often measure volume in cubic units.

The volume of this cube is 8 cubic units. Count each of the cubes to verify the volume.

What is the volume? Count the cubes in an orderly manner to determine the volume. You might want to use cubes to build the solid figures if you need help.

1

30 cubic units

3

75 cubic units

2

24 cubic units

4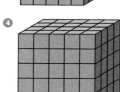

100 cubic units

462

Textbook This lesson is available in the *eTextbook*.

What is the volume? Count the cubes.

5

1 cubic unit

8

64 cubic units

6

8 cubic units

9

125 cubic units

7

27 cubic units

10 In Problems 5–9, the space figures are cubes. Describe any patterns you might have noticed.
One possible answer is that because they are cubes, their volume is $n \times n \times n$.

Chapter 11 • Lesson 13

463

Teaching Lesson 11.13

Assign Student Pages, continued

Pages 464–465

Have students complete the exercises on pages 464 and 465 independently.

Monitoring Student Progress

| **If . . .** students have difficulty visualizing the volume, | **Then . . .** have them build the solids with real cubes. |

As Students Finish

Building Blocks *Shapes Part 7*

LESSON 11.13 · Volume

The cubic centimeter is a unit of volume. This cube has a volume of 1 cubic centimeter.

1 cm
1 cm 1 cm

1 cubic centimeter

Find out how many cubic centimeters are in each box. Then give the volume of the box.

⑪

1 cm
5 cm
3 cm

15 cubic centimeters

⑫
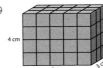
4 cm
5 cm
3 cm

60 cubic centimeters

⑬
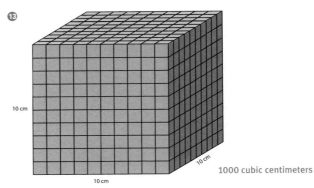
10 cm
10 cm
10 cm

1000 cubic centimeters

464

Textbook This lesson is available in the *eTextbook*.

The liter and milliliter are units of volume.

There are 1,000 milliliters in 1 liter.

1,000 milliliters (mL) = 1 liter (L)

One milliliter is about the same volume as 1 cubic centimeter.

Review **Write** the equivalent amounts.

⑭ 1 L = ■ mL   1,000
⑮ ■ L = 1,000 mL   1
⑯ 2 L = ■ mL   2,000
⑰ ■ L = 3,000 mL   3
⑱ 7 L = ■ mL   7,000
⑲ ■ L = 5,000 mL   5

⑳ 4 L = ■ mL   4,000
㉑ ■ L = 8,000 mL   8
㉒ 1 L = ■ cubic centimeters   1,000
㉓ ■ L = 5,000 cubic centimeters   5
㉔ 2 L = ■ cubic centimeters   2,000
㉕ ■ L = 8,000 cubic centimeters   8

Chapter 11 • Lesson 13

465

---

③ **Reflect** 5 ⏱

Guided Discussion UNDERSTANDING

Whole Group

Discuss with students how they determined the volume for each of the figures on the student pages.

The measure of a cubic unit is one unit on every side. The measure of a cubic inch is one inch on every side. Ask students what they would call the measuring unit that is one foot on every side. cubic foot

 Cumulative Review: For cumulative review of previously learned skills, see page 467–468.

 Family Involvement: Assign the *Practice, Reteach,* or *Enrichment* activities depending on the needs of your students.

Encourage students to explore how many different things have volume with a friend or a relative.

 Concept/Question Board: Have students attempt to answer any unanswered questions on the Concept/Question Board.

 Math Puzzler: Mr. Pappas was stacking canned soup on a shelf in his grocery store. First, he placed a group of cans that was 5 cans long and 2 cans wide. Then, he stacked the same number of cans on top of the first layer. How many cans did he stack altogether? 20; 5 + 5 or 2 × 5 = 10; 10 + 10 or 2 × 10 = 20

4 Assess and Differentiate

 Assess Use *eAssess* to record and analyze evidence of student understanding.

A Gather Evidence

Use the Daily Class Assessment Records in *Assessment* or *eAssess* to record daily observations.

Informal Assessment
☑ **Guided Discussion**

Did the student UNDERSTANDING
- ☐ make important observations?
- ☐ extend or generalize learning?
- ☐ provide insightful answers?
- ☐ pose insightful questions?

Informal Assessment
☑ **Student Pages**

Did the student APPLYING
- ☐ apply learning in new situations?
- ☐ contribute concepts?
- ☐ contribute answers?
- ☐ connect mathematics to real-world situations?

B Summarize Findings

Analyze and summarize assessment data for each student. Determine which Assessment Follow-Up is appropriate for each student. Use the Student Assessment Record in *Assessment* or *eAssess* to update assessment records.

Assessment Page T41

C Assessment Follow-Up ● DIFFERENTIATE INSTRUCTION

Based on your observations, use these teaching strategies for assessment follow-up.

INTERVENTION

Review student performance on *Intervention* Lesson 11.A to see if students have mastered prerequisite skills for this lesson.

ENGLISH LEARNER

Review

Use Lesson 11.13 in *English Learner Support Guide* to review lesson concepts and vocabulary.

ENRICH

If . . . students are proficient in the lesson concepts,

Then . . . encourage them to work on chapter projects or *Enrichment* Lesson 11.13.

Enrichment Lesson 11.13

PRACTICE

If . . . students would benefit from additional practice,

Then . . . assign *Practice* Lesson 11.13.

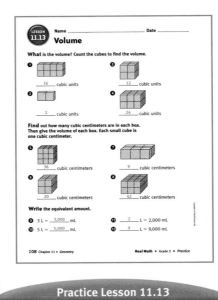

Practice Lesson 11.13

RETEACH

If . . . students struggle with visualizing the solids illustrated in the lesson,

Then . . . have them build the solids with real cubes. They should count the cubes in each solid in a systematic manner. Suggest that they count the cubes in one layer and calculate the rest either by multiplying the layers or by repeated addition. If necessary, they should count all the cubes to check the answer.

Exploring Problem Solving

Objectives

- To solve a nonroutine problem involving the relationship between two-dimensional and three-dimensional forms
- To explore how shape affects volume and surface area
- To see that space figures of different sizes and shapes can have the same volume
- To provide practice with multiplying and finding factors of whole numbers

Materials

- Cubes (64 per group)
- Graph paper
- Scissors

Context of the Lesson In the second problem-solving lesson in Chapter 3, students solved a problem in which they tried to use fencing efficiently to enclose an area. In this lesson they solve an analogous problem in three dimensions, in which they explore using surface area efficiently to enclose a space. The lesson also continues the home theme from pages 422–423 and 444–445.

 **Develop** 5

Tell Students In Today's Lesson They Will

- build models of a playhouse.
- decide which model will cost the least to paint.

Guided Discussion

Recall previous activities involving home design in the Chapter Introduction and the first problem-solving lesson. Have students talk about playhouses. Ask questions such as the following:

■ **What kind of playhouse would you like to have?**
■ **What shape would it be?**
■ **What color would you paint it?**

Tell students they will be exploring the design of playhouses by building several models.

Exploring Problem Solving

You are designing a playhouse for your backyard. The playhouse will be in the shape of a rectangular box. To explore possible shapes, you are using cubes to build different models.

Each model will

- be a rectangular box.
- use exactly 64 cubes.

Work with your group to answer the following questions.

❶ How many different playhouse shapes can you make?

❷ Which playhouse shape will cost the least to paint? How do you know?

❸ Suppose the side of each cube in your model stands for 1 yard. What will be the volume of your playhouse?   64 cubic yards

❹ Does the answer to Problem 3 depend on which of the shapes you choose? Explain.

The 6 possible arrangements are the following:

$64 \times 1 \times 1$ 64

$32 \times 2 \times 1$

$16 \times 4 \times 1$

$16 \times 2 \times 2$

$8 \times 4 \times 2$

$4 \times 4 \times 4$

❶ 6, not counting different orientations of the same arrangement of cubes, otherwise many more—see list above

❷ 8 by 4 by 2 or 4 by 4 by 4; They each have 80 square units of exposed surface area if the 8 by 4 by 2 shape is placed with its large face down.

❹ No; each model uses the same number of cubes, so the playhouse will have the same volume no matter which of the shapes it is.

466   🖥 Textbook This lesson is available in the *eTextbook*.

2 Exploring Problem Solving 30

Using Student Pages

Have students look at and discuss the illustration and information on page 466. Make sure students understand the situation and the conditions that each model must satisfy. Ask questions such as the following:

■ **What shape is each face of a rectangular box?** rectangle
■ **Can two or more of the faces be squares?** Yes, a square is a type of rectangle.
■ **What are some things in the classroom that are shaped like a rectangular box?** cartons, books, and so on
■ **Do all rectangular boxes look the same?** Help students see that while all rectangular boxes share certain characteristics, they can look different. Some may be long and narrow, others more like a cube. They can also be different sizes.
■ **If you made a model 2 cubes long, 2 cubes wide, and 2 cubes high, would it count?** No, it would contain only 8 cubes, and we need to use 64 cubes.
■ **When you make a rectangular box with 64 cubes, are you finished?** No, we need to make other box shapes that have 64 cubes.
■ **How will you remember each model?** draw diagrams; make a table to record the length, width, and height
■ **If you were painting the outside of a playhouse shaped like a rectangular box, how many faces would you paint?** Students should see that the bottom would not be painted, but they may disagree over whether they would paint the roof. Tell them that for this situation they will include painting the roof.

Give each group 64 cubes. Have graph paper and scissors available for those groups that wish to use them.

Have the groups work on Problems 1–4. Provide help as needed. Before students take apart a model to build a new one, you may wish to have them show you their record of its dimensions.

If students seem to be having difficulty making additional models, encourage them to try modifying the one they have made, moving cubes from one section to another to make another rectangular box.

3 Reflect 10

Effective Communication Have students present their results, including the methods they used to discover and record new shapes. Also have them prove that the shape they say will cost the least to paint actually will.

Keep a record on the board of each shape that has not been presented before.

Help students understand the following points:

● Different boxes can have the same volume but different shapes. Some of these shapes use surface area more efficiently than others.
● When you think about how surface area and volume are related, it may help to think about how perimeter and area are related.
● When it is difficult to visualize a 3-dimensional shape, making a 3-dimensional model is often useful.

Sample Solutions Strategies

Students might use one or more of the following strategies.

Draw a Diagram

Students might draw nets to record the different models they make and to help them compare how much paint each would require.

Make an Organized List

Students might begin with the longest, narrowest shape and then change it in a systematic way. There are several patterns they might use to organize the list, for example, the list shown as a sample answer on the reproduction of student page 466.

Break the Problem into Parts

Students might write all the factors of 64, including 1 ($2 \times 2 \times 2 \times 2 \times 2 \times 2 \times 1$), and then combine them in different ways.

Make a Table

Students might use a table to record the dimensions of the various models they build.

Number of cubes long	Number of cubes wide	Number of cubes high
8	4	2
4	4	4

4 Assess 10

When evaluating student work, focus on whether students thought rationally about the problem. Questions to consider include the following:

● Did the student understand the problem?
● Was the student able to record the shape and size of a 3-dimensional box?
● Did the student have some organized way of planning and constructing models?
● Was the student able to explain his or her thinking?
● Did the student check the answers to see that they made sense?

Cumulative Review

Assign Pages 467–468

Use the Cumulative Review as a review of concepts and skills that students have previously learned.

Here are different ways you can assign these problems to your students as they work through the chapter:

- With some of the lessons in the chapter, assign a set of Cumulative Review problems to be completed as practice or for homework.
  Lesson 11.7—Problems 1–2
  Lesson 11.8—Problems 3–4
  Lesson 11.9—Problems 5–7
  Lesson 11.10—Problems 8–10
  Lesson 11.11—Problems 11–13
  Lesson 11.12—Problems 14–18
  Lesson 11.13—Problems 19–20
- At any point during the chapter, assign part or all of the Cumulative Review problems to be completed as practice or for homework.

Cumulative Review

Problems 1–2 review inverse functions using addition, subtraction, multiplication, and division, Lesson 6.4.

Problems 3–4 review dividing decimals including money, Lesson 10.8.

Problems 5–7 review multiplying by 9, Lesson 5.3.

Problems 8–10 review comparing fractions of time, Lesson 8.4.

Problems 11–13 review using decimals in weights, measures, and money, Lesson 10.1.

Problems 14–18 review dividing three-digit numbers by one-digit numbers, Lesson 7.8.

Problems 19–20 review metric capacity and converting measures, Lesson 9.5.

Monitoring Student Progress

If . . . students miss more than one problem in a section, **Then . . .** refer to the indicated lesson for remediation suggestions.

Cumulative Review

Inverse Functions (Reversing the Arrow) Lesson 6.4

Use inverse-arrow operations to find the value of *n*.

1 $n \longrightarrow \boxed{\times 11} \longrightarrow 110 \quad n = \blacksquare \quad 10$

2 $n \longrightarrow \boxed{\div 5} \longrightarrow m \longrightarrow \boxed{\times 3} \longrightarrow 9 \quad n = \blacksquare \quad 15$

Dividing Decimals Lesson 10.8

Solve. If you cannot solve, explain why.

3 The girls from the Pink team bought a present for one of the team members. Including tax, the gift cost $22.05. If 5 girls are sharing the cost equally, what is each person's share? $4.41

4 The children in the neighborhood organized a 5-kilometer relay race. Each relay team has 4 children. How far will each child run? Write your answer in kilometers and meters.   1.25 kilometers; 1,250 meters

Multiplying by 9 Lesson 5.3

Solve the following problems.

Mr. and Mrs. Hoffman challenged their 5 children to read 9 stories per week.

5 In 2 weeks how many stories will 1 child read?   18 stories

6 How many stories will 2 of the children read in 2 weeks?   36 stories

7 How many stories will all the children read in 1 week?   45 stories

Chapter 11 • Cumulative Review   467

Cumulative Review

Fractions of Time Lesson 8.4

Which is a longer period of time?

8 $\frac{1}{5}$ of an hour or $\frac{1}{4}$ of an hour? $\frac{1}{4}$ of an hour

9 $\frac{3}{4}$ of an hour or $\frac{3}{3}$ of an hour? $\frac{3}{3}$ of an hour

10 $\frac{2}{2}$ of an hour or 1 hour?   same

Where Do We See Decimals? Lesson 10.1

Solve these problems.

11 At the aviary, the average African gray parrot weighs about 520 grams. About how much do 3 parrots weigh? Write your answer in kilograms.   about 1.560 kilograms

12 If 1 bag of apples costs 321 cents, how much do 2 bags cost? Write the answer using dollars and cents. $6.42

13 The nature preserve is shaped like a square. Each side is 942 meters long. What is the perimeter of the nature preserve? Write your answer in kilometers.   3.768 kilometers

Dividing Three-Digit Numbers by One-Digit Numbers Lesson 7.8

Divide.

14 $654 \div 6$ 109
15 $2\overline{)578}$ 289
16 $798 \div 7$ 114
17 $8\overline{)344}$ 43
18 $216 \div 9$ 24

Metric Capacity Lesson 9.5

Convert each measure.

19 $6\,L = \blacksquare\,mL$ 6,000
20 $\blacksquare\,L = 2{,}500\,mL$ 2.5

468   Textbook This lesson is available in the *eTextbook.*

Wrap-Up

1 Discuss   5

Concept/Question Board

Review the Concept/Question Board with students.

- Discuss students' contributions to the Concept side of the Board.
- Have students re-pose their questions, and lead a discussion to find satisfactory answers.

Chapter Projects APPLYING

Provide an opportunity for students who have worked on one or more of the projects outlined on page 423C to share their work with the class. Allow each student or student group five minutes to present or discuss their projects. For formal assessment, use the rubrics found in *Across the Curriculum Math Connections;* the rubric for **Create a Map of Your Neighborhood** is on page 115, and the rubric for **Create a Presentation about Houses** is on page 121. For informal assessment, use the following rubric and questions.

	Exceeds Expectations	Meets Expectations	Minimally Meets Expectations
Applies mathematics in real-world situations:	❑	❑	❑
Demonstrates strong engagement in the activity:	❑	❑	❑

Create a Map of Your Neighborhood

- What information did you include on your map?
- How did you use polygons in your map?
- What symbols did you use to label items on your map?
- How did you create balance on your map?
- What do the symbols on your map represent?

Create a Presentation about Houses

- How are houses around the world different from the houses where you live?
- What houses did you choose for your presentation? Why did you choose those houses?
- What slides, flips, and turns did you identify in the architecture of your houses?
- What architectural ornamentations did you write about?
- What information did you include in your paragraph?
- How would your presentation help your clients choose a house style? How could presentations be used in other jobs?
- How is geometry related to architecture? Why would it be important to understand concepts such as slides, flips, and turns if you were an architect?

2 Assign Student Pages 25

Key Ideas Review ✓ UNDERSTANDING

Have students complete the Review questions independently or in small groups. Then discuss each question as a class.

Possible Answers

Problem ❶ Problems 1–5 review different geometrical figures. The answer to Problem 1 is angle.

Problem ❷ The answer is line.

Problem ❸ The answer is triangle or right triangle.

Problem ❹ The answer is pentagon.

Problem ❺ The answer is octagon.

Problem ❻ Problems 6–7 review concepts of rotation, reflection, and translation. The answer is rotation.

Problem ❼ The answer is reflection.

Problem ❽ Problems 8–9 review lines of symmetry. The answer to Problem 8 is 3.

Problem ❾ The answer is 5.

Problem ❿ Answers could be a variation of this:

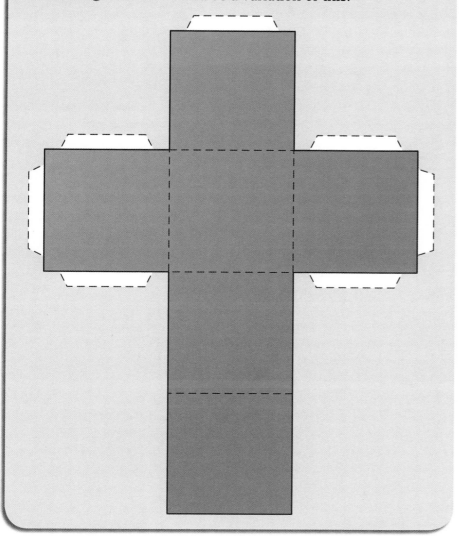

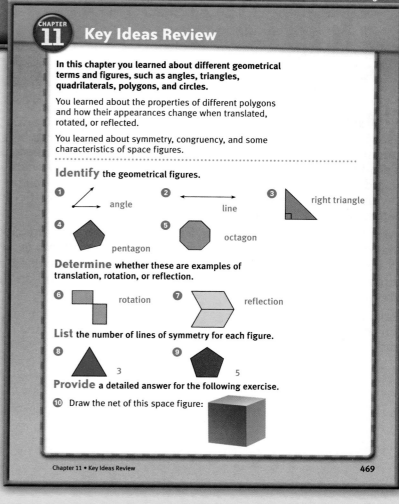

CHAPTER 11 Key Ideas Review

In this chapter you learned about different geometrical terms and figures, such as angles, triangles, quadrilaterals, polygons, and circles.

You learned about the properties of different polygons and how their appearances change when translated, rotated, or reflected.

You learned about symmetry, congruency, and some characteristics of space figures.

Identify the geometrical figures.

❶ angle   ❷ line   ❸ right triangle

❹ pentagon   ❺ octagon

Determine whether these are examples of translation, rotation, or reflection.

❻ rotation   ❼ reflection

List the number of lines of symmetry for each figure.

❽ 3   ❾ 5

Provide a detailed answer for the following exercise.

❿ Draw the net of this space figure:

Chapter 11 • Key Ideas Review   469

Chapter Review

Use the Chapter 11 Review to indicate areas in which each student is having difficulty or in which the class may need help. If students do well on the Chapter 11 Review, you may wish to skip directly to the Chapter Test; if not, you may want to spend a day or so helping students overcome their individual difficulties before taking the Practice Test.

Next to each set of problems is a list of the lessons in the chapter that covered those concepts. If they need help, students can refer to a specific lesson for additional instruction. You can also use this information to make additional assignments based on the previous lesson concepts.

Have students complete pages 470–471 on their own. For review purposes, you may want to do some of the word problems on page 471 as a class.

Monitoring Student Progress

Problems 1–20 Lessons 11.1–11.5

If . . . students miss four or more of these geometry problems,

Then . . . have students create flash cards to practice grouping, categorizing, and naming each of the figures in these lessons.

Problems 21–23 Lesson 11.7

If . . . students miss more than one of these translation problems,

Then . . . review rotation, reflection, and translation, and give students more practice with these concepts.

Problem 24 Lesson 11.10

If . . . students miss this circle problem,

Then . . . give students more opportunities to practice the terminology associated with circles.

Problems 25–28 Lessons 11.11 and 11.13

If . . . students miss more than one of these space figure problems,

Then . . . review the vocabulary, and use manipulatives to reinforce the names of the space figures.

CHAPTER 11 — Chapter Review

Lesson 11.1 ❶ Draw a line, and label two points on the line. One possible answer:
$\overleftrightarrow{A\ B}$

Lesson 11.2 ❷ Perpendicular lines intersect to form what kind of angles? **90°, or right**

Possible answer:

❸ Draw two rays intersecting to form an angle.

❹ Label the vertex in your angle from Problem 3 as point Q. **Possible answer:**
Q

Lesson 11.3 ❺ Isosceles triangles have ▢ equal sides. **2**

❻ ▢ triangles have 3 equal sides. **Equilateral**

❼ Right triangles have how many right angles? **1**

❽ **Extended Response** Draw an example of an isosceles triangle. Draw an example of an equilateral triangle.
Possible answers:

Lesson 11.4 **Answer** yes or no.

❾ Is a rhombus a parallelogram? **yes**

⓫ Is a rhombus a quadrilateral? **yes**

❿ Is a trapezoid a quadrilateral? **yes**

⓬ Is a trapezoid a parallelogram? **no**

Lesson 11.5 **Fill** in the blank.

⓭ A triangle has ▢ sides. **3**

⓱ A rhombus has ▢ sides. **4**

⓮ A rectangle has ▢ sides. **4**

⓲ An octagon has ▢ sides. **8**

⓯ A parallelogram has ▢ sides. **4**

⓳ An isosceles triangle has ▢ sides. **3**

⓰ A hexagon has ▢ sides. **6**

⓴ A pentagon has ▢ sides. **5**

eTextbook This lesson is available in the *eTextbook*.

Lesson 11.7

Determine whether the following diagrams show a reflection, a rotation, or a translation.

㉑ **translation**

㉒ **reflection**

㉓ **reflection**

Lesson 11.10

㉔ **Extended Response** Draw a circle, and label the center point P. Draw a diameter, and label it AD. Draw a radius, and label it PL. **Possible answer:**

Lesson 11.11

㉕ What is the name of this space figure?
sphere

㉖ What is the name of this space figure?
cylinder

㉗ What is the name of this space figure?
rectangular prism

Lesson 11.13

㉘ What is the volume of this figure? **15 cubic centimeters**

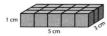
1 cm · 5 cm · 3 cm

3 **Chapter Tests** 40

Practice Test

Student Pages 472–475

- The Chapter 11 Practice Test on *Student Edition* pages 472–475 provides an opportunity to formally evaluate students' proficiency with concepts developed in this chapter.
- The content is similar to the Chapter 11 Review, in standardized format.

Problems 22 – 25 Extended Response

Students apply their understanding of geometric relationships to identify and construct congruent shapes. For the problems students must identify which two shapes appear congruent based on visual perception and why the shapes can be considered congruent. Students need to construct a figure that appears to be congruent to a given shape. While it is likely that students' shapes will not be perfectly congruent, the shapes drawn should appear congruent. The answer to Problem 22 is figures X and Y. The answer to Problem 24 is figures 1 and 3.

CHAPTER

11 **Practice Test**

Write the word or words that make the sentences true.

1. This is an example of ▇ lines. *intersecting*

2. Lines that are the same distance apart and will never cross one another are ▇ lines. *parallel*

3. This cube has ▇ faces and ▇ vertices. *6; 8*

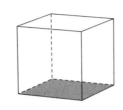

4. A square pyramid has ▇ faces and ▇ edges. *5; 8*

5. What would the area of a square be if one side measured 5 inches? *25 square inches*

Answer these questions.

6. How many milliliters are in 5 liters? *5,000 milliliters*

7. How many liters equal 12,000 milliliters? *12 liters*

Write the letter of the correct answer.

8. What kind of angle is formed by the hands on this clock?

Ⓐ acute Ⓑ obtuse
Ⓒ right Ⓓ straight

9. Gisele says the hands on the clock form a right angle. Of the following choices, what time could it be?
Ⓐ 11:35 Ⓑ 12:30
Ⓒ 3:00 Ⓓ 10:00

10. What kind of angle is formed by the hands on this clock?

Ⓐ acute Ⓑ obtuse
Ⓒ right Ⓓ straight

11. Donna drew this triangle. What kind of triangle did she draw?

Ⓐ equilateral
Ⓑ isosceles
Ⓒ right
Ⓓ obtuse

12. What is the name of this shape?

Ⓐ hexagon Ⓑ square
Ⓒ triangle Ⓓ pentagon

13. What is the name of this shape?

Ⓐ hexagon Ⓑ square
Ⓒ triangle Ⓓ pentagon

CHAPTER 11 Practice Test

14. Maya turned a shape around a point. How did she transform the shape?
- Ⓐ translation
- Ⓑ reflection
- Ⓒ rotation
- Ⓓ tessellation

15. Peter flipped his shape over an imaginary line. How did he transform his shape?
- Ⓐ translation
- Ⓑ reflection
- Ⓒ rotation
- Ⓓ tessellation

16. What transformation was carried out on the trapezoid?

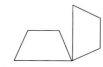

- Ⓐ rotation
- Ⓑ translation
- Ⓒ tessellation
- Ⓓ reflection

Use this circle to answer Questions 17–19.

17. How can this circle be named?
- Ⓐ Circle M
- Ⓑ Circle AB
- Ⓒ Circle CM
- Ⓓ Circle EF

18. Which is the diameter?
- Ⓐ M
- Ⓑ AB
- Ⓒ CM
- Ⓓ EF

19. Which is neither the radius nor the diameter?
- Ⓐ AM
- Ⓑ AB
- Ⓒ CM
- Ⓓ EF

20. Find the quotient. $72 \div 8 = $ ▧
- Ⓐ 12
- Ⓑ 11
- Ⓒ 9
- Ⓓ 8

21. How many pints are in 3 gallons?
- Ⓐ 12 pints
- Ⓑ 24 pints
- Ⓒ 38 pints
- Ⓓ 40 pints

Ⓢ**Textbook** This lesson is available in the **eTextbook**.

Extended Response **Solve.**

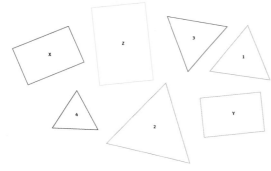

Look at the pictures, and list pairs of congruent figures.

22. Which rectangles are congruent? How do you know?

23. Draw a rectangle that is congruent to rectangle Z.

24. Which triangles are congruent? How do you know?

25. Draw a triangle that is congruent to triangle 4.

Chapter Test COMPUTING

For further evaluation instead of or in addition to this test, you might want to have students take the Chapter 11 Test provided in **Assessment**.

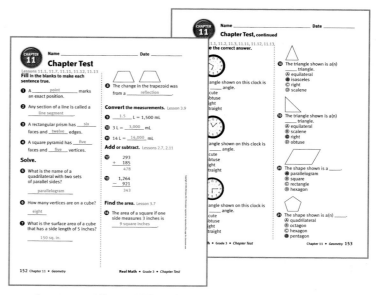

Assessment Pages 152–153

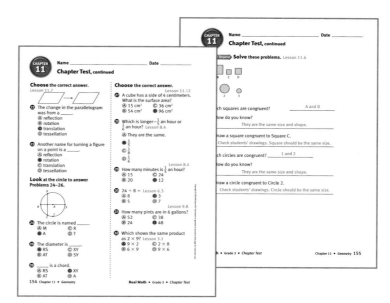

Assessment Pages 154–155

CHAPTER 11 Assessment

4 Assess and Differentiate

 Assess Use **eAssess** to record and analyze evidence of student understanding.

A Gather Evidence

Use the Daily Class Assessment Records in **Assessment** or **eAssess** to record Informal and Formal Assessments.

Informal Assessment
✓ **Key Ideas Review**

Did the student
- ☐ make important observations?
- ☐ extend or generalize learning?
- ☐ provide insightful answers?
- ☐ pose insightful questions?

Informal Assessment
✓ **Project** APPLYING

Did the student
- ☐ meet the project objectives?
- ☐ communicate clearly?
- ☐ complete the project accurately?
- ☐ connect mathematics to real-world situations?

Formal Assessment
✓ **Chapter Test**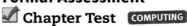

Score the test, and record the results.

B Summarize Findings

Analyze and summarize assessment data for each student. Determine which Chapter Follow-Up is appropriate for each student. Use the Student Assessment Record in **Assessment** or **eAssess** to update assessment records.

C Chapter Follow-Up • DIFFERENTIATE INSTRUCTION

Based on your observations, use these teaching strategies for chapter follow-up.

ENRICH	PRACTICE	RETEACH	INTERVENTION
If . . . students demonstrate **secure understanding** of chapter concepts,	**If . . .** students demonstrate **competent understanding** of chapter concepts,	**If . . .** students demonstrate **emerging understanding** of chapter concepts,	**If . . .** students demonstrate **minimal understanding** of chapter concepts,
Then . . . move on to the next chapter.	**Then . . .** move on to the next chapter.	**Then . . .** move on to the next chapter, but continue to provide cumulative review.	**Then . . .** intensive intervention is still needed before they start the next chapter.

A Paneful Story

Context of the Thinking Story Mr. Breezy figures out how many panes of glass are needed for each window.

Lesson Planner

OBJECTIVES
To develop logical thinking while integrating reading skills with mathematics

NCTM STANDARDS
Geometry
- Reasoning about the results of subdividing, combining, and transforming shapes
- Drawing geometric objects
- Creating and describing mental images of objects, patterns, and paths
- Using geometric models to solve problems in other areas of mathematics, such as number

Problem Solving
- Building new mathematical knowledge through problem solving
- Solving problems that arise in mathematics and in other contexts

READING STANDARDS
- Listening for details
- Predicting what will happen in a story
- Drawing conclusions
- Making inferences
- Evaluating information

Using the Thinking Story

The Thinking Story may be used anytime throughout the chapter. Read the Thinking Story "A Paneful Story" to your class as they follow along in the *Student Edition* on pages 474–477. As you read the story, give students time to think about each question, but not so much that they forget the point being made. Students will need paper and pencils to do some of the problems in this story. Students will also need red, blue, and green crayons. Do not show the illustration on page 476 until after the students have worked on the problems by themselves.

A Paneful Story

A fly kept buzzing around Mr. Breezy's window at his house in the country. Every time Mr. Breezy tried to hit it with the fly swatter, he missed. He would take careful aim, but by the time he swatted, the fly would always be somewhere else on the window.

"I know what the trouble is," said Mr. Breezy. "Every time the fly is on one pane of the window and I swat at it there, it zips over to another pane of the window. I need something so that I can swat at all the panes of the window at the same time. Then I'll get the fly."

What could Mr. Breezy use to do this? ❶

Mr. Breezy found a board that was as big as the whole window, and he waited for the fly to land.

What do you think happened when he swatted at the fly? ❷

"Oh, oh," said Mr. Breezy. "That fly was a little problem, but now I have a big problem. I've broken every pane of glass in the window. But at least I taught that fly a lesson it won't forget."

Mr. Breezy went to a hardware store. "I broke a window, and I need some panes of glass to fix it," he said. "The window is square, and all the panes are square too."

The woman in the hardware store said she could cut squares of glass that were just the right size for Mr. Breezy's window. "How many do you need?" she asked.

"Let me think," said Mr. Breezy. "All the panes in the window are broken, so I need 2 pieces of glass for the top of the window, 2 pieces for the left-hand side of the window, 2 pieces for the bottom, and 2 pieces for the right-hand side."

How many pieces of glass do you think Mr. Breezy needs altogether? ❸

Be careful. Draw the window before you answer.

"You say you need 2 pieces for the top, 2 for the left-hand side, 2 for the bottom, and 2 for the right-hand side," said the woman. "That makes 8 pieces of glass. Something must be wrong. I thought you said

476

the window was square and all the panes in it were square."

"That's right," said Mr. Breezy.

What's wrong? ❹

Try to draw a square window with 8 panes that are all square.

"You can't make a square window out of 8 squares," said the woman. "Are you sure there aren't 9 squares?"

"No," said Mr. Breezy. "As a matter of fact, there are only 4 squares."

"But you said there were 2 on the top, 2 on the bottom, and 2 on each side."

How is that possible? Draw a picture of the window to show how. ❺

"It's very simple," said Mr. Breezy. He drew a picture of a square window divided into 4 squares. "You see, there are 4 squares—2 on the top, 2 on the bottom, and 2 on each side."

"I think you could have told me that a little more clearly at the beginning," said the woman.

How could Mr. Breezy have told what he wanted in a way that would have been easier to understand? ❻

After Mr. Breezy fixed his window, he went for a walk to where a new house was being built. He asked one of the workers what he was doing. "I'm trying to figure out how many different-colored pieces of glass I need to put in this

stained-glass window," said the worker.

"You're very lucky," said Mr. Breezy. "I happen to be an expert on windows and can help you with any window problem."

"I could use some help," said the worker. "These plans don't tell me how many pieces of glass I need. I know the window is square and all the panes of glass are square, and they're all the same size. I know there are more than 7 panes and fewer than 15, but I don't know exactly how many."

Draw a picture to show how many panes the window might have. Remember, the window is square, and all the panes are square too, and the same size. There must be more than 7 panes and fewer than 15. How many panes could there be? ❼

Mr. Breezy looked at the plans. "These plans show three sizes of square windows," he said. "One has 4 panes of glass, just like my window back home. Another has 9 panes. And the other has

477

Guided Discussion

As students answer the questions in the story, ask them to communicate how they decided on their answers. Allow students to debate the answers if necessary.

❶ Possible answers might include a door or other large object.

❷ He broke the window.

❸ 4

❹ You cannot make a square window out of 8 squares.

❺ Mr. Breezy is talking about a square window divided into 4 squares.

❻ He could have told her it was a square window with 4 square panes.

❼ 9

❽ Nine is the only one of the sizes that is more than 7 and fewer than 15.

❾ Reread Mr. Breezy's instructions, allowing time between phrases for students to color the panes.

❿ in the center

⓫ Mr. Breezy is counting some of the panes twice.

⓬ 4

⓭ 4

⓮ Repeat Mr. Breezy's last instructions if necessary.

⓯ the pane in the top left-hand corner

⓰ the one in the bottom right-hand corner

---

16 panes. The window you're making must have 9 panes."

How could Mr. Breezy decide that? ❸

"You might be right," said the worker, "because 9 is the only one of the sizes that's more than 7 and fewer than 15. Thanks a lot. You really seem to know everything about windows."

"Only square windows," said Mr. Breezy. "I'm a smashing success with them."

The next day, Mr. Breezy went back to the house where the worker was making a window. "How is your stained-glass window coming along?" Mr. Breezy asked.

"I think I need your help again," the worker said. "I'm making a square window, and I know I need 9 panes of glass in it—you helped me figure that out yesterday, remember? And I know that some panes are supposed to be blue and some green and some red, but when I read the plans, I can't figure out how many I need of each kind."

"I'll try to help," said Mr. Breezy, reading over the plans. "Ah, I see. It's easy. You need 3 pieces of blue glass for the top of the window. You need 3 pieces of green glass for the bottom of the window. You need 2 pieces of blue glass on the left-hand side of the window and 2 pieces of green glass on the right-hand side of the window. And you need 1 piece of red glass."

Draw a picture of the window the way you think it is supposed to look. Color in the panes. ❾

Where does the piece of red glass go? ❿

"This doesn't work," said the worker. "You said I need 3 blue pieces for the top and 2 blue pieces for one side. That's 5 blue panes. Then you said I need 3 green pieces for the bottom and 2 green pieces for the other side. That's 5 more panes, which makes 10, plus a pane of red glass, which makes 11. I thought we'd already decided there were only 9 panes in the whole window!"

Can you explain why the numbers don't work out right? ⓫

How many blue panes should there be altogether? ⓬

How many green panes should there be altogether? ⓭

478

"It's very simple. I'll draw you a picture," said Mr. Breezy, taking some colored pencils from his pocket. He drew a square divided into 9 little squares. He colored all the top squares blue and all the bottom squares green. Then he colored the left-hand square in the middle row blue and the right-hand square in the middle row green. He colored the square in the middle red.

Is your picture just like the one Mr. Breezy drew? If not, draw another picture. ⓮

"I see," said the worker. "There are just 4 panes of blue glass altogether."

"Yes," said Mr. Breezy. "That's what I've been telling you: 3 blue panes on top and 2 blue panes on the left side."

"But," protested the worker, "you counted one of the panes twice."

Which pane was counted twice? ⓯

"Now you're getting the idea," Mr. Breezy told him. "This pane up in the corner is on the top and on the left-hand side at the same time."

"And the same thing happened with the green panes," said the

worker. "There are only 4, and this one was counted twice."

Which green pane was counted twice? ⓰

"Very good," said Mr. Breezy. "This green pane down in the corner is on the bottom and on the right-hand side at the same time."

"It's all clear to me now," said the worker, "and I think I'll figure out the rest of the windows myself."

"Good luck," said Mr. Breezy. "If you need any more expert help, just get a telephone book, open it to where the Bs are, find the name Breezy, look at the third Breezy on the list, then count down two more Breezys, then …"

"Never mind," said the worker, "I don't think I'll need more help. I think I'll get out of the window-making business and do something simpler—like build spaceships."

Chapter 11 • Thinking Story   479

Lesson Study

Reflect on each of the lessons you taught in this chapter. Rate each one on the following scale, and then consider ways to maintain or improve positive teaching experiences in the future.

Lessons	Very Effective	Effective	Less Effective	What Worked	Ways to Improve
11.1 Points and Lines					
11.2 Angles					
11.3 Triangles					
11.4 Quadrilaterals					
11.5 Polygons					
11.6 Congruence					
11.7 Slides, Flips, and Turns					
11.8 Symmetry					
11.9 Circles I					
11.10 Circles II					
11.11 Space Figures					
11.12 Nets and Surface Area					
11.13 Volume					

Lessons

Data Analysis and Probability

Teaching for Understanding

This chapter develops students' knowledge of probability. Students will be formally introduced to data analysis before exploring the concepts of probability. Students will then investigate the relationship between probability and data analysis.

Prerequisite Skills and Concepts

● Reading a Graph ● Dividing by a One-Digit Number ● Comparing Fractions

Data Analysis and Probability Skills Trace

Before Grade 3	Grade 3	After Grade 3
Grades K–2 Informally introduced to graphs and probability	**This chapter** formally introduces students to the relationship among fractions, data analysis, and probability.	Formally introduces students to fractions, probability, and measurements

Problem solving is in every lesson. This chapter includes the following:

CHAPTER INTRODUCTION Students will examine visual models of average (pp. 480I–481C).

EXPLORING PROBLEM SOLVING The first lesson explores the Organize Data (with a table and a graph) strategy (pp. 498–499, 499A). The second lesson compares methods for determining probability (pp. 512A, 513–514).

THINKING STORY In "A Chancy Birthday Party" students help a character develop strategies for opening packages (pp. 528–531).

Develop reasoning skills, and provide extensive practice.

Have students play previously introduced games.

Math Background
Data Analysis and Probability

What is Data Analysis?

"Describing data involves reading displays of data (e.g., tables, lists, graphs); that is, finding information explicitly stated in the display, recognizing graphical conventions and making direct connections between the original data and the display. the process is essentially what has been called *reading the data*…The process of organizing, and reducing, data incorporates mental actions such as ordering, grouping, and summarizing. Data reduction also includes the use of representative measures of center (often termed *measures of central tendency*) such as mean, mode, or median, and measures of spread such as range or standard deviation."

Kilpatrick, J., Swafford, J. and Findell, B. eds. *Adding It Up: Helping Children Learn Mathematics.* Washington, D.C.: National Research Council/National Academy Press, 2001, p. 289.

Collecting, organizing, displaying, and interpreting data, as well as using the information to make decisions and predictions, are skills that students will use throughout their lives. Statistical instruction should be carried out in a spirit of investigation and exploration so students can understand the data they have gathered or received. Students should develop not only the routine skills of tabulating and graphing results, but also at a higher level, the ability to detect patterns and trends in poorly organized data either before or after reorganization.

Measures of Central Tendency

MEAN
The mean can be found by adding the numbers in a set and dividing by the number of addends.

MEDIAN
The median is the middle number in a set when the numbers are arranged in numerical order. If there are an even number of numbers in the set, the median is halfway between the two middle numbers.

MODE
The mode is the most frequently occurring number in a set. A set may have more than one mode. If all numbers occur the same number of times, the set has no mode.

Tools for Organizing Data

BAR GRAPH
A bar graph is a chart with bars whose lengths are proportional to the quantities they represent.

CIRCLE GRAPH
A circle graph is a circular graph having radii dividing the circle into sectors proportional in angle and area to the relative size of the quantities represented.

TREE DIAGRAM
A tree diagram shows possible choices at each decision point, or "branch."

STEM-AND-LEAF PLOT
A stem-and-leaf is a list of numbers arranged according to their first digits. The first digits are written in the left-hand column (the "stems") and the remaining digits are arranged in rows in the right-hand column (the "leaves").

SCATTER PLOT
A scatter plot uses one dot on a coordinate grid to represent each piece of data. If the measurements used for the x-axis and y-axis are related, the dots will lie approximately along a straight line.

Basics of Probability

- Probability is the measure of how likely it is for an event to occur. The probability of an event is always a number from zero to one.

- As they work through the probability lessons in this chapter, students should recognize that whereas predicting the outcome of only one chance event is not generally possible, we can usually predict the approximate outcomes of a large number of repeated events. Informal intuitive work with this concept has been included since the Kindergarten program.

- If an event cannot happen, its probability is zero. If an event is certain to happen, its probability is one. However, the converse is not true. If the probability of an event is zero, the event could still occur.

What Research Says

About Probability and Statistics

How Children Learn About Data Analysis and Probability

"Data analysis contains one big idea: classifying, organizing, representing, and using information to ask and answer questions. The developmental continuum for data analysis includes growth in classifying and counting to sort objects and quantify their groups....Children eventually become capable of simultaneously classifying and counting, for example, counting the number of colors in a group of objects."

Clements, Douglas and J. Sarama, eds. *Engaging Young Children in Mathematics: Standards for Early Childhood Mathematics Education.* Mahwah, New Jersey: Lawrence Erlbaum Associates, Publishers, 2004, p. 56.

"Representing data in visual displays requires the generation of different organizations of data according to certain conventions. Many elementary students have difficulty creating visual displays of data. First and second graders' knowledge of how to represent data appears to be constrained by difficulties in sorting and organizing data, and technology has been found to be helpful in overcoming those difficulties. Studies of middle school students have revealed substantial gaps in their abilities to construct graphs from given data. Processes like organizing data and conventions like labeling and scaling are crucial to data representation and are strongly connected to the concepts and processes of measurement. Given the difficulties students experience, instruction might need to differentiate these processes and conventions more sharply and utilize the potential of technology to make them more accessible to students."

Kilpatrick, J., J. Swafford, and B. Findell, eds. *Adding It Up: Helping Children Learn Mathematics.* Washington, D.C.: National Research Council/ National Academy Press, 2001, p. 290.

"Elementary school students have difficulty analyzing and interpreting data. In one study, 80% of the first and second graders interviewed gave idiosyncratic or incomplete responses when they attempted to analyze data from a line plot and a bar graph. In another study, almost all the fourth and fifth graders could describe bar graphs, but fewer could interpret them, and many fewer still could use the graphs to predict."

Kilpatrick, J., J. Swafford, and B. Findell, eds. *Adding It Up: Helping Children Learn Mathematics.* Washington, D.C.: National Research Council/ National Academy Press, 2001, p. 291.

Research-Based Teaching Techniques

"The interdependency of the states of data analysis places high demands on young students and their teachers. The students are only beginning to learn how to turn observations into data and are not yet aware of how they can probe data to answer questions. Unlike the expert, novices have little relevant experience they can use to plan ahead. Helping students raise questions that interest them and that they can productively pursue is a challenge for the teacher. Left on their own, students are often overwhelmed given too much structure and assistance, or they can lose sight of the big picture and their motivation for looking at data. The challenge for teachers is to "help students keep hold of the big picture as they explore the "parts." Doing so requires finding ways to manage complexity so that students can think about the questions they are pursuing, focusing not on "features of the graph" per se, but on "its implications as a representation of something real.""

Konold, Clifford and Higgins, Traci in Kilpatrick, Jeremy, Martin, W. Gary, and Schifter, Deborah, eds. *A Research Companion to Principles and Standards for School Mathematics.* Reston, VA: National Council of Teachers of Mathematics, Inc. 2003, pp. 212–213.

"Overall, comparisons of event probabilities are difficult for students and seem to be linked to their proficiency with rational numbers."

Kilpatrick, J., J. Swafford, and B. Findell, eds. *Adding It Up: Helping Children Learn Mathematics.* Washington, D.C.: National Research Council/ National Academy Press, 2001, p. 292.

 RESEARCH IN ACTION

Graphs In Chapter 12 students develop ability to analyze data. Lessons on misleading graphs develop their awareness of real-world applications of statistical information.

Real World Data Chapter 12 provides thorough development of statistics in real world contexts so that students make the connections between data representation and interpretation and the real world applications of that data.

Vocabulary

data (Lesson 12.1) information from which conclusions can be drawn; facts and figures

frequency (Lesson 12.2) the number of times something happens

line graph (Lesson 12.7) a graph that represents data as ordered pairs connected with a line

line plot (Lesson 12.8) a data graph showing frequency on a number line

median (Lesson 12.4) the middle number in a set of data

mean (Lesson 12.4) the typical or usual amount, which is found by dividing the sum of two or more quantities by the number of quantities; another name for average

mode (Lesson 12.4) the number appearing most frequently in a set of data

outlier (Lesson 12.3) a number that is far off from all other numbers in a data set

probability (Lesson 12.10) the ratio of the number of chances favoring the occurrence of a particular event to the total number of possible

range (Lesson 12.3) difference between the greatest and least numbers in a set of data

sample (Lesson 12.1) a smaller set of data that belongs to a larger set of data and reflects the characteristics of members in the larger set

scatter plot (Lesson 12.9) a graph that represents data as ordered pairs

stem-and-leaf plot (Lesson 12.8) a graph showing data from least to greatest using the digits from the greatest place value to group the data

tally (Lesson 12.2) a series of marks to keep a record of data

tree chart (Lesson 12.12) a display of data that shows possible combinations, where the *trunk* represents the first set of choices and the *branches* represent the second, third, etc. set of choices

variability (Lesson 12.3) the likelihood that something will change

English Learner

Cognates

For English learners, a quick way to acquire new English vocabulary is to build on what is known in the primary language.

English	Spanish
false	falso
information	información
common	común
range	rango
mode	modo
median	mediana
results	resultados
table	tabla
to compare	comparar
impossible	imposible
certain	cierto
predictions	predicciones

Access Vocabulary

English learners may understand words in different contexts or not understand idioms. Review chapter vocabulary for this concern. For example:

census	a count of all the U.S. residents every ten years
above average	more than the average
below average	less than the average
table	a chart used to organize data
increase	to get larger
decrease	to get smaller
false statement	a statement that is intentionally misleading, incorrect, or not factual
pick	to select
sum	the answer to an addition problem
outcome	the result of some combination or action

Chapter Planner

Lessons	Objectives	NCTM Standards	State Standards
12.1 Collecting Data—Samples pages 482A–483A	To introduce students to graphs and data analysis	Data Analysis and Probability, Communications	
12.2 Collecting Data—Tally Marks pages 484A–485A	To introduce students to tally marks and data analysis	Data Analysis and Probability, Connections	
12.3 Summarizing Data pages 486A–487A	To introduce the terms variability, range, and outlier	Data Analysis and Probability, Communications	
12.4 Mean, Median, and Mode pages 488A–489A	To introduce the terms mean, median, and mode	Data Analysis and Probability, Connections	
12.5 Displaying Data pages 490A–491A	To explore how to display data in a table	Geometry, Data Analysis and Probability, Connections	
12.6 Graphs That Compare pages 492A–493A	To explore pictographs, single bar graphs, and circle graphs	Data Analysis and Probability, Representation	
12.7 Graphs Showing Change pages 494A–497B	To explore line graphs	Data Analysis and Probability, Connections	
12.8 Graphs Showing How Data Is Grouped pages 502A–503A	To investigate different ways to group data	Data Analysis and Probability, Communication	
12.9 Interpreting and Analyzing Data pages 504A–505A	To explore scatter plots	Data Analysis and Probability, Connections	
12.10 Probability—Impossible to Certain pages 506A–507A	To introduce students to probability	Data Analysis and Probability, Communication, Connections	
12.11 Probability—Predictions and Experiments pages 508A–509A	To explore the concept of probability	Data Analysis and Probability, Communication, Connections	
12.12 Displaying and Analyzing Outcomes pages 510A–511A	To explore tree diagrams and stem-and-leaf plots	Algebra, Data Analysis, Probability	

Vocabulary	Manipulatives and Materials	Games to reinforce skills and concepts
data sample	Response Wheels	
tally frequency	Response Wheels	
variability range outlier	Response Wheels	
median mode mean	• Response Wheels • Guided Discussion on transparency or worksheet (optional)	
	• Response Wheels • Coloring items such as crayons, markers, and coloring pencils	
	Response Wheels	
line graph	Response Wheels	
line plot stem-and-leaf plot	Response Wheels	
scatter plot	Response Wheels	
probability	Number Cubes	
	Number Cubes (optional)	
tree chart	Response Wheels	

Additional Resources

Differentiated Instruction

Intervention Support Guide Provides instruction for the following prerequisite skills:

- Lesson 12.A Reading a Graph
- Lesson 12.B Dividing by a One-Digit Number
- Lesson 12.C Comparing Fractions

Enrichment Support Guide Extends lesson concepts

Practice Reinforces lesson skills and concepts

Reteach Support Guide Provides alternate instruction for lesson concepts

English Learner Support Guide Previews and reviews lesson concepts and vocabulary for English learners

Technology

The following electronic resources are available:

- Planner Lessons 12.1–12.12
- Presentation Lessons 12.1–12.12
- Textbook Lessons 12.1–12.12
- Assess Lessons 12.1–12.12
- MathTools *Graphing Tool* Lessons 12.6 and 12.7
  Probability Lessons 12.10 and 12.11

Assessment

Informal Assessment rubrics at the end of each lesson provide daily evaluation of student math proficiency.

Chapter Planner, continued

Problem Solving

Problem Solving	When to Use	Objectives	NCTM Standards	Skills Covered
Chapter Introduction pp. 480I–481C 15–30 minutes	Use after the Chapter 12 Pretest.	To introduce chapter concepts in a problem-solving setting	Data Analysis and Probability, Connections	Averages
Exploring Problem Solving pp. 498–499, 499A 30–45 minutes	Use anytime during the chapter.	To explore methods of solving nonroutine problems	Data Analysis and Probability, Communication	Data Organization
Exploring Problem Solving pp. 512–512A 45–60 minutes	Use anytime after first Exploring Problem Solving	To explore methods of solving nonroutine problems	Data Analysis and Probability, Connections	Probability
Thinking Story—A Chancy Birthday Party pp. 522–523, 524–525 20–30 minutes	Use anytime during the chapter.	To develop logical reasoning while integrating reading skills with mathematics	Data Analysis and Probability	Collecting data Predicting probability

Review

Review	When to Use	Objectives	NCTM Standards	Skills Covered
Cumulative Review (p. 500–501) 15–30 minutes	Use anytime after Lesson 12.7.	To review concepts and skills taught earlier in the year	Data Analysis and Probability, Connections	Metric weight, arrays, multidigit subtraction, multidigit division, ordered pairs, equalities, inequalities, and angles
Cumulative Review (p. 513–514) 15–30 minutes	Use anytime after Lesson 12.12.	To review concepts and skills taught earlier in the year	Data Analysis and Probability, Communication	Subtracting decimals, fractions of linear measure, transformations, and arrow notation
Chapter 12 Review (pp. 516A, 516–517) 30–45 minutes	Use after Lesson 12.12.	To review concepts and skills taught in the chapter	Data Analysis and Probability, Connections, Communication	Sampling, tally marks, stem-and-left plots, and probability

Assessment

Assessment	When to Use	Objectives	NCTM Standards	Skills Covered
Informal Assessment Rubrics (pp. 483A–511A) 5 minutes per student	Use at the end of each lesson.	To provide daily evaluation of math proficiency	Data Analysis and Probability, Connections, Communication	Computer, Understanding, Reasoning, Applying, Engaging
Pretest Assessment (*Assessment* pp. 157–158) 15–30 minutes	Use prior to Chapter 12.	To provide assessment of prerequisite and chapter topics	Data Analysis and Probability	Arithmetic Computations
Individual Oral Assessment (pp. 501A) 5 minutes per student	Begin use after Lesson 12.7.	To provide alternate means of assessing students' progress	Data Analysis and Probability, Connections, Communication	Probability and Graphing
Mastery Checkpoint (*Assessment* p. T77) 5 minutes per student	Use after Lesson 12.7.	To provide assessment of mastery of key skills	Data Analysis and Probability, Connections, Communication	Probability and Graphing
Chapter 12 Practice Test (pp. 518–519, 520–521) 30–45 minutes	Use after or in place of the Chapter 12 Review.	To provide assessment or additional practice of the lesson concepts	Data Analysis and Probability, Connections, Communication	Probability and Graphing
Chapter 12 Test (*Assessment* pp. 165–168) 30–45 minutes	Use after or in place of the Chapter 12 Review.	To provide assessment of the chapter concepts	Data Analysis and Probability, Connections, Communication	Probability and Graphing

Technology Resources and Support

Visit SRAonline.com for online versions of the **Real Math** eSuite.

Technology for Teachers

e Presentation	**Lessons 12.1–12.12** Use the **ePresentation** to interactively present chapter content.
e Planner	Use the Chapter and Lesson Planners to outline activities and time frames for Chapter 12.
e Assess	Students can take the following assessments in **eAssess**: • Chapter Pretest • Mastery Checkpoint • Chapter Test Teachers can record results and print reports for all assessments in this chapter.
e MathTools	**Graphing Tool Lessons 12.6 and 12.7** **Probability Tool Lessons 12.10 and 12.11**

Technology for Students

e Textbook	An electronic, interactive version of the **Student Edition** is available for all lessons in Chapter 12.
e MathTools	**Graphing Tool Lessons 12.6 and 12.7** **Probability Tool Lessons 12.10 and 12.11**
e Games	Encourage students to play games previously introduced in the book.
TECH KNOWLEDGE	**TechKnowledge** Level 3 provides lessons that specifically teach the Unit 10 Internet applications that students can use in this chapter's projects.

Data Analysis and Probability

1 Introduce Chapter 12 10

Chapter Objectives
Explain to students that in this chapter they will build on what they already know about data analysis and probability. Explain that in this chapter students will

- learn about the properties of graphs.
- learn about probability.
- predict outcomes.

Pretest COMPUTING

Administer the Pretest on **Assessment** pages 157 and 158. The Pretest covers the following skills and topics from the chapter:

- Comparing numbers (Problems 1–3)
- Ordering whole numbers (Problems 4 and 5)
- Addition and subtraction (Problems 6–8)
- Finding area and perimeter (Problems 9 and 10)
- Finding range, median, mean, and mode (Problems 11–14)
- Reading a coordinate grid (Problems 15–17)
- Determine the probability (Problems 18–22)

Chapter 12 Pretest

Access Prior Knowledge UNDERSTANDING

Have students share any experiences they have had on farms or seeing or reading about farms in movies, in books, and on television. Ask them how they think farms in other parts of the world might be different from farms in the United States and how they might be similar.

2 Exploring Problem Solving 30

Tell Students In Today's Lesson They Will
- look at papayas from two different farms.
- decide which farm grows larger papayas.

Materials
None

Using Student Pages

Have students look at page 480 and talk about what they see that is different from what they know about U.S. farms and what they see that is similar.

Read with students the information on page 481. Go over the problem and information on page 481.

Students may be interested in the following information about papayas:

- Papayas are also called *pawpaws*.
- A single papaya can grow as large as 20 pounds.
- Some cultures make medicine from the seeds and leaves of papayas.
- Papayas can be used to make meat tenderizer.

To make sure students understand the information on page 481, ask questions such as the following:

- **Look at the papayas from the González farm. How many different sizes are there?** three
- **If the smallest papaya weighs 1 pound, how many pounds do you think the next larger size weighs?** about 2 pounds; Some students may realize that if one papaya is twice as heavy as another, it will be less than twice as wide.
- **From which farm do the papayas seem to be closer in size?** Answers may vary, but students should agree that the three papayas from the Gonzalez farm are close in size and the ones from the Castillo farm are also close except for one very large papaya.
- **Do you know how these papayas were picked at each farm?** No information is given about how they were picked.

Go over Problems 1–3 with students.

CHAPTER 12 — Data Analysis and Probability

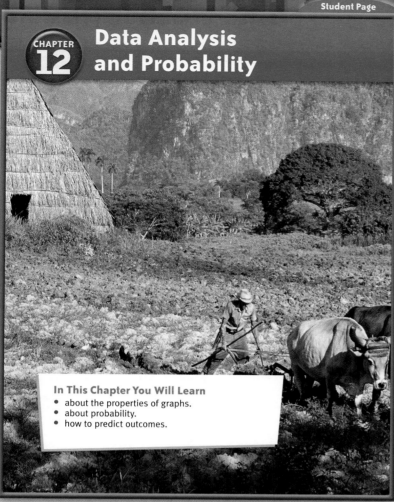

In This Chapter You Will Learn
- about the properties of graphs.
- about probability.
- how to predict outcomes.

Problem Solving

Have you ever tasted a papaya? It is a sweet and nutritious fruit picked from fast-growing plants that can grow 6 to 10 feet tall in less than a year.

Areas of the world where papayas are grown.

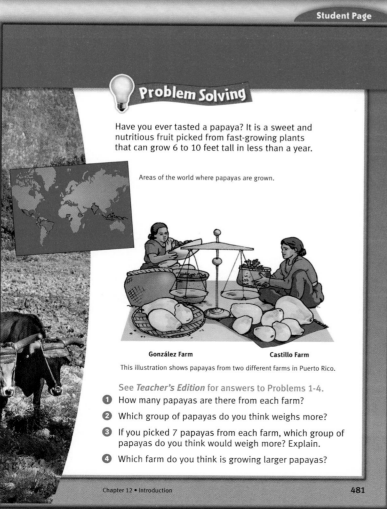

González Farm   **Castillo Farm**

This illustration shows papayas from two different farms in Puerto Rico.

See *Teacher's Edition* for answers to Problems 1-4.
1. How many papayas are there from each farm?
2. Which group of papayas do you think weighs more?
3. If you picked 7 papayas from each farm, which group of papayas do you think would weigh more? Explain.
4. Which farm do you think is growing larger papayas?

Chapter 12 • Introduction   481

Answer to Problem 1
Through counting students should determine that three papayas are from the González farm and seven from the Castillo farm.

Answer to Problem 2
Based on visual estimation, the ones from the Castillo farm seem to weigh more.

Answer to Problem 3
Students might use visual estimation and some direct comparison. For example, students can draw or imagine four more papayas from the González farm like the three that are already shown. They might reason that each papaya from the González farm is larger than any of the six smaller papayas from the Castillo farm, and the one large papaya from the Castillo farm is not large enough to make up the difference. However, there is no guarantee that the papayas shown are representative of the papayas on the farm, especially since there are only three from one farm and seven from the other.

Have students work in groups to answer Problem 4. Provide help as needed. Encourage students to estimate.

Answer to Problem 4
Students may offer several reasons for choosing either farm. The González farm appears to produce larger papayas on a regular basis. On the other hand, the Castillo farm does show a potential for yielding very large papayas. To make matters even more uncertain, no information is given about how the papayas were sampled or whether they are all at the same stage of maturity (except for what you can infer from the illustration).

Concept/Question Board APPLYING

Questions
Have students think of and write three questions they have about data analysis and probability and how they can be used. Then have them select one question to post on the Question side of the Board.

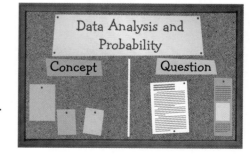

Concepts
As students work through the chapter, have them collect examples of how data analysis and probability are used in everyday situations. For each example, have them write a problem that relates to the item(s). Have them display their examples on the Concept side of the Board. Suggest the following:
- weather trends
- height
- fund raising

Answers
Throughout the chapter, have students post answers to the questions and solutions to the problems on the Board.

CHAPTER 12 Introduction

3 Reflect 10

Effective Communication Have groups present their answer to Problem 4 and reasons for their answer. After each group presents, ask questions such as the following:

■ **Did the group give specific reasons for their answer?**
■ **Were there additional factors that the group could have considered?**

Afterward, discuss why groups came up with different answers and how the answers can all be reasonable.

Tell students that in the lessons to come they will learn more about choosing and using samples to draw conclusions.

 Home Connection

At this time, you may want to send home the letter on pages 46–49 of *Home Connection.* This letter describes what students will be learning and what activities they can do at home to support their work in school.

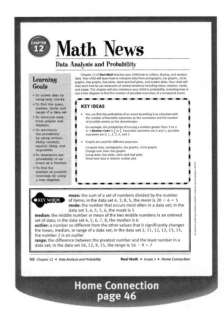

Home Connection
page 46

Assess and Differentiate

 Assess Use **eAssess** to record and analyze evidence of student understanding.

A Gather Evidence

Use the Daily Class Assessment Record in **Assessment** or **eAssess** to record Informal and Formal assessments.

Informal Assessment
✓ **Access Prior Knowledge**
Did the student UNDERSTANDING
- ❏ make important observations?
- ❏ extend or generalize learning?
- ❏ provide insightful answers?
- ❏ pose insightful questions?

Informal Assessment
✓ **Concept/Question Board**
Did the student APPLYING
- ❏ apply learning in new situations?
- ❏ contribute concepts?
- ❏ contribute answers?
- ❏ connect mathematics to real-world situations?

Formal Assessment
✓ **Pretest** COMPUTING
Review student answers in each problem set.
- ❏ Comparing numbers (Problems 1–3)
- ❏ Ordering whole numbers (Problems 4 and 5)
- ❏ Addition and subtraction (Problems 6–8)
- ❏ Finding area and perimeter (Problems 9 and 10)
- ❏ Reading a coordinate grid (Problems 15–17)
- ❏ Determine the probability (Problems 18–22)

B Summarize Findings

Analyze and summarize assessment data for each student. Determine which Assessment Follow-Up is appropriate for each student. Use the Student Assessment Record in **Assessment** or **eAssess** to update assessment records.

C Assessment Follow-Up • DIFFERENTIATE INSTRUCTION

Based on your observations of each student, use these teaching strategies for a general approach to the chapter. Look for specific Differentiate Instruction and Monitoring Student Progress strategies in each lesson that relate specifically to the lesson content.

ENRICH	PRACTICE	RETEACH	INTERVENTION	ENGLISH LEARNER
If . . . students demonstrate **secure understanding** of chapter concepts, **Then . . .** move quickly through the chapter or use **Enrichment** Lessons 12.1–12.12 as assessment follow-up to extend and apply understanding.	**If . . .** students grasp chapter concepts with **competent understanding,** **Then . . .** use **Practice** Lessons 12.1–12.12 as lesson follow-up to develop fluency.	**If . . .** students have prerequisite understanding but demonstrate **emerging understanding** of chapter concepts, **Then . . .** use **Reteach** Lessons 12.4 and 12.10 to reteach lesson concepts.	**If . . .** students are not competent with prerequisite skills, **Then . . .** use **Intervention** Lessons 12.A–12.C before each lesson to develop fluency with prerequisite skills.	Use **English Learner Support Guide** Lessons 12.1–12.12 for strategies to preteach lesson vocabulary and concepts.

Math Across the Curriculum

Preview the chapter projects with students. Assign projects to extend and enrich concepts in this chapter.

Categorize Sheep Facts

SCIENCE WebQuest

3–4 weeks

MATH OBJECTIVE
To reinforce studies of tally charts by using tally charts to categorize sheep facts

SCIENCE OBJECTIVE
To reinforce studies of animals by researching facts about sheep

TECHNOLOGY OBJECTIVE
To use the Internet to research breeds of sheep

Have students use technology to

- research sheep.
- record research by using tally marks in tables.
- print photographs of sheep breeds.

For this project, students use the Internet to investigate the following information:

- facts about sheep
- sheep breed information

For specific step-by-step instructions for this project, see *Across the Curriculum Math Connections* pages 122–127.

Knowledge Age Skills

Effective Communication Students create exhibits to clearly communicate their research.

Teamwork Students work together to select and research sheep breeds.

TECH KNOWLEDGE *TechKnowledge* Level 3 provides lessons that specifically teach the Unit 10 Internet applications that students can use in this project.

Research Horse Farming

SOCIAL STUDIES

3 weeks

MATH OBJECTIVE
To reinforce studies of data collection by collecting and calculating data about horse farming

SOCIAL STUDIES OBJECTIVE
To reinforce studies of careers by researching horse farming

TECHNOLOGY OBJECTIVE
To use a spreadsheet program to create a spreadsheet of horse farming costs

Have students use mathematics to collect and calculate data about horse farming. To broaden the social studies concept, have students research information about careers you are currently studying.

As part of the project, students should consider the following issues:

- types of work horse farmers do
- kinds of horse farms
- costs associated with starting a horse farm

For specific step-by-step instructions for this project, see *Across the Curriculum Math Connections* pages 128–131.

Knowledge Age Skills

Problem Formulation, Planning, and Strategizing Students find information about what is needed to start a horse farm.

Effective Communication Students create spreadsheets to communicate information about the costs of starting a horse farm.

Lesson Planner

OBJECTIVES
- To review graphing and data collecting through gathering and interpreting samples
- To begin organizing data in a manner that will assist in data interpretation

NCTM STANDARDS
Data Analysis and Probability
Collecting data using observations, surveys, and experiments

Communications
Using the language of mathematics to express mathematical ideas precisely

MATERIALS
Examples of various tables of information (optional)

TECHNOLOGY
ⓔPresentation Lesson 12.1

TEST PREP
Cumulative Review
Mental Math reviews comparing fractions (Lesson 8.6).

Extended Response
Problems 1–4

Collecting Data— Samples

Context of the Lesson Students have experienced informal gathering of samples for surveys in Grade 2. In this chapter students will begin exploring ways to organize the data to make gathering information practical. Throughout the chapter, students will work with various tables and graphs to give them a wealth of organizational tables from which to draw. In Grade 4 students will use line graphs also in coordinate graphing.

See page 480B for Math Background for teachers for this lesson.

Planning for Learning ● DIFFERENTIATE INSTRUCTION

INTERVENTION

If . . . students lack the prerequisite skill of reading a graph,

Then . . . teach *Intervention* Lesson 12.A.

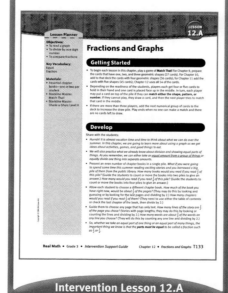

Intervention Lesson 12.A

ENGLISH LEARNER

Preview

If . . . students need language support,

Then . . . use Lesson 12.1 in *English Learner Support Guide* to preview lesson concepts and vocabulary.

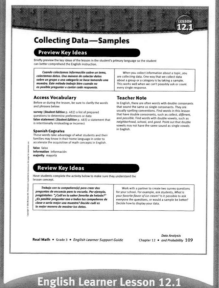

English Learner Lesson 12.1

ENRICH

If . . . students are proficient in the lesson concepts,

Then . . . emphasize the student pages.

PRACTICE

If . . . students would benefit from additional practice,

Then . . . extend Strategy Building before assigning the student pages.

RETEACH

If . . . students are having difficulty understanding data and sampling,

Then . . . extend Guided Discussion before assigning the student pages.

Vocabulary

data \dā´ta\ *pl. n.* information from which conclusions can be drawn; facts and figures

sample \sam´pel\ *n.* a smaller set of data that belongs to a larger set of data and reflects the characteristics of members in the larger set.

Spanish Cognates
false falso
information información
majority mayoría

Mental Math 10

Review comparing fractions with students. Have students use thumbs-up if the comparison is greater than, thumbs-down if the comparison is less than, and open hand if the comparison is equal to. Use examples such as the following:

a. $\frac{1}{2} \ \blacksquare \ \frac{1}{4}$ up

b. $\frac{2}{5} \ \blacksquare \ \frac{3}{5}$ down

c. $\frac{3}{4} \ \blacksquare \ \frac{1}{3}$ up

d. $\frac{3}{6} \ \blacksquare \ \frac{1}{2}$ open

e. $\frac{7}{7} \ \blacksquare \ \frac{8}{8}$ open

f. $\frac{0}{9} \ \blacksquare \ \frac{4}{5}$ down

g. $\frac{1}{17} \ \blacksquare \ \frac{1}{4}$ down

h. $\frac{11}{12} \ \blacksquare \ \frac{1}{2}$ up

1 Develop 20

Tell Students In Today's Lesson They Will

explore data gathering and ways to begin organizing that data.

Guided Discussion UNDERSTANDING Whole Group

Students have been gathering data since the start of their school years. However, they may not be proficient in organizing that data. On the board, record the results from the class question *In what month were you born?* Be sure to just list the data/answers, being aware of not trying to organize it for students. After each student has answered the question, discuss with students some of the ways they think the data could be better organized. Accept all reasonable answers, and talk about the good points of each idea. Ask questions such as the following:

■ **What is the most common month in this classroom?**
■ **Will this be the most common month for other classes in our grade level? Why or why not?**
■ **Will this be the most common month for other grades in our school? Why or why not?**
■ **What would be a way to find the most common month for the students in the whole school?** Accept all reasonable answers, exploring each suggestion.

Introduce students to the term *data* by showing the information that was collected on the board or overhead projector. Talk about other times they have gathered data; for example, gathering drink orders at a party, asking people what their favorite color is, finding probability, and so on.

Ask students if they believe this classroom is a good example of what the most common birth month is for third graders. Introduce the word *sample,* explaining that a sample should allow us to use the data to see what month the majority of third graders in the school were born. Ask questions such as the following about other samples:

■ **Would this classroom be a good sampling of third graders in the school? Why or why not?** most likely yes because they are one section of the overall third grade

■ **Would this classroom be a good sampling of third graders in the United States? Why or why not?** most likely yes because they live in one area of the United States.
■ **Would this classroom be a good sampling of the third graders in the world? Why or why not?** most likely no because many schools outside of the United States don't have levels labeled as third grade
■ **What are some ways to get an even better sampling of the third graders in the United States?** Accept all reasonable ideas. Discuss each suggestion for its positive points no matter what the probability is of performing the task.

If it hasn't been discussed, suggest ideas such as mailing out surveys, posting a survey on the Internet, researching similar studies in different parts of the United States, and so on.

Strategy Building   REASONING Small Group

Have students come to the board to write their *one* favorite color. If you have a small class, you may want students to write more than one color or perhaps gather data from other classes as well. Have students break into small groups, and as a group, have them create a chart to organize the data. Encourage students to be creative. There is no right or wrong way as long as the data is organized in a readable manner. Post various examples of types of charts throughout the classroom, and suggest students look at the charts if they are stuck on how to organize their data. When the class has finished, discuss each chart, and then post them for reference so students can see growth as the chapter progresses.

2 Assign Student Pages 20

Pages 482–483   APPLYING

Have students complete the exercises on pages 482 and 483 independently.

Monitoring Student Progress

If . . . students have a difficult time creating the table on page 483,

Then . . . have them use a smaller amount of data.

As Students Finish

 Game

Allow students to play any previously introduced game, or assign games based on needed skills practice.

LESSON 12.1 Collecting Data—Samples

Key Ideas

When you collect information about a topic, you are collecting data. Data can be collected in many different ways and for many different reasons.

If you are collecting a large group of data, such as from the students in your school or about the animals in your neighborhood, you often take a **sample**. A sample is a smaller portion of a larger set of data; it allows you to make an estimate of what the data would show if you collected and analyzed all of it. Since it is impossible to ask questions of every single person, it is important that your sample reflects properties of the larger group of data as much as possible.

Extended Response **Answer** the following questions.

Imagine that your teacher has a can that is filled with 24 marbles.

❶ Your teacher pulls out 2 marbles and they are both blue. Based on this, what portion of the marbles in the can do you think are blue? Are there other colors of marbles in the can?

❷ Your teacher replaces the two marbles, shakes the can, and then pulls out 6 marbles — 3 blue and 3 red. Based on this, what portion of the marbles in the can do you think are blue?

❸ Your teacher replaces the 6 marbles, shakes the can, and then pulls out 18 marbles — 6 blue and 12 red. Which color of marble do you think there is more of in the can, red or blue?

❹ How could you know the exact amount of each color of marble in the can? Would you want to do that for a can with 1,000 marbles in it?

❶ possible answer: all of them cannot say

❷ possible answer: half

❸ this result would indicate red

❹ pull out all 24 marbles probably not; it would take a long time

482   **Textbook** This lesson is available in the *eTextbook*.

Sometimes the surveys and samples have already been gathered for you; it is up to you to organize the data. Putting the information in a chart or a table will help you organize the information and find important items from the data.

Create a table for the information below.

❺ Mr. Anakin's science class saw the following birds on their field trip two weeks ago. The class also recorded how many times they saw each type of bird.
Cardinal—6 times
Blue Jay—8 times
Robin—10 times
Woodpecker—2 times
Canary—7 times
Red-Tailed Hawk—1 time
Turkey Vulture—3 times
Barn Owl—1 time
Hummingbird—4 times
Finch—4 times
Bald Eagle—1 time
Peregrine Falcon—1 time

❻ Write one true and one false statement about the information above. Accept all reasonable answers.

Accept all reasonable tables that show a grouping of birds and the number of times each appeared.

Chapter 12 • Lesson 1   483

---

3 Reflect

10

Guided Discussion **REASONING**

Whole Group

Ask the class what they think is the most common of the 26 letters in the English language. Allow students to make suggestions and explain why they think their choices are correct. After a few minutes, ask the class how they could find out, without looking up the answer (for example, on the internet). If it is not mentioned by students, suggest that they could count how often each letter appears in a sample of writing. Ask questions such as the following:

■ **Would a page in their math book be a good sample?**
■ **Would a page in their reading book be a good sample?**
■ **How many pages would they need to count to be confident that their answers are correct?**

It is not necessary to have an answer at this time; it is only useful to raise the question and have students think about what constitutes a fair sample.

Extended Response

Problems 1–4 These problems are meant to give students a qualitative feel for data sampling. Contradictory conclusions may be correctly deduced depending on which sample is used—the marbles are all blue (Problem 1), half of the marbles are blue (Problem 2), or the marbles are mostly red (Problem 3). The level of confidence should increase with the sample size; the only way to know the exact distribution of colors would be to sample all the marbles. This is acceptable for a small number of marbles but would quickly become cumbersome for increasing numbers.

SOCIAL STUDIES **Curriculum Connection:** The United States census is a very large survey taken every ten years. Students may be interested in researching the history and data from the census for their state or another.

Review **Cumulative Review:** For cumulative review of previously learned skills, see page 500–501.

Family Involvement: Assign the *Practice, Reteach,* or *Enrichment* activities depending on the needs of your students.
Encourage students to gather and graph data with a friend or a relative.

Concept/Question Board: Have students look for additional examples using graphing and post them on the Concept/Question Board.

Math Puzzler: Write two numbers with a sum greater than 70 and less than 80 and a difference greater than 10 and less than 20. Possible answers are 44 and 30, 42 and 30, 43 and 30.

Assess and Differentiate

 Assess Use *eAssess* to record and analyze evidence of student understanding.

A Gather Evidence

Use the Daily Class Assessment Records in *Assessment* or *eAssess* to record daily observations.

Informal Assessment

✓ **Strategy Building**

Did the student **REASONING**

- ❏ provide a clear explanation?
- ❏ communicate reasons and strategies?
- ❏ choose appropriate strategies?
- ❏ argue logically?

Informal Assessment

✓ **Student Pages**

Did the student **APPLYING**

- ❏ apply learning in new situations?
- ❏ contribute concepts?
- ❏ contribute answers?
- ❏ connect mathematics to real-world situations?

B Summarize Findings

Analyze and summarize assessment data for each student. Determine which Assessment Follow-Up is appropriate for each student. Use the Student Assessment Record in *Assessment* or *eAssess* to update assessment records.

Assessment page T41

C Assessment Follow-Up ● DIFFERENTIATE INSTRUCTION

Based on your observations, use these teaching strategies for assessment follow-up.

INTERVENTION

Review student performance on *Intervention* Lesson 12.A to see if students have mastered prerequisite skills for this lesson.

ENGLISH LEARNER

Review

Use Lesson 12.1 in *English Learner Support Guide* to review lesson concepts and vocabulary.

ENRICH

If . . . students are proficient in the lesson concepts,

Then . . . encourage them to work on chapter projects or *Enrichment* Lesson 12.1.

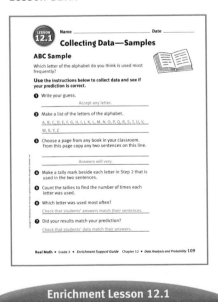

Enrichment Lesson 12.1

PRACTICE

If . . . students would benefit from additional practice,

Then . . . assign *Practice* Lesson 12.1.

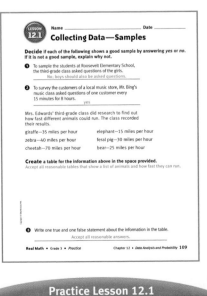

Practice Lesson 12.1

RETEACH

If . . . students struggle with the idea of collecting data samples,

Then . . . have them discuss possible samples for answering specific questions. For example, if they wanted to know the girls' favorite store, would they ask the football team?

OBJECTIVES
To explore tally charts and how they can be used to organize data

NCTM STANDARDS
Data Analysis and Probability
Collecting data using observations, surveys, and experiments

Connections
Recognizing and using connections among mathematical ideas

MATERIALS
*Response Wheels

TECHNOLOGY
Presentation Lesson 12.2

TEST PREP
Cumulative Review
Mental Math reviews area (Lesson 3.7).

Multistep Problems
Problem 9

Extended Response
Problems 1, 4, 6, 8, and 10

Writing + Math
Journal

Collecting Data— Tally Marks

Context of the Lesson Tally marks have been used previously in Grade 2. In this lesson students will gather the data and put the data into a table. Tally marks will be the basis for many of the sampling and data gathering for future graphs in this chapter. Tally marks are used in Grade 4 to collect data for various graphs.

See page 480B for Math Background for teachers for this lesson.

Planning for Learning ● DIFFERENTIATE INSTRUCTION

INTERVENTION
If . . . students lack the prerequisite skill of reading a graph,

Then . . . teach *Intervention* Lesson 12.A.

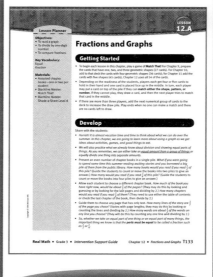

Intervention Lesson 12.A

ENGLISH LEARNER
Preview

If . . . students need language support,

Then . . . use Lesson 12.2 in *English Learner Support Guide* to preview lesson concepts and vocabulary.

English Learner Lesson 12.2

ENRICH
If . . . students are proficient in the lesson concepts,

Then . . . emphasize the Journal.

PRACTICE
If . . . students would benefit from additional practice,

Then . . . extend Strategy Building before assigning the student pages.

RETEACH
If . . . students are having difficulty understanding tally charts,

Then . . . extend Guided Discussion before assigning the student pages.

Vocabulary
tally \tal´ē\ *n.* a series of marks to keep a record of data
frequency \frē´kwən sē\ *n.* the number of times something happens

Access Vocabulary
fill in the chart complete by writing in missing information

Spanish Cognates
common común
method método

---

*Manipulative Kit Item

Mental Math 10

  Review area of squares and rectangles. You may want to demonstrate one or two problems. Use examples such as the following:

a. a square with one side of 4 units 16 square units

b. a rectangle with length of 5 units and width of 4 units 20 square units

c. a rectangle with length of 10 units and width of 8 units 80 square units

d. a square with one side of 8 units 64 square units

1 Develop 20

Tell Students In Today's Lesson They Will
use tally marks to gather and organize data.

Guided Discussion UNDERSTANDING Whole Group

On the board, draw a basic two-column table. Ask students to tell you their favorite day of the week. As a day is mentioned for the first time, write that day of the week in the left-hand column. Then, each time that day is mentioned again, write a single tally mark. When there are four tally marks, be sure to make the fifth a diagonal tally to keep the marks "bundled" together. After every student has had his or her data recorded, count each amount. List this as the *frequency* to the right of the tally column. Students can also count the total tallies to see if they match the number of students that gave responses. Ask questions such as the following about the graph:

- **Which day is the most popular?**
- **Which day(s) was (were) not mentioned in the survey?**
- **How many votes are there total?**
- **Why do you think we cross the tallies to make bundles of 5?** Possible answer: It is easier to count by 5s.
- **Do you think this class's results would be the same as those of another third-grade class? Why or why not?** Accept all reasonable answers. Possible answer: no, because not all third graders have the same favorite day

Strategy Building REASONING Small Group

Make a bar graph of the data using the tally table about favorite days of the week, and have students choose a title for this graph. Then, individually or in small groups, have them create a series of questions of their own about the graph. Have them also list some true and false statements about this graph. Have the other students in the class answer the questions.

2 Assign Student Pages 20

Pages 484–485 APPLYING

Have students complete the exercises on pages 484 and 485 independently.

As Students Finish

 Game Have students play a previously introduced game.

LESSON 12.2 Collecting Data—Tally Marks

Key Ideas

One of the easiest ways to collect data is to create a table using tally marks. The total number of tally marks in each category represents the **frequency**, or how often a particular response occurred.

Marc surveyed his third-grade class to see what transportation they used most often to arrive at school. The results are as follows:

Method	Tally	Frequency
Bus	𝍸𝍸𝍸 𝍸𝍸𝍸 𝍸𝍸𝍸	15
Car	IIII	4
Walk	𝍸𝍸𝍸 I	6
Other	III	3
	Total	28

Use the table to answer the following questions.

1 [Extended Response] How many students did Marc survey? Explain how you know.   28; There are a total of 28 tallies, and the total reads 28.

2 What is the most common method of getting to school?   bus

3 How many students in Marc's class do *not* get to school by bus?   13

4 [Extended Response] What methods of transportation to school might the *Other* category include?   bike, taxi, and so on

484   Textbook This lesson is available in the *eTextbook*.

Use the following information to create a table using tally marks.

5 [Extended Response] Star surveyed her gym class to see what their favorite colors are. She chose the top four colors and then decided on an *Other* category for the remaining colors. The top four colors are *blue, green, yellow,* and *red*. When Star counted each category, she found that 11 students liked blue, 9 students liked red, 7 students liked green, and 8 students liked yellow. There are 38 students in her gym class. see Reflect in *Teacher's Edition*.

Other

Answer the following questions about your completed table from Star's survey.

6 [Extended Response] What would be a good title for this survey?   One possible answer is *Favorite Colors of Star's Gym Class*.

7 What is the most common favorite color in the survey?   blue

8 [Extended Response] Do you think this is the favorite color of the entire school? Why or why not?

9  Are there more students who like blue and green or students who like yellow, red, and *Other*?   yellow, red, and *Other*

10 [Extended Response] Write a true statement about the table you made from Star's survey.

[Writing + Math] **Journal**

In your own words, describe what a table with tally marks is and when you might use one.

8 Accept reasonable answers. One possible answer is not necessarily, because it is not a random (or fair) sampling of the entire student body.

10 Accept reasonable answers. One possible answer is that this table is a survey of the four most common favorite colors of the students in Star's gym class.

Chapter 12 • Lesson 2   485

---

3 Reflect   10

Guided Discussion [REASONING]   Whole Group

Discuss why we "bundle" tallies in groups of 5 rather than some other number, such as 7, 10, 3, or 20.

Two groups of 5 make 10, and, because we have a number system based on 10, counting by 10 is easy. If we grouped by 10, however, we would have to do a lot of counting to be sure we have 9 before drawing the line across, and we would have to count groups of 9, 8 and 7 in table created on page 485. Groups of 4 or fewer are easily counted without great effort. If we would bundle in groups of 2, then there would be too many bundles. A group of 5 is the best compromise of all the factors mentioned.

Extended Response

Problem 5 Accept any table showing the correct number of tallies and frequencies, with a total frequency of 38.

[Writing + Math] **Journal** ✓ [REASONING]

A tally chart is used to record data as it is collected. Accept any reasonable example of when a tally chart might be useful.

Cumulative Review: For cumulative review of previously learned skills, see page 500–501.

Family Involvement: Assign the **Practice, Reteach,** or **Enrichment** activities depending on the needs of your students.

Encourage students to gather data using a tally chart with a friend or a relative.

Concept/Question Board: Have students look for additional examples using graphing and post them on the Concept/Question Board.

Math Puzzler: At the local market 7 farmers each had 7 bags that each held 7 oranges. How many oranges were there altogether? 343 oranges; $7 \times 7 = 49$; $49 \times 7 = 343$

4 Assess and Differentiate

 Assess Use **eAssess** to record and analyze evidence of student understanding.

A Gather Evidence

Use the Daily Class Assessment Records in **Assessment** or **eAssess** to record daily observations.

Informal Assessment

☑️ **Student Pages**

Did the student **APPLYING**
- ❑ apply learning in new situations?
- ❑ contribute concepts?
- ❑ contribute answers?
- ❑ connect mathematics to real-world situations?

Portfolio Assessment

☑️ **Journal**

Did the student **REASONING**
- ❑ provide a clear explanation?
- ❑ communicate reasons and strategies?
- ❑ choose appropriate strategies?
- ❑ argue logically?

B Summarize Findings

Analyze and summarize assessment data for each student. Determine which Assessment Follow-Up is appropriate for each student. Use the Student Assessment Record in **Assessment** or **eAssess** to update assessment records.

Assessment page T41

C Assessment Follow-Up • DIFFERENTIATE INSTRUCTION

Based on your observations, use these teaching strategies for assessment follow-up.

INTERVENTION

Review student performance on **Intervention** Lesson 12.A to see if students have mastered prerequisite skills for this lesson.

ENGLISH LEARNER

Review

Use Lesson 12.2 in **English Learner Support Guide** to review lesson concepts and vocabulary.

ENRICH

If . . . students are proficient in the lesson concepts,

Then . . . encourage them to work on chapter projects or **Enrichment** Lesson 12.2.

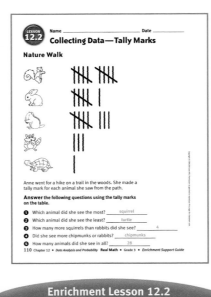

Enrichment Lesson 12.2

PRACTICE

If . . . students would benefit from additional practice,

Then . . . assign **Practice** Lesson 12.2.

Practice Lesson 12.2

RETEACH

If . . . students struggle making tally marks,

Then . . . have them take turns surveying the class on different questions. For example, how many classmates have blue, brown, or green eyes? How many walk to school or ride the bus? What is their favorite food?

OBJECTIVES
To begin to assess the information in graphs by exploring the terms *variability, range,* and *outlier*

NCTM STANDARDS
Data Analysis and Probability
Describing the important features of a set of data and comparing related data sets with an emphasis on how the data are distributed

Communication
Organizing and consolidating mathematical thinking through communication

MATERIALS
*Response Wheels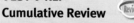

TECHNOLOGY
ⓔPresentation Lesson 12.3

TEST PREP
Cumulative Review
Mental Math reviews subtracting decimals (Lesson 10.6).

Extended Response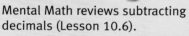
Problem 3

Summarizing Data

Context of the Lesson In this chapter students will be introduced to some of the characteristics of data more formally than in Grade 2. Students will explore various collections of data to determine how the desired characteristics change depending on the data presented.

See page 480B for Math Background for teachers for this lesson.

Planning for Learning ● DIFFERENTIATE INSTRUCTION

INTERVENTION
If . . . students lack the prerequisite skill of reading a graph,

Then . . . teach *Intervention* Lesson 12.A.

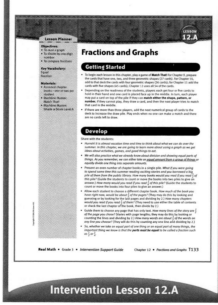

Intervention Lesson 12.A

ENGLISH LEARNER
Preview

If . . . students need language support,

Then . . . use Lesson 12.3 in *English Learner Support Guide* to preview lesson concepts and vocabulary.

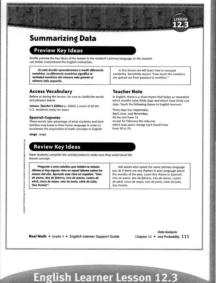

English Learner Lesson 12.3

ENRICH
If . . . students are proficient in the lesson concepts,

Then . . . emphasize the student pages.

PRACTICE
If . . . students would benefit from additional practice,

Then . . . extend Guided Discussion before assigning the student pages.

RETEACH
If . . . students are having difficulty understanding how to summarize data,

Then . . . extend Using Student Pages before assigning the student pages.

Vocabulary
variability \var´i a bil´ i tē\ *n.* the likelihood that something will change

range \rānj\ *n.* difference between the greatest and least numbers in a set of data

outlier \aut lī r\ *n.* a number that is far off from all other numbers in a data set.

Access Vocabulary
census a count of all US residents every ten years

Spanish Cognates
range rango

Mental Math 10

 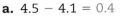 Review subtracting decimals. Have students use their finger to represent the decimal point on the **Response Wheel.** Use examples such as the following:

a. $4.5 - 4.1 = 0.4$ **b.** $0.6 - 0.4 = 0.2$ **c.** $9.9 - 3.3 = 6.6$

d. $8.1 - 0.1 = 8.0$ **e.** $5.5 - 5.5 = 0.0$ **f.** $21.8 - 20.1 = 1.7$

g. $10.9 - 7.9 = 3.0$ **h.** $8.7 - 3.5 = 5.2$ **i.** $0.7 - 0.1 = 0.6$

1 Develop 20

Tell Students In Today's Lesson They Will

begin to analyze the data in graphs by using terms such as *variability, range,* and *outlier.*

Guided Discussion UNDERSTANDING   Whole Group

According to the *Western Regional Climate Center,* the following are the monthly maximum temperature averages (in Fahrenheit) for the city of Valdez, Alaska:

January	27.9
February	30.7
March	36.7
April	45.0
May	53.6
June	60.4
July	62.6
August	61.1
September	53.9
October	43.5
November	32.9
December	28.9

List this information on the board for students to see. Discuss whether the temperatures are hot, cold, or comfortable. Compare the monthly averages to the local monthly averages. Ask students questions such as the following:

- **What does *average temperature* indicate?**
- **Are the monthly averages *hot, cold,* or *comfortable*?**
- **Are there any average monthly temperatures that are repeated?** no
- **What is the highest average monthly temperature?** 62.6 in July
- **What is the lowest average monthly temperature?** 27.9 in January
- **What is the difference between the highest average monthly temperature and the lowest average monthly temperature?** 34.7 degrees

Introduce the term *range* and the definition. The *range* for the average monthly temperatures for Valdez, Alaska is 34.7 degrees Fahrenheit. Ask students questions such as the following:

- **Why would finding the range be helpful when dealing with average monthly temperatures?** if the range is a large amount, it can be assumed the temperatures vary greatly annually
- **Would you consider this a big difference in the range or a not so big difference in the range?** Accept all reasonable answers and explanations, reminding students that this data deals with temperature of a city in Alaska.

An *outlier* would be any number that is far from the rest of the numbers if you were to plot the numbers on a number line. Ask students if there are any outliers for this set of data. Accept all reasonable answers, and discuss both points of view if students answer both *yes* and *no.*

Using Student Pages APPLYING   Whole Group

Have students read through the Key Ideas on student page 486. Discuss what the table on page 486 represents. Ask questions such as the following:

- **Are there any numbers of sick days that are repeated?** no
- **Can these numbers be put in numerical order?** yes

Have students put the data in numerical order to assist with the questions on page 486. Go through each question with students, discussing their responses, especially to Problems 3 and 4.

2 Assign Student Pages 20

Pages 486–487 APPLYING

Have students complete the exercises on page 487 independently.

Problem 7 If we excluded the attendance for Game 7 (which could be argued to be an outlier), this is false. Game 7 was the only game with a vastly different attendance; the range of attendance for the other seven games was only 5,253. (This is not a significant amount when the average attendance for those seven games was about 32,000.)

As Students Finish

 Have students play a previously introduced game.

LESSON 12.3 Summarizing Data

Key Ideas

The numbers in a set can be written in order from least to greatest. How much the data are spread out is called the *variability*. The *variability* of the data also can be measured by the range and the outliers.

The **range** of a set of numbers is the difference between the greatest number in the data and the smallest number in the data. A small number for the range means the data are close together.

An **outlier** is a number that seems to be too far out at one end of the range. Sometimes an outlier can affect how we interpret the data.

❸ 4 (and possibly 17) appear far out from the rest of the data; possible answers: Maybe school is more fun in June or students are more likely to get sick in the winter.

The following is a table showing the number of student sick days at Valley Alternative Elementary School for the 2008–2009 school year.

Use the table to answer the following questions.

❶ What is the least number of student sick days? What is the greatest number of student sick days? 4 days; 45 days

❷ What is the range for the student sick days for the 2008–2009 school year? 41 days

❸ **Extended Response** What number or numbers might be considered an outlier? What might be a reason for the outlier? Explain.

❹ True or False. You could say the number of student sick days varied greatly from month to month. true

Month	Student Sick Days
August	17
September	21
October	28
November	25
December	22
January	30
February	45
March	35
April	34
May	26
June	4

486   **Textbook** This lesson is available in the *eTextbook*.

The 1919 World Series between the Chicago White Sox and the Cincinnati Reds was an infamous World Series due to eight White Sox players being accused of cheating (trying to lose the World Series on purpose). It is also a unique series because, due to the country being happy about the end of World War I, the baseball commissioner declared this particular series would be the best of nine games, instead of the normal best of seven games. This meant the World Series champion would be the first team to win five games—which the Reds did in the eighth game. Listed below are the attendance numbers for the eight games of the 1919 World Series.

❺ What was the least attendance? What was the greatest attendance?
13,923; 34,379

❻ What is the range for the attendance numbers in the 1919 World Series?
20,456

❼ True or False. You could say the number of people in attendance for the 1919 World Series varied greatly from game to game. See *Teacher's Edition.*

❽ Which attendance number might be considered an outlier? Game 7: 13,923

Game	Attendance
Game 1	30,511
Game 2	29,690
Game 3	29,126
Game 4	34,363
Game 5	34,379
Game 6	32,006
Game 7	13,923
Game 8	32,930

Chapter 12 • Lesson 3   487

---

3 Reflect   10

Guided Discussion REASONING   Whole Group

Call attention to the table of sick days on student page 486. Ask the students if they can estimate the total number of students who attend Valley School. Have students explain the basis for their estimates. Then guide them through a strategy based on sampling and proportions. Ask questions such as the following (the answers given are examples):

- **About how many students in our class are absent in January because of sickness?** perhaps 3 every month
- **How many students are in our class?** 20
- **Our class of 20 students has 3 student sick days in January. If Valley school has 30 student sick days, about how many students could they have?** if the proportion is the same, Valley School would have about 200 students
- **How did we calculate this?** Valley School's sick days are ten times that of our school, so we estimate that they also have ten times as many students.

Be sure to listen to different suggestions as many students will likely have interesting and defensible explanations for their estimates.

Extended Response

Problem 3 The sick days for June (4)—and perhaps even August (17)—make a strong case for an outlier. Possible explanations; students are less likely to get sick in the summer months, school is more fun in June, and so on.

 Curriculum Connection: Students may be interested in reading about the alleged scandal revolving around the 1919 World Series, and how it impacts baseball even today.

 Cumulative Review: For cumulative review of previously learned skills, see page 500–501.

 Family Involvement: Assign the **Practice, Reteach,** or **Enrichment** activities depending on the needs of your students.

Encourage students to look through a newspaper, in a book, or online at a graph of numerical data and find the ranges with a friend or a relative.

 Concept/Question Board: Have students look for additional examples using graphing and post them on the Concept/Question Board.

 Math Puzzler: There are 8 coins in a box. Their total value is $1.50. What coins could be in the box? Possible answers: 5 quarters, 2 dimes, and 1 nickel; 2 half-dollars, 1 quarter, and 5 nickels; or 1 dollar coin, 3 dimes, and 4 nickels

Chapter 12 • Lesson 3   **486–487**

4 Assess and Differentiate

e Assess Use *eAssess* to record and analyze evidence of student understanding.

A Gather Evidence

Use the Daily Class Assessment Records in *Assessment* or *eAssess* to record daily observations.

Informal Assessment
☑ **Guided Discussion**

Did the student `UNDERSTANDING`
- ❏ make important observations?
- ❏ extend or generalize learning?
- ❏ provide insightful answers?
- ❏ pose insightful questions?

Informal Assessment
☑ **Student Pages**

Did the student `APPLYING`
- ❏ apply learning in new situations?
- ❏ contribute concepts?
- ❏ contribute answers?
- ❏ connect mathematics to real-world situations?

B Summarize Findings

Analyze and summarize assessment data for each student. Determine which Assessment Follow-Up is appropriate for each student. Use the Student Assessment Record in *Assessment* or *eAssess* to update assessment records.

Assessment page T41

C Assessment Follow-Up ● DIFFERENTIATE INSTRUCTION

Based on your observations, use these teaching strategies for assessment follow-up.

INTERVENTION

Review student performance on *Intervention* Lesson 12.A to see if students have mastered prerequisite skills for this lesson.

ENGLISH LEARNER

Review

Use Lesson 12.3 in *English Learner Support Guide* to review lesson concepts and vocabulary.

ENRICH

If . . . students are proficient in the lesson concepts,

Then . . . encourage them to work on chapter projects or *Enrichment* Lesson 12.3.

Enrichment Lesson 12.3

PRACTICE

If . . . students would benefit from additional practice,

Then . . . assign *Practice* Lesson 12.3.

Practice Lesson 12.3

RETEACH

If . . . students struggle with summarizing data,

Then . . . have them look at recent quiz grades to determine the variability of the grades. What is the range? Are there any outliers? What would the outliers represent? Why might the outliers exist? Encourage students to practice finding range and outliers for other data sets that are important to them.

Lesson Planner

OBJECTIVES
To represent data by using mean, median, and mode

NCTM STANDARDS
Data Analysis and Probability
Using measures of center, focusing on the median, and understanding what each does and does not indicate about the data set

Connections
Recognizing and applying mathematics in contexts outside of mathematics

MATERIALS
*Response Wheels

TECHNOLOGY
ⓔ **Presentation** Lesson 12.4

TEST PREP
Cumulative Review
• Mental Math reviews fractions of time (Lesson 8.4).
• Problems 5 and 10 review range (Lesson 12.3).

Writing + Math
Journal

Mean, Median, Mode

Context of the Lesson In Grade 2 students informally discussed mean and mode. In this chapter students also explore the characteristic of median. These three characteristics are used to report information from sampling and data gathering.

See page 480B for Math Background for teachers for this lesson.

Planning for Learning ● DIFFERENTIATE INSTRUCTION

INTERVENTION	ENGLISH LEARNER	ENRICH
If . . . students lack the prerequisite skill of dividing by a one-digit number, **Then . . .** teach *Intervention* Lesson 12.B.	**Preview** **If . . .** students need language support, **Then . . .** use Lesson 12.4 in *English Learner Support Guide* to preview lesson concepts and vocabulary.	**If . . .** students are proficient in the lesson concepts, **Then . . .** emphasize the student pages.

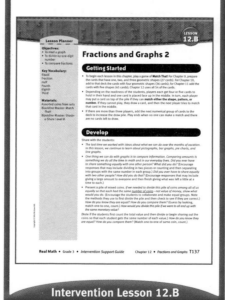

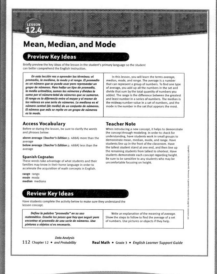

Intervention Lesson 12.B

English Learner Lesson 12.4

PRACTICE
If . . . students would benefit from additional practice,

Then . . . extend Guided Discussion before assigning the student pages.

RETEACH
If . . . students are having difficulty understanding mean, median, or mode,

Then . . . extend Guided Discussion before assigning the student pages.

Vocabulary
median \mēˊdē ən\ *n.* the middle number in a set of data
mode \mōd\ *n.* the number appearing most frequently in a set of data

mean \mēn\ *n.* the typical or usual amount, which is found by dividing the sum of two or more quantities by the number of quantities; another name for average

Access Vocabulary
above average more than the average
below average less than the average

Spanish Cognates
range rango
mode modo
median mediana

Mental Math 10

 Review with students fractions of time. Use examples such as the following:

a. $\frac{1}{2}$ of 60 30   **b.** $\frac{2}{2}$ of 60 60

c. $\frac{1}{3}$ of 60 20   **d.** $\frac{2}{3}$ of 60 40

e. $\frac{0}{3}$ of 60 0   **f.** $\frac{1}{4}$ of 60 15

g. $\frac{2}{4}$ of 60 30   **h.** $\frac{3}{4}$ of 60 45

1 Develop 20

Tell Students In Today's Lesson They Will

represent information obtained through data by using mean, median, and mode.

Guided Discussion UNDERSTANDING
Whole Group

List on the board or the overhead projector the following $\frac{1}{4}$-mile times driven by national drag racers for August 2005. The times are in seconds.

14, 15, 9, 13, 12, 11, 14, 14, 16

As a class, have students put the times in order from least to greatest. 9, 11, 12, 13, 14, 14, 14, 15, 16

Have students find the time that occurs most often, and tell them we call this the mode. 14 Discuss with students ways to remember that mode means most. One suggestion might be to point out that mode and most both begin with *m–o*. It may be confusing to students once mode, median, and mean are all introduced as vocabulary. Word associations may be helpful for students and their recollection of the words.

Because the numbers are already in order, have students find the *median*, or middle number. 14

Discuss with students the meaning of median in nonmathematical terms. Where else might they have heard the word median? One of the more common uses of the term refers to the median in a road.

To find the mean, or average of the numbers, add them. Then divide by the number of entries. In this instance, add the times. The total is 118 seconds, and there are 9 entries. Work with students on dividing 118 by 9:

$9\overline{)118}$

Your answer should be 13 R1. The average time, or mean time, is about 13 seconds.

Make a table with the following items:

Mean: 13 seconds
Median: 14 seconds
Mode: 14 seconds

It might be helpful to have this information visible as students work on the student pages.

Using Student Pages APPLYING
Whole Group

Have students open to student page 488. Discuss the information in the Key Ideas. Have students look at the information in the table for Mrs. Hartman's third-grade class to see that they understand the information. Walk around the room, assisting students with the computations as they complete the student pages.

2 Assign Student Pages 20

Pages 488–489 APPLYING

Have students complete the exercises on pages 488 and 489 independently.

Monitoring Student Progress

If . . . students are having difficulties remembering the difference between mean, median, and mode,

Then . . . have them create flash cards with the word on the front and the definition and a word association or example on the back.

As Students Finish

 Have students play a previously introduced game.

LESSON 12.4 Mean, Median, Mode

Key Ideas

Median, mode, and mean are often used to represent data.

Thom measured the 7 plants in the classroom greenhouse. Their heights, measured in centimeters, were 11, 7, 3, 18, 7, 8, and 9. When Thom put them in order from shortest to tallest, he was able to find the middle value, or the median.

3   7   7   **8**   9   11   18

The median for this group of measurements is 8 centimeters.

The mode, or most frequently occurring height, is 7 centimeters.

Thom was also able to find the average, or mean, of the measurements by adding their heights and dividing by the total number of plants. The sum of their heights is 63 centimeters, and there are 7 plants total.

$63 \div 7 = 9$

The average, or mean, of the plant heights is 9 centimeters.

Mrs. Hartman's third-grade class recorded their ages in months. Here are the ages of all the students.

134	137	127	134	128	129	136	132	130	130
129	134	128	131	132	125	128	126	135	132
126	142	130	130	139	137	136	126	130	129

488   Textbook This lesson is available in the *eTextbook*.

Student Page

Use the table of ages of Mrs. Hartman's students (on page 488) to answer the following questions.

1. List the numbers in order from least to greatest.

2. What is the least number in your list? What is the greatest number?   125; 142

3. Which number appears most often (the mode)?   130

4. What is the mean, or average age, for the students (in months)?   about 131

5. What is the range?   17

Here are the students' scores on Mrs. Hartman's math test.

83 85 91 62 85 74 95 68 92 94

85 97 73 78 80 86 88 91 93 87

81 79 76 83 82 96 84 82 85 86

6. What is the mode for this group of scores?   85

7. What is the average score (the mean)?   about 84

8. What are the least and greatest scores?   62; 97

9. What score is the median, or middle, score?   85

10. What is the range?   35

Writing + Math Journal
Describe in your own words the terms *mean, median,* and *mode.*

1. 125, 126, 126, 126, 127, 128, 128, 128,
129, 129, 129, 130, 130, 130, 130, 130,
131, 132, 132, 134, 134, 134, 135,
136, 136, 137, 137, 139, 142

3 Reflect   10

Guided Discussion   REASONING

Whole Group

Write the age in months of the youngest and oldest students on the chalkboard. Calculate the age to the first of the current month. Thus an 8 year old who was born in March would be 97 months old in April. Then ask the class to estimate the median age, the modal age and the mean age of the class. Begin with a general discussion, but then have each student or small group write down their estimates. Finally, record all of the data on the board and have students organize the data and check their estimates against the actual data.

 **Journal** ✓ **REASONING**

Accept all reasonable correct definitions of mean, median, and mode. Possible answers: Mode is the most common; median is the middle one; mean is when you add all the numbers and then divide by the number of them; mean is the number you would get if you "evened" out all the numbers so that each number was the same

---

 Curriculum Connection: Students may be interested in finding out some of the largest and smallest plants recorded in history.

 Cumulative Review: For cumulative review of previously learned skills, see page 500–501.

 Family Involvement: Assign the *Practice, Reteach,* or *Enrichment* activities depending on the needs of your students.

Encourage students to find real-world examples of mean, median, and mode with a friend or a relative.

 Concept/Question Board: Have students look for additional examples using graphing and post them on the Concept/Question Board.

 Math Puzzler: The sum of the digits of a two-digit number is 13. If the digits are reversed, the new number is 9 more than the first. What are the two numbers?   67, 76

4 Assess and Differentiate

 Assess Use *eAssess* to record and analyze evidence of student understanding.

A Gather Evidence

Use the Daily Class Assessment Records in *Assessment* or *eAssess* to record daily observations.

Informal Assessment
☑ **Guided Discussion**

Did the student **UNDERSTANDING**
- ❑ make important observations?
- ❑ extend or generalize learning?
- ❑ provide insightful answers?
- ❑ pose insightful questions?

Portfolio Assessment
☑ **Journal**

Did the student **REASONING**
- ❑ provide a clear explanation?
- ❑ communicate reasons and strategies?
- ❑ choose appropriate strategies?
- ❑ argue logically?

B Summarize Findings

Analyze and summarize assessment data for each student. Determine which Assessment Follow-Up is appropriate for each student. Use the Student Assessment Record in *Assessment* or *eAssess* to update assessment records.

Assessment page T41

C Assessment Follow-Up • DIFFERENTIATE INSTRUCTION

Based on your observations, use these teaching strategies for assessment follow-up.

INTERVENTION

Review student performance on *Intervention* Lesson 12.B to see if students have mastered prerequisite skills for this lesson.

ENGLISH LEARNER

Review

Use Lesson 12.4 in *English Learner Support Guide* to review lesson concepts and vocabulary.

ENRICH

If . . . students are proficient in the lesson concepts,

Then . . . encourage them to work on chapter projects or *Enrichment* Lesson 12.4.

Enrichment Lesson 12.4

PRACTICE

If . . . students would benefit from additional practice,

Then . . . assign *Practice* Lesson 12.4.

Practice Lesson 12.4

RETEACH

If . . . students are having difficulty with mean, median, or mode,

Then . . . reteach the concept using *Reteach* Lesson 12.4.

Reteach Lesson 12.4

Lesson Planner

OBJECTIVES
To explore how to display data in a table

NCTM STANDARDS

Geometry
Making and using coordinate systems to specify locations and to describe paths

Data Analysis and Probability
Representing data using tables and graphs

Connections
Recognizing and using connections among mathematical ideas

MATERIALS
- *Response Wheels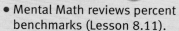
- Guided Discussion on transparency or worksheet (optional)

TECHNOLOGY
Presentation Lesson 12.5

TEST PREP

Cumulative Review
- Mental Math reviews percent benchmarks (Lesson 8.11).
- Problems 7–11 review coordinate grids (Lesson 6.6).

Extended Response
Problem 12

Writing + Math
Journal

*Manipulative Kit Item

Displaying Data

Context of the Lesson In this chapter students will create tables they believe would best display given data. From these tables, students will explore concepts previously encountered in the chapter.

See page 480B for Math Background for teachers for this lesson.

Planning for Learning ● DIFFERENTIATE INSTRUCTION

INTERVENTION

If . . . students lack the prerequisite skill of reading a graph,

Then . . . teach **Intervention** Lesson 12.A.

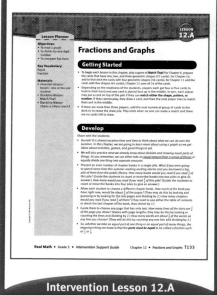

Intervention Lesson 12.A

ENGLISH LEARNER

Preview

If . . . students need language support,

Then . . . use Lesson 12.5 in **English Learner Support Guide** to preview lesson concepts and vocabulary.

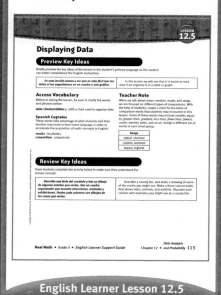

English Learner Lesson 12.5

ENRICH

If . . . students are proficient in the lesson concepts,

Then . . . emphasize the student pages.

PRACTICE

If . . . students would benefit from additional practice,

Then . . . extend Strategy Building before assigning the student pages.

RETEACH

If . . . students are having difficulty understanding how to display data,

Then . . . extend Guided Discussion before assigning the student pages.

Access Vocabulary
table a chart used to organize data

Spanish Cognates
results resultados
competition competición

Mental Math 10

  Review with students which percent benchmark is closest to each percent. Use the percent slider on the **Response Wheel.** Use examples such as the following:

a. 45% 50%   **b.** 68% 75%   **c.** 99% 100%
d. 12% 0%   **e.** 21% 25%   **f.** 60% 50%
g. 3% 0%   **h.** 88% 100%   **i.** 89% 100%

1 Develop 20

Tell Students In Today's Lesson They Will
explore displaying data in a table.

Guided Discussion UNDERSTANDING   Small Group

Read the following story once to gain an overall understanding. Ask students to list as many facts as they can remember. Read the story a second time to fill in any missing pieces of information.

Tammy and her after-school club entered their projects in the local science fair. When they got back to school on Monday, they compared their individual results. Christine won 2 superior ratings, 4 outstanding ratings, and 2 excellent ratings; Denni won 3 superior ratings, 3 outstanding ratings, and 2 excellent ratings; Adam won 4 superior ratings, 1 outstanding rating, and 2 excellent ratings; Shane won 3 superior ratings, 2 outstanding ratings, and 1 excellent rating; and Tammy won 2 superior ratings, 3 outstanding ratings, and 4 excellent ratings.

Ask questions such as the following:

- **How many people were comparing results?** 5
- **What kind of sections or groupings would be possible for this collection of data?** Possible answers: name, superior, outstanding, and excellent.

Strategy Building REASONING   Small Group

In small groups, have students create a table they believe would adequately display the information they have obtained. It might be helpful to have the paragraph with the information on an overhead transparency or on a worksheet for reference. Have students show the tables to the class and explain how they decided to create their tables.

When the tables are complete, have students create a list of questions that could be asked about their table. For example, how many ribbons did Tammy win? If time allows, have groups exchange lists and see if they can answer each other's questions. If time does not allow, combine the graphs and the questions in a booklet for students to work on later.

Monitoring Student Progress

If . . . students are having difficulties coming up with questions about their tables,

Then . . . give them a few more examples of questions, allowing them to use one or two of your suggestions in their list.

2 Assign Student Pages 20

Pages 490–491 APPLYING

Have students complete the exercises on pages 490 and 491 independently.

As Students Finish

 Have students play a previously introduced game.

LESSON 12.5 Displaying Data

Key Ideas
Data can be displayed in various kinds of graphs or tables.

The Local County Fair was held this past weekend. Here are the results from Sunday's competitions.

The Happy Valley Farms took home 8 first-place ribbons, 2 second-place ribbons, and 9 third-place ribbons. Merry Acres Meadows acquired 7 first-place ribbons, 4 second-place ribbons, and 1 third-place ribbon. First-time contestant Weary Wanderer's Rest received 3 first-place ribbons, 1 second-place ribbon, and 3 third-place ribbons.

Copy the following table. Use the information from the newspaper clipping to complete the table.

Contestant	1st Place	2nd Place	3rd Place
1. Happy Valley Farms	8	2	9
2. Merry Acres Meadows	7	4	1
3. Weary Wanderer's Rest	3	1	3

④ How many second- and third-place ribbons did Merry Acres Meadows win? 5

⑤ How many ribbons did Weary Wanderer's Rest win total? 7

⑥ Who won the most ribbons? Happy Valley Farms

490

Textbook This lesson is available in the *eTextbook*.

This grid shows a small section of Anytimetown. Each location can be named with an ordered pair—a number from the bottom number line, (axis) of the graph and a number from the left-hand number line (axis) of the graph.

Answer the following questions by using the section map of Anytimetown. The first one has been done for you.

⑦ Where is the school located? (2, 7) Once you locate the school, go down to the bottom axis to find the first number, 2. From the school, go to the left axis to find the second number, 7.

⑧ Where is Bree's house located? (5, 5)

⑨ Who lives farther north, Alphie or Charles? Charles

⑩ Where is the grocery store located? (3, 3)

⑪ If you were traveling from the grocery store to the bank, would you travel east or west? east

⑫ Extended Response What would be a good title for this graph?
Accept reasonable answers. Possible answer: *Anytimetown*

Writing + Math Journal
Describe a situation in which you might use a table to organize your information.

Chapter 12 • Lesson 5

491

---

3 Reflect 10

Guided Discussion REASONING

Whole Group

Provide students with different results to the table on page 490:

	1st	2nd	3rd
Happy Valley Farms	8	3	5
Merry Acres Meadows	9	4	0
Weary Wanderer's Rest	4	7	9

Ask students which group should be declared the winner of the competition—Weary Wanderer's Rest (won the most ribbons altogether), Merry Acres Meadows (won the most first place ribbons), or Happy Valley Farms (won more total ribbons than Merry Acres Meadows and had twice as many first place ribbons as Weary Wanderer's Rest).

Allow students to express their ideas and be sure to listen to unorthodox approaches. One solution that you might suggest is to award 5 points for each first place ribbon, 3 points for each second place ribbon and 1 point for each 3rd place ribbon.

If that were the case, Happy Valley Farms would have 54 points, Merry Acres Meadows would have 57 points, and Weary Wanderer's Rest would have 50 points. When students see this type of solution, they will likely suggest a different point system that might award first place to a different group.

Writing + Math Journal REASONING

Accept any reasonable answer describing a situation that would allow for use of a table to organize the data.

 Curriculum Connection: Many types of maps are commonly used every day. Students may be interested in looking at and comparing different kinds of maps of their city, state, or other areas.

 Cumulative Review: For cumulative review of previously learned skills, see page 500–501.

 Family Involvement: Assign the *Practice, Reteach,* or *Enrichment* activities depending on the needs of your students.

Encourage students to create tables for various items with a friend or a relative.

 Concept/Question Board: Encourage students to continue to post questions, answers, and examples on the Concept/Question Board.

 Math Puzzler: Jane's school locker has a three-digit number on it. The first digit is double the second digit. The third digit is half the second digit. What could Jane's locker number be? 000, 421, 842

Assess and Differentiate

e Assess Use *eAssess* to record and analyze evidence of student understanding.

A Gather Evidence

Use the Daily Class Assessment Records in *Assessment* or *eAssess* to record daily observations.

Informal Assessment
☑ **Guided Discussion**

Did the student **UNDERSTANDING**
- ❏ make important observations?
- ❏ extend or generalize learning?
- ❏ provide insightful answers?
- ❏ pose insightful questions?

Portfolio Assessment
☑ **Journal**

Did the student **REASONING**
- ❏ provide a clear explanation?
- ❏ communicate reasons and strategies?
- ❏ choose appropriate strategies?
- ❏ argue logically?

B Summarize Findings

Analyze and summarize assessment data for each student. Determine which Assessment Follow-Up is appropriate for each student. Use the Student Assessment Record in *Assessment* or *eAssess* to update assessment records.

Assessment page T41

C Assessment Follow-Up ● DIFFERENTIATE INSTRUCTION

Based on your observations, use these teaching strategies for assessment follow-up.

INTERVENTION
Review student performance on *Intervention* Lesson 12.A to see if students have mastered prerequisite skills for this lesson.

ENGLISH LEARNER
Review
Use Lesson 12.5 in *English Learner Support Guide* to review lesson concepts and vocabulary.

ENRICH

If . . . students are proficient in the lesson concepts,

Then . . . encourage them to work on chapter projects or *Enrichment* Lesson 12.5.

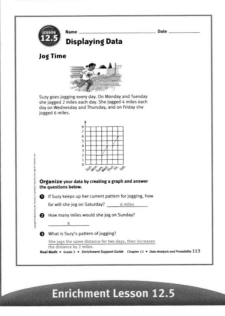

Enrichment Lesson 12.5

PRACTICE

If . . . students would benefit from additional practice,

Then . . . assign *Practice* Lesson 12.5.

Practice Lesson 12.5

RETEACH

If . . . students are having difficulty making ordered pairs,

Then . . . review with them that the *x* (horizontal) coordinate is listed first and the *y* (vertical) coordinate is listed second. Then have them practice naming points on a grid.

Lesson Planner

OBJECTIVES
- To review pictographs, single bar graphs, and circle graphs
- To create a pictograph, a single bar graph, and a circle graph
- To interpret the data from graphs that compare

NCTM STANDARDS

Data Analysis and Probability
- Representing data using tables and graphs such as line plots, bar graphs, and line graphs
- Comparing different representations of the same data

Representation
Creating and using representations to organize, record, and communicate mathematical ideas

MATERIALS

- *Response Wheels
- Coloring items such as crayons, markers, coloring pencils
- Centimeter graph paper (optional)

TECHNOLOGY
Presentation Lesson 12.6
MathTools Graphing Tool

TEST PREP
Cumulative Review
- Mental Math reviews multiplying by powers of 10 (Lesson 7.1).
- Problem 1 reviews tally marks (Lesson 12.2).
- Problem 3 reviews interpreting bar graphs (Lesson 3.10).

Extended Response
Problem 6

Writing + Math
Journal

Graphs That Compare

Context of the Lesson Students have encountered pictographs, single bar graphs, and circle graphs in Grade 2. In this chapter students will compare data using these graphs. Students will continue to use bar graphs and circle graphs in Grade 4.

See page 480B for Math Background for teachers for this lesson.

Planning for Learning • DIFFERENTIATE INSTRUCTION

INTERVENTION

If . . . students lack the prerequisite skill of reading a graph,

Then . . . teach *Intervention* Lesson 12.A.

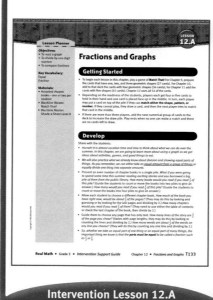

Intervention Lesson 12.A

ENGLISH LEARNER

Preview

If . . . students need language support,

Then . . . use Lesson 12.6 in *English Learner Support Guide* to preview lesson concepts and vocabulary.

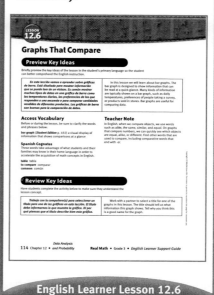

English Learner Lesson 12.6

ENRICH

If . . . students are proficient in the lesson concepts,

Then . . . emphasize the Journal.

PRACTICE

If . . . students would benefit from additional practice,

Then . . . extend Strategy Building before assigning the student pages.

RETEACH

If . . . students are having difficulty with comparison graphs,

Then . . . extend Guided Discussion before assigning the student pages.

Spanish Cognates
table tabla

to compare comparar
common común

Teaching Lesson 12.6

Mental Math 10

 Review multiplying by 10, 100, or 1,000. Use examples such as the following:

a. $4 \times 10 = 40$ **b.** $14 \times 10 = 140$ **c.** $27 \times 10 = 270$
d. $8 \times 100 = 800$ **e.** $38 \times 100 = 3,800$ **f.** $10 \times 100 = 1,000$
g. $9 \times 1,000 = 9,000$ **h.** $27 \times 1,000 = 27,000$ **i.** $1,000 \times 10 = 10,000$

1 Develop 20

Tell Students In Today's Lesson They Will

use various sets of data to create pictographs, single bar graphs, and circle graphs to compare the data.

Guided Discussion UNDERSTANDING Whole Group

Review with students the terms *sampling*, *surveys*, and *data*. Have students give examples when they might encounter these words. For example, if the cafeteria were going to change its menu, the staff may pass out a survey of what students considered their favorite cafeteria lunch. Ask students questions such as the following:

■ **What are some of the ways the cafeteria staff could record those results?** Possible answer includes writing it in a table, a tally graph, a notebook, and so on.
■ **What information might the data show?** possible answer might be that the majority of students prefer cheese pizza and very few students like spaghetti, or other food items

As a whole class, create a tally table showing what cafeteria foods are preferred. It might be easier to limit their choices to five possibilities. Create a two column table labeled **Favorite Food** and **Tallies**. When the class has been surveyed, write the word *frequency* to the right of each collection of tally marks, and review with students the word. Have students discuss some of the results of their survey. Discuss with students the *mode* of the data and what they can conclude from it. Have students create a few questions about the data that other students in the room can answer.

Review with students a *pictograph* and some of the parts of a pictograph; for example, the title, the Key, and the labels. On the board, draw a basic pictograph with a blank box for the Key. Refer to Student Edition page 492 for an example. Have students create a title for the graph. As a class, decide on what Key to use. Some students may prefer to use one figure to represent one person. While this is acceptable, encourage students to explore using a Key that has a non-one-to-one correspondence. Discuss how a figure that represents 4 people can be drawn as half to represent 2 people. After the Key has been decided, fill in the Key box with the figure and what it represents. Have students copy the graph and fill in the information on their papers. Walk around the room answering questions and assisting where needed. When the class has finished their graphs, display them and discuss similarities and differences.

Strategy Building APPLYING Small Group

Divide the class into small groups. Pass out unlined paper to the groups along with coloring items such as crayons, markers, coloring pencils. Review with the class *bar graphs* and the elements of each. Be sure to emphasize choosing a title, labeling the axis correctly, and making sure the divisions are an equal distance apart. Remind students that if their divisions are too close or too far apart, the information obtained from their graphs may be misleading. Using centimeter graph paper might help students. On the board or by using *eMathTools: Graphing Tool,* draw a basic bar graph such as this:

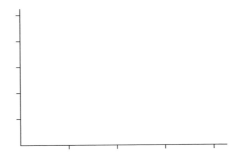

Have students copy the graph in their groups, filling in the labeling and the title. Choose the first favorite food item and draw the bar for that item remembering to color in the bar. Have students create the first bar on their graphs. Check to see that the graphs are correct. Have students finish the bar graph with the information obtained from the survey. Discuss with students any difficulties they may have had creating the graph. When the class has finished their graphs, share them and discuss similarities and differences. Show an example of the same data but in a circle graph, using the *eMathTools: Graphing Tool.*

2 Assign Student Pages 20

Pages 492–493 APPLYING

Have students complete the exercises on pages 492 and 493 independently.

As Students Finish

 Have students play a previously introduced game.

LESSON 12.6 Graphs That Compare

Key Ideas

Three common kinds of graphs are pictographs, bar graphs, and circle graphs.

Qmariz surveyed 50 fellow students on their favorite type of sport to play. Basketball got 14 votes, baseball/softball got 12 votes, soccer got 16 votes, and football got 8 votes.

❶ Create a table of tallies using Qmariz's information on a separate piece of paper.

❷ Use the information from the table you created in Problem 1 to copy and complete the pictograph. Remember to refer to the key to determine the number of figures to use.

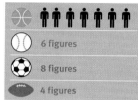

⚾	6 figures
⚽	8 figures
🏈	4 figures

KEY
🧍 = 2 students

492   📖 **Textbook** This lesson is available in the *eTextbook*.

Copy the following bar graph on your paper. Use the information from page 492 to complete the bar graph.

❸
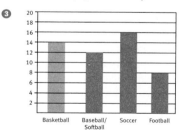

Basketball   Baseball/Softball   Soccer   Football

Qmariz also created a circle graph to show the percentages of the total votes for each favorite sport to play.

Answer the following questions.

 ❹ Write each of the percents as fractions.

❺ How many students were surveyed altogether?   **50**

❻ **Extended Response** Write one true statement and one false statement about the information from the circle graph.   Accept reasonable answers.

Football 16%   Basketball 28%   Soccer 32%   Baseball/Softball 24%

❹ $16\% = \frac{16}{100} = \frac{8}{50}$; $28\% = \frac{28}{100} = \frac{14}{60}$; $24\% = \frac{24}{100} = \frac{12}{50}$; $32\% = \frac{32}{100} = \frac{16}{50}$

Writing + Math **Journal**
How are pictographs, bar graphs, and circle graphs alike? How are they different?

---

3 Reflect   10 ⏱

Guided Discussion **REASONING**   Whole Group

Ask students why we did not calculate the mean, median, and range for the data about the favorite foods.

Discuss with students how the set of data is categories (pizza, spaghetti, and so on), where the only numbers available were how often each category was chosen. So, you could decide which category of food was chosen as favorite most often, but finding the average of a hamburger and a dish of spaghetti, for example, is silly. Such data is sometimes called categorical data and doing arithmetic with it does not make sense.

 **Writing + Math** Journal ✓ **REASONING**

Accept any reasonable answer showing an understanding of the differences and similarities between pictographs, bar graphs, and circle graphs.

 Curriculum Connection: Sports play an important role in the lives of many students. Students may be interested in researching the history, rules, and famous players of sports that are unfamiliar to them.

 Cumulative Review: For cumulative review of previously learned skills, see page 500–501.

 Family Involvement: Assign the *Practice, Reteach,* or *Enrichment* activities depending on the needs of your students.

Encourage students to find examples of pictographs, bar graphs, and circle graphs with a friend or a relative.

 Concept/Question Board: Encourage students to continue to post questions, answers, and examples on the Concept/Question Board.

 Math Puzzler: One kilogram of raisins has 1,000 grams in it. How many grams does a kilogram of peanuts have? 1,000 grams because a kilogram always has 1,000 grams

LESSON 12.6

Assess and Differentiate

 Assess Use *eAssess* to record and analyze evidence of student understanding.

A Gather Evidence

Use the Daily Class Assessment Records in **Assessment** or **eAssess** to record daily observations.

Informal Assessment
☑ **Strategy Building**

Did the student **APPLYING**
- ☐ apply learning in new situations?
- ☐ contribute concepts?
- ☐ contribute answers?
- ☐ connect mathematics to real-world situations?

Portfolio Assessment
☑ **Journal**

Did the student **REASONING**
- ☐ provide a clear explanation?
- ☐ communicate reasons and strategies?
- ☐ choose appropriate strategies?
- ☐ argue logically?

B Summarize Findings

Analyze and summarize assessment data for each student. Determine which Assessment Follow-Up is appropriate for each student. Use the Student Assessment Record in **Assessment** or **eAssess** to update assessment records.

Assessment page T41

C Assessment Follow-Up ● DIFFERENTIATE INSTRUCTION

Based on your observations, use these teaching strategies for assessment follow-up.

INTERVENTION

Review student performance on *Intervention* Lesson 12.A to see if students have mastered prerequisite skills for this lesson.

ENGLISH LEARNER

Review

Use Lesson 12.6 in *English Learner Support Guide* to review lesson concepts and vocabulary.

ENRICH

If . . . students are proficient in the lesson concepts,

Then . . . encourage them to work on chapter projects or *Enrichment* Lesson 12.6.

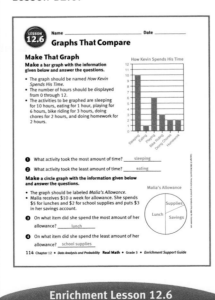

Enrichment Lesson 12.6

PRACTICE

If . . . students would benefit from additional practice,

Then . . . assign *Practice* Lesson 12.6.

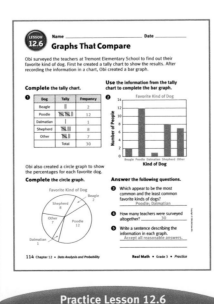

Practice Lesson 12.6

RETEACH

If . . . students struggle comparing information in a graph,

Then . . . have them find examples of pictographs, single bar graphs and circle graphs in newspapers and magazines. Have students discuss the data that is shown in the graphs.

Have them transfer the data to tally charts if they need help analyzing the data. Students can also transfer the data to another type of graph. They can use this data to see which type of graph would portray the data most effectively.

OBJECTIVES
- To review reading line graphs
- To use line graphs to compare data that changes over time
- To interpret the data from graphs that show change

NCTM STANDARDS

Data Analysis and Probability
Representing data using tables and graphs such as line plots, bar graphs, and line graphs

Connections
Recognizing and applying mathematics in contexts outside of mathematics

MATERIALS
*Response Wheels

TECHNOLOGY
e **Presentation** Lesson 12.7
e **MathTools** Graphing Tool

TEST PREP
Cumulative Review
Mental Math reviews multiplication and division facts (Chapter 5).

Extended Response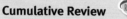
Problems 1, 16, and 24

Graphs Showing Change

Context of the Lesson Students have explored line graphs in Grade 2 and in Chapter 6 of Grade 3. In this chapter students will see that line graphs are one way to show change over time. In Grade 4 students will continue to use line graphs in coordinate graphing. This lesson contains a Mastery Checkpoint.

See page 480B for Math Background for teachers for this lesson.

Planning for Learning ● DIFFERENTIATE INSTRUCTION

INTERVENTION

If . . . students lack the prerequisite skill of reading a graph,

Then . . . teach *Intervention* Lesson 12.A.

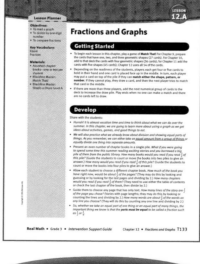

Intervention Lesson 12.A

ENGLISH LEARNER

Preview

If . . . students need language support,

Then . . . use Lesson 12.7 in *English Learner Support Guide* to preview lesson concepts and vocabulary.

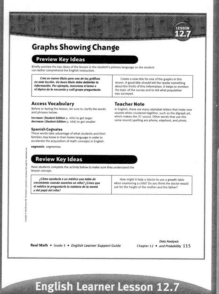

English Learner Lesson 12.7

ENRICH

If . . . students are proficient in the lesson concepts,

Then . . . emphasize the student pages.

PRACTICE

If . . . students would benefit from additional practice,

Then . . . extend Using Student Pages before assigning the student pages.

RETEACH

If . . . students are having difficulty understanding graphs showing change,

Then . . . extend Guided Discussion before assigning the student pages.

Vocabulary
line graph *n.* a graph that represents data as ordered pairs connected with a line

Access Vocabulary
increase to get larger
decrease to get smaller

Spanish Cognates
segments segmentos

---

*Manipulative Kit Item

Mental Math 10

  Review with students basic multiplication and division facts. Use examples such as the following:

a. $4 \times 5 = 20$

b. $18 \div 6 = 3$

c. $9 \times 10 = 90$

d. $7 \times 2 = 14$

e. $20 \div 4 = 5$

f. $3 \times 6 = 18$

g. $90 \div 10 = 9$

h. $14 \div 2 = 7$

i. $10 \times 10 = 100$

1 Develop 20

Tell Students In Today's Lesson They Will

interpret the data on different line graphs that show change over time.

Guided Discussion UNDERSTANDING
Whole Group

Review with students what kind of graphs they have used in this chapter and in other chapters, or graphs they have seen in places other than in mathematics. One type of graph should be a line graph. A line graph is often used to show change over time. If we graph the cost of something and the line goes up, we would say the cost has increased. And likewise, if the line goes down, then we would say the cost has decreased. You may want to have other examples (from magazines, newspapers, reports, and so on) of line graphs, bar graphs, pictographs, and circle graphs to display during this lesson or show examples using the *eMathTools: Graphing Tool.*

Using Student Pages APPLYING
Whole Group

Have students look at the graph of Todd's height on student page 494. Discuss the graph and observations students may make. Ask questions such as the following:

■ **What is the measurement used for his height?** centimeters

■ **What is the spacing between height marks?** 10 cm

■ **Is this graph easy to read? Why or why not?**

As a class, answer the questions on page 494, and discuss them. Accept all reasonable title suggestions, such as *Todd's Height from Birth to Age 15.*

On page 495, work together as a class to answer Problems 3–6. Answer any questions, and see that students are understanding before proceeding to assign the student pages.

2 Assign Student Pages

20 🌙

Pages 494–495 APPLYING

Have students complete the exercises on page 495 independently.

Graphs Showing Change

Key Ideas

A line graph shows change over a period of time.

Along the bottom line, or *axis,* of a line graph is the measure of time (minutes, hours, years, centuries, and so on). On the left line, or *axis,* is usually another type of measurement (pounds, amount of something, number of something, and so on). It is important that in any graph, the spaces always represent equal amounts; if not, your graph may be misleading.

This line graph shows the change in Todd's height from his birth, which could be considered 0 years, through age 15. Notice the bottom axis is labeled *Age in Years,* and the left-hand axis is labeled *Height in Centimeters.*

❶ **Extended Response** What would be a good title for this graph?

❷ Does this line graph show an *increase* in Todd's height or a *decrease* in Todd's height over the years? increase

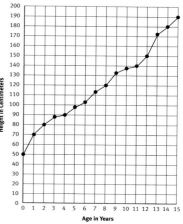

❶ Accept all reasonable answers. Possible answer: *Todd's Height*

494　　　　　　　　　　　 📖 **Textbook** This lesson is available in the *eTextbook.*

Use the graph to answer these questions.

About how tall was Todd on his

❸ first birthday? 70 cm

❹ fifth birthday? 98 cm

❺ eighth birthday? 120 cm

❻ fourteenth birthday? 180 cm

How old was Todd when he was

❼ 90 centimeters tall? 4 years old

❽ 115 centimeters tall? 7 years old

❾ 140 centimeters tall? 11 years old

❿ 180 centimeters tall? 14 years old

About how many centimeters did Todd grow between his

⓫ first and fifth birthdays? 28 cm

⓬ fifth and eighth birthdays? 22 cm

⓭ eighth and fourteenth birthdays?
60 cm

⓮ first and fourteenth birthdays?
110 cm

⓯ If Todd continues to grow at the same rate as he grew between his thirteenth and fifteenth birthdays, how tall do you think he will be on his sixteenth birthday? about 200 cm tall

　　　　　　　　　　　　　　　495

Teaching Lesson 12.7

Assign Student Pages, continued

Pages 496–497 APPLYING

Have students complete the exercises on pages 496 and 497 independently.

As Students Finish

 Game Have students play a previously introduced game.

LESSON 12.7 • Graphs Showing Change

This line graph shows the change in Wendy's weight from her birth.

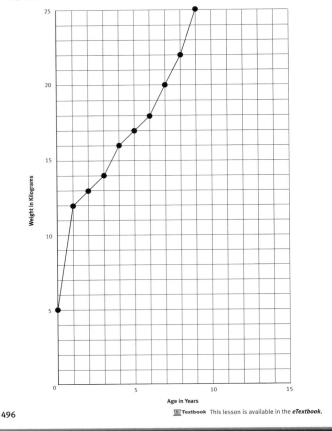

Weight in Kilograms

Age in Years

496   **[eTextbook]** This lesson is available in the *eTextbook*.

---

16 **Extended Response** What would be a good title for this graph? Accept all reasonable answers.
Possible answer: Wendy's Weight

17 Does this line graph show an *increase* in her weight or a *decrease* in her weight over the years? increase

Use the line graph to answer these questions.

About how much did Wendy weigh on her

18 first birthday? 12 kg

19 third birthday? 14 kg

20 seventh birthday? 20 kg

21 ninth birthday? 25 kg

22 About how much do you think Wendy weighed when she was $7\frac{1}{2}$ years old? 21 kg

23 About how old do you think Wendy was when she weighed 24 kilograms? between 8 and 9 years old; Accept all reasonable answers.

24 **Extended Response** Write one true statement about this graph. Accept all reasonable answers.

25 When will Wendy reach 100 kg?
probably never

③ Reflect 10

Guided Discussion REASONING

Whole Group

Have students refer back to the graph of Todd's height on page 494. Ask students to focus on the graph between age 0 (birth) and age 1. Ask questions such as the following:

- **How much did Todd grow between birth and age 1?** 20 cm
- **If this was the only data we had, how tall would we predict him to be at age 5? Explain your answer.** 150 cm; 20 cm per year for another four years would be 70 + 80 = 150.
- **What was Todd's actual height at age 5? How much of a difference is this from the estimate we made based on his first year of growth?** around 98 cm; for an estimate of 150 cm, this overestimates his height by about 50 cm
- **Why is the estimate based on his first year of growth so far off?** Todd does not grow a constant amount each year
- **If Todd is 190 cm at age 15, do you expect him to be 380 cm at age 30?** No; that would mean Todd would be almost 12.5 ft. tall. His growth will most likely level out near his age 15 height.

✓ Use Mastery Checkpoint 23 found in **Assessment** to evaluate student mastery of interpreting line graphs. By this time students should be able to correctly answer eighty percent of the Mastery Checkpoint items.

 Curriculum Connection: Students may be interested in researching what determines genetic traits such as height, eye color, hair color, and so on.

 Cumulative Review: For cumulative review of previously learned skills, see page 513–514.

 Family Involvement: Assign the *Practice, Reteach,* or *Enrichment* activities depending on the needs of your students.

Encourage students to find other examples of line graphs with a friend or a relative.

 Concept/Question Board: Encourage students to continue to post questions, answers, and examples on the Concept/Question Board.

 Math Puzzler: Catherine worked for 7 hours on Friday, and Lorien worked for 4 hours. Catherine earned $5 an hour, and Lorien earned $8 an hour. Who earned more money on Friday? How much more? Catherine; $3 more

Assess and Differentiate

 Assess Use *eAssess* to record and analyze evidence of student understanding.

A Gather Evidence

Use the Daily Class Assessment Records in **Assessment** or **eAssess** to record daily observations.

Formal Assessment

☑ **Mastery Checkpoint 23**

Did the student
☐ use correct procedures?
☐ respond with at least 80% accuracy?

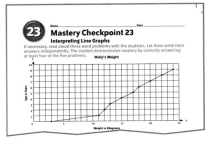

Assessment Page T77

B Summarize Findings

Analyze and summarize assessment data for each student. Determine which Assessment Follow-Up is appropriate for each student. Use the Student Assessment Record in **Assessment** or **eAssess** to update assessment records.

Assessment page T41

C Assessment Follow-Up ● DIFFERENTIATE INSTRUCTION

Based on your observations, use these teaching strategies for assessment follow-up.

INTERVENTION

Review student performance on *Intervention* Lesson 12.A to see if students have mastered prerequisite skills for this lesson.

ENGLISH LEARNER

Review

Use Lesson 12.7 in *English Learner Support Guide* to review lesson concepts and vocabulary.

ENRICH

If . . . students are proficient in the lesson concepts,

Then . . . encourage them to work on chapter projects or *Enrichment* Lesson 12.7.

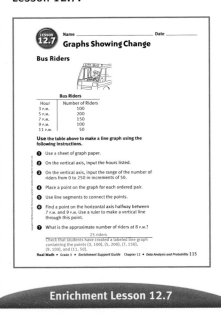

Enrichment Lesson 12.7

PRACTICE

If . . . students would benefit from additional practice,

Then . . . assign *Practice* Lesson 12.7.

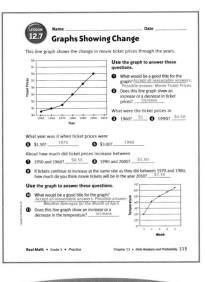

Practice Lesson 12.7

RETEACH

If . . . students struggle with interpreting line graphs,

Then . . . give them lists of data showing changes over time and have them make graphs to represent the data. Have students work in pairs or small groups. This data can be found in encyclopedias and on the Internet.

Exploring Problem Solving

Objectives
- To explore the problem-solving strategy Organize Data
- To provide practice solving nonroutine problems that involve interpreting data to make decisions

Materials
- Graph paper
- Counters or other objects (optional)

Context of the Lesson This lesson helps students prepare for the upcoming lessons on graphs that show how data is grouped. It also provides an opportunity for students to continue to apply what they have been learning about organizing data with tables and graphs.

1 Develop 5

Tell Students In Today's Lesson They Will
- read a problem about a farm business in Thailand.
- look at how two students use two different ways to solve the problem.
- solve the problem themselves and show how they solved it.

Guided Discussion

Help students recall the chapter opener in which they solved problems about papayas grown in Puerto Rico. Tell them that they will solve a problem today about fruit grown on a farm in another part of the world.

2 Exploring Problem Solving 30

Using Student Pages

Read the problem on page 498 with the class.

To help make sure students understand the problem and the records illustrated on page 499, ask questions such as the following:

- **What does Ms. Riley sell and ship?** star fruit
- **How many kilograms of star fruit are in a basket?** however many kilograms a customer orders

---

Exploring 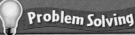 Problem Solving

Ms. Riley sells baskets of star fruit that she grows on her farm in Thailand. People tell her how many kilograms they want, and she makes up a basket with that amount. She keeps records such as the ones below so she knows the different amounts people order.

Ms. Riley has decided to make her business simpler. She will sell baskets of star fruit in only three sizes—small, medium, and large. How many kilograms should she put in each size?

Tuesday	
Number of Baskets	Amount in Each Basket
1	2 kg
1	4 kg
2	10 kg
1	15 kg

Wednesday	
Number of Baskets	Amount in Each Basket
2	3 kg
1	5 kg
1	8 kg
1	12 kg

Thursday	
Number of Baskets	Amount in Each Basket
2	4 kg
1	7 kg
2	8 kg
1	15 kg

Friday	
Number of Baskets	Amount in Each Basket
2	3 kg
1	9 kg
3	10 kg
2	15 kg

Saturday	
Number of Baskets	Amount in Each Basket
2	2 kg
1	6 kg
2	8 kg
3	15 kg
1	18 kg

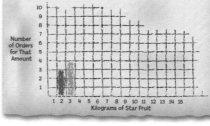

Eric organized the data in a table to help solve the problem.

Amount	Number of Baskets
2 kg	3
3 kg	4
4 kg	

Textbook This lesson is available in the *eTextbook*.

Think about Eric and LeAnne's strategies. Answer the following questions.

1. Why did Eric write the number 3 next to 2 kg?
to show that three 2-kg baskets of star fruit were sold
2. What number do you think Eric is about to write? Why?
3; because that's how many 4-kg baskets were sold
3. Do you think Eric's way of organizing the data helps?

4. How would you solve the problem?

LeAnne organized the data in a different way.

5. What do the two bars that LeAnne made so far show?
Three 2-kg baskets were sold; four 3-kg baskets were sold.
6. How is LeAnne's strategy different from Eric's?

7. How are the two strategies alike?

8. How could LeAnne use her graph to solve the problem?
See *Teacher's Edition*.
9. Use one of the strategies shown or a strategy of your own to decide how heavy each size should be. Explain your reasoning. See *Teacher's Edition*.

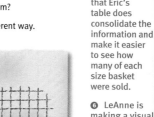

3. Students should see that Eric's table does consolidate the information and make it easier to see how many of each size basket were sold.

6. LeAnne is making a visual display, or bar graph, to show the data; Eric used numbers in a table.

7. Both involve putting information from several documents into a single one.

- **What does Ms. Riley want to change?** She wants to sell only three sizes.
- **What information will she use to help her decide which sizes to sell?** how many kilograms people ordered recently
- **What information does each of the records give you?** how many kilograms of star fruit were ordered and how many times that amount was ordered
- **Can you tell quickly if customers ordered more 6-kilogram baskets or more 10-kilogram baskets?** no, not quickly, because the information is spread out and mixed up
- **How might you organize the information to help you see which sizes were the most popular?** Allow students to share whatever suggestions come to mind, such as making tally marks, making a table, making a bar graph, or making a pictograph.

Guide students through Eric's strategy by going over Problems 1–4 on page 499. For Problem 4, encourage students to suggest different strategies, but move to the next sample strategy if they cannot come up with any ideas. Guide students through LeAnne's strategy by going over Problems 5–8.

Answer to Problem 8

LeAnne could look at the bars on the graph and try to find three sizes that would please most of her customers.

Have students work in pairs or small groups to answer Problem 9. Tell them they may use graph paper to organize the data in whatever way they think will help. As students work on the problem, circulate around the room providing support as needed. Commend students who persist when they are stuck.

Answer to Problem 9

Students should give valid reasons for their choices. For example, they might complete LeAnne's graph and look for three groupings.

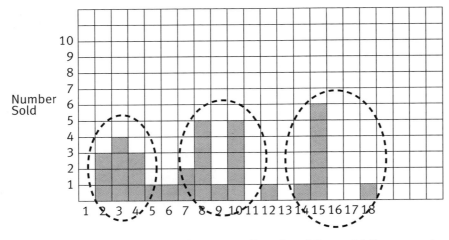

Some students might say that Ms. Riley should put 3 kilograms in the small size, 9 kilograms in the medium size (the average of 8 and 10), and 15 kilograms in the large size.

Other students may say that she should choose 8 or 10 kilograms for the medium size, not 9, because 9 will not give many people exactly what they want. Some students may say Ms. Riley should pick the three most popular amounts: 8 kilograms, 10 kilograms, and 15 kilograms. Help them see that more customers would be better served by having a small size in the 2 to 4 kilogram range.

Effective Communication Have groups present how they organized the information, what sizes they decided to make, and why they chose those sizes. In discussion, bring out the following points:

- There are different ways to organize information.
- Different people may prefer different ways of organizing information.
- Math can help us make good business decisions and many other kinds of decisions. To use math in this way, we need to think about the meaning of the numbers we are working with.
- When making decisions in real-life situations, answers may not be clear-cut.
- Different people may look at the same information and come to different conclusions, and both conclusions may be reasonable.

Sample Solutions Strategies

Use Tally Marks

Students may keep track of the number of each amount ordered by making a tally and then counting the tally marks.

Make a Pictograph

Students may use pictures to show how many of each size was ordered.

4 **Assess**   15

When evaluating student work, focus on whether students thought rationally about the problem. Questions to consider include the following:

- Did the student understand the problem?
- Did the student organize the data in a clear way?
- Was the student able to explain the reasoning used?
- Did the student listen carefully to other students' explanations?

Cumulative Review

Assign Pages 500–501

Use the Cumulative Review as a review of concepts and skills that students have previously learned.

Here are different ways that you can assign these problems to your students as they work through the chapter:

- With some of the lessons in the chapter, assign a set of cumulative review problems to be completed as practice or for homework.
  Lesson 12.1—Problems 1–5
  Lesson 12.2—Problems 6–7
  Lesson 12.3—Problems 8–11
  Lesson 12.4—Problems 12–17
  Lesson 12.5—Problems 18–20
  Lesson 12.6—Problems 21–26
  Lesson 12.7—Problems 27–30
- At any point during the chapter, assign part or all of the cumulative review problems to be completed as practice or for homework.

Cumulative Review

Problems 1–5 review conversions of metric weight, Lesson 9.3.

Problems 6–7 review problem solving using arrays, Lesson 4.5.

Problems 8–11 review subtracting three-digit numbers, Lesson 2.8.

Problems 12–17 review dividing two-digit numbers by one-digit numbers, Lesson 7.7.

Problems 18–20 review graphing ordered pairs to answer questions, Lesson 6.6.

Problems 21–26 review equalities and inequalities, Lesson 1.4.

Problems 27–30 review obtuse, acute, and right angles, Lesson 11.2.

Monitoring Student Progress

If . . . students miss more than one problem in a section,   **Then . . .** refer to the indicated lesson for remediation suggestions.

Cumulative Review

Metric Weight Lesson 9.3

Convert each measure from kilograms to grams or from grams to kilograms. Write the new measure.

❶ ▊ g = 10 kg 10,000
❷ 4 kg = ▊ g 4,000
❸ 17 kg = ▊ g 17,000
❹ ▊ g = 8 kg 8,000
❺ ▊ g = 3 kg 3,000

Arrays Lesson 4.5

Draw the array, and then answer the question.

❻ In the winter, Amanda uses straw to help keep her llamas warm. She has 6 rows with 12 bales of straw each. Draw the array.

❼ Amanda uses 3 bales to cover each shelter floor. If she used all the straw, how many shelter floors could she cover? 24

Subtracting Three-Digit Numbers Lesson 2.8

Subtract.

❽ 261 − 199 ▊ 62
❾ 354 − 275 ▊ 79
❿ 613 − 535 ▊ 78
⓫ 707 − 488 ▊ 219

Dividing Two-Digit Numbers by One-Digit Numbers Lesson 7.7

Divide.

⓬ 96 ÷ 2 48
⓭ 69 ÷ 3 23
⓮ 49 ÷ 7 7

⓯ 68 ÷ 4 17
⓰ 96 ÷ 4 24
⓱ 52 ÷ 4 13

eTextbook This lesson is available in the *eTextbook*.

Graphing Ordered Pairs Lesson 6.6

Fill in the blanks by finding the letters in the graph that match the ordered pairs.

⓲ To move animals, a farmer might use this.
▊▊▊▊▊▊▊ trailer
(0, 6) (10, 5) (3, 7) (5, 8) (8, 2) (7, 6) (10, 5)

⓳ Many horse ▊▊▊▊▊▊ are made of leather. saddles
(7, 9) (3, 7) (0, 0) (0, 0) (8, 2) (7, 6) (7, 9)

⓴ You might find this shelled animal at a reptile farm.
▊▊▊▊▊▊ turtle
(0, 6) (4, 4) (10, 5) (0, 6) (8, 2) (7, 6)

Equalities and Inequalities Lesson 1.4

Use <, >, or = to make a true comparison.

㉑ 875 ▊ 877 <
㉔ 86 − 8 ▊ 68 − 6 >
㉒ 9 + 185 ▊ 12 + 186 <
㉕ 1,235 ▊ 1,235 =
㉓ 4,325 ▊ 4,442 <
㉖ 617 − 9 ▊ 619 − 7 <

Angles Lesson 11.2

Label each angle as either *right, obtuse,* or *acute.*

㉗   ㉘   ㉙   ㉚

obtuse   acute   right   obtuse

Individual Oral Assessment

Purpose of the Test

The Individual Oral Assessment is designed to measure students' growing knowledge of chapter concepts. It is administered individually to each student, and it requires oral responses from each student. The test takes about five minutes to complete.

See **Assessment** for detailed instructions for administering and interpreting the test, and record students' answers on the Student Assessment Recording Sheet.

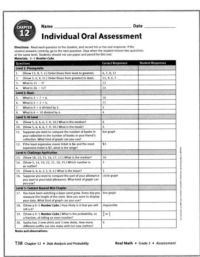

Assessment Page T38

Directions

Read each question to the student, and record his or her oral response. If the student answers correctly, go to the next question. Stop when the student misses two questions at the same level. Students should not use scrap paper.

Materials

0–5 **Number Cube**

Questions

Level 1: Prerequisite

1. (Show 12, 8, 7, 4.) Put these numbers in order from least to greatest. 4, 7, 8, 12
2. (Show 3, 6, 9, 11.) Put these numbers in order from greatest to least. 11, 9, 6, 3
3. What is 15 − 3? 12
4. What is 26 − 12? 14

Level 2: Basic

5. Add 3 + 7 + 6. 16
6. Add 5 + 2 + 4. 11
7. Add 9 + 6, and then divide the sum by 3. 5
8. Add 6 + 10, and then divide the sum by 4. 4

Level 3: At Level

9. (Show 5, 6, 6, 6, 7, 9, 10.) What is the median of this set of values? 6
10. (Show 5, 6, 6, 6, 7, 9, 10.) What is the mode of this set of values? 6
11. Suppose you want to compare the number of books in your collection to the number of books in your friend's collection. What kind of graph can you use? bar graph
12. You want to compare movie ticket prices. The least expensive ticket is $4. The most expensive ticket is $7. What is the range? $3

Level 4: Challenge Application

13. (Show 18, 12, 15, 14, 17, 17.) What is the median? 16
14. (Show 5, 14, 19, 22, 21, 18, 20.) Which number is an outlier? 5
15. (Show 4, 6, 6, 2, 5, 8, 4.) What is the mean of this set of values? 5
16. Suppose you want to compare the part of your allowance you save to your total allowance. Which kind of graph could you use? circle graph

Level 5: Content Beyond Mid-Chapter

17. You have been watching a bean seed grow. Every day you measure the length of the stem. Now you want to display your data. What kind of graph can you use? line
18. (Show a 0–5 **Number Cube.**) How likely is it that you will roll a 6? impossible
19. (Show a 0–5 **Number Cube.**) What is the probability, as a fraction, of rolling an odd number? $\frac{3}{6}$ or $\frac{1}{2}$
20. Sasha has 2 new shirts and 3 new skirts. How many different outfits can she make with her new clothes? 6

OBJECTIVES
- To explore graphs that show another way data is grouped
- To review the terms range, mode, and outliers

NCTM STANDARDS
Data Analysis and Probability
Representing data using tables and graphs such as line plots, bar graphs, and line graphs

Communication
Using the language of mathematics to express mathematical ideas precisely

MATERIALS
*Response Wheels

TECHNOLOGY
ⓔ **Presentation** Lesson 12.8

TEST PREP
Cumulative Review
- Mental Math reviews adding decimals (Lesson 10.5).
- Problem 1 reviews creating bar graphs (Lesson 12.6).
- Problem 2 reviews mode and range (Lessons 12.3 and 12.4).

Extended Response
Problems 4 and 8

Graphs Showing How Data Is Grouped

Context of the Lesson In this lesson students will explore line plots and stem-and-leaf plots. Characteristics previously discussed will be reviewed using these types of graphs.

See page 480B for Math Background for teachers for this lesson.

Planning for Learning ● DIFFERENTIATE INSTRUCTION

INTERVENTION
If . . . students lack the prerequisite skill of reading a graph,

Then . . . teach *Intervention* Lesson 12.A.

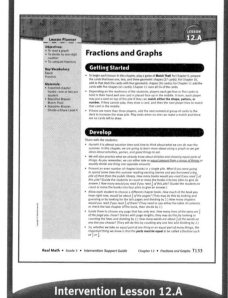

Intervention Lesson 12.A

ENGLISH LEARNER
Preview

If . . . students need language support,

Then . . . use Lesson 12.8 in *English Learner Support Guide* to preview lesson concepts and vocabulary.

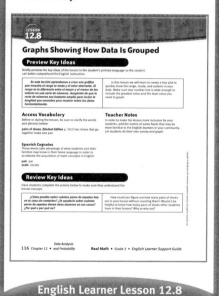

English Learner Lesson 12.8

ENRICH
If . . . students are proficient in the lesson concepts,

Then . . . emphasize the student pages.

PRACTICE
If . . . students would benefit from additional practice,

Then . . . extend Using Student Pages before assigning the student pages.

RETEACH
If . . . students are having difficulty understanding graphs showing data groupings,

Then . . . extend Guided Discussion before assigning the student pages.

Vocabulary

line plot *n.* a data graph that shows frequency along a number line

stem-and-leaf plot *n.* a graph showing data from least to greatest using the digits from the greatest place value to group the data

Spanish Cognates
pair pares
scale escala

---

*Manipulative Kit Item

Mental Math   10

  Review with students adding decimals. Have students represent the decimal point with their finger. Use examples such as the following:

a. $4.1 + 0.3 = 4.4$ **b.** $6.3 + 6.3 = 12.6$

c. $7.5 + 3.0 = 10.5$ **d.** $3.8 + 0.2 = 4.0$

e. $8.2 + 0.2 = 8.4$ **f.** $0.6 + 0.4 = 1.0$

1 Develop 20

Tell Students In Today's Lesson They Will

explore graphs that show how data can be graphed and some of the terms associated with those graphs.

Guided Discussion   UNDERSTANDING   Whole Group

Review with students a number line and the properties of a number line. For example, the markings are always the same distance apart, a number line can start and end anywhere, it can include all sorts of numbers including whole numbers, negative numbers, decimals, and so on. Draw a number line on the board with 10 markings but with no labeling. On either side of the board, create a tally table of the number of pencils (or other writing instruments) each student has in his or her desk. After you feel there is an adequate number of answers, explain that you need to transfer this data to a graph. This particular graph is called a line plot.

Label your number-line markings to reflect the data collected in your survey. Then, proceed to place an x above each place on the number line that would correspond with one of your tally marks. For example, if you had two students who said 2, two students who said 3, and one student who said 4, your line plot would look like this:

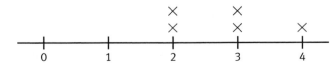

Transfer the data from your table to your line plot. Ask students to give a good title for this line plot such as "number of pencils in desks." Then discuss with students some of the data on this plot, having them create questions and answering them.

Skill Building APPLYING   Small Group

Present the following scenario: A third grade class is selling greeting cards (packed 20 to a box) for a fundraiser. Twenty students sold the following amounts of greeting cards: 20, 60, 80, 120, 100, 120, 200, 140, 60, 120, 80, 120, 200, 200, 180, 140, 120, 80, 120, and 60.

Have students work in small groups to create a line plot of the amounts of cards sold. Ask questions such as the following:

- **What is the mode? What is the range?** 120; 180
- **What number might be considered an outlier?** 20

Have students compare their line plots to see if other groups derived similar results.

Using Student Pages UNDERSTANDING   Whole Group

Refer students to the information about stem-and-leaf plots on page 503. With students, work through the example, even drawing it on the board or overhead projector. Discuss some of the patterns and discoveries about the data from this plot. Have students create and answer questions about this graph. Check for understanding before assigning student pages.

Monitoring Student Progress

If . . . students are having difficulty with stem-and-leaf plots,

Then . . . create one together as a class before assigning student pages.

2 Assign Student Pages 20

Pages 502–503   APPLYING

Have students complete the remaining exercises on pages 502 and 503 independently.

Problem 1 The bar graph will have the same shape as the line plot. The only differences will be the addition of a y-axis from 0 to (at least) 8 and, instead of vertically stacking x's, there will be bars of equivalent heights.

As Students Finish

 Have students play a previously introduced game.

LESSON **12.8** **Graphs Showing How Data is Grouped**

Key Ideas

There are times when you want to show the spread of data quickly to help identify the range, mode, or any outliers. One easy way to do this is by creating a line plot.

To create a line plot, begin by drawing a number line. Make sure your number line has a scale that includes the greatest value and the least value you need to graph. For each piece of information to graph, draw an x above the corresponding value. Look at the following line plot Zampa made of the pairs of shoes the students counted in their houses.

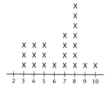

Use the information from Zampa's line plot to answer the following questions.

 1 Create a bar graph showing how frequently you would expect to find a certain number of pairs of shoes in a student's house. **See Teacher's Edition.**

 2 What is the mode? What is the range? **8; 7**

3 What number of pairs of shoes might be considered an outlier? **There is not an outlier.**

 4 **Extended Response** Write one true and one false statement about the line plot. **See Reflect in the Teacher's Edition.**

502   **Textbook** This lesson is available in the **eTextbook**.

Student Page

Another type of plot that allows you to organize and group data is a stem-and-leaf plot.

The following are the ages of ten faculty at the News Review Journalism Camp.

35, 28, 19, 45, 51, 48, 31, 34, 18, 50

When we put the ages in numerical order, they are 18, 19, 28, 31, 34, 35, 45, 48, 50, and 51. The least value is 18, and the greatest value is 51. This will help us determine our first and last stem.

In this stem-and-leaf plot, the stems will be the digits in the tens place and the leaves will be the digits in the ones place.

Copy and list the stems to the left of the dividing line. Then list the leaves to the right of the dividing line so that they match up with the appropriate stem.

Stem	Leaves
1	8 9
2	8
3	1 4 5
4	5 8
5	0 1

The row 1 | 8 9 represents 18 and 19, 2 | 8 represents 28, and so on. By looking at this stem-and-leaf plot, we can tell that the most frequently occurring ages are between 30 and 39 and the median is 34.

The following are extra-credit points awarded in Ms. Pi's third-grade class for the entire year: 10, 21, 26, 8, 33, 41, 43, 28, 19, 17, 7, 22, 25, 31, 30, 20, 17, 50, and 44.

5 Use the extra-credit points listed above to create a stem-and-leaf plot. **See plot in Teacher's Edition.**

6 Is it now easier to find the least, greatest, and most common number of extra-credit points? **yes**

7 How many students had extra credit this year in Ms. Pi's third-grade class? **19**

8 **Extended Response** Write one true statement about the stem-and-leaf plot. **See Reflect in Teacher's Edition.**

---

3 Reflect   10

Guided Discussion REASONING   Whole Group

Refer students to the line plots they made in class about the greeting card fundraiser. Ask how the line plot would change if, instead of plotting the number of cards, the students plotted the number of boxes (remind them that there were 20 greeting cards to a box).

Through discussion help students to see that the shape of the graph does not change – only the numbers on the number line (horizontal axis) change. Even though each data point is divided by 20, the relative relationships remain the same. For example, a data point that is twice as much as another remains so (40 vs. 20 becomes 2 vs. 1).

Extended Response

Problems 4 and 8 Verify with the class that each of the true and false statements about these graphs is indeed true or false. Discuss why the false statements are this way and what might need to be done to change them.

Problem 5

```
0 | 7 8
1 | 0 7 7 9
2 | 0 1 2 5 6 8
3 | 0 1 3
4 | 1 3 4
5 | 0
```

 Cumulative Review: For cumulative review of previously learned skills, see page 513–514.

 Family Involvement: Assign the **Practice, Reteach,** or **Enrichment** activities depending on the needs of your students.

 Concept/Question Board: Encourage students to continue to post questions, answers, and examples on the Concept/ Question Board.

 Math Puzzler: When you multiply these two numbers together, you get 16, and when you add them, you get 8. What are these two numbers? **4, 4**

4 Assess and Differentiate

 Assess Use *eAssess* to record and analyze evidence of student understanding.

A Gather Evidence

Use the Daily Class Assessment Records in *Assessment* or *eAssess* to record daily observations.

Informal Assessment

☑ **Guided Discussion**

Did the student `UNDERSTANDING`
- ☐ make important observations?
- ☐ extend or generalize learning?
- ☐ provide insightful answers?
- ☐ pose insightful questions?

Informal Assessment

☑ **Student Pages**

Did the student `APPLYING`
- ☐ apply learning in new situations?
- ☐ contribute concepts?
- ☐ contribute answers?
- ☐ connect mathematics to real-world situations?

B Summarize Findings

Analyze and summarize assessment data for each student. Determine which Assessment Follow-Up is appropriate for each student. Use the Student Assessment Record in *Assessment* or *eAssess* to update assessment records.

Assessment page T41

C Assessment Follow-Up ● DIFFERENTIATE INSTRUCTION

Based on your observations, use these teaching strategies for assessment follow-up.

INTERVENTION

Review student performance on *Intervention* Lesson 12.A to see if students have mastered prerequisite skills for this lesson.

ENGLISH LEARNER

Review

Use Lesson 12.8 in *English Learner Support Guide* to review lesson concepts and vocabulary.

ENRICH

If . . . students are proficient in the lesson concepts,

Then . . . encourage them to work on chapter projects or *Enrichment* Lesson 12.8.

Enrichment Lesson 12.8

PRACTICE

If . . . students would benefit from additional practice,

Then . . . assign *Practice* Lesson 12.8.

Practice Lesson 12.8

RETEACH

If . . . students struggle with making a line graph,

Then . . . draw a number line on the board. Give each student a card with a data point on it. Have students come up one at a time and tape their data point on the number line where it belongs. If there is already a value there, have them tape their value above the existing. When they are finished they will have made a line plot for the data. Have them discuss what the outliers mean and what the range and mode of the data are. If possible, use data that is pertinent to the students such as test scores or shoe sizes.

OBJECTIVES
To introduce the scatter plot as a way of organizing and studying data

NCTM STANDARDS
Data Analysis and Probability
- Describing the shape and important features of a set of data and comparing related data sets, with an emphasis on how the data are distributed
- Representing data using tables and graphs

Connections
Recognizing and using connections among mathematical ideas

MATERIALS
*Response Wheels

TECHNOLOGY
ⓔ Presentation Lesson 12.9

TEST PREP
Cumulative Review
- Mental Math reviews fractions of sets (Lesson 8.3).
- Problem 2 reviews the basic shape of a line (Lesson 11.1).

Interpreting and Analyzing Data

Context of the Lesson In this lesson students will explore scatter plots and their characteristics.
See page 480B for Math Background for teachers for this lesson.

Planning for Learning ● DIFFERENTIATE INSTRUCTION

INTERVENTION

If . . . students lack the prerequisite skill of reading a graph,

Then . . . teach *Intervention* Lesson 12.A.

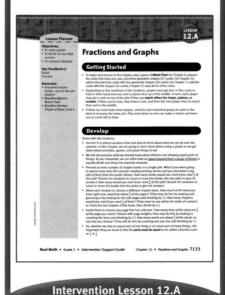

Intervention Lesson 12.A

ENGLISH LEARNER

Preview

If . . . students need language support,

Then . . . use Lesson 12.9 in *English Learner Support Guide* to preview lesson concepts and vocabulary.

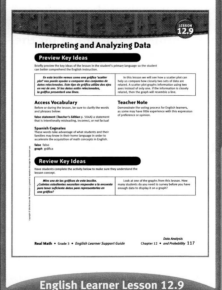

English Learner Lesson 12.9

ENRICH

If . . . students are proficient in the lesson concepts,

Then . . . emphasize the student pages.

PRACTICE

If . . . students would benefit from additional practice,

Then . . . extend Guided Discussion before assigning the student pages.

RETEACH

If . . . students are having difficulty understanding how to interpret and analyze data,

Then . . . extend Guided Discussion before assigning the student pages.

Vocabulary	**Access Vocabulary**	**Spanish Cognates**
scatter plot *n.* a graph that represents data as ordered pairs	**false statement** a statement that is intentionally misleading, incorrect, or not factual	**false** falso **graph** gráfica

---

*Manipulative Kit Item

Mental Math 10

 Review fractions of whole numbers. Use examples such as the following:

a. $\frac{1}{2}$ of 10 5

b. $\frac{1}{2}$ of 12 6

c. $\frac{1}{3}$ of 12 4

d. $\frac{2}{3}$ of 12 8

e. $\frac{1}{5}$ of 20 4

f. $\frac{3}{5}$ of 20 12

1 Develop 20

Tell Students In Today's Lesson They Will

interpret the data in a scatter plot to determine how closely the data is related.

Using Student Pages UNDERSTANDING Whole Group

Go over the graph of age versus height on page 504. Have students explain to you what information that graph is displaying. You may wish to have them clarify their reasoning by asking questions such as the following:

- **What information did Julia collect for each of the 25 girls?** height and age
- **Why are there sometimes many points on the graph for the same age (for example, the three points at age 4)?** each point represents the height of a different girl; it is likely that most heights for the same age will be within a range of heights, but within that range, the height will likely vary from girl to girl
- **Can you imagine one straight line that all the points on this graph would fall on or near?** yes
- **Would this straight line slant upward or downward as the age of a girl increases?** upward
- **What does this say about how a girl's height is related to her age?** the height increases as the age increases

Emphasize to students that because the points on this scatter plot look as though they could fall on (or near) one straight line we say the two variables being plotted are *closely related*. Ask students if the conclusion that height and age are closely related makes sense. Yes, it does; you would expect a person to get taller as they get older and grow.

For comparison, review the graph of age versus number of family members on page 505. Guide students through a related discussion using questions such as the following:

- **What additional information did Julia collect for each of the 25 girls?** the number of family members
- **Can you imagine one straight line that all the points on this graph would fall on or near?** no (particularly when compared to the graph on page 504); if students answer yes, ask them to describe a straight line they believe would work. For any straight line they come up with, you should be able to identify points that are not near to it.

- **Would you say the number of members in a girl's family increases or decreases with her age?** cannot say
- **Would you have expected a girl's age to be closely related to the number of people in her family?** Students may wish to make arguments that you might have a brother or sister born into your family when you are younger or a family member may pass away as you get older, but those events are not dependent on a girl's age and could happen at a variety of times.
- **Based on this scatter plot, would you say that a girl's age and the number of members of her family are closely related?** no

2 Assign Student Pages 20

Pages 504–505 APPLYING

Have students answer the questions on pages 504 and 505 independently.

As Students Finish

 Have students play a previously introduced game.

LESSON 12.9 Interpreting and Analyzing Data

Key Ideas

One way to see how closely two sets of data are related is to use a scatter plot. If the information is closely related, then the graph will resemble a line.

Julia recorded the age and height of twenty-five girls. Rather than make two separate graphs for age and height, she created a scatter plot comparing a girl's age to that girl's height.

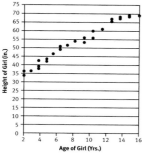

❶ As a girl's age increases, does her height generally increase or decrease?   increase

❷ True or False. The points are fairly close to being on a line.   true

❸ Based on your answer to Problem 2, would you consider the age and height of a girl to be closely related?   Yes

❹ What would be a good title for this scatter plot?
Possible answer: *Age of a Girl Compared to Her Height*

504   📖 **Textbook** This lesson is available in the *eTextbook*.

Julia also recorded how many members were in each girl's family. She decided to plot that information compared to each girl's age on a different scatter plot.

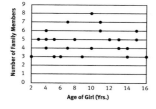

❺ As a girl's age increases, does the number of members in her family generally increase or decrease?   cannot say

❻ True or False. The points are fairly close to being on a line.   false

❼ Based on your answer to Problem 6, would you consider the age of a girl and the number of members in her family to be closely related?   no

❽ What would be a good title for this scatter plot?
Possible answer: *Age of a Girl Compared to Her Family Size*

---

3 Reflect   10 ⏰

Guided Discussion   **REASONING**   Whole Group

Have students give examples of data that, when plotted on a scatter plot, should be closely related (for example, practice time versus performance, amount of daily study versus quiz scores, and so on).

Have students talk about any times they may have seen a scatter plot, if any. Remind students that since it is a graph, a scatter plot should have each axis labeled and should be given an appropriate scale.

 Cumulative Review: For cumulative review of previously learned skills, see page 513–514.

Family Involvement: Assign the *Practice, Reteach,* or *Enrichment* activities depending on the needs of your students.

Encourage students to find real-world examples of scatter plots with a friend or a relative.

Concept/Question Board: Encourage students to continue to post questions, answers, and examples on the Concept/Question Board.

Math Puzzler: Mr. Mohammed is building a bookshelf. Each shelf is 3 feet long, and there are 6 shelves. He also has to buy 4 brackets for each shelf. If wood is $1.00 a foot and brackets cost $0.50 each, how much will Mr. Mohammed spend? $30.00

Assess and Differentiate

e Assess Use *eAssess* to record and analyze evidence of student understanding.

A Gather Evidence

Use the Daily Class Assessment Records in **Assessment** or **eAssess** to record daily observations.

Informal Assessment
☑ Using Student Pages

Did the student **UNDERSTANDING**
- ❏ make important observations?
- ❏ extend or generalize learning?
- ❏ provide insightful answers?
- ❏ pose insightful questions?

Informal Assessment
☑ Student Pages

Did the student **APPLYING**
- ❏ apply learning in new situations?
- ❏ contribute concepts?
- ❏ contribute answers?
- ❏ connect mathematics to real-world situations?

B Summarize Findings

Analyze and summarize assessment data for each student. Determine which Assessment Follow-Up is appropriate for each student. Use the Student Assessment Record in **Assessment** or **eAssess** to update assessment records.

Assessment page T41

C Assessment Follow-Up ● DIFFERENTIATE INSTRUCTION

Based on your observations, use these teaching strategies for assessment follow-up.

INTERVENTION	ENRICH	PRACTICE	RETEACH
Review student performance on **Intervention** Lesson 12.A to see if students have mastered prerequisite skills for this lesson.	**If . . .** students are proficient in the lesson concepts, **Then . . .** encourage them to work on chapter projects or **Enrichment** Lesson 12.9.	**If . . .** students would benefit from additional practice, **Then . . .** assign **Practice** Lesson 12.9.	**If . . .** students struggle with interpreting and analyzing data, **Then . . .** have them find examples of graphs in the newspaper and magazines. Have students discuss the graphs and what information is portrayed. Could another graph have been better utilized for that data?

ENGLISH LEARNER

Review

Use Lesson 12.9 in **English Learner Support Guide** to review lesson concepts and vocabulary.

Enrichment Lesson 12.9

Practice Lesson 12.9

Lesson Planner

OBJECTIVES
- To begin a formal introduction to probability
- To introduce the concepts of certain and impossible in probability

NCTM STANDARDS
Data Analysis and Probability
- Discuss the degree of likelihood using such words as certain and impossible
- Understanding that the measure of the likelihood of an event can be represented by a number from 0 through 1

Communication
Using the language of mathematics to express mathematical ideas precisely

Connections
Recognizing and applying mathematics in contexts outside of mathematics

MATERIALS
Number Cubes

TECHNOLOGY
Presentation Lesson 12.10
MathTools Probability Tool

TEST PREP
Cumulative Review
Mental Math reviews angles (Lesson 11.2).

Writing + Math
Journal

Probability— Impossible to Certain

Context of the Lesson Students have had some experience with predictions and probability since kindergarten. In this chapter students will be formally introduced to some of the terminology related to probability. In Grade 4 students will further explore probability in the form of fractions and percentages.

See page 480B for Math Background for teachers for this lesson.

Planning for Learning • DIFFERENTIATE INSTRUCTION

INTERVENTION
If . . . students lack the prerequisite skill of comparing fractions,

Then . . . teach *Intervention* Lesson 12.C.

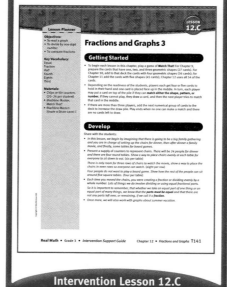

Intervention Lesson 12.C

ENGLISH LEARNER
Preview

If . . . students need language support,

Then . . . use Lesson 12.10 in *English Learner Support Guide* to preview lesson concepts and vocabulary.

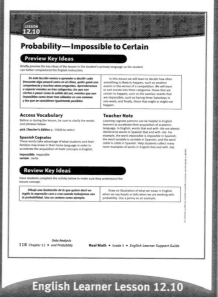

English Learner Lesson 12.10

ENRICH
If . . . students are proficient in the lesson concepts,

Then . . . emphasize the Journal.

PRACTICE
If . . . students would benefit from additional practice,

Then . . . extend Skill and Strategy Building before assigning the student pages.

RETEACH
If . . . students are having difficulty understanding probability,

Then . . . extend Guided Discussion before assigning the student pages.

Vocabulary
probability *n.* the ratio of the number of favorable outcomes to the total number of possible outcomes.

Access Vocabulary
pick to select

Spanish Cognates
impossible imposible
certain cierto

---

*Manipulative Kit Item

Mental Math 10

  Review with students right angles. Use thumbs-up if the angle is greater than a right angle, thumbs-down if the angle is less than a right angle, and open hand if the angle is equal to a right angle. It is optional to use the right angle symbol in the angle. Use examples such as the following:

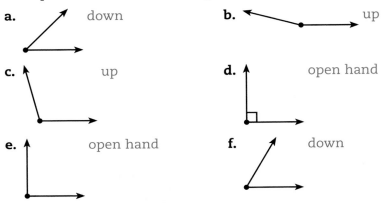

a. down

b. up

c. up

d. open hand

e. open hand

f. down

1 Develop 20

Tell Students In Today's Lesson They Will

begin a formal introduction to probability and some of the terms related to probability.

Guided Discussion UNDERSTANDING Whole Group

Students should recognize the terms *probability* and *predictions* already. Predictions occur when they hear the weather forecast or when there is talking about some events in the news and so on. Ask students if they know how the weather forecaster is able to predict the weather for tomorrow, the next day, and the next week. Discuss the fact that many forecasters rely on data that has been collected in previous years and previous days, and that is still being collected as they give their weather forecasts. Ask students if they have ever experienced a time when the weather forecast was not correct. Emphasize the fact that a weather forecast is a *prediction* and a prediction is not a guarantee.

Ask students if they believe the following statement to be true: *Today is a day that, when named in English, ends in y.* Students should agree that it is a true statement. Since this is a guaranteed true statement, we would say this is a *certain* statement.

Ask students if they believe the following statement to be true: *If I have a bag that contains only green marbles, eventually I will pull out a blue marble.* Students should agree that this statement is a false statement. Since this is a guaranteed false statement, we would say this is an *impossible* event or a false statement .

Explain to students that events that are *impossible* and *certain* will have the minimum (0) and maximum (1) probability, respectively. If an event is not at one of these extremes, then its probability will fall somewhere between 0 and 1.

An event that is neither impossible nor certain will always have the possibility of occurring. Students may sometimes see the terms *unlikely* and *likely* used to describe events, but it may be more accurate at this time to describe events that are neither impossible nor certain using statements such as *less likely* or *more likely.*

For example, students may wish to say a probability of 17% is *unlikely*, given that, in their estimation, a probability of 50% is *equally likely*. However, a probability of 50% is only equally likely if there are two events, such as when flipping a coin. If you were rolling a number cube, the same percentage of (about) 17% could be described as *equally likely*, because each of the six faces is equally likely to be rolled ($\frac{1}{6}$).

Use less likely and more likely to describe situations such as the following:

- **I have a bag with thirty green marbles, three blue marbles, and three red marbles, and I pick out a green marble.** more likely because the majority of the marbles are green.
- **You have one brother and six sisters in your family, and a male family member answers the phone.** less likely because although it is possible that the one brother could answer the phone, there are more females than males in the family

Skill and Strategy Building UNDERSTANDING Whole Group

Begin an introduction to probability using a 0–5 **Number Cube.** Ask students to predict what number they think will be rolled. Accept all reasonable answers, and have students give reasons for their predictions. Ask questions such as the following:

- **Is it possible to roll a number greater than 5?** no
- **Is it possible to roll a number less than 5?** yes
- **What are the possible numbers that could be rolled on a 0–5 Number Cube?** 0, 1, 2, 3, 4, or 5

Roll the **Number Cube** or use the **eMathTools: Probability Tool,** and record the roll on the board. Ask students to make a prediction as to what the number will be when you roll it a second time. All predictions are reasonable at this point as long as the numbers are between 0 and 5. Roll the **Number Cube** or use the **eMathTools: Probability Tool,** and record the roll on the board with the first roll. Roll the **Number Cube** or use the **eMathTools: Probability Tool,** a total of 10 times, asking for predictions before each roll, and recording the result after each roll. Discuss with students what they predict the 11th roll might be. Discuss all answers, and roll to see how well students did with their predictions. Try to elicit from students the fact that they had only one chance in six of predicting correctly.

2 Assign Student Pages 20

Pages 506–507 APPLYING

Have students complete the exercises on pages 506 and 507 independently.

As Students Finish

 Game Have students play a previously introduced game.

Probability—Impossible to Certain **LESSON**

LESSON 12.10 Probability—Impossible to Certain

Key Ideas

People often make predictions about the future that are based on the probability that an event will happen.

If an event is certain to happen, such as the sun rising the next morning, we say it has a probability of 1.

If an event is impossible, such as rolling a 6 on a **Number Cube** which only has the numbers 0–5, we say that it has a probability of 0.

Most events are neither certain nor impossible, and they have a probability between 0 and 1.

Use the term *certain, impossible,* or *neither certain nor impossible* to label each of the following scenarios.

1. If today is May 3, then tomorrow is May 4.   certain

2. If today is the 30th day of the month, then tomorrow is the 31st day of the month.   neither certain nor impossible

3. The day school starts has a name (in English) that doesn't end with the letter "*y.*"   impossible

4. If I walk into a family restaurant, the first person I see will be a male.   neither certain nor impossible

5. When I roll a 5–10 **Number Cube**, I will roll an even number or an odd number.   certain

506   Textbook This lesson is available in the *eTextbook*.

Probabilities are expressed with fractions.

What is the probability that you will roll a 4 with a fair 0–5 **Number Cube?** There are 6 possible outcomes—0, 1, 2, 3, 4, and 5—but only 1 of the outcomes is a 4. We say that the probability of rolling a 4 is $\frac{1}{6}$.

What is the probability that you will roll a 7? The probability of rolling a 7 is $\frac{0}{6}$ or 0. It is impossible to roll a 7 with a 0–5 **Number Cube.**

What is the probability of rolling either a 0, 1, 2, 3, 4, or 5? The probability of rolling one of those numbers is $\frac{6}{6}$, or 1. It is certain that one of those numbers will be rolled.

Answer the following based on a 0–5 **Number Cube.**

6. What is the probability of rolling a 2? $\frac{1}{6}$

7. What is the probability of rolling a 5? $\frac{1}{6}$

8. What is the probability of rolling a 6? $\frac{0}{6}$

Answer the following based on a regular penny with heads and tails.

9. How many possible outcomes are there when you flip the penny?   Two; You might want to discuss that although the penny *may* land on the edge, we assume that will not happen.

10. What is the probability of the penny landing on heads? $\frac{1}{2}$

11. What is the probability of the penny landing on tails? $\frac{1}{2}$

12. What is the probability of the penny landing on either heads or tails? $\frac{2}{2}$

 Journal

Describe how you would determine the probability of rolling a 7 on a 5–10 **Number Cube.**

3 Reflect   10

Guided Discussion   REASONING   Whole Group

Flip a coin in front of the class and call out whether it lands heads or tails. Repeat several times, each time writing the result on the board. After many flips, your results might look like the following:

H T T H H T T H

Keep flipping until you get 4 heads (or 4 tails in a row.) At that point, stop and ask the class what the probability is of flipping that same result again. Many students will think that since one result has occurred 4 times in a row, the probability of the other result occurring next will now be greater. However, despite flipping 4 heads (or tails) in a row, the probability of getting either heads or tails on the next flip is still $\frac{1}{2}$.

Through discussion, help the students understand that the probability of getting heads is always $\frac{1}{2}$ and the probability of getting a tail is always $\frac{1}{2}$. The coin, of course, does not remember what was flipped previously. This is a difficult idea, but an important one and worth discussing.

Writing + Math **Journal** ✓

The probability is $\frac{1}{6}$ and to find it is the same process used to find the probability of rolling a 4 on a 0-5 **Number Cube.**

Cumulative Review: For cumulative review of previously learned skills, see page 513–514.

Family Involvement: Assign the **Practice, Reteach,** or **Enrichment** activities depending on the needs of your students.

Concept/Question Board: Have students attempt to answer any unanswered questions on the Concept/Question Board.

Math Puzzler: Shirley's hair is longer than Jennifer's, and Shannon's hair is longer than Shirley's. Who has the longest hair?
Shannon

4 Assess and Differentiate

e Assess Use **eAssess** to record and analyze evidence of student understanding.

A Gather Evidence

Use the Daily Class Assessment Records in **Assessment** or **eAssess** to record daily observations.

Informal Assessment
☑ **Guided Discussion**

Did the student **UNDERSTANDING**
- ☐ make important observations?
- ☐ extend or generalize learning?
- ☐ provide insightful answers?
- ☐ pose insightful questions?

Portfolio Assessment
☑ **Journal**

Did the student **REASONING**
- ☐ provide a clear explanation?
- ☐ communicate reasons and strategies?
- ☐ choose appropriate strategies?
- ☐ argue logically?

B Summarize Findings

Analyze and summarize assessment data for each student. Determine which Assessment Follow-Up is appropriate for each student. Use the Student Assessment Record in **Assessment** or **eAssess** to update assessment records.

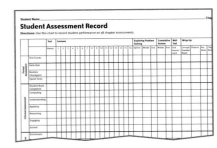

Assessment page T41

C Assessment Follow-Up ● DIFFERENTIATE INSTRUCTION

Based on your observations, use these teaching strategies for assessment follow-up.

INTERVENTION

Review student performance on **Intervention** Lesson 12.C to see if students have mastered prerequisite skills for this lesson.

ENGLISH LEARNER

Review

Use Lesson 12.10 in **English Learner Support Guide** to review lesson concepts and vocabulary.

ENRICH

If . . . students are proficient in the lesson concepts,

Then . . . encourage them to work on chapter projects or **Enrichment** Lesson 12.10.

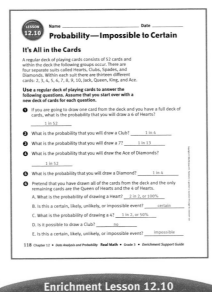

Enrichment Lesson 12.10

PRACTICE

If . . . students would benefit from additional practice,

Then . . . assign **Practice** Lesson 12.10.

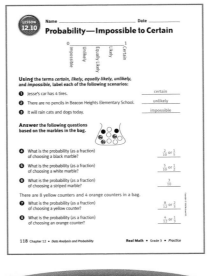

Practice Lesson 12.10

RETEACH

If . . . students are having difficulty with probability,

Then . . . reteach the concept using **Reteach** Lesson 12.10.

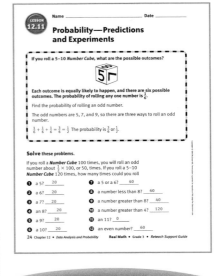

Reteach Lesson 12.10

OBJECTIVES
- To continue the study of probability
- To introduce the idea that we can use a knowledge of probability to predict the outcomes of multiple events

NCTM STANDARDS

Data Analysis and Probability
Predicting the probability of outcomes of simple experiments and testing the predictions

Communication
Using the language of mathematics to express mathematical ideas precisely

Connections
Recognizing and applying mathematics in contexts outside of mathematics

MATERIALS
Number Cubes (optional)

TECHNOLOGY
e Presentation Lesson 12.11
e MathTools Probability Tool

TEST PREP
Cumulative Review
- Mental Math reviews quadrilaterals (Lesson 11.4).
- Problem 1 reviews probability (Lesson 12.10).

Probability—Predictions and Experiments

Context of the Lesson In this lesson students will more formally explore predictions. Reviewing concepts from the previous lesson and fractions of sets, students will determine the probability of multiple events.
See page 480B for Math Background for teachers for this lesson.

Planning for Learning ● DIFFERENTIATE INSTRUCTION

INTERVENTION

If . . . students lack the prerequisite skill of comparing fractions,

Then . . . teach *Intervention* Lesson 12.C.

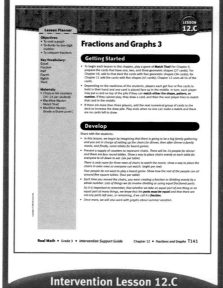

Intervention Lesson 12.C

ENGLISH LEARNER

Preview

If . . . students need language support,

Then . . . use Lesson 12.11 in *English Learner Support Guide* to preview lesson concepts and vocabulary.

English Learner Lesson 12.11

ENRICH

If . . . students are proficient in the lesson concepts,

Then . . . emphasize the student pages.

PRACTICE

If . . . students would benefit from additional practice,

Then . . . extend Skill and Strategy Building before assigning the student pages.

RETEACH

If . . . students are having difficulty understanding predictions and probability,

Then . . . extend Guided Discussion before assigning the student pages.

Access Vocabulary
sum the answer to an addition problem

Spanish Cognates
predictions predicciones
experiments experimentos

Teaching Lesson 12.11

Mental Math　　　10

  Review quadrilaterals. Use thumbs-up if the shape is a quadrilateral and thumbs-down if the shape is not a quadrilateral. Use examples such as the following:

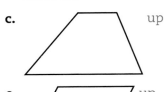
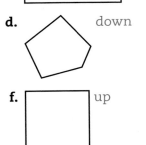

a. down   b. up

c. up   d. down

e. up   f. up

1 Develop　　　20

Tell Students In Today's Lesson They Will
review probability as a fraction and predict the number of times you expect a desired result.

Guided Discussion   UNDERSTANDING　Whole Group

Probability Race—Single Number
Write the numbers 0–5 across the board. Place eight rows beneath the numbers and add the label "FINISH" to the last row.

Tell students that they are going to participate in a Roll-a-Number Race. One red 0–5 **Number Cube** will be rolled repeatedly, and the number that comes up for each roll will be marked on the board with an "X." The first number to get 8 marks will cross the finish line and be the winner.

Discuss with students which number they think will win. Do they believe one has a better chance than the other? Have volunteers explain their reasoning to the class.

When you have finished the discussion, perform the race to test the class's predictions. The **Number Cube** may be rolled by successive students one at a time. Have students announce their roll to the rest of the class.

Regardless of which number wins, ask the students, if the number race was performed again, would the same number win again? not necessarily; each face of the number cube has an equally likely chance of being rolled.

As time permits, you could repeat the race to test their predictions.

Strategy Building ENGAGING　　Whole Group　Small Group

Probability Race—Sums
Now tell students that they are going to participate in a more complex race—a Roll-a-Sum Race. For this race, two **Number Cubes** will be rolled—one red 0–5 **Number Cube** and one blue 5–10 **Number Cube**. The numbers showing on both **Number Cubes** will be added together to make a sum.

Ask students what the least possible sum would be. 0 + 5 = 5 What about the greatest possible sum? 5 + 10 = 15. All the sums from 5 to 15 are possible.

Ask students again which sum (5 – 15) they believe has the greatest chance of being rolled and why.

Perform the Roll-a-Sum Race to test the predictions of the class. Have all the students roll a blue and a red **Number Cube** at the same time. Then have them announce their results one at a time to the rest of the class. Record sums on the race grid.

Discuss the results of the Roll-a-Sum Race. Did any of the sums seem more likely to be rolled? If so, have students try to explain why. unlike the single number probability race, the probabilities for the different sums are not equal. The "middle" sums (9, 10, 11) have more ways to be rolled and are expected to occur more often than the other sums. At this time, it is most important for students to get a qualitative feel for the difference between the two experiments. The table and exercises on page 509 will give students the opportunity to count the number of possibilities and attempt to assign numerical values to the different probabilities.

2 Assign Student Pages　　　20

Pages 508–509 APPLYING
Have students complete the exercises on pages 508 and 509 independently.

Problems 6–10 Students are not expected to calculate these probabilities. Rather, once they have completed the addition table they should be able to count the number of times a given sum appears. Students may need help realizing that the denominator of the fraction is 36. Point out to them that the table shows all the possible sums, or 36 total.

As Students Finish

 Have students play a previously introduced game.

LESSON 12.11 Probability—Predictions and Experiments

Key Ideas

The probability of an event occurring can be written as a fraction from 0 through 1. The probability of a fair penny landing on heads when flipped is $\frac{1}{2}$, which can be read *one out of two.*

What would happen if you flipped a penny 10 times? The number of times you expect the penny to land heads would be $\frac{1}{2}$ of 10, or 5 times. If you flipped the penny 20 times, the number of times you expect the penny to land on heads would be $\frac{1}{2}$ of 20, or 10 times. In general, it will not land heads *exactly* $\frac{1}{2}$ the time, but in the long run we expect it to land heads *about* $\frac{1}{2}$ the time.

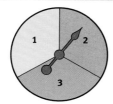

Use the spinner to answer the following questions.

1. What is the probability that you will spin a 1? A 2? A 3? $\frac{1}{3}; \frac{1}{3}; \frac{1}{3}$

2. If you were to spin the spinner 6 times, what is the number of times that you would expect to spin a 1? A 2? A 3? 2; 2; 2

3. If you were to spin the spinner 12 times, what is the number of times that you would expect to spin a 3? 4

4. If you were to spin the spinner 8 times, what is the number of times that you would expect to spin a 5? 0

508 Textbook This lesson is available in the *eTextbook.*

Suppose you roll a 0–5 *Number Cube* and a 5–10 *Number Cube.*

5. Copy the following table and use your knowledge of sums to complete the table.

+	5	6	7	8	9	10
0	5	6	7	8	9	10
1	6	7	8	9	10	11
2	7	8	9	10	11	12
3	8	9	10	11	12	13
4	9	10	11	12	13	14
5	10	11	12	13	14	15

6. What is the probability that you would roll a sum of 5? $\frac{1}{36}$

7. What is the probability that you would roll a sum of 15? $\frac{1}{36}$

8. What is the probability that you would roll a sum of 0? $\frac{0}{36}$

9. What is the probability that you would roll a sum of 10? $\frac{6}{36}$ or $\frac{1}{6}$

10. What is the probability that you would roll a sum of 13? $\frac{3}{36}$ or $\frac{1}{12}$

Chapter 12 • Lesson 11   509

---

3 Reflect   10

Guided Discussion REASONING   Whole Group

Draw the outlines of three spinners on the board:

- A spinner that is $\frac{1}{2}$ red and $\frac{1}{2}$ blue
- A spinner that is $\frac{2}{4}$ red and $\frac{2}{4}$ blue (alternating)
- A spinner that is $\frac{3}{6}$ red and $\frac{3}{6}$ blue (alternating)

Pointing to each spinner in turn, ask what the probability is of spinning and landing on red or blue. Through discussion establish that the probabilities are the same for each spinner as the fraction colored in red in each circle is $\frac{1}{2}$ and the fraction colored in blue is also $\frac{1}{2}$.

 Cumulative Review: For cumulative review of previously learned skills, see page 513–514.

 Family Involvement: Assign the *Practice, Reteach,* or *Enrichment* activities depending on the needs of your students.

 Concept/Question Board: Have students attempt to answer any unanswered questions on the Concept/Question Board.

 Math Puzzler: Stan is not older than Geraldo. Tanya and Penny are younger than Stan, but Tanya is not younger than Penny. Write the names of the children in order from youngest to oldest.
Penny, Tanya, Stan, Geraldo

4 Assess and Differentiate

 Assess Use **eAssess** to record and analyze
evidence of student understanding.

A Gather Evidence

Use the Daily Class Assessment Records in **Assessment** or **eAssess**
to record daily observations.

Informal Assessment
☑ **Guided Discussion**

Did the student `UNDERSTANDING`

- ❑ make important
  observations?
- ❑ extend or generalize
  learning?
- ❑ provide insightful answers?
- ❑ pose insightful questions?

Informal Assessment
☑ **Student Pages**

Did the student `APPLYING`

- ❑ apply learning in new
  situations?
- ❑ contribute concepts?
- ❑ contribute answers?
- ❑ connect mathematics to
  real-world situations?

B Summarize Findings

Analyze and summarize assessment data for each student.
Determine which Assessment Follow-Up is appropriate for each
student. Use the Student Assessment Record in **Assessment** or
eAssess to update assessment records.

Assessment page T41

C Assessment Follow-Up ● DIFFERENTIATE INSTRUCTION

Based on your observations, use these teaching strategies for assessment follow-up.

INTERVENTION	ENRICH	PRACTICE	RETEACH
Review student performance on **Intervention** Lesson 12.C to see if students have mastered prerequisite skills for this lesson.	**If . . .** students are proficient in the lesson concepts, **Then . . .** encourage them to work on chapter projects or **Enrichment** Lesson 12.11.	**If . . .** students would benefit from additional practice, **Then . . .** assign **Practice** Lesson 12.11.	**If . . .** students struggle with writing probability as a fraction, **Then . . .** have them use **Number Cubes** to act out the second half of the lesson. Have them practice writing the probability of different events. Make sure they write all their probabilities in fraction form.

ENGLISH LEARNER

Review

Use Lesson 12.11 in
**English Learner Support
Guide** to review lesson
concepts and vocabulary.

Enrichment Lesson 12.11

Practice Lesson 12.11

Lesson Planner

OBJECTIVES
To display possible outcomes using tree diagrams

NCTM STANDARDS

Algebra
Modeling problem situations with objects and using representations such as graphs, tables, and equations to draw conclusions

Data Analysis and Probability
Predicting the probability of outcomes of simple experiments and testing the predictions

Connections
Recognizing and applying mathematics in contexts outside of mathematics

MATERIALS
*Response Wheels

TECHNOLOGY
Presentation Lesson 12.12

TEST PREP
Cumulative Review
Mental Math reviews percent benchmarks (Lesson 8.11).

Extended Response
Problem 2

Displaying and Analyzing Outcomes

Context of the Lesson In this lesson students will create and display possible outcomes using tree diagrams.
See page 480B for Math Background for teachers for this lesson.

Planning for Learning ● DIFFERENTIATE INSTRUCTION

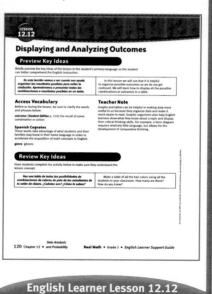

INTERVENTION
If . . . students lack the prerequisite skill of reading graphs,

Then . . . teach *Intervention* Lesson 12.A.

Intervention Lesson 12.A

ENGLISH LEARNER
Preview
If . . . students need language support,

Then . . . use Lesson 12.12 in *English Learner Support Guide* to preview lesson concepts and vocabulary.

English Learner Lesson 12.12

ENRICH
If . . . students are proficient in the lesson concepts,

Then . . . emphasize the student pages.

PRACTICE
If . . . students would benefit from additional practice,

Then . . . extend Strategy Building before assigning the student pages.

RETEACH
If . . . students are having difficulty understanding outcomes,

Then . . . extend Guided Discussion before assigning the student pages.

Vocabulary
tree diagram *n.* a display of data that shows possible combinations, with subsequent possibilities branching from previous ones

Access Vocabulary
outcome the result of some combination or action

Spanish Cognates
genre género

Mental Math 10

Review percent benchmarks with students. Use examples such as the following:

a. 65% 75%
b. 20% 25%
c. 40% 50%
d. 3% 0%
e. 98% 100%
f. 88% 100%

1 Develop 20

Tell Students In Today's Lesson They Will

display outcomes using tree diagrams and stem-and-leaf plots.

Guided Discussion UNDERSTANDING Whole Group

Present this situation to the class:

When Christy went through the cafeteria line at school, she was presented with the following choices:

For an entrée she could have cheese pizza, macaroni and cheese, or grilled cheese. For her side item, she could have a small salad, applesauce, or pears. Her drink choices were milk, juice, or lemonade.

Ask students for one combination Christy could choose for her lunch. Accept all combinations that include one item from each section. Write them as listed on the board. When students think they have given all of the possible combinations, discuss ways that they can be certain they have all the combinations without repeating any. Students should suggest creating a table even if they aren't sure what kind of table to create. Introduce tree diagrams explaining that you start with an initial decision, and then "branch" out through all the possible combinations of choices. The diagram of all these possible choices looks like a tree on its side.

Write on the board, in one column, *pizza, macaroni and cheese,* and *grilled cheese,* leaving space between each item to extend the "branches." Start from a point to the left of this column and draw lines to each choice (pizza, macaroni and cheese, and grilled cheese). Ask questions such as the following:

■ **How many entrée choices are there?** 3
■ **How many side choices does Christy have?** 3
■ **How many dessert choices are there?** 3

Draw three "branches" or lines from the pizza entrée choice. At the end of each line, write the three side choices *salad, applesauce,* and *pears.* Do this for the macaroni and cheese option and the grilled cheese option. Ask questions such as the following:

■ **How many outcomes were there with only the entrées?** 3
■ **How many possible outcomes are there now with the entrée and side dishes?** 9

■ **If there are 3 entrees with 3 side-dish choices each, how could we write this as a math sentence?** 3 × 3
■ **How many total outcomes do you think there will be when we include the drink options?** 27

Strategy Building UNDERSTANDING Small Group

In small groups, have students copy the tree diagram that was started in Guided Discussion and make a prediction as to how many total outcomes there will be. Then have the small groups finish the tree diagram. Have students share with the class their tree diagrams and the results of how many total outcomes there are.

In small groups have students create their own tree diagrams, using a sample problem such as one with clothing choices:

● either a blue or red t-shirt
● either blue jeans, shorts, or corduroy pants
● either black tennis shoes, white tennis shoes, sandals, or boots

Have students share their predictions, their tree diagrams, and the mathematical sentences describing the choices for outfits. There are 24 total outcomes.

2 Assign Student Pages 20

Pages 510–511 APPLYING

Have students complete the exercises on pages 510 and 511 independently.

Monitoring Student Progress

If . . . students have difficulty finishing the tree chart on page 511,

Then . . . have them list each option (some more than once) on individual index cards and physically create their tree diagrams.

As Students Finish

Game Have students play a previously introduced game.

LESSON 12.12 Displaying and Analyzing Outcomes

Key Ideas

There are times when counting the possible outcomes can be confusing. Making a diagram might help you organize the information and make the counting a little easier.

Janice had the following choices for painting her room: blue, red, and green.

Her choices for decorations were flowers, animals, and shapes.

She made a diagram to show all the combinations (possible outcomes) she had for her new room.

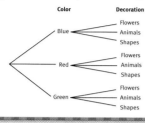

Use the diagram above to answer the following questions.

❶ How many possible color and decoration combinations (for example, blue and animals) are there for Janice's room? 9

❷ **Extended Response** Describe what mathematical sentence would give the same answer and why it would describe this diagram. 3×3; There are 3 possible decorations for each of 3 colors.

510   Textbook This lesson is available in the *eTextbook*.

The name for this type of diagram is a tree diagram. A tree diagram helps to give the total number of possible outcomes.

Mrs. Godbey offered her class the following options for their free-writing assignment. They could choose the setting as the beach, the mountains, or the ocean; their characters could be robots or children; and their story genre could be science fiction or mystery.

❸ Create a tree diagram with the information offered by Mrs. Godbey.   See *Teacher's Edition* for tree diagram.

Use your completed tree diagram to answer the following questions.

❹ How many possible outcomes are there?   12

❺ If a student wants to write only a science fiction story, how many possible outcomes are there?   6

❻ If a student wants to write only about a story on the beach, how many possible outcomes are there?   4

❼ Is it possible for a student to write a mountain story about robots?   yes

❽ If a student wants to write only about robots in the mountains, how many possible outcomes are there?   2

---

3 Reflect   10

Guided Discussion   REASONING   Whole Group

Tell the class about a women's clothing store that advertised 24 different outfits, but included only 3 skirts, 4 blouses and 2 pairs of shoes. Could the store be telling the truth? How can you have 24 different outfits with so few pieces of clothing?

Through discussion, help students to see that if there were 3 different colors of skirts, 4 different kinds of blouses and 2 different colors of shoes, there are, in fact, 24 possible combinations or 24 outfits. Help the students list the combinations on the board using a tree diagram.

Extended Response

Problem 3 One possible tree diagram is the following:

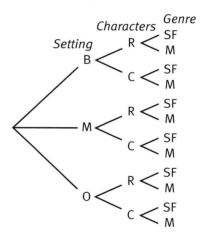

Cumulative Review: For cumulative review of previously learned skills, see page 513–514.

Family Involvement: Assign the *Practice, Reteach,* or *Enrichment* activities depending on the needs of your students.

Concept/Question Board: Have students attempt to answer any unanswered questions on the Concept/Question Board.

Math Puzzler: Dmitri's scout troop camped overnight in the woods. There were 31 other scouts in Dmitri's troop. How many 4-person tents did they need to house all of the scouts? 8; $32 \div 4 = 8$

Assess and Differentiate

 Assess Use **eAssess** to record and analyze evidence of student understanding.

A Gather Evidence

Use the Daily Class Assessment Records in **Assessment** or **eAssess** to record daily observations.

Informal Assessment
☑ **Strategy Building**

Did the student UNDERSTANDING
- ❑ make important observations?
- ❑ extend or generalize learning?
- ❑ provide insightful answers?
- ❑ pose insightful questions?

Informal Assessment
☑ **Student Pages**

Did the student APPLYING
- ❑ apply learning in new situations?
- ❑ contribute concepts?
- ❑ contribute answers?
- ❑ connect mathematics to real-world situations?

B Summarize Findings

Analyze and summarize assessment data for each student. Determine which Assessment Follow-Up is appropriate for each student. Use the Student Assessment Record in **Assessment** or **eAssess** to update assessment records.

Assessment page T41

C Assessment Follow-Up • DIFFERENTIATE INSTRUCTION

Based on your observations, use these teaching strategies for assessment follow-up.

INTERVENTION

Review student performance on **Intervention** Lesson 12.A to see if students have mastered prerequisite skills for this lesson.

ENGLISH LEARNER

Review

Use Lesson 12.12 in **English Learner Support Guide** to review lesson concepts and vocabulary.

ENRICH

If . . . students are proficient in the lesson concepts,

Then . . . encourage them to work on chapter projects or **Enrichment** Lesson 12.12.

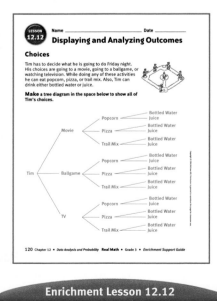

Enrichment Lesson 12.12

PRACTICE

If . . . students would benefit from additional practice,

Then . . . assign **Practice** Lesson 12.12.

Practice Lesson 12.12

RETEACH

If . . . students are having difficulty drawing tree diagrams,

Then . . . give students shapes and multiple pieces of different colored paper. Have them physically model a tree diagram that shows possible combinations of shapes and colors.

Exploring Problem Solving

Objectives
- To provide practice listing outcomes and determining probability
- To compare methods for finding probability
- To provide practice solving and justifying solutions to nonroutine problems

Materials
Counters, spinners, number cards (1–5), or paper and markers (for students who wish to find the probability by carrying out an experiment)

Context of the Lesson This lesson provides an opportunity for students to apply some of the skills they have been working on in this chapter to solve a challenging problem involving probability.

 Develop 5

Tell Students In Today's Lesson They Will
figure out how likely it is that they will help with two particular chores.

Guided Discussion
Remind students of the problems they have already solved on pages 481 and 499 about farms and about what they have learned in the last few lessons. Explain that today they will pretend they are visiting a farm in Nepal, a country in Asia.

 Exploring Problem Solving 30

Using Student Pages
Read the information on the top of page 512 together. To make sure students understand the problem, ask questions such as the following:

- **How many farm chores will you get a chance to help with?** two
- **Can you choose the chores you want?** No, we will be picking two at random; we will not know which ones we are getting.
- **Could you pick the same chore twice?** No, we will be selecting two different chores.

Exploring Problem Solving

All over the world, people grow food on farms. Some farming methods are different from country to country. But some things are the same, such as the need to do chores.

Suppose you are visiting a small farm thousands of miles away in Nepal. You are going to get a chance to help with farm chores. The names of five chores are placed in a paper bag, and you will reach in and pick two of them.

Work with your group to solve this problem.

1. What is the probability that you will pick milking buffalos and feeding goats? $\frac{1}{10}$

2. How did you solve the problem?
   Methods may vary. See *Teacher's Edition*.

3. Make up and exchange your own problem about chores on a farm in Nepal.

512　　Ⓖ Textbook　This lesson is available in the *eTextbook*.

- **If you were picking just one chore at random, what would be the probability of picking the chore of feeding goats? Why?**
$\frac{1}{5}$, because feeding goats is 1 of 5 chores and there would be an equal chance of picking any of them

Have students work on Problems 1–3 in pairs or small groups.

Have spinners, number cards, or counters of different colors available for students who wish to find the probability by carrying out an experiment. Alternatively, students can make their own number cards or simply put marks on pieces of paper.

Circulate around the room, and provide support as needed.

Effective Communication Have groups present their answers and methods. (See Sample Solutions Strategies below.)

In discussion, bring out the following points:

- Students can solve some problems by acting out the situation with a probability experiment. This is called doing a *simulation*, which is one way of modeling the problem situation.
- When students do a simulation, as with any modeling, they must make sure they are representing the problem accurately. For example, in this problem, they need to account for the fact that getting the same chore twice is not a possibility. So, if they are using number cards, they should not return a drawn card to the pile until after they have drawn the second card.
- When students do simulations, they should repeat the activity enough times to make the results valid. For example, suppose students simulated picking two chores by drawing a pair of number cards. If they picked only ten times and they never got the numbers one and three together, they might mistakenly conclude that the probability of getting those two numbers (or the two chores they represent) is zero.

Sample Solutions Strategies

Students might use one of the following strategies to solve the problem.

Make a Physical Model

Students might carry out an experiment to simulate the process of choosing two chores. There are many ways for them to do this—they simply need to set up five choices that can be picked at random and some way of distinguishing two of them. For example:

- Place five folded scraps of paper in a bag—two of them marked and the others plain.
- Place five cubes or other counters in a bag—two of them red and the rest blue (or even five different colors).
- Make five cards numbered 1 to 5.

By repeating the drawing many times and keeping track of the results, students can estimate the probability.

Make an Organized List

Students might use a pattern to write down all the possible pairings. They might use different letters to stand for the different chores. In using this strategy, students might need to look back and cross out pairs that are listed twice. They might also need to cross out pairs, such as AA and BB, that don't count because they are the same chore repeated.

Pairs with A	Pairs with B	Pairs with C	Pairs with D	Pairs with E
~~AA~~	~~BA~~	~~CA~~	~~DA~~	~~EA~~
AB	~~BB~~	~~CB~~	~~DB~~	~~EB~~
AC	BC	~~CC~~	~~DC~~	~~EC~~
AD	BD	CD	~~DD~~	~~ED~~
AE	BE	CE	DE	~~EE~~

Draw a Diagram / Use a Pattern

Students might begin to make a tree diagram to show all the possible pairings. They might notice a pattern that they can use to find the number of possibilities.

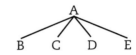

After drawing this much of a diagram, students might see that each chore has four other chores it can be paired with, making a total of 5 × 4, or 20 pairs. Of course, half of the pairs are duplicates; for example, AB is the same as BA because in this context it does not matter in which order you choose the chores.

Write an Equation

Students might write a word equation to help them focus on what they need to find and how to find it.

Probability of picking chores A and D = $\dfrac{\text{number of ways of picking that pair}}{\text{number of different pairs of chores that might be picked}}$

When evaluating student work, consider not only whether the answer was correct, but whether the student thought rationally about the problem. Questions to think about include the following:

- Did the student understand the problem?
- Did the student approach the problem in a reasonable way?
- Was the student able to explain his or her reasoning?
- Did the student check to see that the answer made sense?
- Did the student use any particularly sophisticated reasoning to solve the problem?

Cumulative Review

Assign Pages 513–514

Use the Cumulative Review as a review of concepts and skills that students have previously learned.

Here are different ways that you can assign these problems to your students as they work through the chapter:

- With some of the lessons in the chapter, assign a set of cumulative review problems to be completed as practice or for homework.
  Lesson 12.8—Problems 1–6
  Lesson 12.9—Problems 7–10
  Lesson 12.10—Problems 11–13
  Lesson 12.11—Problems 14–16
  Lesson 12.12—Problems 17–20
- At any point during the chapter, assign part or all of the cumulative review problems to be completed as practice or for homework.

Cumulative Review

Problems 1–6 review subtracting decimals, Lesson 10.6.

Problems 7–10 review fractions of linear measure, Lesson 8.2.

Problems 11–13 review problem-solving applications, Lesson 7.9.

Problems 14–16 review rotations, reflections, and translations of figures, Lesson 11.7.

Problems 17–20 review arrow notations to solve equations, Lesson 6.3.

Monitoring Student Progress

If . . . students miss more than one problem in a section,

Then . . . refer to the indicated lesson for remediation suggestions.

Cumulative Review

Subtracting Decimals Lesson 10.6
Subtract.

1. $18.53 - 11.26$ 7.27
2. $8.79 - 6.32$ 2.47
3. $20.00 - 10.5$ 9.50
4. $1.33 - 0.88$ 0.45
5. $9.17 - 3.4$ 5.77
6. $81.38 - 26.5$ 54.88

Fractions of Linear Measure Lesson 8.2
What fraction of the line is shaded?

7. $\frac{3}{4}$
8. $\frac{6}{6}$ or 1
9. $\frac{4}{8}$ or $\frac{1}{2}$
10. $\frac{1}{8}$

Problem-Solving Applications Lesson 7.9

Tell whether you would add, subtract, multiply, or divide to solve each problem. Then solve each problem. If it is not possible to solve the problem, tell why.

11. **Extended Response** Every five years the Tucker family moves half of their livestock to another farm. They moved 68 head of cattle this time. How many cattle did they have this year before they moved the livestock?
    multiply; $68 \times 2 = 136$ cattle

12. **Extended Response** Emma milked 3 cows every morning. She collected about 12 liters of milk each day. About how many liters of milk did she collect from each cow?
    divide; $12 \div 3 = 4$; 4 liters

13. **Extended Response** Now Emma has 4 cows to milk. About how many liters of milk will she collect each day?
    multiply; $4 \times 4 = 16$ liters

Chapter 12 • Cumulative Review   513

Cumulative Review

Slides, Flips, and Turns Lesson 11.7

Describe the change from position A to position B for each figure. Determine if the change was from a translation, reflection, rotation, or a combination of two different changes.

14. translation or reflection
15. rotation
16. translation

Using Arrow Notation to Solve Equations Lesson 6.3

Find the value of n. In Problem 20, find the value of n and the value of m.

17. $48 \to \div 4 \to n$
    $n = \square$ 12

19. $9 \to \times 11 \to n$
    $n = \square$ 99

18. $n \leftarrow \times 8 \leftarrow 20$
    $n = \square$ 160

20. $7 \to +8 \to n \to \times 4 \to m$
    $n = \square$ 15
    $m = \square$ 60

514

Chapter 12 • Data Analysis and Probability   513–514

Wrap-Up

1 Discuss 5

Concept/Question Board

Review the Concept/Question Board with students.

- Discuss students' contributions to the Concept side of the Board.
- Have students re-pose their questions, and lead a discussion to find satisfactory answers.

Chapter Projects APPLYING

Provide an opportunity for students who have worked on one or more of the projects outlined on page 481C to share their work with the class. Allow each student or student group five minutes to present or discuss their projects. For formal assessment, use the rubrics found in *Across the Curriculum Math Connections;* the rubric for **Categorize Sheep Facts** is on page 127, and the rubric for **Research Horse Farming** is on page 131. For informal assessment, use the following rubric and questions.

	Exceeds Expectations	Meets Expectations	Minimally Meets Expectations
Applies mathematics in real-world situations:	❏	❏	❏
Demonstrates strong engagement in the activity:	❏	❏	❏

Categorize Sheep Facts

- What was the most interesting thing you learned about sheep?
- How did you use tally marks to record information about sheep?
- What breeds of sheep did you choose? Why did you choose those breeds?
- How did you organize your information?
- What did you include in your exhibit?
- If you could raise one breed of sheep you researched, which would it be? Why?
- What would you add to your exhibit to make it even more interesting?

Research Horse Farming

- What do horse farmers do?
- What items are needed to run a horse farm?
- How many horses were on your farm?
- What were the total costs to run your horse farm?
- Was a spreadsheet program a useful way to organize your data? Why or why not?
- Would you like to become a horse farmer? Why or why not?

2 Assign Student Pages 25 ◑

Key Ideas Review UNDERSTANDING

Have students complete the Review questions independently or in small groups. Then discuss each question as a class.

Possible Answers

Extended Response

Problem ❶ Tally charts are used to collect samples. The information from a tally chart can easily convert to a single bar graph. Both types of graphs (charts) can help with comparisons of data. Here is the bar graph:

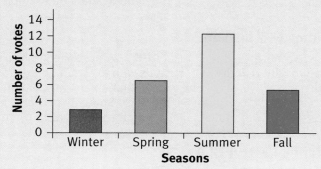

Extended Response

Problem ❷ Understanding what a table records is essential to reading the table. One possible true statement is that summer is the favorite season. One possible false statement is that winter is the favorite season.

Problem ❸ Problem 3 involves students ordering the numbers first before obtaining the answers. The answers to Problem 3 are 25 inches for range and 36 inches for mode.

Problem ❹ The answer is $\frac{2}{5}$ for landing on red because there are two red sections, and the probability is $\frac{3}{5}$ for not landing on a red section.

Extended Response

Problem ❺ The answer is 2 because in one spin the probability of landing on yellow is $\frac{1}{5}$. In ten spins, it would be $\frac{1}{5}$ of 10, or 2.

Extended Response

Problem ❻ The answer is 8 because in one spin the probability of landing on red is $\frac{2}{5}$. In twenty spins, it would be $\frac{2}{5}$ of 20, or 8.

CHAPTER 12 Key Ideas Review

In this chapter, you explored various graphs and their properties and probability.

You learned about collecting and summarizing data. You learned about many types of graphs. You learned about predictions, probability, and outcomes.

Use the following information about Susanne's class's favorite seasons.

In Susanne's class 3 people chose winter, 7 people chose spring, 12 people chose summer, and 6 people chose fall.

❶ Create a tally table and a single bar graph from the information gathered in Susanne's class.

❷ **Extended Response** Write one true statement and one false statement from the data in Susanne's class.

Use the list of heights (in inches) of Shane's classmates to answer the following questions.

Height in inches of Shane's class:
36, 36, 48, 48, 41, 50, 57, 38, 32, 42, 43, 55, 42, 41, 36

❸ What is the range? The mode? The median? The mean?
25 inches; 36 inches; 42 inches; 43 inches

❹ What is the probability (as a fraction) of the spinner landing on red with only one spin? What is the probability (as a fraction) of the spinner *not* landing on red with only one spin? $\frac{2}{5}; \frac{3}{5}$

❺ **Extended Response** If you spin the spinner ten times, what is the number of times that you would expect to land on yellow? Explain your answer.

❻ **Extended Response** If you spin the spinner twenty times, what is the number of times that you would expect to land on red? Explain your answer.

❺ 2; $\frac{1}{5}$ of 10 is 2.

❻ 8; $\frac{2}{5}$ of 20 is 8.

Chapter Review

Use the Chapter 12 Review to indicate areas in which each student is having difficulty or in which the class may need help. If students do well on the Chapter 12 Review, you may wish to skip directly to the Chapter Test; if not, you may want to spend a day or so helping students overcome their individual difficulties before taking the Practice Test.

Next to each set of problems is a list of the lessons in the chapter that covered those concepts. If they need help, students can refer to a specific lesson for additional instruction. You can also use this information to make additional assignments based on the previous lesson concepts.

Have students complete pages 516–517 on their own. For review purposes, you may want to do some of the word problems on page 517 as a class.

Monitoring Student Progress

Problems 1–2 Lesson 12.1

If . . . students miss more than one of these sample problems,

Then . . . have students explain why they chose their answer.

Problem 3 Lesson 12.2

If . . . students are having difficulty creating a tally chart,

Then . . . give them a tally chart to copy and help students fill in the correct data.

Problems 4–5 Lesson 12.3

If . . . students are having difficulty with the vocabulary,

Then . . . have them create flash cards with the word on the front and the definition and an example on the back.

Problems 6–7 Lesson 12.4

If . . . students are having difficulty with the vocabulary,

Then . . . have them create flash cards with the word on the front and the definition and an example on the back. Students may also need assistance with division when finding the *mean*.

Problem 8 Lesson 12.8

If . . . students are having a hard time creating a line plot or a stem-and-leaf plot,

Then . . . give them a model to copy, and assist them with getting their own graph started.

Problems 9–12 Lesson 12.10

If . . . students are finding it hard to list the probability as a fraction,

Then . . . have them demonstrate with manipulatives and then write their answer as a fraction.

Problems 13–14 Lesson 12.11

If . . . students are having difficulty with probability that involves more than one spin,

Then . . . review with students how to find fractions of a set from Chapter 8.

CHAPTER 12 Chapter Review

Lesson 12.1 **Decide** if each of the following shows a good sample by answering *yes* or *no*. If it is not a good sample, explain why.

1 Students in Mr. Young's health class asked every fourth student entering the school cafeteria questions about the school lunch menu.   yes

2 **Extended Response** Three students from Ms. Theus's homeroom stood in the hallway asking girls wearing glasses to list their favorite class in school.   no, because it is limited to a specific gender and only girls wearing glasses

Lesson 12.2 **Use** the following information to create a tally table.

3 Sara surveyed her art class to see what their favorite pastime activity is. The top five pastime activities are *Television, Games, Reading, Drawing,* and *Biking.* When Sara counted her results, she found that 9 students like television, 11 students like games, 2 students like reading, 3 students like drawing, 4 students like biking, and 3 students like activities other than the ones mentioned.

Lesson 12.3 **Answer** the questions using the following data from Hydepark Elementary School.

For the current school year, there are 117 kindergartners, 121 first graders, 105 second graders, 110 third graders, 108 fourth graders, 43 fifth graders, and 120 sixth graders at Hydepark Elementary School.

4 How many students are there total? What is the range of students?   724; 78

5 Is there an outlier amount? If so, what is it?

yes; 43 fifth graders

ⓔTextbook This lesson is available in the *eTextbook.*

Lesson 12.4 **Solve.**

Judith listed the number of days in each month on a piece of paper: 31, 28, 31, 30, 31, 30, 31, 31, 30, 31, 30, 31.

6 What is the mode? What is the median?   31; 31

7 **Extended Response** Describe how you would find the mean.

Find the total, and divide by the number of months.

Lesson 12.8 **Create** a line plot and a stem-and-leaf plot using the following information.

Misty counted the genres of books she had in her family library. She discovered there were 23 poetry books, 17 mysteries, 10 science fiction books, 21 romance novels, 12 biographies, 14 other types of nonfiction, and 17 other types of fiction.

Lesson 12.10 **Using** the terms *certain, neither certain nor impossible,* and *impossible,* label each of the following scenarios.

8 If today is March 3, then yesterday was March 2.   certain

9 If I have a box with a pair of shoes, what is the probability I will pick out the left shoe?   neither certain nor impossible

Lesson 12.11 **Answer** questions 10 and 11 based on a 5–10 *Number Cube.*

10 What is the probability (as a fraction) that you will roll a 10? $\frac{1}{6}$

11 What is the probability (as a fraction) that you will roll a 0? $\frac{0}{6}$

12 What is the probability (as a fraction) that your one spin will land on a green section? On a red section? On a blue section?

13 If you were to spin the spinner 8 times, what is the number of times that you would expect it to land on a green section? On a red section? On a blue section?   2; 2; 4

12 $\frac{1}{4}$; $\frac{1}{4}$; $\frac{2}{4}$, or $\frac{1}{2}$

 Chapter Tests 40 ⦿

Practice Test

Student Pages 518–521

- The Chapter 12 Practice Test on **Student Edition** pages 518–521 provides an opportunity to formally evaluate students' proficiency with concepts developed in this chapter.
- The content is similar to the Chapter 12 Review, in standardized format.

Problem ㉕   **Extended Response**

Students apply their understanding of data analysis and probability concepts. For Problem 25, students display data in a graph and then analyze and interpret the data presented graphically. The graph should look like the information listed.

Problem ㉖   **Extended Response**

For Part a, students consider all possible outcomes in a real-life situation. They draw a tree diagram to list all outcomes and then consider different configurations of options. The answer for Part b is 9; the answer for Part c is 2. One possible explanation for Part d is no, because Darcy can get only one scoop of ice cream, and chocolate and vanilla are two scoops. The answer for Part e is that adding sprinkles will double the number of options available because you can get each combination with or without sprinkles.

 Practice Test

Answer the questions.

1. Look at this set of data. What is the range? 10

   3, 7, 5, 8, 2, 9, 10, 12

2. Look at this set of data. Which number is an outlier?

   42, 44, 73, 36, 40, 38, 40   73

Use this set of data for Problems 3–6.

   10, 8, 14, 14, 15, 9, 17

3. What is the mode? 14

4. What is the median? 14

5. What is the range? 9

6. Ally collected data about her friends' favorite sports and put them in this tally chart. She wants to display the data in a graph. What kind of graph should she use?
   bar graph or pictograph

Sport	
Basketball	卌
Soccer	卌 II
Baseball	IIII
Football	卌

7. Carla has a 0–5 **Number Cube.** Using the terms *certain*, *impossible*, or *neither*, what is the probability that she will roll a number greater than 5?
   impossible

8. Maya will flip a coin. What is the probability, as a fraction, that the coin will land heads up? $\frac{1}{2}$

Use this table to answer the following questions.

Mr. Krishnan's Room (Eye Colors)	
Eye Color	**Number of Students**
Blue	12
Brown	10
Hazel	2
Green	1

9. What is the most common eye color in Mr. Krishnan's class?
   Ⓐ blue   Ⓑ brown
   Ⓒ hazel   Ⓓ green

10. How many students are in Mr. Krishnan's class?
    Ⓐ 22   ⬤Ⓑ 25
    Ⓒ 23   Ⓓ 20

Choose the situation that shows an example of good sampling.

11. An ice-cream shop wants to test a new flavor.

    Ⓐ The owner gives a sample to one person every 30 minutes for 2 hours.

    Ⓑ The owner gives a sample to every third person who comes to the store.

    Ⓒ The owner gives a sample to each boy who comes to the store.

    Ⓓ The owner gives a sample to his next-door neighbor.

12. A student wants to find out what color car is most popular. What is the best way to get a good sample?

    Ⓐ She tallies the colors of the cars that pass by her school for one hour each day for a week.

    Ⓑ She tallies the colors of the cars owned by her family.

    Ⓒ She asks all the girls in her class what their favorite color is.

    Ⓓ She tallies the color of every car that passes by her school in a thirty-minute period.

Use this bar graph to answer the following questions.

13. What is the mode?
    Ⓐ 4   Ⓑ 6   Ⓒ 1   Ⓓ 8

14. What is the range?
    Ⓐ 6   Ⓑ 10   ⬤Ⓒ 8   Ⓓ 7

Use this bar graph to answer the following questions.

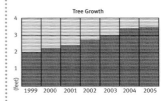

15. In what year did the tree grow the most?
    Ⓐ 2001   Ⓑ 2003
    ⬤Ⓒ 2004   Ⓓ 2005

CHAPTER 12 Practice Test

Find the probability of each event.

16. If today is Monday, then tomorrow will be Tuesday.
Ⓐ certain
Ⓑ likely
Ⓒ impossible
Ⓓ unlikely

17. After you turn ten, you will be nine on your next birthday.
Ⓐ certain
Ⓑ likely
Ⓒ impossible
Ⓓ unlikely

18. You roll a 0–5 **Number Cube.** What is the probability, as a fraction, of rolling either a 3 or a 4?
Ⓐ $\frac{1}{6}$ Ⓑ $\frac{2}{6}$
Ⓒ $\frac{4}{6}$ Ⓓ $\frac{5}{6}$

19. You roll a **Number Cube** with sides numbered 2, 2, 2, 3, 4, 6. What is the probability, as a fraction, of rolling an even number?
Ⓐ $\frac{1}{6}$ Ⓑ $\frac{2}{6}$
Ⓒ $\frac{3}{6}$ Ⓓ $\frac{5}{6}$

20. How many minutes is $\frac{3}{5}$ of an hour?
Ⓐ 24 minutes
Ⓑ 30 minutes
Ⓒ 36 minutes
Ⓓ 42 minutes

21. Find the quotient of 72 ÷ 9.
Ⓐ 5   Ⓑ 8
Ⓒ 9   Ⓓ 7

22. Find the sum of 7 + 6 + 4 + 3.
Ⓐ 18   Ⓑ 16
Ⓒ 20   Ⓓ 24

23. How many decimeters are in 72 meters?
Ⓐ 70   Ⓑ 7.2
Ⓒ 7,200   Ⓓ 720

24. There are 6 shelves filled with 120 books. If each shelf holds the same number of books, how many books are on each shelf?
Ⓐ 20   Ⓑ 26
Ⓒ 12   Ⓓ 6

520   ⓔTextbook This lesson is available in the **eTextbook.**

Extended Response Create the graph described.

25. Make a bar graph using the information in this tally chart.

Favorite Animal	
Lion	𝍷𝍷𝍷 𝍷𝍷𝍷 𝍷𝍷
Tiger	𝍷𝍷𝍷 𝍷𝍷𝍷
Giraffe	𝍷𝍷𝍷 𝍷𝍷𝍷𝍷
Seal	𝍷𝍷𝍷 𝍷𝍷

26. **Extended Response** The frozen yogurt shop has 3 flavors—strawberry, chocolate, and vanilla. The shop offers waffle cones, sugar cones, and bowls. Darcy wants to get one scoop of frozen yogurt.

a. Draw a tree diagram to show all the combinations she can choose from.

b. How many possible combinations can Darcy choose from?

c. Darcy has decided she will get a cone with vanilla ice cream. How many combinations does she have to choose from now?

d. Is it possible to get a 1-scoop bowl with chocolate and vanilla ice cream? Explain.

e. The ice-cream shop can also top the ice cream with sprinkles. How does this affect the number of possible combinations?

Chapter Test COMPUTING

For further evaluation instead of or in addition to this test, you might want to have students take the Chapter 12 Test provided in **Assessment.**

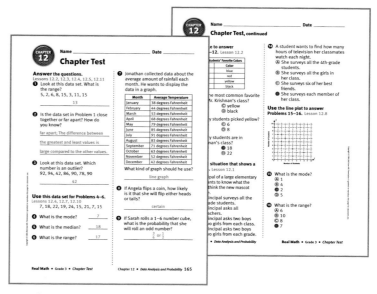

Assessment Pages 165–166

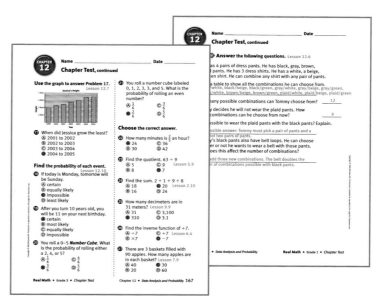

Assessment Pages 167–168

4 Assess and Differentiate

 Assess Use *eAssess* to record and analyze evidence of student understanding.

A Gather Evidence

Use the Daily Class Assessment Records in *Assessment* or *eAssess* to record Informal and Formal Assessments.

Informal Assessment

☑ **Key Ideas Review** UNDERSTANDING

Did the student
- ❏ make important observations?
- ❏ extend or generalize learning?
- ❏ provide insightful answers?
- ❏ pose insightful questions?

Informal Assessment

☑ **Project** APPLYING

Did the student
- ❏ meet the project objectives?
- ❏ communicate clearly?
- ❏ complete the project accurately?
- ❏ connect mathematics to real-world situations?

Formal Assessment

☑ **Chapter Test** COMPUTING

Score the test, and record the results.

B Summarize Findings

Analyze and summarize assessment data for each student. Determine which Chapter Follow-Up is appropriate for each student. Use the Student Assessment Record in *Assessment* or *eAssess* to update assessment records.

C Chapter Follow-Up • DIFFERENTIATE INSTRUCTION

Based on your observations, use these teaching strategies for chapter follow-up.

ENRICH	PRACTICE	RETEACH	INTERVENTION
If . . . students demonstrate **secure understanding** of chapter concepts,	**If . . .** students demonstrate **competent understanding** of chapter concepts,	**If . . .** students demonstrate **emerging understanding** of chapter concepts,	**If . . .** students demonstrate **minimal understanding** of chapter concepts,
Then . . . move on to the next chapter.	**Then . . .** move on to the next chapter.	**Then . . .** move on to the next chapter, but continue to provide cumulative review.	**Then . . .** intensive intervention is still needed before they start the next chapter.

A Chancy Birthday Party

Context of the Thinking Story Willy takes his chances on getting presents while opening packages at his birthday party.

Lesson Planner

OBJECTIVES
To develop logical thinking while integrating reading skills with mathematics

NCTM STANDARDS
Data Analysis and Probability
- Collecting data by using observations
- Proposing and justifying conclusions and predictions that are based on data
- Describing events as *likely* or *unlikely*
- Predicting the probability of outcomes of simple experiments

READING STANDARDS
- Listening for details
- Predicting what will happen in a story
- Drawing conclusions
- Making inferences
- Evaluating information

Using the Thinking Story

The Thinking Story may be used anytime throughout the chapter. Read the Thinking Story "A Chancy Birthday Party" to your class as they follow along in the **Student Edition** on pages 528–531. As you read the story, give students time to think about each question, but not so much that they forget the point being made.

A Chancy Birthday Party

"I've been wishing for a surprise birthday party," said Willy, "but I'm afraid my wish won't come true. My birthday is only a week away, and no one has said anything about a party for me yet."

Is that a good reason for Willy to think he won't have a surprise birthday party? ❶

How long will he have to wait to see if his wish comes true? ❷

What makes you think so? ❸

Seven days later there was a knock on Willy's door. When Willy opened the door, he heard a loud "Surprise!"

"What a big surprise," said Willy, as the crowd of people came in. "I'm glad no one told me about my party."

"Since you like to wish so much," Portia told him, "Ferdie and I brought you a special present. Here are 4 packages."

"That's more than I could have wished for," Willy said.

"But there's a catch," said Ferdie. "Only 3 of the packages have presents in them. One of the packages is empty."

"That's all right," said Willy. "Three presents are enough."

522

"But you may not get all 3," Portia explained. "It depends on how lucky you are. You have to point to and then open the packages one at a time, and when you open the empty package you have to stop. You get only the presents that you open."

"This is going to take some hard wishing," said Willy. "If my wishing works, I'll get lots of presents."

If Willy is really lucky, how many presents will he get from Portia and Ferdie? ❹

"I wish I knew which package is empty," said Willy. "I wouldn't open it until the end. That way I'd get 3 presents."

If Willy is really unlucky, how many presents will he get from Portia and Ferdie? ❺

Willy picked one of the packages and started to open it. "I hope my wishing works," he said. "If this package is empty, I won't get any presents."

Is the package more likely to be empty or more likely to have a present in it? ❻

Why? ❼

"The wishing worked!" screamed Willy. "I got a present!"

Guided Discussion

As students answer the questions in the story, ask them to communicate how they decided on their answers. Allow students to debate the answers if necessary.

1 no

2 until his birthday

3 because it is supposed to be a surprise

4 3; it will help to draw the 4 packages on the board and mark each one as it is opened, showing whether it is empty or contains a present

5 none

6 to have a present in it

7 Willy has 3 chances in 4 of getting a present.

8 3

9 2

10 a present

11 2

12 The chances are the same.

13 Only 1 package has not been opened yet, and it has to have a present in it.

14 3

15 2

16 somewhat lucky, because he got a present when his chances were greater than 1 in 2

"I'm glad you did," said Marcus, "but that was pretty easy. There were 4 packages, and only 1 is empty. So you had 3 chances of picking a present and only 1 chance of picking the empty box."

"I hope I'm lucky again," said Willy. "Here goes."

How many packages are left? **8**

How many packages have presents in them? **9**

Is Willy more likely to pick a present or an empty box? **10**

"I got another present!" shouted Willy. "Now do you believe wishing works, Marcus?"

"I doubt it very much," said Marcus. "There were 3 packages, and 2 of them had presents in them. You had 2 chances of picking a present and only 1 chance of picking an empty box."

How many packages are left now? **11**

Is Willy more likely to pick the one with a present in it or the one that is empty? **12**

524

This time when Willy opened the package, he found it was empty. "I wish I had one more chance," he said. "I'm sure my luck would work next time, and I'd pick the package with a present in it."

How can Willy be so sure? **13**

How many packages did Willy open? **14**

How many presents did he get? **15**

Would you say he was very lucky, somewhat lucky, or not lucky at all? Why? **16**

The End

Lesson Study

Reflect on each of the lessons you taught in this chapter. Rate each one on the following scale, and then consider ways to maintain or improve positive teaching experiences in the future.

Lessons	Very Effective	Effective	Less Effective	What Worked	Ways to Improve
12.1 Collecting Data—Samples					
12.2 Collecting Data—Tally Marks					
12.3 Summarizing Data					
12.4 Mean, Median, Mode					
12.5 Displaying Data					
12.6 Graphs That Compare					
12.7 Graphs Showing Change					
12.8 Graphs Showing How Data Is Grouped					
12.9 Interpreting and Analyzing Data					
12.10 Probability—Impossible to Certain					
12.11 Probability—Predictions and Experiments					
12.12 Displaying and Analyzing Outcomes					

Handbook

![SRA] **Real Math**

Student Handbook

Problem-Solving Tips

If you need help solving a math problem, try this:

- Write the problem in your own words.
- Write what you are trying to find out.
- List the information you already know.
- List the information you need to find out.
- Discuss the problem with other people.
- Write possible ways you can find out what you need to know.
- Have you solved problems like this before? If so, how did you do it?
- Try to solve the problem.

After you think you have solved the problem, ask yourself:

- Does the answer make sense?
- Is there more than one answer?
- Is there a different way to solve the problem?
- Would a different way have been easier or better for some reason?
- What have you learned that will help you solve other problems?

Handbook

Handwriting Models

 Starting point, straight down

 Starting point, around right, slanting left and straight across right

 Starting point, around right, in at the middle, around right

Starting point, straight down, straight across right. Starting point, straight down, crossing line

 Straight down, curve around right and up. Starting point, straight across right

 Starting point, slanting left, around the bottom curving up around left and into the curve

 Starting point, straight across right, slanting down left

 Starting point, curving left, curving down and around right, slanting up right to starting point

 Starting point, curving around left all the way, straight down

 Starting point, straight down. Starting point, curving left all the way around to starting point

---

Number Line

Number lines show numbers in order.

−10 −9 −8 −7 −6 −5 −4 −3 −2 −1 0 1 2 3 4 5 6 7 8 9 10

You can use a number line to

- count on.
- count back.
- skip count by 2s or 3s or any number.
- add.
- subtract.

Number Names

0	Zero				15	Fifteen	Ten and five	15th	Fifteenth
1	One		1st	First	16	Sixteen	Ten and six	16th	Sixteenth
2	Two		2nd	Second	17	Seventeen	Ten and seven	17th	Seventeenth
3	Three		3rd	Third	18	Eighteen	Ten and eight	18th	Eighteenth
4	Four		4th	Fourth	19	Nineteen	Ten and nine	19th	Nineteenth
5	Five		5th	Fifth	20	Twenty	Two tens	20th	Twentieth
6	Six		6th	Sixth	30	Thirty	Three tens	30th	Thirtieth
7	Seven		7th	Seventh	40	Forty	Four tens	40th	Fortieth
8	Eight		8th	Eighth	50	Fifty	Five tens	50th	Fiftieth
9	Nine		9th	Ninth	60	Sixty	Six tens	60th	Sixtieth
10	Ten		10th	Tenth	70	Seventy	Seven tens	70th	Seventieth
11	Eleven	Ten and one	11th	Eleventh	80	Eighty	Eight tens	80th	Eightieth
12	Twelve	Ten and two	12th	Twelfth	90	Ninety	Nine tens	90th	Ninetieth
13	Thirteen	Ten and three	13th	Thirteenth	100	One hundred	Ten tens	100th	One hundredth
14	Fourteen	Ten and four	14th	Fourteenth					

Handbook

Place Value

A place-value table tells you how many hundreds, tens, and ones. Place value is important. Look what happens when the 5 is in the hundreds place or the ones place.

Hundreds	Tens	Ones
5	4	1

Hundreds	Tens	Ones
1	4	5

Big Numbers

Numbers go on forever. After trillions come quadrillions and then quintillions. A googol is written as 1 followed by 100 zeros. A googolplex is written as 1 followed by one googol zeros.

1	One	10,000,000	Ten million
10	Ten	100,000,000	One hundred million
100	One hundred		
1,000	One thousand	1,000,000,000	One billion
10,000	Ten thousand	10,000,000,000	Ten billion
100,000	One hundred thousand	100,000,000,000	One hundred billion
1,000,000	One million	1,000,000,000,000	One trillion

Addition Table

You can use the Addition Table to find basic addition and subtraction facts.

+	0	1	2	3	4	5	6	7	8	9	10
0	0	1	2	3	4	5	6	7	8	9	10
1	1	2	3	4	5	6	7	8	9	10	11
2	2	3	4	5	6	7	8	9	10	11	12
3	3	4	5	6	7	8	9	10	11	12	13
4	4	5	6	7	8	9	10	11	12	13	14
5	5	6	7	8	9	10	11	12	13	14	15
6	6	7	8	9	10	11	12	13	14	15	16
7	7	8	9	10	11	12	13	14	15	16	17
8	8	9	10	11	12	13	14	15	16	17	18
9	9	10	11	12	13	14	15	16	17	18	19
10	10	11	12	13	14	15	16	17	18	19	20

Handbook

Addition and Subtraction Facts

Addition Fact Helpers

These strategies can help with many of the addition facts.

To add:	Think of:
0	No change
1	Counting on 1
2	Counting on 2
4	One less than adding 5
5	Finger sets—one more hand
6	One more than adding 5
9	One less than adding 10
10	Write 1 in the tens place

Subtraction Fact Helpers

These strategies can help with some of the subtraction facts. For other subtraction facts, think of the corresponding addition fact.

To subtract:	Think of:
0	No change
1	Counting back 1
5	Finger sets—taking away one hand
9	One more than subtracting 10
10	Subtracting 1 from the tens digit

Addition

One Way to Add

$$\begin{array}{r} 685 \\ + 267 \\ \hline \end{array}$$

We start at the right because it is easier that way. Add ones.
5 + 7 = 12. 12 ones = 1 ten and 2 ones.

$$\begin{array}{r} 1 \\ 685 \\ + 267 \\ \hline 2 \end{array}$$

Add tens. 1 + 8 + 6 = 15. 15 tens = 1 hundred and 5 tens.

$$\begin{array}{r} 11 \\ 685 \\ + 267 \\ \hline 52 \end{array}$$

Add hundreds. 1 + 6 + 2 = 9.

$$\begin{array}{r} 11 \\ 685 \\ + 267 \\ \hline 952 \end{array}$$

Handbook

Addition Laws

Commutative Law of Addition
The order of two numbers does not affect their sum. For example, the sum of $1 + 3$ is the same as the sum of $3 + 1$.

Associative Law of Addition
When adding three numbers, it does not matter whether the first pair or the last pair is added first.
$5 + 4 + 3 = (5 + 4) + 3 = 5 + (4 + 3)$

$9 + 3$ $5 + 7$

Additive Identity
Adding a number to 0 gives that number.
$6 + 0 = 6$

Additive Inverse
Adding a positive number and a negative number with the same absolute value (distance from 0) gives 0.
$4 + (-4) = 0$.

Subtraction
One Way to Subtract

$$\begin{array}{r} 365 \\ -178 \end{array}$$

Start at the right because it is easier.

There are not enough ones to subtract 8, so rename 6 tens as 5 tens and 10 ones.

$$\begin{array}{r} ^{5\ 15} \\ 36\!\!\!/5 \\ -178 \end{array}$$

Subtract ones.

$$\begin{array}{r} ^{5\ 15} \\ 36\!\!\!/5 \\ -178 \\ \hline 7 \end{array}$$

There are not enough tens to subtract 7, so rename 3 hundreds as 2 hundreds and 10 tens.
Subtract tens.

$$\begin{array}{r} ^{2\ 15\,15} \\ 3\!\!\!/6\!\!\!/5 \\ -178 \\ \hline 87 \end{array}$$

Subtract hundreds.

$$\begin{array}{r} ^{2\ 15\,15} \\ 3\!\!\!/6\!\!\!/5 \\ -178 \\ \hline 187 \end{array}$$

Handbook

Multiplication Table

You can use the Multiplication Table to find basic facts.

×	0	1	2	3	4	5	6	7	8	9	10	11	12
0	0	0	0	0	0	0	0	0	0	0	0	0	0
1	0	1	2	3	4	5	6	7	8	9	10	11	12
2	0	2	4	6	8	10	12	14	16	18	20	22	24
3	0	3	6	9	12	15	18	21	24	27	30	33	36
4	0	4	8	12	16	20	24	28	32	36	40	44	48
5	0	5	10	15	20	25	30	35	40	45	50	55	60
6	0	6	12	18	24	30	36	42	48	54	60	66	72
7	0	7	14	21	28	35	42	49	56	63	70	77	84
8	0	8	16	24	32	40	48	56	64	72	80	88	96
9	0	9	18	27	36	45	54	63	72	81	90	99	108
10	0	10	20	30	40	50	60	70	80	90	100	110	120
11	0	11	22	33	44	55	66	77	88	99	110	121	132
12	0	12	24	36	48	60	72	84	96	108	120	132	144

Multiplication Facts
Fact Helper Strategies
To multiply by:

10   Write a "0" after the number.

9   Subtract the number from 10 times the number.

0   The answer is 0.

1   The answer is the number.

2   Add the number to itself.

5   Multiply half the number by 10 if it is even. If the number is odd, multiply half of the next smaller number by 10 and add 5.

4   Double the number, and then double that answer.

3   Add the number to its double.

8   Double 4 times the number, or subtract the number from 9 times the number.

6   Double 3 times the number.

7   If you've learned all the other facts and can remember that $7 \times 7 = 49$, you know all the multiples of 7.

Fact Families
Fact families show how multiplication and division are related.

$2 \times 3 = 6$	$6 \div 2 = 3$
$3 \times 2 = 6$	$6 \div 3 = 2$

Handbook

Multiplication

Think of multiplication as finding many areas.

	100	100	100	10	10	10	10	6
10								
10								
10	$300 \times 50 = 15{,}000$			$40 \times 50 = 2{,}000$				
10								
10								
2	$300 \times 2 = 600$			$40 \times 2 = 80$				

$6 \times 2 = 12$

$6 \times 50 = 300$

Partial Products

Multiplying using partial products may help you keep track of place values. Starting with the rightmost column, multiply each position in the top number by the ones-column digit, then the tens-column digit, and so on. Then add the partial products to find the final product. You could start with any column, but it is easier if you start on the right.

$$\begin{array}{r} 346 \\ \times\ 52 \\ \hline \end{array}$$

$2 \times 6 = 12$	12
$2 \times 40 = 80$	80
$2 \times 300 = 600$	600
$50 \times 6 = 300$	300
$50 \times 40 = 2{,}000$	2000
$50 \times 300 = 15{,}000$	+ 15000
Add partial products.	17992

A Shorter Way to Multiply

Beginning at the rightmost column, find the product. Write the ones digit of the product below the line in the ones column, and write the tens digit at the top of the tens column. Then repeat this process for each digit of the second factor.

$$\begin{array}{r} 346 \\ \times\ 52 \\ \hline \end{array}$$

Multiply 2 times the ones. $6 \times 2 = 12$
12 ones = 1 ten and 2 ones
Multiply 2 times 4 tens, and add the carried ten. $(2 \times 4) + 1 = 9$

$$\begin{array}{r} 1 \\ 346 \\ \times\ 52 \\ \hline 2 \end{array} \qquad \begin{array}{r} 1 \\ 346 \\ \times\ 52 \\ \hline 92 \end{array}$$

Multiply 2 times 3 hundreds. $2 \times 3 = 6$

$$\begin{array}{r} 1 \\ 346 \\ \times\ 52 \\ \hline 692 \end{array}$$

Multiply 5 tens times 6 ones. $5 \times 6 = 30$
30 tens = 3 hundreds and 0 tens
Multiply 5 tens times 4 tens, and add the carried hundreds. $(5 \times 4) + 3 = 23$
23 = 2 thousands and 3 hundreds

$$\begin{array}{r} 3 \\ 346 \\ \times\ 52 \\ \hline 692 \\ 00 \end{array} \qquad \begin{array}{r} 2\ 3 \\ 346 \\ \times\ 52 \\ \hline 692 \\ 300 \end{array}$$

Multiply 5 tens times 3 hundreds, and add the carried thousands. $(5 \times 3) + 2 = 17$
17 thousands = 1 ten thousand and 7 thousands

$$\begin{array}{r} 2\ 3 \\ 346 \\ \times\ 52 \\ \hline 692 \\ 17300 \end{array}$$

Add partial products.

$$\begin{array}{r} 2\ 3 \\ 346 \\ \times\ 52 \\ \hline 692 \\ + 17300 \\ \hline 17992 \end{array}$$

Handbook

Division

One Way to Divide

$$5\overline{)423}$$

Five does not divide into 4, but it will divide into 42 eight times.

$$\begin{array}{r} 8 \\ 5\overline{)423} \\ 40 \end{array}$$

Subtract 40 from 42.

$$\begin{array}{r} 8 \\ 5\overline{)423} \\ -\ 40 \\ \hline 2 \end{array}$$

Bring down the next digit, 3.

$$\begin{array}{r} 8 \\ 5\overline{)423} \\ -\ 40 \\ \hline 23 \end{array}$$

Five divides into 23 four times.

$$\begin{array}{r} 84 \\ 5\overline{)423} \\ -\ 40 \\ \hline 23 \\ 20 \end{array}$$

Subtract 20 from 23.

$$\begin{array}{r} 84 \\ 5\overline{)423} \\ -\ 40 \\ \hline 23 \\ -\ 20 \\ \hline 3 \end{array}$$

$423 \div 5 = 84$ R3

Divisibility Patterns

Divisibility by 2

An even number is a number divisible by 2. We can recognize even numbers because their last digit must also be divisible by 2 (the last digit must be 0, 2, 4, 6, or 8). For example, 78,950 has a 0 as its last digit; therefore, it's divisible by 2.

Divisibility by 3

A number is divisible by 3 if the sum of its digits is divisible by 3. The number 492,603 has a digit sum of 24. Twenty-four is divisible by 3; therefore, 492,603 is divisible by 3.

Divisibility by 5

We can recognize a number that is divisible by 5 because its last digit must be either a 0 or a 5. The number 47,825 has a 5 as its last digit; therefore, it's divisible by 5.

Divisibility by 11

A two-digit number is divisible by 11 if the two digits are equal to each other. Take 33, for example: 3 = 3, so 33 is divisible by 11. There are patterns for divisibility by 11 for numbers greater than 100. Can you find them?

Handbook

Geometric Figures

Plane Figures

Circle A circle is composed of all points in a plane the same distance from the center.

Polygon A polygon is a closed figure with sides that are all line segments.

Angles Angles are measured based on the amount of turn they represent. A quarter turn is a right angle. Angles of less than a quarter turn are acute angles. Angles of more than a quarter turn but less than half a turn are obtuse angles.

Triangle A triangle is a polygon with three sides.

right   acute   obtuse

Polygons

Quadrilateral A polygon with four sides

Rectangle A rectangle has four sides with opposite pairs of sides of equal length and four right angles.

Square A square is a quadrilateral with four equal sides and four right angles.

Rhombus A rhombus is a quadrilateral with four equal sides.

Trapezoid A trapezoid is a quadrilateral with two sides parallel.

Pentagon A pentagon is a polygon with five sides.

Hexagon A hexagon is a polygon with six sides.

pentagon

hexagon

Space Figures

Cube A cube is a space figure with six square faces.

Sphere A sphere is a space figure composed of all points in space the same distance from its center.

Cone A cone is a space figure made by connecting every point on a circle or other plane figure to a point not on the figure.

Cylinder A cylinder is a space figure with two parallel bases (usually circles).

Polyhedron A polyhedron is a closed space figure whose faces are all polygons.

cube

sphere

cone

cylinder   polyhedron

Measurements

Decimal and Metric Prefixes

1000 = thousand = *kilo-*   0.10 = tenth = *deci-*
100 = hundred = *hecto-*   0.01 = hundredth = *centi-*
10 = ten = *deca-*   0.001 = thousandth = *milli-*

The basic units in the metric system are *meter, gram,* and *liter.*

Measuring Length

Metric	Equivalency
1 millimeter (mm)	1mm: -
1 centimeter (cm)	10 millimeters
1 decimeter (dm)	10 centimeters
1 meter (m)	100 centimeters
1 dekameter (dam)	10 meters
1 hectometer (hm)	100 meters
1 kilometer (km)	1,000 meters

Customary	Equivalency
1 inch (in.)	1 inch: ———
1 foot (ft)	12 inches
1 yard (yd)	3 feet
1 mile (mi)	5,280 feet 1,760 yards

Measuring Temperature

Celsius		Fahrenheit
0	Water Freezes	32
100	Water Boils	212

Handbook

Measuring Weight (Mass)

Metric	Equivalent
1 gram (g)	a dollar bill weighs about 1 gram
1 dekagram (dag)	10 grams
1 hectogram (hg)	100 grams
1 kilogram (kg)	1,000 grams
1 metric ton (t)	1,000 kilograms

Customary	Equivalent
1 ounce (oz)	11 pennies weigh about 1 ounce
1 pound (lb)	16 ounces
1 ton	2,000 pounds

Measuring Capacity

Metric	Equivalent
1 milliliter (mL)	an eyedropper holds about 1 milliliter
1 centiliter (cL)	0.01 liter
1 deciliter (dL)	0.1 liter
1 liter (L)	1,000 milliliters
1 dekaliter (daL)	10 liters
1 hectoliter (hL)	100 liters
1 kiloliter (kL)	1,000 liters

Customary	Equivalent
1 fluid ounce (fl oz)	approximately the volume of 1 ounce of water
1 cup (c)	8 fluid ounces
1 pint (pt)	2 cups
1 quart (qt)	2 pints
1 gallon (gal)	4 quarts

Time

Months of the Year

Month	Number of Days
January	31
February	28, except in leap year every four years when there are 29
March	31
April	30
May	31
June	30
July	31
August	31
September	30
October	31
November	30
December	31

Equivalents of Time

60 seconds	1 minute
60 minutes	1 hour
24 hours (the time it takes Earth to rotate)	1 day
7 days 168 hours	1 week
12 months $52\frac{1}{7}$ weeks 365.25 days (the time it takes Earth to revolve around the sun)	1 year

A.M. (ante meridiem; before midday) means between midnight and noon

P.M. (post meridiem; after midday) means between noon and midnight

Military or 24-Hour Time Equivalents

1:00	1 A.M.	7:00	7 A.M.	13:00	1 P.M.	19:00	7 P.M.
2:00	2 A.M.	8:00	8 A.M.	14:00	2 P.M.	20:00	8 P.M.
3:00	3 A.M.	9:00	9 A.M.	15:00	3 P.M.	21:00	9 P.M.
4:00	4 A.M.	10:00	10 A.M.	16:00	4 P.M.	22:00	10 P.M.
5:00	5 A.M.	11:00	11 A.M.	17:00	5 P.M.	23:00	11 P.M.
6:00	6 A.M.	12:00	12 Noon	18:00	6 P.M.	24:00	12 Midnight

A.D. or C.E. means the common era, after the year 0

B.C. or B.C.E. means before the common era, before the year 0

Handbook

Frequency Tables

A frequency table shows tally marks and how often each kind of data occurs in a set of data.

Our Pets

Dogs	Cats	Other

Tally Marks

Tally marks are used to keep count. |||

Tallies of Five

Tally marks represent 5 when four tallies are combined with one diagonal mark.

Graphs

Bar Graph

A bar graph is a graph with bars of lengths that represent amounts.

Circle Graph

A circle graph has sectors that represent different categories.

Favorite Color

Line Graph

A line graph connects points to show change over time.

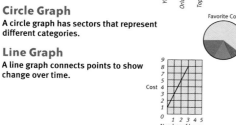

Fractions, Decimals, and Percentages

Fractions, decimals, and percentages are called *rational numbers* because they can be written as ratios. Whole numbers, counting numbers, integers, fractions, decimals, improper fractions, and mixed numbers are all examples of rational numbers.

Percentages are special ratios that compare a number to 100.

A ratio is the comparison of two quantities by division, such as a fraction.

Ratios are commonly used to relate one number to another. Ratios have no labels. There are three major representations of ratios: 3 out of 4, 3:4, and $\frac{3}{4}$. Probabilities are represented most often by ratios.

The ratio of blue to red dots can be written $\frac{2}{5}$.
The ratio of blue dots to the total number of dots is $\frac{2}{7}$.

A number line helps you think about rational numbers. You can see whole numbers, negative numbers, and fractions as belonging to the same system.

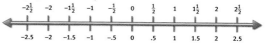

Benchmark for Fractions, Decimals, and Percentages

Fractions, decimals, and percentages can all represent the same rational number or part of a whole.

$1 = 1.0 \ = 100\%$
$\frac{3}{4} = 0.75 = 75\%$
$\frac{1}{2} = 0.5 \ = 50\%$

$\frac{1}{4} = 0.25 \ = 25\%$
$\frac{1}{8} = 0.125 = 12.5\%$

$\frac{3}{4}$ — numerator
— denominator

Handbook

Algebraic Functions

A function pairs a number (the input) with a second number (the output).
A function table lists the pairs of numbers.

If a girl is 3 years older than her brother, you can say:
Brother's age + 3 = Sister's age
No matter how old they are, the sister will always be three years older than her brother.

in	out
1	4
2	5
3	6
4	7
5	8

A **function machine** shows the input, output, and rule for a function. A **function rule** tells how the input of a function is related to the output of a function.

Composite functions involve more than one step in the function rule.

$x \to \times 3 \to n \to +3 \to y$

Linear functions create a straight line when graphed.

An **equation** is a mathematical statement showing that one quantity or expression is equal to another quantity or expression. These are the sentences of mathematical language.

Math Symbols

+	Plus / Add	$7 + 3 = 10$
−	Minus / Subtract	$10 - 3 = 7$
× or * on the computer	Times / Multiply	$3 \times 2 = 6$
÷, ⌐, or / on the computer	Divided by	$6 \div 2 = 3$
=	Is equal to	$4 + 2 = 6$
¢	Cents	39¢
$	Dollars	$1.00
°F	Degrees Fahrenheit	100°F
°C	Degrees Celsius	25°C
>	Greater than	$47 > 39$
<	Less than	$2 + 6 < 10$
4^3 ← exponent, ↑ base	Exponents are used as a shorthand notation to show repeated multiplication.	$4^3 = 4 \times 4 \times 4 = 64$
∠	Angle	$\angle ABC$
Δ	Triangle	$\triangle JKL$
≅	Is congruent to	$\angle ABC \cong \angle DEF$
∽	Is similar to	$\triangle JKL \backsim \triangle ABC$

Glossary

A

acute angle \ə kūr'\ *n.* an angle which measures between 0° and 90°

These are acute angles:

addend \ad' end\ *n.* any number or quantity that is to be added to another; for example:

```
 35  —— addend       7 + 8 = 15 —sum
+ 48  —— addend           |        addend
 83  —— sum               |        addend
```

A.M. (ante meridiem) *abbr.* before noon; the time from midnight to noon

angle \ang'gəl\ *n.* the figure formed by two rays extending from the same point

approximate \ə prok' sə māt'\ *v.* to come near or close. \ə prok' sə mit\ *adj.* nearly correct or exact

approximation \ə prok' sə mā' shən\ *n.* something that is nearly correct, as an estimated amount

area \âr' ē ə\ *n.* the measure of the interior, or inside, of a figure; the area of this rectangle is 6 square centimeters:

3 cm
2 cm

array \ə rā'\ *n.* a group of objects arranged in an orderly way in rows and columns

associative \ə sō"shē ā'tiv\ *adj.* a law stating that the sum or product of two or more quantities will be the same regardless of the way in which they are grouped

axes (of a graph) \ak' sēs\ *n.* the two zero lines of a graph that give the coordinates of points

B

bar graph \bär\ *n.* a graph that uses bars (rectangles) to represent data

benchmark \bench märk\ *n.* something that serves as a standard or reference by which something else can be measured or compared

C

capacity \kə pas' i tē\ *n.* the amount (of anything) a container can hold

center \sen 'tər\ *n.* a point within a circle equally distant from every point on the circle

centimeter \sen" tə mē' tər\ *n.* a unit of length equal to one-hundredth of a meter; The prefix *centi-* means "one hundredth."

circle \sûr' kəl\ *n.* a continuous, closed curved line, every point of which is equally distant from the center

Commutative Law of Multiplication *n.* the order of factors does not affect the product when multiplying; generally, for any numbers a and b, $a \times b = b \times a$

congruent \kən grü' ənt\ *adj.* figures that are the same size and same shape; that is, they fit perfectly when placed on top of one another

coordinates \kō ôr" də nits\ *n.* a pair of numbers that gives the location of a point on a graph; also called an ordered pair of numbers. In the figure shown, for example, the coordinates of point A are (2, 3). The x–coordinate is 2 and the y–coordinate is 3.

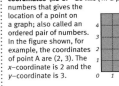

Glossary

cube \kūb\ *n.* a solid figure with six equal, square sides

cubic units *n.* units that are used to measure volume

cup \kup\ *n.* a customary measure of capacity equal to 16 fluid ounces

cylinder \sil' ən dər\ *n.* a solid geometric figure bounded by two equal, parallel circles and a curved surface that is formed by a straight line moving parallel to itself with its ends always on the circumferences of the circles

D

data \dā' tə, dat' ə\ *pl. n.* information from which conclusions can be drawn; facts and figures

decimal point *n.* a dot used in separating the ones digit from the tenths digit

decimeter \de sə\ *n.* a metric measure of length equal to one-tenth of a meter

degree \di grē\ *n.* a unit of measurement for angles or temperature

denominator \di nom' ə nā' tər\ *n.* a number below the line in a fraction that indicates the number of equal parts into which the whole is divided

diameter \dī am' i tər\ *n.* a straight line passing through the center of a circle or sphere, from one side to the other

difference \dif' rəns\ *n.* remainder left after subtracting one quantity from another For example:

```
 43 __ minuend      10 − 7 = 3 —difference
− 16 __ subtrahend        |         subtrahend
 27 __ difference         |         minuend
```

digit \dij' it\ *n.* any of the ten Arabic numerals from 0 through 9

Distributive Law *n.* a law stating that the product of multiplication is the same when the operation is performed on a whole set as when it is performed on the individual members of the set: $4 \times (2 + 5) = 4 \times 2 + 4 \times 5$

dividend \div' i dend\ *n.* the number that is to be divided; for example:

```
6 ÷ 3 = 2 —— quotient
      |   divisor
      |   dividend
```

```
            43        —— quotient
divisor — 8)347       —— dividend
          − 32
          ——
            27
          − 24
          ——
             3
```

division \di vizh' ən\ *n.* the act of separating into parts or pieces; in mathematics, the process of dividing two numbers to show how many times one number contains the other number

divisor \di vī' zər\ *n.* the number the dividend is to be divided by

double \dub' əl\ *n.* to make a number twice as great by adding the number to itself (multiplying by 2)

E

edge \ej\ *n.* a line or place where an object or area begins or ends; extreme or outermost border; a line segment where two faces meet or a planar area begins or ends

---

Glossary

elapsed \i lapst'\ *n.* the amount of time that has passed

equation \i kwā' zhən\ *n.* a mathematical statement showing that one quantity or expression is equal to another quantity or expression

equilateral \ē' kwə lat'ər əl\ *adj.* having all sides equal in length

equivalent \i kwiv' ə lənt\ *adj.* having the same value

equivalent fractions \i kwiv' ə lənt\ *n.* fractions that name the same rational number

estimate *n.*, es' tə mit; *v.*, es' tə māt'\ *n.* a judgment or opinion, as of the value, quality, extent, size, or cost of something. *v.* to form a judgment or opinion (based on available information) about the extent or size of something; calculate

even number *n.* a number that can be divided exactly by two

exponent \ek spō' nənt\ *n.* a numeral or symbol placed at the upper right side of another numeral or symbol to indicate the number of times it is to be used as a factor

F

face \fās\ *n.* a plane figure that serves as one side of a space figure

fact family \fakt fam'ə lē\ *n.* a group of number sentences that uses the same numbers to relate addition and subtraction

factor \fak' tər\ *n.* numbers you multiply to get a product; for example:
3 (multiplier) $\times$ 5 (multiplicand) = 15 (product)

foot \fu̇t\ *n.* a customary measure of length equal to 12 inches

fraction \frak' shən\ *n.* a quantity expressing the division of one number by a second number, written as two numerals separated by a line

frequency \frē' kwen sē\ *n.* the number of times something happens

function \fungk' shən\ *n.* a relationship that pairs every element of one set with an element of a second set; for example, a relationship that pairs any number with another number

function machine *n.* a machine (sometimes imaginary) that does the same thing to every number that is put into it

G

gallon \ga' lən\ *n.* a customary measure of capacity equal to 4 quarts

graph \graf\ *n.* a diagram showing the relationship between two or more sets of data

greatest common factor *n.* the greatest factor shared by a pair of numbers

grid \grid\ *n.* a pattern of intersecting lines that divides a map or table into small squares

H

halfway \haf' wā\ *n.* in the middle

heptagon \hep' tə gon'\ *n.* a plane figure having seven sides and seven angles

hexagon \hek' sə gon'\ *n.* a plane figure having six sides and six angles

hour \au(ə)r\ *n.* a measure of time equal to 60 minutes

Glossary

hundredth \hun' dridth\ *n.* one of a hundred equal parts; $\frac{1}{100}$

hypotenuse \hī pot' ə nūs'\ *n.* the side of a right triangle opposite the right angle

I

improper fraction *n.* a fraction whose numerator is greater than, or equal to, its denominator

inequality \in' i kwol' i tē\ *n.* mathematical statement showing that two numbers are not equal or that one number is greater than or less than another number

integer \in' ti jər\ *n.* any positive or negative whole number or zero

intersecting lines *n.* lines that meet and cross each other

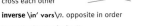

inverse \in' vərs\ *n.* opposite in order

isosceles \ī säs' lēz\ *adj.* having two equal sides. These are isosceles triangles:

K

kilo– \kē' lo; kil' ō\ *prefix* one thousand

kilometer \ki lom' i tər, kil' ə mē' tər\ *n.* a unit of length in the metric system equal to 1,000 meters

L

least common multiple *n.* the smallest multiple of a pair of numbers

length \lengkth\ *n.* describes how long something is

line \līn\ *n.* a straight path that extends infinitely in opposite directions, thought of as having length but no thickness

line graph *n.* a graph that represents data as ordered pairs connected with a line

line of symmetry *n.* a line on which a figure can be folded into two or more congruent parts

line plot *n.* a data graph showing frequency on a number line

line segment *n.* a part of a line with two endpoints

M

mean \mēn\ *n.* the typical or usual amount, which is found by dividing the sum of two or more quantities by the number of quantities

median \mē' dē ən\ *n.* the middle number in a set of data

metric system *n.* a decimal system of measurement that uses the meter as the fundamental unit of length

milliliter \mil' ə lē' tər\ *n.* a metric measure of capacity equal to one thousandth of a liter

millimeter \mil' ə mē' tər\ *n.* a metric measure of length equal to one thousandth of a meter

minuend \min' ū end'\ *n.* the number from which another is to be subtracted

minute \min' it\ *n.* a measure of time equal to 60 seconds

mixed number *n.* a number consisting of a whole number and a fraction

mode \mōd\ *n.* the number appearing most frequently in a set of data

Glossary

multiple \mul′ tə pəl\ *n.* a number that is some whole number times another number; for example, 12 is a multiple of 2 because $2 \times 6 = 12$

multiplicand \mul tə pli kand\ *n.* a number multiplied by another number, the multiplier

For example:

```
  5 ——— multiplicand
× 3 ——— multiplier
 15 ——— product
```

$3 \times 5 = 15$ —product
multiplicand
multiplier

multiplier \mul′ tə plī ər\ *n.* a factor of a product

multiply \mul′ tə plī′\ *v.* to find the product of a number that is repeatedly added to itself $(4 + 4 + 4 + 4 = 4 \times 4 = 16)$

N

negative \neg′ tiv\ *n.* less than zero

net \net\ *n.* a pattern used to create a space figure

number line *n.* a line of infinite extent whose points correspond to the real numbers according to their distance in a positive or negative direction from a point arbitrarily taken as zero

numeral \nü′ mər əl\ *n.* a symbol that represents a number, such as 7 or VII

numerator \nü′ mə rā′ tər\ *n.* the part of a fraction written above the line; the numerator tells how many parts are being referred to

O

obtuse angle *n.* an angle that is greater than 90°

These are obtuse angles:

octagon \ok′ tə gon′\ *n.* a polygon having eight sides and eight angles

odd number *n.* a whole number that cannot be divided into two equal whole numbers

ordered pair *n.* a set of numbers that describes the location of a point on a graph; an example is (3, 4)

outcome \out′ kum\ *n.* a result or consequence

outlier \out′ līər\ *n.* a number that is far off from all other numbers in a data set

P

parallel lines *n.* lines that are the same distance apart and that go in the same direction and never meet

parallelogram \par′ ə lel′ ə gram′\ *n.* a quadrilateral that has two pairs of parallel sides

parentheses \pə ren′ thə sēz\ *n.* curved marks ( ) used to enclose symbols or numbers to indicate which expression to evaluate first

partial product *n.* the product that comes from multiplying the multiplicand by one of the digits of the multiplier: for example:

```
    36   ⎱ This partial product comes from
  × 12   ⎰ multiplying 36 by 2 ones.
    72   ⎱ This partial product comes from
         ⎰ multiplying 36 by 1 ten.
  +360   ⎱ This product comes from adding the
   432   ⎰ partial products.
```

Glossary

pattern \pat′ ərn\ *n.* an arrangement or design of colors, shapes, or lines

pentagon \pen′ tə gon′\ *n.* a polygon with five line segments as sides

percent \pər sent′\ *n.* a fraction with a denominator of 100; the number of parts in every hundred

perimeter \pə rim′ i tər\ *n.* the length of the path around a figure

perpendicular lines *n.* lines that intersect at right angles

pictograph \pik′ tə graf\ *n.* a graph that uses pictures or symbols to represent data

pint \pīnt\ *n.* a customary measure of capacity equal to 2 cups

place value *n.* the value of a digit determined by its position within a number

plane \plān\ *n.* a flat surface wholly containing every line connecting any two points on it

plane figure *n.* a figure having only height and width

P.M. (post meridiem) *abbr.* after noon; the time from noon to midnight

point \point\ *n.* something having position but no length, width, or height

polygon \pä′ lē gän′\ *n.* a closed plane figure with three or more line segments as sides

polyhedron \pä′ lē hē′ drən\ *n.* a space figure that has only flat faces, which are polygons

pound \paůnd\ *n.* a customary measure of weight equal to 16 ounces

prism \priz′ əm\ *n.* a solid having two congruent and parallel faces, and whose other faces are parallelograms

prisms

probability \prob′ ə bil′ i tē\ *n.* how likely it is for something to happen

product \prod′ əkt\ *n.* the result of multiplying two (or more) numbers together

profit \prof′ it\ *n.* the amount remaining after all the costs of a business have been paid

pyramid \pir′ ə mid′\ *n.* a solid figure having a polygon for a base and triangular sides intersecting at a point

Q

quadrilateral \kwod′ rə lat′ ər əl\ *n.* a polygon with four sides and four angles

quart \kwort\ *n.* a customary measure of capacity equal to 2 pints

quarter \kwôr′ tər\ *n.* one-fourth of an hour; fifteen minutes

quotient \kwō′ shənt\ *n.* the answer to a division problem

R

radius \rā′ dē əs\ *n.* a line segment going from the center to the outside of a circle or sphere

---

Glossary

range \rānj\ *n.* the difference between the greatest and least numbers in a set of data

ray \rā\ *n.* a set of points that has one endpoint and extends forever in one direction

rectangle \rek′ tang′ gəl\ *n.* a parallelogram having four right angles

reflection \ri flek′ shən\ *n.* a change in the location of a figure when it is flipped over a line

regroup \rē grüp′\ *v.* to rename a number to make adding and subtracting easier

$$\begin{array}{r} \overset{1\ \ 15}{25} \\ -\ 17 \\ \hline 8 \end{array}$$

(To subtract in the ones column, 2 tens and 5 are regrouped as 1 ten and 15.)

regular polygon *n.* a polygon with sides of equal length

relation signs *n.* the three basic relation signs are > (greater than), < (less than), and = (equal to)

remainder \ri mān′ dər\ *n.* the number left over when a set of objects is shared equally or separated into equal groups. For example, when you divide 25 by 4, the quotient is 6 with a remainder of 1

$$\begin{array}{r} 6\ \ R1 \\ 4\overline{)25} \\ -\ 24 \\ \hline 1 \end{array}$$

rhombus \räm′ bəs\ *n.* a parallelogram whose sides are all the same length

right angle *n.* an angle measuring 90°

right triangle *n.* a triangle with one right angle

rotation \rō tā′ shən\ *n.* a change in the location of a figure when it is turned in a circle around a point

rounding \round ing\ *v.* changing a number to another number that is easier to work with and that is close enough for the purpose

S

sample \sam′ pəl\ *n.* a smaller set of data that belongs to a larger set of data and reflects the characteristics of members in a larger set

scale \skāl\ *n.* a series of marks made along a line at regularly spaced intervals; used in measuring

scatter plot *n.* a graph that represents data as ordered pairs

segment \seg′ mənt\ *n.* a part of a line with two endpoints

set \set\ *n.* a collection of numbers, points, objects, or other things that are grouped together

similar \sim′ ə lər\ *adj.* figures that have the same shape, but that differ in size

sphere \sfîr\ *n.* a round three-dimensional figure having all the points at an equal distance from the center

square \skwâr\ *n.* a plane figure having four sides of equal length and four right angles

---

Glossary

standard \stan′ dərd\ *adj.* widely accepted and used as a model

stem-and-leaf plot *n.* a data graph showing data from least to greatest using the digits from the greatest place value to group the data

subtrahend \sub′ trə hend\ *n.* the number that is to be subtracted from another

sum \sum\ *n.* a result obtained from addition

surface area *n.* the sum of the areas of the faces of a space figure

symmetry \sim′ i trē\ *n.* having the same size and shape across a dividing line

T

table \tā′ bəl\ *n.* graphic display of information

tally \tal′ ē\ *n.* a series of marks to keep a record of data

tenth \tenth\ *n.* one of ten equal parts

term \tûrm\ *n.* a number or other symbol that is connected by addition or subtraction to another term

translation \tranz lā′ shən\ *n.* a change in the location of a figure when it slides without being turned

trapezoid \trap′ ə zoid′\ *n.* quadrilateral with exactly one pair of parallel lines

tree chart *n.* a display of data that shows possible combinations where the trunk represents the first set of choices and the branches represent the second, third, and so on set of choices

triangle \trī′ ang gəl\ *n.* a plane figure with three sides and three angles

U

unit cost *n.* the cost of one out of a number of goods or services

upper and lower bounds *n.* numbers that an answer must be less than or greater than

V

variable \vâr′ ē ə bəl\ *n.* a symbol representing a quantity that can have any of a set of values

variability \vâr′ ē ə bil ity\ *n.* the likelihood that something will change

vertex \ver′ teks\ *n.* 1. the point of intersection of two rays 2. the point of intersection of three edges of a space figure

volume \vol′ ūm\ *n.* the amount of space anything fills

W

weight \wāt\ *n.* describes how much something weighs

withdrawal \with drô′ əl\ *n.* the act of taking away or removing

whole number *n.* a number that tells how many complete things there are

Y

yard \yärd\ *n.* a customary measure of length equal to 3 feet

Z

zero \zîr′ ō\ *n.* the number that leaves any number unchanged when it is added to it

Appendix

This appendix provides additional information about key issues in mathematics education and how they are addressed in *Real Math.*

About Mathematics

> "Genuine mathematics...constitutes one of the finest expressions of the human spirit. The great areas of mathematics—algebra, real analysis, complex analysis, number theory, combinatorics, probability theory, statistics, topology, geometry, and so on—have undoubtedly arisen from our experience of the world around us, in order to systematize that experience, to give it order and coherence, and thereby to enable us to predict and perhaps control future events."
>
> Hilton, Peter. *"Mathematics in Our Culture"* in Gullberg, Jan. Mathematics: From the Birth of Numbers. New York: W.W. Norton & Company, 1997.

Mathematics is a way of describing relationships between numbers and other measurable quantities. As the language of science, mathematics communicates ideas in universally accepted terminology. It can express simple equations or explain relationships among the farthest objects in the known universe. Mathematics has helped make advances in medicine, technology, astronomy, meteorology, biology, physics, economics, and political science.

Mathematics has two main branches: pure mathematics, the study of abstract relationships, and applied mathematics, which applies mathematical analysis to real-world problems. The relationship between pure and applied mathematics is a complex one, and is constantly shifting.

Mathematics continues to grow at a phenomenal rate. There is no end in sight, and the application of mathematics to science becomes greater all the time.

Key Events in the Time Line of Mathematics

- Counting was the earliest mathematical activity. Early humans needed counting to keep track of herds and for trade. Early counting systems used the fingers of one or both hands, as evidenced by the predominance of the numbers 5 and 10 as the bases for most number systems today. Advances were in the concept of numbers, the invention of addition, subtraction, multiplication, and division, and concepts such as the line and the circle in geomoetry.

  - **2000 B.C.** The Babylonians of ancient Mesopotamia and the ancient Egyptians developed principles of arithmetic, measurement, and calculation.

    - **1400 B.C.** The first true evidence of mathematical activity in China can be found in numeration symbols on tortoise shells and oracle bones from the Shang dynasty. These inscriptions contain both tally and code symbols based on a decimal system. Early Chinese mathematics had a great influence on later civilizations.

      - **1000 B.C.** The Maya used a base-20 number system, which probably descended from early times when people counted on both fingers and toes and may have been the first to have a special symbol for zero. The Maya also developed two types of calendars, calculating the length of the lunar month and the solar year with remarkable precision.

- **6th Century B.C.** The Greeks adopted elements of mathematics from the Babylonians and the Egyptians and invented abstract mathematics founded on a logical structure of definitions, axioms (propositions accepted as self-evident), and proofs. Thales and Pythagoras were famous mathematicians.

  - **300 B.C.** Euclid, a Greek mathematician, deduced some 500 theorems comprising all the important results of Greek mathematics to that time. Euclid began by defining terms, such as line, angle, and circle. He stated ten self-evident truths, such as "The whole is greater than any of its parts."

    - **1st Century A.D.** After the decline of Greece and Rome, mathematics flourished for hundreds of years in India and the Islamic world. Their mathematical masterpieces and those of the Greeks were translated into Arabic in the centers of Islamic learning, where mathematical discoveries continued during the Middle Ages. Our present numeration system, with each digit having a value and a place value (ones, tens, hundreds, and so forth), is known as the Hindu-Arabic system.

      - **8th Century A.D.** Translators in Baghdad produced Arabic versions of Greek and Indian mathematical works. Many of the ancient Greek works on mathematics were preserved during the Middle Ages through Arabic translations and commentaries. Europe acquired much of this learning during the 12th century, when Greek and Arabic works were translated into Latin, the written language of the educated Europeans.

"Number rules the universe."

—Pythagoras, Greek philosopher and mathematician, 580–520 B.C.

> **"Mathematics is one of humanity's great achievements. By enhancing the capabilities of the human mind, mathematics has facilitated the development of science, technology, engineering, business, and government. Mathematics is also an intellectual achievement of great sophistication and beauty that epitomizes the power of deductive reasoning. For people to participate fully in society, they must know basic mathematics."**
>
> Kilpatrick, J., Swafford, J., and Findell, B. eds. *Adding It Up: Helping Children Learn Mathematics.* Washington, D.C.: National Research Council/National Academy Press, 2001, p. 1.

Real Math and Mathematics

Real Math has been developed with a keen respect for the history and the beauty of mathematics. Careful attention has been paid to developing children's understanding of mathematics in a coherent and logical fashion to demonstrate the connections among the different strands and branches of mathematics. *Real Math* aims for children to develop a positive attitude toward mathematics. Specific abilities and understandings will be of little value to children unless accompanied by two convictions: (a) that mathematics does what it was invented to do —solve real, interesting problems; and (b) that it is a tool that can be used confidently and well. Also, we hope that students will find mathematics enjoyable to do and that they will appreciate it aesthetically.

- **9th Century A.D.** Arab mathematician al-Khwārizmī wrote a systematic introduction to algebra. The English word *algebra* comes from *al-jabr* in the title. A 12th-century Latin translation of al-Khwārizmī's treatise was crucial for the later development of algebra in Europe. Al-Khwārizmī's name is the source of the word *algorithm*.

  - **16th Century** Mathematicians began to use symbols to make algebraic thinking and writing more concise. These symbols included $+$, $-$, $\times$, $=$, $>$ (greater than), and $<$ (less than). The most significant innovation, by French mathematician François Viète, was the systematic use of letters for variables in equations.

    - **17th Century** The founders of modern science—Nicolaus Copernicus, Johannes Kepler, Galileo, and Isaac Newton— studied the natural world as mathematicians, and they looked for its mathematical laws. Over time, mathematics grew more and more abstract as mathematicians sought to establish the foundations of their fields logically. The most important development in geometry during the 17th century was the discovery of analytic geometry by René Descartes and Pierre de Fermat, which makes it possible to study geometric figures using algebraic equations. The discovery of differential and integral calculus by Sir Isaac Newton and Gottfried Wilhelm Leibniz ranks as the crowning achievement of 17th-century mathematics. Calculus allowed the solution of many problems that had been previously insoluble, including the determination of the laws of motion and the theory of electromagnetism.

- **18th Century** During the 18th century, calculus became the cornerstone of mathematical analysis on the European continent. Mathematicians applied the discovery to a variety of problems in physics, astronomy, and engineering. In the course of doing so, they also created new areas of mathematics. The greatest mathematician of the 18th century, Leonhard Euler of Switzerland, was also the most prolific writer on mathematical subjects of all time. His treatises covered essentially the entire fields of pure and applied mathematics.

  - **The 19th Century** was a period of intense mathematical activity. It began with German mathematician Carl Friedrich Gauss, considered to be the last complete mathematician because of his contributions to all branches of the field. The century saw a great effort to place all areas of mathematics on firm theoretical foundations. The support for these foundations was logic—the deduction of basic propositions from a limited set of assumptions and definitions. Mathematicians also discovered the existence of additional geometries and algebras, and more than one kind of infinity.

    - **During the 20th Century** mathematics made rapid advances on all fronts. The foundations of mathematics became more clearly defined, while at the same time mathematics advanced the development of symbolic logic. Philosophy and physics, too, benefited from the contributions of mathematicians to the Relativity Theory and Quantum Theory. Indeed, mathematics achieved broader applications than ever before as new fields developed within mathematics (computational mathematics, game theory, and chaos theory), and other branches of knowledge, including economics and physics, achieved firmer grounding through the application of mathematics. Even the most abstract mathematics seemed to find application, and the boundaries between pure mathematics and applied mathematics grew ever fuzzier.

Content Strands of Mathematics

"One reason why mathematics enjoys special esteem, above all other sciences, is that its laws are absolutely certain and indisputable, while those of other sciences are to some extent debatable and in constant danger of being overthrown by newly discovered facts."

—Albert Einstein, physicist, 1879–1955

Algebra

Algebra is the branch of mathematics that uses symbols to represent arithmetic operations. Algebra extends arithmetic through the use of symbols and other notations, such as exponents and variables. Algebraic thinking involves understanding patterns, equations, and relationships, and includes concepts of functions and inverse operations. Because algebra uses symbols as well as numbers, it can produce general rules that apply to all numbers. What most people commonly think of as algebra involves the manipulation of equations and the solving of equations. Exposure to algebraic ideas can and should occur well before students first study algebra in middle school or high school. Even primary-grade students are capable of understanding many algebraic concepts. Developing algebraic thinking in the early grades smoothes the transition to algebra in middle school and high school and ensures success in future math and science courses, as well as in the workplace.

> "Algebra begins with a search for patterns. Identifying patterns helps bring order, cohesion, and predictability to seemingly unorganized situations and allows one to make generalizations beyond the information directly available. The recognition and analysis of patterns are important components of the young child's intellectual development because they provide a foundation for the development of algebraic thinking."

Clements, Douglas and Sarama, J. eds. *Engaging Young Children in Mathematics: Standards for Early Childhood Mathematics Education.* Mahwah, New Jersey: Lawrence Erlbaum Associates, Publishers, 2004, p. 52.

Real Math and Algebra

Goal: Understanding of functional relationships between variables that represents real-world phenomena in a constant state of change

Children should be able to draw the graphs of functions and to derive information about functions from their graphs. They should understand the special importance of linear functions and the connection between the study of functions and the solution of equations and inequalities.

The algebra readiness strand that begins in the PreK level is designed to prepare students for future work in algebra by exposing them to algebraic thinking, including looking for patterns, using variables, working with functions, using integers and exponents, and being aware that mathematics is far more than just arithmetic.

Arithmetic

Arithmetic, one of the oldest branches of mathematics, arises from the most fundamental of mathematical operations: counting. The arithmetic operations—addition, subtraction, multiplication, and division—form the basis of the mathematics that we use regularly.

> "Although some educators once believed that children memorize their 'basic facts' as conditioned responses, research now shows that children do not move from knowing nothing about sums and differences of numbers to having the basic number combinations memorized. Instead, they move through a series of progressively more advanced and abstract methods for working out the answers to simple arithmetic problems. Furthermore, as children get older, they use the procedures more and more efficiently."

Kilpatrick, J., Swafford, J. and Findell, B. eds. *Adding It Up: Helping Children Learn Mathematics.* Washington, D.C.: National Research Council/National Academy Press, 2001, p. 182–183.

Real Math and Arithmetic

Goal: Mastery of the basic operations with whole numbers (addition, subtraction, multiplication, and division)

Whatever other skills and understandings children acquire, they must have the ability to calculate a precise answer when necessary. This fundamental skill includes not only knowledge of the appropriate arithmetic algorithms, but also mastery of the basic addition, subtraction, multiplication, and division facts and understanding of the positional notation (base ten) of the whole numbers.

Mastery Checkpoints occur throughout the program to indicate when mastery of concepts and skills is expected. Skills are often introduced at least one grade level before mastery is expected and then reviewed in Mental Math and subsequent grade levels. Once taught, arithmetic skills are also integrated into other topics, such as functions and geometry.

Data Collection and Organization

Goal: Ability to organize information to make it easier to use and the ability to interpret data and graphs

"Describing data involves reading displays of data (e.g., tables, lists, graphs); that is, finding information explicitly stated in the display, recognizing graphical conventions, and making direct connections between the original data and the display. The process is essentially what has been called reading the data.... The process of organizing and reducing data incorporates mental actions, such as ordering, grouping, and summarizing. Data reduction also includes the use of representative measures of center (often termed *measures of central tendency*), such as mean, mode, or median, and measures of spread, such as range or standard deviation."

Kilpatrick, J., Swafford, J. and Findell, B. eds. *Adding It Up: Helping Children Learn Mathematics*. Washington, D.C.: National Research Council/National Academy Press, 2001, p. 289.

Real Math and Data Organization

Goal: Ability to organize and arrange data for greater intelligibility

Children should develop not only the routine skills of tabulating and graphing results, but also, at a higher level, the ability to detect patterns and trends in poorly organized data, either before or after reorganization. Children need to develop the ability to extrapolate and interpolate from data and from graphic representations. Children should also know when extrapolation or interpolation is justified and when it is not.

In *Real Math,* students work with graphs beginning in PreK. In each grade, the program emphasizes understanding what data shows.

Geometry

Geometry is the branch of mathematics that deals with the properties of space. Plane geometry is the geometry of flat surfaces, and solid geometry is the geometry of three-dimensional space figures. Geometry has many more fields, including the study of spaces with four or more dimensions.

"Geometry can be used to understand and to represent the objects, directions, and locations in our world, and the relationships between them. Geometric shapes can be described, analyzed, transformed, and composed and decomposed into other shapes."

Clements, Douglas and Sarama, J. eds. *Engaging Young Children in Mathematics: Standards for Early Childhood Mathematics Education*. Mahwah, New Jersey: Lawrence Erlbaum Associates, Publishers, 2004, p. 39.

Real Math and Geometry

Goals: Understanding of and ability to use geometric concepts in a variety of contexts

Appreciating how geometry can help to explain algebraic concepts

Measurement

Goal: Understanding of what a measurement is and how units relate to measurement

"Measurement is one of the main real-world applications of mathematics...counting is a type of measurement—it measures how many items in a collection. Measurement of continuous quantities involves assigning a number to attributes, such as length, area, and weight. Together, number and measurement are components of quantitative reasoning. In this vein, measurement helps connect the two realms of number and geometry, each providing conceptual support to the other."

Clements, Douglas and Sarama, J. eds. *Engaging Young Children in Mathematics: Standards for Early Childhood Mathematics Education.* Mahwah, New Jersey: Lawrence Erlbaum Associates, Publishers, 2004, p. 43–50.

Real Math and Measurement

Goal: Firm understanding of magnitude with respect to measurements and of the role of units in assigning numerical magnitudes to physical quantities

Children should, for example, understand the need for standard units of measurement and know how to use appropriate measurement tools (rulers, balances, liquid volume measures, and thermometers).

In *Real Math,* students work extensively with estimating measures and making actual measurements. They work with both the customary system (inches, pounds, cups) and the metric system (meters, grams, liters) separately so that they develop an intuitive feel for measurements in both systems.

Number Sense and Place Value

Goal: Understanding of the significance and use of numbers in counting, measuring, comparing, and ordering

"It is very important for teachers to provide children with opportunities to recognize the meaning of mathematical symbols, mathematical operations, and the patterns or relationships represented in the child's work with numbers. For example, the number sense that a child acquires should be based upon an understanding that inverse operations, such as addition and subtraction, undo the operations of the other. Instructionally, teachers must encourage their students to think beyond simply finding the answer and to actually have them think about the numerical relationships that are being represented or modeled by the symbols, words, or materials being used in the lesson."

Kilpatrick, J., Swafford, J. and Findell, B. eds. *Adding It Up: Helping Children Learn Mathematics.* Washington, D.C.: National Research Council/National Academy Press, 2001, p. 270–271.

Real Math and Number Sense

Goals: Firm understanding of the significance and use of numbers in counting, measuring, comparing, and ordering

The ability to think intelligently, using numbers

This basic requirement of numeracy includes the ability to recognize given answers as absurd, without doing a precise calculation, by observing that they violate experience, common sense, elementary logic, or familiar arithmetic patterns. It also includes the use of imagination and insight in using numbers to solve problems. Children should be able to recognize when, for example, a trial-and-error method is likely to be easier to use and more manageable than a standard algorithm.

Developing number sense is a primary goal of *Real Math* in every grade. Numbers are presented in a variety of representations and integrated in many contexts so that students develop thorough understanding of numbers.

Probability and Statistics

Probability and statistics deal with events where outcomes are uncertain, and they assess the likelihood of possible outcomes. Statistics is the organization and analysis of data for the purpose of simplification, comparison, and prediction.

Real Math and Probability and Statistics

Goal: The ability to use probabilistic ideas in ordinary, elementary applications

Children should understand the reasons for (and something of the dangers of) using sampling techniques; they should have the ability to describe a population in terms of some simple statistic (mean, median, range); and they should understand the difference between intelligent risk taking, based on reasonable estimates of probabilities, and foolish risks, based on unsupported guesswork or wishful thinking.

Rational Numbers—Fractions, Decimals, and Percents

Goal: Understanding fractions, decimals, and percents and their relationships to each other, including the ability to perform calculations and to use rational numbers in measurement

"Children need to learn that rational numbers are numbers in the same way that whole numbers are numbers. For children to use rational numbers to solve problems, they need to learn that the same rational number may be represented in different ways, as a fraction, a decimal, or a percent. Fraction concepts and representations need to be related to those of division, measurement, and ratio. Decimal and fractional representations need to be connected and understood. Building these connections take extensive experience with rational numbers over a substantial period of time. Researchers have documented that difficulties in working with rational numbers can often be traced to weak conceptual understanding....Instructional sequences in which more time is spent at the outset on developing

meaning for the various representations of rational numbers and the concept of unit have been shown to promote mathematical proficiency."

—Kilpatrick, J., Swafford, J. and Findell, B. eds. *Adding It Up: Helping Children Learn Mathematics.* Washington, D.C.: National Research Council/National Academy Press, 2001, p. 415–416.

Real Math and Rational Numbers

Goal: Understanding of rational numbers and of the relationship of fractions to decimals

Included here are the ability to do appropriate calculations with fractions or decimals (or both, as in fractions of decimals); the use of decimals in (metric unit) measurements; and the multiplication of fractions as a model for the "of" relation and as a model for areas of rectangles.

Goal: Understanding of the meaning of rates and of their relationship to the arithmetic concept of ratio

Children should be able to calculate ratios, proportions, and percentages; understand how to use them intelligently in real-life situations; understand the common units in which rates occur (such as kilometers per hour, cents per gram); understand the meaning of *per*; and be able to express ratios as fractions.

In **Real Math,** understanding of rational numbers begins in the earliest grades with sharing activities and develops understanding of rational numbers with increasing sophistication at each grade.

Mathematics Research Overview

For decades, people have been studying mathematics instruction to figure out what is and what is not effective. In the last few years, two compendiums of reliable research have been published; this research is relevant, sound, and generalizable.

Kilpatrick, J., Swafford, J. and Findell, B. eds. *Adding It Up: Helping Children Learn Mathematics*. Washington, D.C.: National Research Council/National Academy Press, 2001.

Kilpatrick, Jeremy, Martin, W. Gary, and Schifter, Deborah, eds. *A Research Companion to Principles and Standards for School Mathematics*. Reston, VA: National Council of Teachers of Mathematics, Inc., 2003.

The purpose of these books has been to synthesize the research on elementary math education to provide recommendations and advice to educators. Research can help to guide decisions about what mathematics to teach and how to teach it to improve the quality of math education and promote interest and achievement in mathematics.

Research has helped to identify

- what mathematics should be learned in elementary school to develop a solid foundation in understanding.
- effective teaching strategies for different strands of mathematics.
- classification of the learning trajectories that describe how children learn mathematics.

"The science of pure mathematics...may claim to be the most original creation of the human spirit."

Alfred North Whitehead, English mathematician and philosopher, 1861–1947

Real Math and Research

Real Math is based on several types of research. Building on mathematics education research findings over the last fifty years, *Real Math* brings the most effective curriculum and strategies to the classroom.

1. *Field Tests* **Real Math** is constantly being tested and improved. It was originally developed one grade level at a time over a ten-year period and was rigorously field-tested to ensure its effectiveness. Used in classrooms for over thirty years, the program has been revised to address current standards and the latest research in mathematics education, and continues its reliance on scientific field-testing and feedback from teachers.

2. *Research on Teaching Strategies* **Real Math** seriously attends to the latest research in mathematics education. Doug Clements's and Julie Sarama's work in early childhood mathematics forms the prekindergarten level of the program, and Joan Moss's work in fractions, decimals, and percents inspired revision of the rational number strand throughout the program. A review of relevant research precedes each chapter, and research-based strategies throughout the program are identified in the **Research in Action** feature.

3. *Research on Learning Trajectories* Much research has been conducted in identifying children's learning trajectories in mathematics. Developmental levels for early mathematics are outlined in Appendix C, and relevant information for teachers about the learning trajectories precedes each chapter. *Real Math* activities, teaching strategies, and lesson progression support the development of children through the developmental levels of the learning trajectories.

Math Proficiencies

Each problem that I solved became a rule which served afterwards to solve other problems.

René Descartes, French philosopher and mathematician, 1596–1650

1. **Understanding** (Conceptual Understanding): Comprehending mathematical concepts, operations, and relations—knowing what mathematical symbols, diagrams, and procedures mean

   Conceptual Understanding refers to an integrated and functional grasp of mathematical ideas. Students with conceptual understanding know more than isolated facts and methods. They understand why a mathematical idea is important and the kinds of contexts in which it is useful. They have organized their knowledge into a coherent whole, which enables them to learn new ideas by connecting those ideas to what they already know. Conceptual understanding also supports retention. Because facts and methods learned with understanding are connected, they are easier to remember and use, and they can be reconstructed when forgotten. If students understand a method, they are unlikely to remember it incorrectly.

   A significant indicator of conceptual understanding is being able to represent mathematical situations in different ways and knowing how different representations can be useful for different purposes.

   Knowledge that has been learned with understanding provides the basis for generating new knowledge and for solving new and unfamiliar problems. When students have acquired conceptual understanding in an area of mathematics, they see the connections among concepts and procedures and can give arguments to explain why some facts are consequences of others. They gain confidence, which then provides a base from which they can move to another level of understanding.

2. **Computing** (Procedural Fluency): Carrying out mathematical procedures, such as adding, subtracting, multiplying, and dividing numbers flexibly, accurately, efficiently, and appropriately

   Procedural Fluency refers to knowledge of procedures, knowledge of when and how to use them appropriately, and skill in performing them flexibly, accurately, and efficiently. In the domain of numbers, procedural fluency is especially needed to support conceptual understanding of place value and the meanings of rational numbers. It also supports the analysis of similarities and differences between methods of calculating. These methods include, in addition to written procedures, mental methods for finding certain sums, differences, products, or quotients, as well as methods that use calculators, computers, or manipulative materials such as blocks, counters, or beads.

   Students need to be efficient and accurate in performing basic computations with whole numbers without always having to refer to tables or other aids. They also need to know reasonably efficient and accurate ways to add, subtract, multiply, and divide multidigit numbers, both mentally and with pencil and paper. A good conceptual understanding of place value in the base-ten system supports the development of fluency in multidigit computation. Such understanding also supports simplified but accurate mental arithmetic and more flexible ways of dealing with numbers than many students ultimately achieve.

3. **Applying** (Strategic Competence): Being able to formulate problems mathematically and to devise strategies for solving them using concepts and procedures appropriately

   Strategic Competence refers to the ability to formulate mathematical problems, represent them, and solve them. This strand is similar to what has been called *problem solving* and *problem formulation*. Although students are often presented with clearly specified problems to solve in the school setting, outside of school they encounter situations in which part of the difficulty is to figure out exactly what the problem is. Then they need to formulate the problem so that they can use mathematics to solve it. Consequently, they are likely to need experience and practice in problem formulating, as well as in problem solving. They should know a variety of solution strategies, as well as which strategies might be useful for solving a specific problem.

   To represent a problem accurately, students must first understand the situation, including its key features. They then need to generate a mathematical representation of the problem that captures the core mathematical elements and ignores the irrelevant features.

Students develop procedural fluency as they use their strategic competence to choose among effective procedures. They also learn that solving challenging mathematics problems depends on the ability to carry out procedures readily, and that problem-solving experience helps them acquire new concepts and skills.

4. **Reasoning** (Adaptive Reasoning): Using logic to explain and justify a solution to a problem or to extend from something known to something not yet known

Adaptive Reasoning refers to the capacity to think logically about the relationships among concepts and situations. Such reasoning is correct and valid, stems from careful consideration of alternatives, and includes knowledge of how to justify the conclusions. In mathematics, adaptive reasoning is the glue that holds everything together and guides learning. One uses it to navigate through the many facts, procedures, concepts, and solution methods, and to see that they all fit together in some way, that they make sense. In mathematics, deductive reasoning is used to settle disputes and disagreements. Answers are right because they follow some agreed-upon assumptions through a series of logical steps. Students who disagree about a mathematical answer need not rely on checking with the teacher, collecting opinions from their classmates, or gathering data from outside the classroom. In principle, they need only check that their reasoning is valid.

Research suggests that students are able to display reasoning ability when three conditions are met: they have a sufficient knowledge base, the task is understandable and motivating, and the context is familiar and comfortable.

5. **Engaging** (Productive Disposition): Seeing mathematics as sensible, useful, and doable—if you work at it—and being willing to do the work

Productive Disposition refers to the tendency to see sense in mathematics, to perceive it as both useful and worthwhile, to believe that steady effort in

learning mathematics pays off, and to see oneself as an effective learner and doer of mathematics. If students are to develop conceptual understanding, procedural fluency, strategic competence, and adaptive reasoning abilities, they must believe mathematics is understandable, not arbitrary; that with diligent effort, it can be learned and used; and that they are capable of figuring it out. Developing a productive disposition requires frequent opportunities to make sense of mathematics, to recognize the benefits of perseverance, and to experience the rewards of sense making in mathematics.

Students' dispositions toward mathematics are a major factor in determining their educational success. Students who have developed a productive disposition are confident in their knowledge and ability. They see that mathematics is both reasonable and intelligible, and believe that, with appropriate effort and experience, they can learn.

Real Math and Math Proficiency

The goals of *Real Math* are to develop the five interwoven proficiencies. In every lesson, activities are designed to address understanding, computing, reasoning, applying, and engaging in an integrated fashion. Most games, for example, can be thought of as one or more mathematical problems. Students must first identify that a problem or problems exist, then provide a structure of the problem and use reasoning to arrive at a solution. At the same time, students are developing fluency in arithmetic. There is little question that students demonstrate engagement with mathematics as well when they are playing a *Real Math* game. Similarly, many activities in *Real Math* are engaging because the situations are those that are real to students. The students are well motivated to learn the mathematics involved in each situation.

Real Math Computational Expectations

At every grade level, **Real Math** develops each strand of mathematics with understanding, teaching children to appreciate and think mathematically. Problem solving, communicating mathematically, algebra, measurement, geometry, probability, and statistics, for example, are explored in every grade. Below are the computational expectations that are developed with understanding at each grade level that build fluency with number.

PreK

There are two key ideas emphasized in number.

1. Numbers can be used to tell us how many, describe order, and measure; they involve numerous relations and can be represented in various ways.

2. Operations with numbers can be used to model a variety of real-world situations and to solve problems; they can be carried out in various ways.

Grade K

- Numbers (cardinal and ordinal) through 100
- Counting; writing numerals
- Measurement with nonstandard units
- One-to-one matching
- Adding and subtracting whole numbers in the 0–100 range

Grade 1

- Numbers 0 through 100
- Addition and subtraction concepts
- Basic addition facts (through 10 + 10)
- Measurement with nonstandard units
- Introductory work with multiplication, fractions, recording data, maps, and inequalities

Grade 2

- Numbers through 10,000
- Basic addition and subtraction facts
- Multidigit addition and subtraction algorithms
- Introduction to multiplication and division
- Measurement with standard units
- Fractions of area and fractions of numbers
- Reading maps

Grade 3

- Numbers through 1,000,000 and beyond
- Fractions and decimals
- Multiplication and division
- Multiplication facts through 10 × 10
- Multidigit multiplication algorithms
- Measurement
- Graphing and functions
- Adding and subtracting decimals

Grade 4

- General multidigit multiplication algorithm
- Division by a one-digit divisor
- Addition and subtraction of common fractions
- Rounding and approximation
- Linear functions and composite and inverse functions
- Graphing such functions
- Multiplying decimals and whole numbers
- Introduction to mixed numbers

Grade 5

- Multidigit division algorithm
- Rounding
- Linear functions and composite and inverse functions
- Graphing such functions
- Introduction of negative numbers
- Rates, ratios, and percentages
- Relation of fractions and decimals
- Addition, subtraction, and multiplication of fractions, mixed numbers, and decimals
- Division with decimal dividends and quotients

Grade 6

- All operations with whole numbers, fractions, and decimals
- Some operations with negative numbers
- Computational shortcuts
- Compass and ruler constructions
- Nonlinear functions
- Graphing such functions
- Exponents

Basic Facts

The "basic" computation facts involve addition expressions in which the addends are whole numbers from 0 through 10, and the corresponding subtraction expressions; multiplication expressions in which the factors are whole numbers from 0 through 10, and the corresponding division expressions. Fluency with basic facts is the ability to use facts quickly, accurately, and appropriately. Fluency is necessary before students can use multidigit algorithms efficiently. *Real Math* uses a variety of methods to ensure that students become fluent with basic facts by developing an understanding of how facts are related rather than by encouraging rote memorization.

If students have difficulty with some basic facts, you can help them by providing (or helping them discover) specific strategies for the facts they have not mastered. If students use their thinking skills and understand our base-ten number system and relationships between numbers, they can use strategies, such as the following, to help with quick and accurate recall.

Note that *Real Math* teaches the addition and multiplication facts systematically to emphasize the relationships between the facts, but the subtraction and division facts are taught as inverses of addition and multiplication. When simple organizing relationships are available, those are also taught.

Addition Fact Helpers

These strategies can help with many of the addition facts.

To add:	Think of:
0	No change
1	Counting up 1
2	Counting up 2
4	One less than adding 5
5	Finger sets
6	One more than adding 5
9	One less than adding 10
10	Write 1 in the tens place

Other strategies which may be helpful include the following:

- **Commutative Law** (for example, 6 + 9 and 9 + 6) Students should recognize that if they can add two numbers in one order, they also know the sum in the opposite order. You can demonstrate this using concrete objects that are arranged in two different ways or a picture of two sets that is turned 180°. This realization cuts roughly in half the number of facts students need to learn.

- **Doubles** (for example, 4 + 4 and 7 + 7) Most students find the doubles facts easy to learn, since only one distinct addend is involved in each fact. The **Roll a Double Game** provides targeted practice with doubles facts.

- **Near doubles** (for example, 4 + 5, 8 + 7, and 7 + 9) When the two addends in a fact differ by 1 or 2, students can relate the fact to a doubles fact. For example, 8 + 7 must be 1 more than 7 + 7, so it is 14 + 1, or 15. One way to find 7 + 9 is to recognize that since 7 is 1 less than 8 and 9 is 1 more than 8, we know 7 + 9 = 8 + 8, or 16.

- **Sums of 10** (for example, 3 + 7 and 2 + 8) Students can become familiar with pairs of numbers that add to 10 by thinking of their fingers—raising 3 fingers then 7 fingers results in all 10 fingers being raised. The **Roll a Ten Game** provides targeted practice with the skill of recognizing sums of 10, which is useful for mental computation.

- **Remaining facts** The strategies above will help with all facts except 8 + 3, 7 + 4, and 8 + 4. If students have trouble with these, you can demonstrate that 8 + 3 and 7 + 4 are both 1 more than 7 + 3, and that 8 + 4 = 8 + 2 + 2 = 10 + 2.

Subtraction Fact Helpers

Strategies that may help with subtraction facts include the following:

- **Subtracting 0** Subtracting 0 leaves a number unchanged.

- **Subtracting 5** Think of taking away one hand worth of fingers (a finger set of 5).

- **Subtracting 9** To subtract 9, you can first subtract 10, then add 1. For example, 16 − 9 = 6 + 1, or 7.

- **Subtracting 10** To subtract 10 from a number between 10 and 20, simply remove the tens digit. For example, 13 − 10 = 3.

- **Differences of 10** (for example, 17 − 7) When two numbers from 0 through 19 have the same ones digit, their difference is always 10.

To find other subtraction facts, think of the corresponding addition fact.

Multiplication Fact Helpers

To multiply by:	Think:
0	The product is 0.
1	The product is the other number.
2	Add the number to itself.
3	Add the number to its double.
4	Double the double.
5	Multiply the number by 10 and take half.
6	Add the number to 5 times the number, or double 3 times the number.
8	Double 4 times the number.
9	Subtract the number from 10 times the number.
10	Write a 0 after the number to indicate that number of tens.

Other strategies which may be helpful include the following:

- **Commutative Law** (for example, 6×9 and 9×6) Students should recognize that if they can multiply two numbers in one order, they also know the product of the numbers in the opposite order. You can demonstrate this using an array that is turned sideways so that rows become columns and columns become rows. This realization cuts roughly in half the number of facts students need to learn.

- **Square facts** (for example, 3×3 and 7×7) Most students find the square facts relatively easy to learn, since only one distinct factor is involved in each fact.

- **Near squares** (for example, 8×7 and 6×8) When the two factors in a fact differ by 1 or 2, students can relate the product to a square fact. When the difference is 1, the product can be found by adding the smaller factor to its square. For example, 8×7 is 7 more than 7×7 — that is, $49 + 7 = 56$. When the difference is 2, students can use the pattern $(n - 1)(n + 1) = n^2 - 1$. They can discover this pattern in the multiplication table even though they cannot prove it algebraically. For example, $6 \times 8 = (7 - 1)(7 + 1) = 49 - 1 = 48$.

- **Multiples of 9** Once students are familiar with most of the multiplication facts, you may want to point out that the sum of the digits in multiples of 9 is always a multiple of 9. They can use this to check their work or to recall a product if they can find the first digit. For example, 7×9 is a little less than 7×10, or 70, so the first digit is 6. Since $6 + 3 = 9$, the product is 63. It is best not to introduce this pattern when students are first learning multiplication facts because they may inappropriately apply it to other factors. It is not true, for instance, that the sum of the digits of a multiple of 8 is a multiple of 8 (although the "rule" does also work for 3).

Another quick way to multiply a whole number (0 through 10) by 9 is to spread out fingers and turn down the finger corresponding to the other factor (for example, the third finger to find 3 times 9). The product is "read" by counting the fingers to the left of the folded finger as tens, and the fingers to the right as ones. Two fingers and seven fingers represents 27. The fact that the sum of the digits of multiples of 9 through 90 is always 9, and the fact that these multiples can be found by subtracting the other number from 10 times, it can be used to show why the finger trick works.

- **Division** Since the division facts do not fall neatly into patterns, the most efficient way to find division facts is to think of the corresponding multiplication fact. For example, $56 \div 7 = 8$ because $8 \times 7 = 56$.

Ways to Practice Facts

Even after students have learned all the basic facts with understanding, they need practice to retain their fluency. There are several useful ways for students to practice facts at school or at home.

- **Games** Playing appropriate games is an excellent way to provide practice with many facts in a brief period of time, while engaging even those students who are already fluent with basic facts.

  Good games for addition practice include **Roll a 15, Addition Table,** and **Addition Crossing.**

  Good games for multiplication practice include **Multiplication Table, Multiple Crossing,** and **Multigo.**

- **Flash Cards** When used appropriately, flash cards are a good way to provide either targeted practice with certain facts or general practice with all facts. Incorrect answers should simply receive no reaction—negative reinforcement is counterproductive since it often leads to frustration.

- **Frequent "quizzing"** If a student or class is struggling with just a few facts, ask about those facts frequently throughout the day. Encourage parents to do the same before and after school.

- **Other Applications through Word Problems, Projects, and Activities** Applications offer opportunities for meaningful fact practice.

- **Mental Math** Frequent mental math exercises encourage cumulative review and abstract thinking practice.

- **Speed Tests** Administer speed tests to encourage automatic recall periodically after most students have learned the basic facts to ensure that students are maintaining and improving their skills. Students should work to improve their own performance, rather than comparing their results to those of others.

Algorithms

> "Step-by-step procedures for adding, subtracting, multiplying, or dividing numbers are called algorithms.... Learning to use algorithms for computation with multidigit numbers is an important part of developing proficiency with numbers. Algorithms are procedures that can be executed in the same way to solve a variety of problems arising from different situations and involving different numbers."
>
> Kilpatrick, J., Swafford, J. and Findell, B. eds. *Adding It Up: Helping Children Learn Mathematics.* Washington, D.C.: National Research Council/National Academy Press, 2001, p. 196.

An algorithm is a set of steps for carrying out a procedure. There are many commonly used algorithms for addition, subtraction, multiplication, and division of multidigit numbers. The beauty and power of our base numeration system is that having learned a procedure for two-digit numbers, we can use the same steps in any place without reference to place value. **Real Math** guides students to discover one standard algorithm for each operation. However, if students have previously learned a different algorithm, or have figured out efficient procedures for some computations on their own, they should not be restricted to the procedures taught in class. In fact, **Real Math** encourages students to avoid using standard algorithms whenever they can find a more efficient procedure.

When developing algorithms, **Real Math** places students in an environment in which they are almost forced to discover an efficient standard algorithm. But when finished, ideally students should believe they would have discovered it with help from the teacher or textbook and would be able to rediscover it if necessary.

Addition

A standard algorithm for addition is introduced using two sets of sticks bundled in groups of ten.

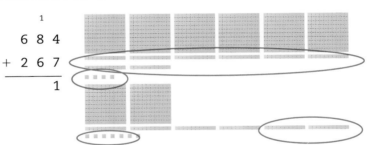

There are 7 tens and 15 ones. Regroup 10 ones as 1 ten.

Now there are 8 tens and 5 ones, so 37 + 48 = 85.

To avoid regrouping at the end, we can start adding with the ones place. We can record each step.

Beginning on the rightmost (ones) column, find the sum of the digits in the column. Write the ones digit of the sum below the addition line, and carry the tens digit to the top of the tens column. Then repeat this process for the tens, hundreds, and so on.

```
  6 8 4
+ 2 6 7
───────
```

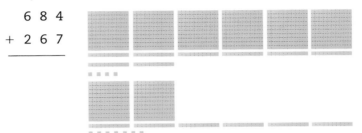

Add the ones: 4 + 7 = 11. Think, 11 ones = 1 ten and 1 one. Write the 1 one below the addition line. Write the 1 ten on top of the tens column.

```
    1
  6 8 4
+ 2 6 7
───────
      1
```

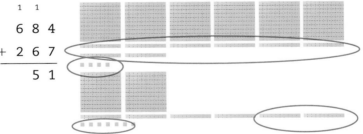

Add the tens: 1 + 8 + 6 = 15. Think, 15 tens = 1 hundred and 5 tens. Write the 5 tens below the addition line. Write the 1 hundred on top of the hundreds column.

```
  1 1
  6 8 4
+ 2 6 7
───────
    5 1
```

Add the hundreds: 1 + 6 + 2 = 9. Write the 9 hundreds below the hundreds column.

```
  1 1
  6 8 4
+ 2 6 7
───────
  9 5 1
```

Note: You may wish to discourage students from writing the "carried" digit if they can get along without it. Extra digits can lead to confusion, especially when students later learn the multiplication algorithm.

Subtraction

As with the addition algorithm, a standard algorithm for subtraction is introduced using a set of sticks bundled in groups of ten.

$$\begin{array}{r} 8\ 5 \\ -\ 3\ 7 \\ \hline \end{array}$$

There are not enough ones to take away 7.

Regroup 1 ten as 10 ones.

$$\begin{array}{r} 8\ 5 \\ -\ 3\ 7 \\ \hline \end{array}$$

There are 4 tens and 8 ones.

$85 - 37 = 48$

It is easiest if we start subtracting with the ones place. We can record each step.

Beginning at the rightmost (ones) column, find the difference of that column. If the difference cannot be found, then rename the number in the next column to the left. Rewrite the tens and ones to reflect renaming. Then repeat this process for the tens, hundreds, and so on.

$$\begin{array}{r} 1\ 1\ 6\ 5 \\ -\ \ \ 4\ 2\ 8 \\ \hline \end{array}$$

Since 8 ones cannot be taken from 5 ones, rename 6 tens as 5 tens and 10 ones.

$$\begin{array}{r} {\scriptstyle 5\ \ 15} \\ 1\ 1\ 6\!\!\!/\ 5\!\!\!/ \\ -\ \ \ 4\ 2\ 8 \\ \hline \end{array}$$

Subtract the ones.

$$\begin{array}{r} {\scriptstyle 5\ \ 15} \\ 1\ 1\ 6\!\!\!/\ 5\!\!\!/ \\ -\ \ \ 4\ 2\ 8 \\ \hline 7 \end{array}$$

Subtract the tens.

$$\begin{array}{r} {\scriptstyle 5\ \ 15} \\ 1\ 1\ 6\!\!\!/\ 5\!\!\!/ \\ -\ \ \ 4\ 2\ 8 \\ \hline 3\ 7 \end{array}$$

Since 4 hundreds cannot be taken from 1 hundred, rename 1 thousand as 10 hundreds.

$$\begin{array}{r} {\scriptstyle 5\ \ 15} \\ 1\ 1\ 6\!\!\!/\ 5\!\!\!/ \\ -\ \ \ 4\ 2\ 8 \\ \hline 3\ 7 \end{array}$$

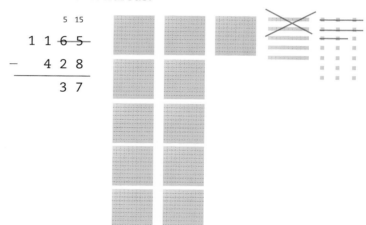

Subtract the hundreds.

$$\begin{array}{r} {\scriptstyle 5\ \ 15} \\ 1\ 1\ 6\!\!\!/\ 5\!\!\!/ \\ -\ \ \ 4\ 2\ 8 \\ \hline 7\ 3\ 7 \end{array}$$

Multiplication

Efficient multiplication of multidigit numbers uses the Distributive Law. To multiply by a multidigit number, you can rewrite the product as a series of partial products. For example, $43 \times 8 = (40 + 3) \times 8 = (40 \times 8) + (3 \times 8) = 320 + 24 = 344$.

Products of two multidigit numbers can be found by writing each factor in expanded form and finding the products of each pair of terms. For example, $46 \times 73 = (40 + 6) \times (70 + 3) = (40 \times 70) + (40 \times 3) + (6 \times 70) + (6 \times 3)$.

Real Math introduces these ideas using area models in which each partial product is shown as a separate area. The product of the numbers (the sum of the areas of each rectangle) is the sum of the partial products.

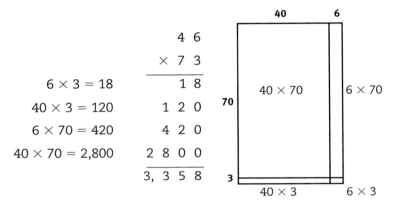

$$
\begin{array}{r}
4\ 3 \\
\times\ \ \ \ 8 \\
\hline
2\ 4 \\
3\ 2\ 0 \\
\hline
3\ 4\ 4
\end{array}
$$

$6 \times 3 = 18$

$40 \times 3 = 120$

$6 \times 70 = 420$

$40 \times 70 = 2,800$

$$
\begin{array}{r}
4\ 6 \\
\times\ 7\ 3 \\
\hline
1\ 8 \\
1\ 2\ 0 \\
4\ 2\ 0 \\
2\ 8\ 0\ 0 \\
\hline
3,\ 3\ 5\ 8
\end{array}
$$

A similar area model can be (and is) used to demonstrate the distributive law.

Standard algorithm

Once students understand the idea of partial products, they are introduced to a more efficient way of recording their work.

Beginning at the rightmost column, find the product. Write the ones digit of the product below the line, and carry the tens digit to the top of the tens column. Then repeat this process for each digit of the second factor.

$$
\begin{array}{r}
4\ 6 \\
\times\ 7\ 3 \\
\hline
\end{array}
$$

Multiply 3 times the ones: $6 \times 3 = 18$.

18 ones = 1 ten and 8 ones

$$
\begin{array}{r}
1 \\
4\ 6 \\
\times\ 7\ 3 \\
\hline
8
\end{array}
$$

Multiply 3 times the tens and add the carried ten:

$(4 \times 3) + 1 = 13$. Record 13 tens.

$$
\begin{array}{r}
1 \\
4\ 6 \\
\times\ 7\ 3 \\
\hline
1\ 3\ 8
\end{array}
$$

Multiply 7 tens times the ones: $7 \times 6 = 42$.

42 tens = 4 hundreds and 2 tens

$$
\begin{array}{r}
4 \\
4\ 6 \\
\times\ 7\ 3 \\
\hline
1\ 3\ 8 \\
2
\end{array}
$$

Multiply 7 tens times 4 tens and add the 4 carried tens:

$(7 \times 4) + 4 = 32$

$$
\begin{array}{r}
4 \\
4\ 6 \\
\times\ 7\ 3 \\
\hline
1\ 3\ 8 \\
3\ 2\ 2
\end{array}
$$

Add the partial products.

$$
\begin{array}{r}
4 \\
4\ 6 \\
\times\ 7\ 3 \\
\hline
1\ 3\ 8 \\
3\ 2\ 2 \\
\hline
3,\ 3\ 5\ 8
\end{array}
$$

To avoid confusion, students should write the "carried" digits only if necessary. If they do write these digits, they should cross out the digits for the first multiplier before writing the digits for the second multiplier.

Division

Division with a multidigit dividend is introduced using an example in which an amount of money (expressed in $100, $10, and $1 bills) is shared as equally as possible by a number of students. As students share the money, they exchange $100 bills for $10 bills and $10 bills for $1 bills as needed.

Share $836 (8 $100 bills, 3 $10 bills, and 6 $1 bills) among 7 students.

Each student gets 1 $100 bill, so write 100 above the dividend. Now $700 has been distributed, so subtract 700 from the total.

$$\begin{array}{r} 100 \\ 7\overline{)836} \\ -700 \\ \hline 136 \end{array}$$

Now there is 1 $100 bill, 3 $10 bills, and 6 $1 bills. Exchange the 1 $100 bill for 10 $10 bills, to leave 13 $1 bills.

Each student gets 1 $10 bill, so write 10 above the dividend and subtract 70.

$$\begin{array}{r} 10 \\ 100 \\ 7\overline{)836} \\ -700 \\ \hline 136 \\ -70 \\ \hline 66 \end{array}$$

Now there are 6 $10 bills and 6 $1 bills left. Exchange the 6 $10 bills for 60 $1 bills, to leave 66 $1 bills.

Each student gets 9 $1 bills, so write 9 above the dividend and subtract 63 (7 × 9).

$$\begin{array}{r} 9 \\ 10 \\ 100 \\ 7\overline{)836} \\ -700 \\ \hline 136 \\ -70 \\ \hline 66 \\ -63 \\ \hline 3 \end{array}$$

The mathematical sciences particularly exhibit order, symmetry, and limitation; and these are the greatest forms of the beautiful.

Aristotle, Greek philosopher, 384–322 B.C.

Since 100 + 10 + 9 = 119, each student gets $119. There will be $3 left over.

This naturally leads to a standard algorithm which involves asking how many times the divisor divides into the thousands, hundreds, tens, and ones of the dividend.

Standard algorithm

Once students understand the steps in division, they are introduced to progressively more efficient ways of writing them. Three different versions of the algorithm are taught. Each uses the same steps, but they differ in the amount of writing they require.

Long Form	Shorter Form	Shorter Form
1,276 Remainder 4	With Zeros	Without Zeros
	Be careful to put the answers in the correct column.	Subtract and "bring down" only the next digit. Be careful to put the answers in the correct columns.

Long Form:

$$\begin{array}{r} 6 \\ 70 \\ 200 \\ 1000 \\ 7\overline{)8936} \\ -7000 \\ \hline 1936 \\ -1400 \\ \hline 536 \\ -490 \\ \hline 46 \\ -42 \\ \hline 4 \end{array}$$

Shorter Form With Zeros:

$$\begin{array}{r} 1276 \ \text{R4} \\ 7\overline{)8936} \\ -7000 \\ \hline 1936 \\ -1400 \\ \hline 536 \\ -490 \\ \hline 46 \\ -42 \\ \hline 4 \end{array}$$

Shorter Form Without Zeros:

$$\begin{array}{r} 1276 \ \text{R4} \\ 7\overline{)8936} \\ -7 \\ \hline 19 \\ -14 \\ \hline 53 \\ -49 \\ \hline 46 \\ -42 \\ \hline 4 \end{array}$$

Shortest Form

Write "remainders" in front of the next digit.

$$\begin{array}{r} 1 \ 2 \ 7 \ 6 \ \text{R4} \\ 7\overline{)8^19^53^46} \end{array}$$

Technology

Technology has changed the world of mathematics. Technological tools have reduced the need for tedious calculations and have enabled significant advances in applications of mathematics. Technology can also help to make teaching more effective and efficient. Well-designed math software activities have proven effective in advancing children's math achievements. Technology can also help teachers organize planning and instruction and manage record keeping.

Real Math Technology for Teachers

ePlanner provides a tool to help teachers plan and organize daily lessons and plot out year-long goals.

- Daily lesson plan with lesson and homework detail
- Weekly lesson plan
- Monthly plan
- Yearly plan with lesson detail
- Lesson summaries and electronic lessons from the *ePresentation* that can be accessed at home
- Program resources (blacklines, technology, manipulatives lists)
- Correlation to state guidelines
- Assign Homework

ePresentation is an electronic presentation of all of the *Real Math* lessons, *eGames,* and *eMathTools.* Teachers can use this daily or periodically to vary instructional presentations.

eAssess enables teachers to record, track, and report on all aspects of students' math performances and progress toward achieving state and national standards.

Professional Development

A series of five courses that teach different aspects of instruction for math proficiency

- Teaching for Understanding
- Teaching Computational Fluency
- Teaching Mathematical Reasoning and Problem Solving
- Teaching Applications of Mathematics
- Teaching Mathematics

Each course covers a definition of the proficiency, what teachers need to know about it, how children learn, effective strategies, differentiating instruction, and assessment.

Real Math Technology for Students

Calculators: Basic arithmetic skills are essential in mathematics. It is important for students to learn how to use calculators wisely and when appropriate. It is also important that students understand arithmetic procedures and are able to do computations by hand when calculators are impractical or unavailable. To this end, *Real Math* teaches students how to use a calculator effectively. Children should be able to recognize when a calculator is useful and when other methods, such as mental approximation or precise calculation, are more appropriate. Students should also be expected to approximate answers and use numbers intelligently so that they can detect absurd answers that might result, for example, from pushing the wrong keys or using an inappropriate calculation.

> "A large number of empirical studies of calculator use, including long-term studies, have generally shown that the use of calculators does not threaten the development of basic skills and that it can enhance conceptual understanding, strategic competence, and disposition toward mathematics....The question...is not whether, but how, calculators should be used."
>
> Kilpatrick, J., Swafford, J. and Findell, B. eds. *Adding It Up: Helping Children Learn Mathematics.* Washington, D.C.: National Research Council/National Academy Press, 2001, p. 354–355.

In *Real Math,* students first learn arithmetic skills and only then use calculators to help them solve more complex problems using those skills. Specific instruction addresses when it is and is not appropriate to use a calculator.

Computer Math Technology for Students

Real Math develops familiarity with the nature and purpose of computers. We believe that children should have the opportunity to use computers. Whether or not children have the advantage of access to a computer, it is essential that they understand the principles on which computers function and the role they are capable of playing in our daily domestic, social, and professional lives. Children should appreciate that computers enable us to obtain numerical answers to large-scale mathematical problems easily and quickly.

eGames, can be accessed apart from or are available within the eTextbook and ePresentation, provide electronic versions of several of the cube games and game mats. eGames are referenced in relevant lessons in the Teacher's Edition.

Building Blocks software provides computer math activities that address specific developmental levels of the math learning trajectories. Building Blocks software is critical to the prekindergarten level of Real Math and provides support activities for specific concepts in Grades K–6.

Some Building Blocks activities have different levels of difficulty, indicated by ranges in the Activity Names below. The list provides an overview of all of the Building Blocks activities, along with the domains, descriptions, and appropriate age ranges.

Domain: Trajectory	Activity Name	Description	Age Range
Geometry: Composition/Decomposition	Create a Scene	Students explore shapes by moving and manipulating them to make pictures.	4–12
Geometry: Composition/Decomposition	Piece Puzzler 1–5, Piece Puzzler Free Explore, and Super Shape 1–7	Students complete puzzles using pattern or tangram shapes.	4–12
Geometry: Imagery	Geometry Snapshots 1–8	Students match configurations of a variety of shapes (e.g., line segments in different arrangements, 3–6 tiled shapes, embedded shapes) to corresponding configurations, given only a brief view of the goal shapes.	5–12
Geometry: Shapes (Identifying)	Memory Geometry 1–5	Students match familiar geometric shapes (shapes in same or similar sizes, same orientation) within the framework of a Concentration card game.	3–5
Geometry: Shapes (Matching)	Mystery Pictures 1–4 and Mystery Pictures Free Explore	Students construct predefined pictures by selecting shapes that match a series of target shapes.	3–8
Geometry: Shapes (Parts)	Shape Parts 1–7	Students build or fix some real-world object, exploring shape and properties of shapes.	5–12
Geometry: Shapes (Properties)	Legends of the Lost Shape	Students identify target shapes using textual clues provided.	8–12
Geometry: Shapes (Properties)	Shape Shop 1–3	Students identify a wide range of shapes given their names, with more difficult distractors.	8–12
Measurement: Length	Comparisons	Students are shown pictures of two objects and are asked to click on the one that fits the prompt (longer, shorter, heavier, and so on).	4–8
Measurement: Length	Deep Sea Compare	Students compare the length of two objects by representing them with a third object.	5–7
Measurement: Length	Reptile Ruler	Students learn about linear measurement by using a ruler to determine the length of various reptiles.	7–10
Measurement: Length	Workin' on the Railroad	Students identify the length (in nonstandard units) of railroad trestles they built to span a gully.	6–9
Multiplication/Division	Arrays in Area	Students build arrays and then determine the area of those arrays.	8–11
Multiplication/Division	Comic Book Shop	Students use skip counting to produce products that are multiples of 10s, 5s, 2s, and 3s. The task is to identify the product, given a number and bundles.	7–9
Multiplication/Division	Egg-stremely Equal	Students divide large sets of eggs into several equal parts.	4–8
Multiplication/Division	Field Trip	Students solve multidigit multiplication problems in a field-trip environment (e.g., equal number of students on each bus; number of tickets needed for all students).	8–11
Multiplication/Division	Snack Time	Students use direct modeling to solve multiplication problems.	6–8
Multiplication/Division	Word Problems with Tools 5–6, 10	Students use number tools to solve single and multidigit multiplication and division problems.	8–11
Multiplication/Division	Clean the Plates	Students use skip counting to produce products that are multiples of 10s, 5s, 2s, and 3s.	7–9
Numbers: Adding and Subtracting	Barkley's Bones 1–10 and 1–20	Students determine the missing addend in $X + \_\_ = Z$ problems to feed bone treats to a dog ($Z = 10$ or less).	5–8

Professional Development

Domain: Trajectory	Activity Name	Description	Age Range
Number: Adding and Subtracting	Double Compare 1–10 and 1–20	Students compare sums of cards (to 10 or 20) to determine which sum is greater.	5–8
Number: Adding and Subtracting	Word Problems with Tools 1–4, 7–9, 11–12	Students use number tools to solve single and multidigit addition and subtraction problems.	8–12
Number: Adding and Subtracting and Counting	Counting Activities (Road Race Counting Game, Numeral Train Game, et. al.)	Students identify numerals or dot amounts (totals to 20) and move forward a corresponding number of spaces on a game board.	3–9
Number: Adding and Subtracting and Multiplying and Dividing	Function Machine 1–4	Students provide inputs to a function and examine the resulting outputs to determine the definition of that function. Functions include either addition, subtraction, multiplication, or division.	6–12
Number: Comparing	Ordinal Construction Company	Students learn ordinal positions (1st through 10th) by moving objects between floors of a building.	5–7
Number: Comparing	Rocket Blast 1–3	Given a number line with only initial and final endpoints labeled and a location on that line, students determine the number label for that location.	6–12
Number: Comparing and Counting	Party Time 1–3 and Party Time Free Explore	Students use party utensils to practice one-to-one correspondence, identify numerals that represent target amounts, and match object amounts to target numerals.	4–6
Number: Comparing and Multiplication and Division	Number Compare 1–5	Students compare two cards and choose the one with the greater value.	4–11
Number: Comparing, Counting, Adding, and Subtracting	Pizza Pizzazz 1–5 and Pizza Pizzazz Free Explore	Students count items, match target amounts, and explore missing addends related to toppings on pizzas.	3–8
Number: Counting (Object)	Countdown Crazy	Students click digits in sequence to count down from 10 to 0.	5–7
Number: Counting (Object)	Memory Number 1–3	Students match displays containing both numerals and collections to matching displays within the framework of a Concentration card game.	4–6
Number: Counting (Object) and Adding and Subtracting	Dinosaur Shop 1–4 and Dinosaur Shop Free Explore	Students use toy dinosaurs to identify numerals representing target amounts, match object amounts to target numerals, add groups of objects, and find missing addends.	4–7
Number: Counting (Objects)	Book Stacks	Students fill an order by counting up from a two-digit number through the next decade. Students count on (through at least one decade) from a given number as they load books onto a cart.	6–8
Number: Counting (Objects)	School Supply Shop	Students count school supplies bundled in groups of ten to reach a target number up to 100.	
Number: Counting (Objects)	Tire Recycling	Students use skip counting by 2s and 5s to count tires as the tires are moved.	6–8
Number: Counting (Strategies)	Build Stairs 1–3, and Build Stairs Free Explore	Students practice counting, sequencing, and ordering by building staircases.	4–7
Number: Counting (Strategies)	Math-O-Scope	Students identify the numbers that surround a given number in the context of a 100s Table.	7–9
Number: Counting (Strategies)	Tidal Tally	Students identify missing addends (hidden objects) by counting on from given addends (visible objects) to reach a numerical total.	6–9
Number: Counting (Verbal)	Count and Race	Students count up to 50 by adding cars to a racetrack one at a time.	3–6
Number: Counting (Verbal)	Before and After Math	Students identify and select numbers that come either just before or right after a target number.	4–7
Number: Counting (Verbal)	Kitchen Counter	Students click on objects one at a time while the numbers from 1 to 10 are counted aloud.	3–6
Number: Subitizing	Number Snapshots 1–10	Students match numerals or dot collections to corresponding numerals or collections given only a brief view of the goal collections.	3–12
Patterning	Marching Patterns 1–3	Students extend a linear pattern of marchers by one full repetition of an entire unit (AB, AAB, ABB, and ABC patterns).	5–7
Patterning	Pattern Planes 1–3	Students duplicate a linear pattern of flags based on an outline that serves as a guide (AB, AAB, ABB, and ABC patterns).	4–6
Patterning	Pattern Zoo 1–3 and Free Explore	Students identify a linear pattern of fruit that matches a target pattern to feed zoo animals (AB, AAB, ABB, and ABC patterns). Students explore patterning by creating rhythmic patterns of their own.	3–6

 **MathTools**

Data Organization and Display Tools

- **Spreadsheet**—allows students to manage, display, sort, and calculate data; links to the graphing tool for further data display

- **Graphing Tool**—displays data in circle graphs, line graphs, or bar graphs

- **Venn Diagram**—allows students to sort data visually

- **Coordinate Grid Tool**—plots points and function rules

Calculation and Counting Tools

- **Calculator**—allows students to launch a calculator to perform mathematical operations

- **Function Machine**—an electronic version of a function machine that students use to solve missing variable problems

- **Multiplication and Division Table**—an interactive version of a table that highlights relationships between multiplication and division facts

- **Addition and Subtraction Table**—an interactive version of a table that highlights relationships between addition and subtraction facts

- **100 Table**—an interactive version of a table that highlights patterns and relationships among numbers

- **Number Line**—an electronic number line that allows students to skip count and see the relationships among whole numbers, fractions, decimals, and percents

- **Number Stairs**—a tool to illustrate counting in units

- **Probability Tool**—uses **Number Cubes,** spinners, or tumble drums to test scenarios of probability

- **Sets Former**—allows students to visually represent and manipulate different sets of objects for a variety of counting and computation activities

- **Base Ten**—allows students to manipulate base-ten blocks for counting and computation

- **Coins and Money**—uses visual representations of coins and money to represent counting

- **Fractions**—represents fractional units for counting and understanding relationships

- **Array Tool**—presents arrays to represent multiplication and division patterns and relationships

Measurement and Conversion Tools

- **Stopwatch**—measures real time for development of counting and time concepts

- **Calendar**—an electronic calendar to develop concepts of time

- **Metric/Customary Conversion**—converts metric and customary measurements in length, distance, mass and weight, time, temperature, and capacity

- **Estimating Proportion Tool**—allows visual representations of proportions in order to develop understanding of ratios, fractions, and decimals

Geometric Exploration Tools

- **Tessellations**—allows students to create tessellation patterns by rotating, coloring, and tiling shapes

- **Net Tool**—allows students to manipulate 2-D shapes and then print them to create 3-D shapes

- **Shape Tool**—explores and manipulates shapes to create designs

- **Geometry Sketch Tool**—allows drawing, manipulating, and measuring a wide variety of shapes

- **Pythagorean Theorem Tool**—launches right triangles to explore the Pythagorean Theorem

- **Shape Creator**—allows students to input specifications and see which shapes result

Using Games

The Role of Games

Games provide enjoyable practice. They give students a way of becoming proficient in the mathematical skills to which they have been introduced. Many **Real Math** games do more. They offer students a chance to recognize situations, real to the student, that can be understood through mathematical thinking, which leads to the identification and solution of strategy problems. This usually leads to in-depth mathematical communication between students regarding the problem and solution.

A benefit of this development through games is that there is no need to teach students the best solution. The process of trying to find a better strategy is the useful activity.

Games also afford teachers the opportunity to monitor progress. By observing game-playing sessions, teachers can assess students' computational fluency, understanding, reasoning, and engagement.

Games allow students of all levels of ability to compete fairly. Winning games requires a mix of chance, skills, and thinking strategies.

Games and Skills

Each of the games in **Real Math** involves the use of specific math skills. When a lesson plan prescribes a game, it does so because the principal skills involved in that game need attention at that time. Most games provide practice in many skills. For example, nearly all the games help students develop and apply intuitive concepts of probability. Many games afford students the opportunity to apply problem-solving strategies, such as recognizing a problem, working backward, or making an approximation.

Types of Games

Cube Games

These games are included in appropriate lessons in the **Student** and **Teacher's Editions.** The games' rules usually appear on the student pages. Many of the cube games have variations that extend the mathematics or provide applications for new strategies. Variations can be learned quickly, making the cube games even more practical. Directions for all cube games are also reproduced in **Home Connection,** as well as in the **Home Connection Game Kit.**

Mat Games

Mat games can be found in the **Game Mat Kit** and are reproduced in Appendix D of this **Teacher's Edition.** The mat games are referenced in appropriate lessons.

Games

These games are electronic versions of some of the cube and mat games. They are referenced in appropriate lessons throughout the program. The **eGames** can be accessed online, on the **eGames** CD-ROM, or through the **eTextbook, ePresentation,** or **ePlanner.**

Multiple Crossing

	5	6	7	8	9	10
4	5	6	7	8	9	10
8	10	12	14	16	18	20
12	15	18	21	24	27	30
16	20	24	28	32	36	40
20	25	30	35	40	45	50
24	30	36	42	48	54	60
28	35	42	49	56	63	70
32	40	48	56	64	72	80
36	45	54	63	72	81	90
40	50	60	70	80	90	100

Math Focus: Practicing basic facts—using factors up to 10

Object of the Game: To be the first to complete a continuous path across the board

Players: Two

MATERIALS

Two cubes · Two cubes · 25 counters of the same color for each player

SET UP

▶ Choose a direction. One of you will move horizontally (left to right), and the other will move vertically (up and down).

▶ Players roll the 0-5 number cube. The person who rolls the higher number chooses his or her counters and is followed by the second player.

HOW TO PLAY

1. Take turns rolling any two cubes. Put a counter on any square that holds the product of the two numbers you rolled.

2. If you roll a 0, you cannot place a counter on a square.

3. The first player to make a continuous path from one side to the opposite side is the winner. Your path can go up, down, forward, backward, or diagonally, as long as all the squares are touching each other.

Sample Game

Building Blocks

These electronic activities are referenced in appropriate lessons throughout the lower grades of **Real Math.** The PreK level of the **Building Blocks** software, which includes the activities appropriate for prekindergarten, is a crucial part of the PreK curriculum. The **Building Blocks** activities referenced in appropriate lessons at the other grade levels reinforce key concepts.

Choosing Games

Some lesson plans suggest a particular game; some suggest that teachers select appropriate games for students based on needed skill practice; and some suggest that students be given a free choice of games. The authors recommend that teachers maintain a balance between selecting games for students and having students choose games for themselves.

To help students choose games, teachers can make a chart of the games that have been introduced to date. The chart can be a simple list or an organized collection of game mats, titles, game rules, materials lists, and illustrations. A group of students might be put in charge of making the display and updating it whenever a new game is introduced.

When you do prescribe games, check the game directory in Appendix D. This listing of the principal skills involved in each game will help you select those games that will give each student an appropriate form of practice.

Learning Game Rules

Rules for each cube game are given in the lesson in which the game is introduced. The directions for game mats are found on the game mats. Here are some tips for making sure that games are played correctly:

- Familiarize yourself with each game before showing students how to play it. Read the instructions, and then play the game by yourself or with a colleague or a friend.

- Demonstrate—do not tell—how a game is played. Even for straightforward games, oral instructions can sound complicated. Introduce a game by demonstrating it in front of the class, with you playing against the class, with you playing against one student (representing the class), or with two students (representing teams) playing against each other. The **ePresentation** allows teachers to present and demonstrate all games to the entire class at one time. Make sure that each student can see while you demonstrate a game.

- Verbalize the rules as you demonstrate games. End the demonstration when all the rules have been covered.

- Supervise to see that students get off to the right start after you have introduced a game.

- Let students teach other students. Those who have grasped the game rules can help those who have not.

Organizing Successful Game Sessions

- Pair children wisely. There are times when it will be appropriate to pair children of the same ability. However, this rule should not become invariable because most games involve some luck. Furthermore, if a student who is not attentive while playing a game plays with one who is, the first student may realize that paying attention may help.

- Change groupings from day to day. Students can learn different things by playing with different partners.

- Be sure students are challenged by a game. Most games have easier and harder variations.

- Assign a referee to each group. When students get so absorbed in their own efforts that they do not follow the rules, a referee can be useful. This is particularly appropriate for kindergarten through second grade. The referee can see that the rules are followed, remind each player when it is his or her turn, settle disputes, keep track of scores, and in some games, act as a banker.

- Make game mats accessible. Store mats so they are easy for the students to find and to return without your help.

- Encourage students to play games during free time, in school, and at home, as well as during the scheduled game sessions.

- Allow students opportunities to create and name their own variations of the games. In some cases, you may want to describe a student's variation to the entire class and ask him or her to name it. Be alert, however, to avoid student-invented variations that reduce the skill practice or thinking value of the game.

- Get help during game-playing sessions. Likely candidates are parents, grandparents, teacher's aides, or students in upper grades. Be sure the helpers know the rules of the games by having them play the chosen games ahead of time.

Game-Playing Behavior

Establishing the proper atmosphere for game playing makes the sessions more effective and easier to manage. Encourage enjoyment rather than competition. Emphasize sportsmanship, fair play, and taking turns. Beginning with the first game-playing session, teach students to control their excitement and to speak using low voices. Cubes, when rolled, should stay within a confined area. Insisting that students roll cubes on an $11'' \times 8\frac{1}{2}''$ pad, cardboard field, or on the backs of their textbooks reduces noise and inappropriate exuberance.

Problem Solving

Problem solving and reasoning are fundamental math proficiencies. Without the ability to reason mathematically, identify problems, and devise appropriate strategies to solve them, computational fluency has little relevance. There are several keys to developing students' problem-solving abilities.

1. Use Real Problems

The first and most important step in helping students become good problem solvers is to provide opportunities to identify and solve problems that are genuinely interesting and, therefore, motivating. We call these *real problems*. To help understand what we mean by *real*, we can consider three types of problems: those that are real, those that are realistic, and those that are contrived.

Contrived Problems appear largely in textbooks — never in real life. They often occur when it is difficult to find an application for a particular type of computation, so a forced, contrived situation is invented. For example, knowing how much antifreeze to add to a radiator that is $\frac{4}{7}$ full and which has a 4-gallon capacity is a contrived problem. One would never know that the radiator was $\frac{4}{7}$ full, and even if one did have that piece of useless information, nobody would calculate how much antifreeze to add. They would simply fill the tank to capacity. When students encounter such problems, they learn the wrong lesson — that mathematics is an endeavor that makes work, not one that saves work and solves useful problems. We avoid using contrived problems in *Real Math.*

Realistic Problems mirror the kind of mathematics that people do in real life. Although not as motivating as real problems, they are an important part of a mathematics program and are the main source of word problems found in our student texts. Unit pricing, comparing or combining quantities or measures, balancing a checkbook, and learning to read a telephone bill are all examples of realistic problems.

Real Problems are developed from the reality of the person being asked to solve the problem; they come from the social situation of the problem solver and his or her desire to find a solution. Thus, what is real to a first grader is not the same as what is real to a third grader or to an adult. The same problem may be real to one person and realistic to another who is engaged in a different activity, but if a problem is real to one person, then it can never be a contrived problem. Carefully selected games are a source of real problems because figuring out a strategy to win a game is of real interest to a school child. Thinking stories, too, can be real, because they have the proper balance of storyline, fantasy, humor, and reality, appropriate for the intended grade level.

Carefully developed activities are another source of real problems.

Finding real problems is one of the more difficult challenges in curriculum development, one that we take seriously and work hard at achieving. But it is here where teachers can help immensely. One of the most important prerequisites for developing real problem-solving opportunities is to know the students — know what they are interested in and know what is real to them. And so **Real Math** is rich in opportunities to individualize mathematics to the interests of the students.

2. Develop Critical-Thinking Skills

Students must have tools that are useful for solving problems. Computational skills are, of course, important, but they are not enough. Students also need an arsenal of critical-thinking skills (sometimes called *problem-solving strategies*, and sometimes called *heuristics*) that they can call upon to solve particular problems. These skills should not be taught in isolation. Rather, students should learn to use them in different contexts. By doing so, students are more likely to recognize in which situations a particular skill will be useful and when it is not likely to be useful.

We can group critical-thinking skills into two categories — those that are useful in virtually all situations and those that are useful in specific contexts.

Strategies for Every Problem-Solving Situation

Identify the problem — The first step in becoming a good problem solver is to learn how to identify when a problem does, in fact, exist. Too often in school mathematics, we give students problems to solve, even many interesting problems, but the problems are always given by the teacher or provided by the textbook—they are never identified by the student as arising from a particular context. That is not the way we encounter problems in the real world. **Real Math** lessons are rich in opportunities for students to identify problems.

Understand the problem — Without exception, students must understand each problem or physical situation and do only what makes sense to them. Applying rules in unthinking ways, using key words that avoid thinking, or using other shortcuts that subvert or eliminate understanding are all counterproductive, and although they might lead to correct answers in contrived situations, such tactics do not help students become good problem solvers, and they are not used in **Real Math.** There are no exceptions.

Reflect on the problem — Students must learn to reflect on problems both before and after solving them. Before a solution is found, students might reflect on problems that they have encountered earlier. A solution to a problem encountered earlier might offer a clue about how to structure the solution to the current problem. Good problem solvers also reflect on problems after they have been solved. What have I learned from this problem that might help with other problems? Was there an easier or a more elegant solution? Can I think of related problems that I have not yet solved? Asking such questions is likely to help students become good problem solvers. Every *Real Math* lesson concludes with an opportunity for students to reflect on what they have learned, expand on what they have learned, or ask new questions that arise from what they have learned.

Revisit the problem — Good problem solvers tend to think about a problem after they have solved it. By doing so they are likely to better understand the processes they used and see things the second and third time that they did not see the first time. One of the central roles of games in *Real Math* is to afford students the opportunity to revisit problems. Students do this by replaying games that allow them to formulate and reformulate winning strategies.

Problem-Solving Strategies

Below is a partial listing of critical-thinking skills that are likely to be useful in specific contexts.

Draw a Picture — Sometimes drawing a picture will help to visualize and hence understand a problem.

Look for a Pattern — Some problems can be solved by looking for and finding patterns.

Guess, Check, and Revise — If a direct procedure cannot be found, it is sometimes useful to make an educated guess and then check to see if that answer makes sense. This procedure often involves making several successive guesses, each based on feedback from earlier guesses. The process of guessing and checking will often lead to a better understanding of the problem and to a procedure for solving it without future guessing.

Make a Table or Graph — Organizing information in a table or graph will often reveal important trends and patterns.

Work Backward — For some problems, working backward helps to reveal a pattern or patterns.

Work an Easier Problem — If a problem appears too difficult, it sometimes helps to solve a related, but easier, problem. Solving the easier problem will often reveal strategies likely to be useful for solving the more difficult problem.

Detect Absurdities — Spotting answers that are contrary to reason, even if the correct answer is not known, is often an important part of the problem-solving process.

Ask the Right Questions — Knowing when necessary information is missing, knowing how to find the information, and knowing how to ask the right questions to find the information is often useful.

Approximate — Many problems do not require precise answers. Knowing when a precise answer is appropriate and when an approximate answer is appropriate is important, as is sufficient knowledge of the number system in order to make approximations.

3. Involve All Students in Problem Solving

Problem solving is an activity that must involve all students, not just those who are more able or who have mastered particular computational skills. *Real Math* lessons are designed to provide many such opportunities.

4. Problem Solving in Every Lesson

If students are to see the usefulness of mathematics for solving interesting problems that are relevant to their own lives, and if they are to have lots of experience solving problems, such activities must be part of every mathematics lesson — not something that is reserved for Fridays or perhaps isolated in one or two chapters of a textbook. That is why we include problem-solving opportunities in every lesson in *Real Math.* There are no exceptions.

Real Math and Problem Solving

Real Math lessons are rich in problem-solving opportunities and are adaptable to many styles of teaching. The principal sources of problem-solving opportunities come from the following:

Games

Real Math games are a principal source for practice of traditional basic skills. Most games do more: they give students an opportunity to work out important mathematical ideas and strategies. Thus, students might start a game by just getting the skill practice, but after a while they might realize that the game involves more than practice — that a winning strategy must be developed. At that point students have identified a problem. Because winning the game is often a real problem for students, there is genuine motivation to find a solution. Moreover, each time students replay the game, there is an opportunity to revisit a problem previously encountered and find alternative and more sophisticated strategies that might have been missed earlier. Although students

Professional Development

compete with each other during game-playing sessions, they often communicate their strategies to each other and discuss them.

Thinking Stories

Thinking Stories found in kindergarten and Grades one, two, and three are an essential part of the *Real Math* approach to developing problem-solving abilities; they develop creativity and common sense in the use of mathematics. The problem-solving skills that are stressed include recognizing absurd answers, recognizing obvious answers (those that don't need calculation), recognizing when a problem can be solved using mathematics and when other, non-mathematical knowledge is needed, and so on. The stories are real stories, designed to be read to the students and discussed. The various characters in the stories have peculiarities in thinking that the students come to know. Mr. Breezy, for example, is always giving more information than what is needed, while Ms. Eng is often vague and provides too little information. Thus when Mr. Breezy appears in a story, students learn to listen and think about what information is not useful, whereas when Ms. Eng appears, students learn to ask questions to get the information that she has failed to give. Because the stories are read to the students, we can use a much richer vocabulary than what would be necessary if students read the stories themselves. Thus we do not divorce language from mathematics — rather we make use of language to build problem-solving skills.

Exploring Problem Solving

Three sets of explorations in every chapter focus specifically on introducing, comparing, and using strategies for identifying and solving problems from many curricular areas or realistic situations. Students analyze solution methods and share other possible solutions.

Activities

The many whole-class and small-group activities allow students to apply mathematics in different contexts, which are often cross-curricular. Such activities are rich in opportunities for students to communicate their ideas within their small groups and also to others from whom they are seeking information.

Mathematics is being lazy. Mathematics is letting the principles do the work for you so that you do not have to do the work for yourself.

George Pólya, mathematician, 1887–1985

Computation Pages

As in most programs, pages that provide needed computation practice are included throughout *Real Math.* But because we frequently include groups of related exercises on these pages, students learn to look for them and use the resulting patterns to avoid tedious computations. For example, an exercise such as $54 + 73 =$ might be followed by $54 + 74 =$ and $54 + 75 =$. Students who notice this pattern can compute the first sum, but then note that each successive sum is one more than the previous sum. Such patterns appear often in *Real Math.*

Word Problems

Realistic word problems appear frequently throughout *Real Math.* They illustrate situations in which mathematics is useful in the real world, and they are a source of much practice. To be certain that students understand the situations described in these problems, we never group problems of the same type together, such as giving problems, which all call for addition. To do so would allow students to simply look for the numbers and use the indicated operation. They would not have to understand the problem and would not have to think. To encourage thinking, we include problems that include too much information, too little information, problems that can be solved by mathematics, and those that cannot. We also include problems in which an approximate answer is more useful than a precise answer, and those in which a precise answer is more useful than an approximate answer. We do not allow students to rely on key words either, because doing so allows students to avoid thinking and to apply procedures that are likely to work only with problems that appear in textbooks.

Guided Discussion

"Discourse should not be confined to answers only, but should include discussion of connections to other problems, alternative representations and solution methods, the nature of justification and argumentation, and the like."

Kilpatrick, J., Swafford, J. and Findell, B. eds. *Adding It Up: Helping Children Learn Mathematics.* Washington, D.C.: National Research Council/National Academy Press. 2001, p. 425–426.

Mathematical discussions have the potential to greatly advance mathematical understanding. A good discussion provides opportunities for students to explain their thinking, to expand or challenge their understanding by listening to others' contributions, and to justify their reasoning. Good mathematical discussions enable teachers to assess and understand student thinking to inform their future instruction.

"Writing and talking enable learners to make their mathematical thinking visible. It is through writing and talking that teachers obtain a window into their students' thinking. Both writing and talking are tools for discovery, enabling learners to make new connections as they engage in the process. The fluid nature of talk allows for the quick brainstorming of many ideas, while the permanent quality of writing provides an important trail of our children's thinking."

Whitin, Phyllis and Whitin, David J. *Math Is Language Too.* Urbana, IL: National Council of Teachers of English. 2000, p. 17.

Discussion Management

These points will help produce more discussions:

1. Restate some or all of what the student has said, and then ask the student to respond and verify whether or not the teacher's restatement is correct. (However, always restating what students say may discourage students from listening to each other the first time.)

2. Ask students to restate someone else's reasoning, which gives the rest of the class another rendition of the first student's contribution and provides evidence that other students could and did hear. It is also evidence for the speaker's points.

3. Ask students to apply and explain their own reasoning to someone else's reasoning. This will involve more students in the discussion and will encourage student interactions.

4. Prompt students by asking for further commentary to support a position.

5. Use free time. This time allows students to think and consider answers to complicated questions before they speak.

Chapin, Suzanne, O'Connor, Catherine, and Anderson, Nancy Canavan. *Classroom Discussions: Using Math Talk to Help Students Learn.* Sausalito, CA: Math Solutions Publications, 2003, p. 12–16.

Real Math and Guided Discussion

Guided Discussion plays a prominent role in the Develop and Reflect parts of virtually every lesson in *Real Math.* Routines for Guided Discussion are included in the Getting Started section of each grade level to develop effective discussion strategies.

Questions that Promote Learning

Not all questions have the same effect. Questions help teachers to learn what students are thinking and to consider instructional implications of that knowledge. Below are ideas for formulating questions to promote learning during Guided Discussion.

Engaging questions to invite students to participate in a discussion

Identify terms, relationships, and methods already known that are connected to the topic.	What is _____? What does _____ mean?
Share opinions about the topic.	What do you think about _____?
Relate concrete experiences that are pertinent to the topic.	Have you ever been asked to do this before?
Verify the results.	How do you know this is true?

Exploratory questions to help students consider connections and consequences

Identify a specific difficulty, and decide how to solve it.	What was the hardest part of the problem? Is there an easier way to solve it?
Relate personal experience in solving the problem.	What did you do in the past to solve the problem?
Draw analogies to other situations.	How is this the same as or different from other problems?
Process and record results.	Write the steps you used to solve the problem.

Synthesizing questions to help students pull ideas together.

Identify patterns.	What pattern do you see in everyone's results?
Generalize.	What is a good way to solve this kind of problem?
Elaborate rules, definitions, and laws that express the generalization.	Explain or justify the steps for solving problems like this.
Argue, prove, or demonstrate assumptions.	Which way is the best way to solve a problem like this? How is it better?
Use references.	Who else solved the problem in this way?

Clarifying questions to help students explain their thinking or to help you understand their thinking

Reflect on examples and analyze results.	Which is the easiest/hardest/most fun way of approaching the problem, and why?
Provide examples.	What is an example of a problem like this?
Describe stages and observations.	What was the thinking process you used to solve the problem?
Understand and accept limitations of personal and peer knowledge, and search for other information sources.	Is there a better way? How could we find out?

Refocusing questions to help students get back on track

Refocusing questions are most useful when students are working in nonproductive ways.	How is this like _____? What does this say about _____?

Knowledge Age Skills and Talents

The twenty-first century is the dawn of the Knowledge Age. In contrast to the Industrial Age or Information Age, the Knowledge Age requires a specific set of skills and talents. These include the ability to write and speak clearly, analyze information, conduct research, and solve difficult problems. According to a February 2005 study conducted by Peter D. Hart Research Associates for Achieve, Inc., of high school graduates

❑ 51% feel that there are some gaps in their science preparation (14% large gaps)

❑ 46% say that there are gaps in their oral communication skills (15% large gaps)

❑ 45% identify some gaps in their ability to do research (13% say there are large gaps)

❑ 41% say that there are some gaps in their mathematics preparation (16% large gaps)

❑ 38% feel that there are some gaps in the quality of writing that is expected (10% large gaps)

Elementary education can help to build these knowledge age skills in the following ways.

Throughout **Real Math,** activities are included to teach, build, apply, and practice knowledge age skills in the course of learning mathematics.

The following competencies are developed in each grade level in the course of the Develop and Reflect sections of each lesson, as well as in the Concept/Question Board and Project activities.

- **High-Level Responsibility**—Helping students to take over more of the high-level parts of the learning process that are traditionally treated as part of the teacher's job; for instance, goal-setting, activating prior knowledge, monitoring, and determining next steps

- **Teamwork**—Encouraging group work and grading on the basis of contributions to the success of group efforts rather than solely on the basis of individual performance

- **Effective Communication**—Taking responsibility for communicating clearly both orally and in writing

- **Creative Work with Ideas**—Emphasizing ideas and idea improvement rather than task completion and getting the right answer

- **Problem Formulation, Planning, and Strategizing**—Recognizing difficulties and opportunities in a situation and converting these into solvable problems. Recognizing a problem as solvable implies having a strategy, a way to proceed, and so strategies become a natural subject of discussion

- **Self-Monitoring and Self- and Group Assessment**—Making students aware of and responsible for achieving mandated learning objectives

Manipulatives and How to Use Them

"The use of concrete materials, sometimes termed manipulatives, for teaching mathematics is widely accepted, particularly in elementary grades. Manipulatives should always be seen as a means and not an end in themselves. They require careful use over sufficient time to allow students to build meaning and make connections....Simply putting materials on desks is not enough to guarantee students will learn appropriate mathematics. The relationship between learning and the use of manipulatives is far more complex than many mathematics educators have thought....When students use a manipulative, they need to be helped to see its relevant aspects and to link those aspects to appropriate symbolism and mathematical concepts and operations....If students do not see the connections among object, symbol, language, and idea, using a manipulative becomes just one more thing to learn rather than a process leading to a larger mathematical learning goal....The evidence indicates...that manipulatives can provide valuable support for student learning when teachers interact over time with the students to help them build links between the object, the symbol, and the mathematical idea that both represent."

Kilpatrick, J., Swafford, J. and Findell, B. eds. *Adding It Up: Helping Children Learn Mathematics.* Washington, D.C.: National Research Council/National Academy Press. 2001, p. 353–354.

"The laws of nature are written in the language of mathematics...the symbols are triangles, circles, and other geometrical figures, without whose help it is impossible to comprehend a single word."

Galileo Galilei, Italian astronomer and physicist, 1564–1642

Real Math and Manipulatives

The purpose of using manipulatives is to help students understand mathematics, not to get answers to problems. Too often students know rules but do not know how or why the rules work. By explaining abstract concepts with manipulatives, students can develop and demonstrate understanding of mathematical concepts. Manipulatives are used whenever appropriate in *Real Math.* Each time they are used, there is also a plan to remove the need for them so that once the understanding is achieved, students focus attention on fluency and the abstract. The power of mathematics is in its abstractness.

Because the goal is to understand and use abstract mathematics, *Real Math* tries to provide several models such as craft sticks and rubber bands, fingers, or play money for base ten. Teachers should feel free to use still other models, but they should be sure to encourage abstract work without the manipulative as soon as students understand the underlying concept and are able to proceed without the physical crutch.

Below are common manipulatives and their principal purposes.

Manipulatives	Description	Purpose	Concepts to Develop
Money	Pennies, nickels, dimes, quarters, half dollars, $1, $5, $10, $20, $50, and $100 bills	Demonstrate concepts and values of money and applications of base-ten arithmetic and develop the division algorithm	• Number sense • Base-ten system • Place value
Pattern Blocks	Colorful blocks in different geometric shapes (hexagons, squares, trapezoids, triangles, and parallelograms, and rhombi) and colors	Create and demonstrate different types of color and shape patterns and to explore the mathematics of tiling and tesselations	• Number sense • Fractions • Geometry • Proportional reasoning
Attribute Blocks	Blocks in five shapes (circle, hexagon, rectangle, square, and triangle), different sizes, thicknesses, and colors	Build shape identification, logical thinking, and comparing and ordering concepts	• Number sense • Geometry
Platonic Solids	Wooden 3-D cone, cube, pyramid, and sphere	Develop geometric concepts of space figures	• Geometry
Mirror	Small nonbreakable mirror	Develop concepts of symmetry	• Geometry
Geoboard	Plastic board with pegs and rubber bands laid out in a square grid	Explore shapes, area, perimeter, symmetry, design, and fractions of shapes	• Geometry • Measurement
Protractor	Clear protractor in graduations from 0–180 degrees	Measure angles	• Geometry • Measurement
Compass	Center point and pencil	Draw and measure circles	• Geometry • Measurement
Gummed Tape	Adhesive paper tape	Create geometric figures and shapes	• Geometry
Fraction Tiles	Plastic tiles in sets of different fractional increments including $\frac{1}{8}, \frac{1}{4}, \frac{1}{3}, \frac{1}{2}$, and 1	Explore parts of wholes and adding and subtracting fractions	• Number sense • Fractions and rational numbers • Measurement
Spinners	Plastic spinners	Explore probability	• Probability • Number operations
Counters	Colored plastic disks	Explore patterns and counting	• Number sense • Counting • Probability • Number operations
Base-Ten Blocks	Plastic shapes in cubes, flats, rods, and units	Explore base-ten systems, counting, and number operations	• Number sense • Counting • Number operation
Craft Sticks and Rubber Bands	Wood sticks	Explore the base-ten system, place value, and standard multidigit addition and subtraction algorithms	• Number sense • Counting • Number operation
Counters	Plastic shapes	Explore counting and ordering numbers	• Number sense • Counting • Number operation
Math-Link Cubes	Plastic cubes that nest together	Explore counting, patterns, number operations, and composing and decomposing numbers	• Number sense • Counting • Patterns • Number operations • Rational number
Ruler and Tape Measure	Plastic customary and metric ruler and tape measure	Explore metric and customary measurements of length	• Measurement • Counting
Measuring Cups and Liter Pitcher	Plastic metric and customary measurement containers	Explore metric and customary measurements of capacity	• Measurement • Geometry • Fractions, decimals, and percents
Double Pan Balance and Platform Scales	Scale and balance and weight set	Explore metric and customary measurements of weight; help understand and solve linear equations	• Measurement
Thermometer	Celsius and Fahrenheit thermometers	Explore temperature measurements	• Measurement
Clock Face	Plastic analog clock face	Explore time measurements	• Measurement
Stopwatch	Electronic stopwatch	Explore time measurements	• Measurement • Fractions, decimals, and percents

Differentiating Instruction

"In the context of education, we define *differentiation as* 'a teacher's reacting responsively to a learner's needs.' A teacher who is differentiating understands a student's need to express humor or work with a group, or to have additional teaching on a particular skill, or to delve more deeply into a particular topic....Differentiation is simply attending to the learning needs of a particular student or small group of students rather than the more typical pattern of teaching the class as though all individuals in it were basically alike. The goal of a differentiated classroom is maximum student growth and individual success."

—Tomlinson, Carol Ann and Allan, Susan Demirsky. *Leadership for Differentiating Schools and Classrooms.* Alexandria, VA: Association for Supervision and Curriculum Development. 2000, p. 4.

All students can benefit from differentiated instruction. Differentiated instruction is dependent on ongoing, daily assessment and an interest in and understanding of how children learn and develop concepts.

How to Differentiate

Instruction can be differentiated in three key ways:

- **Content** What the teacher wants students to learn and the materials or mechanisms through which that is accomplished.

  Differentiating the content may entail teaching prerequisite concepts to students who need intervention or by asking questions that will cause students to think beyond the concepts covered in the lesson.

- **Process** How or what activities the students do to ensure that they use key skills to make sense of the content

  Differentiating the process may include grouping students in different ways, or alternating the pace of the lesson by moving more slowly or more quickly than originally planned. It might also include stressing different modalities: visual, auditory, or kinesthetic.

- **Product** How the student will demonstrate what he or she has come to know

  Differentiating the product may include assigning **Enrichment, Practice,** or **Reteach** activities to complete.

Differentiating instruction does not mean chaos or a classroom devoid of structure with everyone working on different goals. Lessons should have clearly defined purposes with students focused on one key understanding.

Analyzing Student Needs

Teachers successful at differentiating instruction are typically in tune with individual student needs. These needs vary and should be addressed in the context of the key ideas of the lesson. By preparing for differentiation and considering what you as a teacher might do when you encounter different student needs, you can have materials and strategies at the ready.

For a particular concept or lesson, different students may need

- challenge.
- social interaction.
- alternative instruction.
- independence.
- personal attention.
- serious intervention.
- language support.
- creative expression.
- cooperative grouping.
- extra practice.

Real Math and Differentiated Instruction

Every lesson of **Real Math** begins with Planning for Learning: Differentiate Instruction ideas. These include

- *Intervention* that teach prerequisite skills for students who are not ready for the lesson concepts.

- *English Learner* **Preview** lesson that previews lesson concepts and vocabulary for students learning English.

- *Enrichment* ideas for expanding parts of the lesson if, as you are teaching, you realize students are already confident with the lesson concepts.

- *Practice* strategies for extending parts of the lesson, if you realize during the lesson that students would benefit from more practice.

Professional Development

- **Reteach** ideas for re-presenting and reinforcing the key teaching of the lesson, if you realize that students are not grasping the concepts.

During the lesson, Monitoring Student Progress presents tips for addressing specific concerns.

At the end of the lesson, Assessment Follow-Up provides activities to review, reteach, practice, or enrich lesson concepts depending on student performance.

Key Principles of a Differentiated Classroom

- The teacher is clear about what matters in subject matter.
- The teacher understands, appreciates, and builds upon student differences.

- Assessment and instruction are inseparable.
- The teacher adjusts content, process, and product in response to student readiness, interests, and learning profiles.
- All students participate in respectful work.
- Students and teachers are collaborators in learning.
- Goals of a differentiated classroom are maximum growth and individual success.
- Flexibility is the hallmark of a differentiated classroom.

Tomlinson, Carol Ann and Allan, Susan Demirsky. *Leadership for Differentiating Schools and Classrooms.* Alexandria, VA: Association for Supervision and Curriculum Development. 2000, p. 48.

Themes

Each chapter of **Real Math** involves a theme to provide application and context for the mathematics. The theme is evidenced in the Problem Solving activities in the Chapter Opener, the Exploring Problem Solving activities in the middle and end of the chapter, and the Thinking Stories in grades K–3.

Grade	K	1	2	3	4	5	6
Chapter 1	School	Animals	Sharing Stories	Friendship	Risks and Consequences	Cooperation and Competition	Perserverance
Chapter 2	Animals	Animals	Kindness	Friendship	Risks and Consequences	Cooperation and Competition	Perserverance
Chapter 3	Finding Friends	Neighborhood	Kindness	City Wildlife	Dollars and Sense	Astronomy	Ancient Civilizations
Chapter 4	Wind	Games	Kindness	City Wildlife	Dollars and Sense	Astronomy	Ancient Civilizations
Chapter 5	Gardens	Neighborhood	Parks/Picnics	Imagination	From Mystery to Medicine	Heritage	Taking a Stand
Chapter 6	Flags, Parades, and Celebrations	Neighborhood	Zoo	Imagination	From Mystery to Medicine	Heritage	Taking a Stand
Chapter 7	Teamwork	Animals	Museum	Money	Survival	Making a New Nation	Beyond the Notes
Chapter 8	The Sea	Homes	Dinosaurs	Money	Survival	Making a New Nation	Beyond the Notes
Chapter 9		Neighborhood	Courage	Storytelling	Communication	Going West	Ecology
Chapter 10		Weather	Courage	Storytelling	Communication	Going West	Ecology
Chapter 11		Homes	Our Country	Country Life	A Changing America	Journeys and Quests	A Question of Value
Chapter 12			Our Country	Country Life	A Changing America	Journeys and Quests	A Question of Value

Assessment

> "...assessment, whether externally mandated or developed by the teacher, should support the development of students' mathematical proficiency. It needs to provide opportunities for students to learn, rather than taking time away from their learning. Assessments in which students are learning, as well as showing what they have already learned, can provide valuable information to teachers, schools, districts, and states, as well as to the students themselves. Such assessments help teachers modify their instruction to support better learning at each grade level."
>
> Kilpatrick, J., Swafford, J. and Findell, B. eds. *Adding It Up: Helping Children Learn Mathematics.* Washington, D.C.: National Research Council/National Academy Press. 2001, p. 423.

Much has been written about the importance of assessment. The Assessment Standards book from the National Council of Teachers of Mathematics tells us that classroom assessment should

- provide a rich variety of mathematical topics and problem situations.
- give students opportunities to investigate problems in many ways.
- question and listen to students.
- look for evidence of learning from many sources.
- expect students to use concepts and procedures effectively in solving problems.

The goals of assessment are to

- improve instruction by informing teachers of the effectiveness of their lessons.
- promote growth of students by identifying where they need additional instruction and support.
- recognize accomplishments.

Real Math and Assessment

Real Math provides opportunities for formal and informal assessments and convenient ways to record, track, and report on student achievements.

Informal Assessments

Informal assessment involves ongoing observations of student involvement in class activities. Informal assessments are tailored to evaluate students on the five areas of mathematic proficiency: computing, understanding, reasoning, applying, and engaging.

Every lesson includes two **Assessment** checkmarks in the **Teacher's Edition** next to activities tailored to reveal students' math proficiencies. These activities may include Guided Discussion, Skill Building, Strategy Building, Games, or Journals. The checkmarks alert teachers to carefully observe students during the activity. Rubric checklists in Assess and Differentiate of the lesson describe specific positive behaviors to look for as signs of development. As teachers become familiar with the rubric checklists, they can access them through memory. Teachers can record their observations in the Daily Class Assessment Records for each proficiency.

Computing	• respond accurately • respond quickly • respond with confidence • self-correct
Understanding	• make important observations • extend or generalize learning • provide insightful answers • pose insightful questions
Reasoning	• provide a clear explanation • communicate reasons and strategies • choose appropriate strategies • argue logically
Applying	• apply learning in new situations • contribute concepts • contribute answers • connect mathematics to real-world situations
Engaging	• pay attention to others' contributions • contribute information and ideas • improve on a strategy • reflect on and check the accuracy of his or her work

Daily checklist observations can be summarized in the Student Assessment Record for the chapter or in **eAssess** to provide a long-term holistic view of student proficiency. If teachers record these observations, these daily informal assessments can be powerful indicators of student proficiency, and as such help inform instruction, as well as provide feedback to students and their parents.

Professional Development

Formal Assessment

There are several opportunities for formal assessment in every chapter. All assessments can be recorded further in the Student Assessment Record or in **eAssess** for every chapter to provide a comprehensive view of student achievement.

- **Pretests** test prerequisite and chapter concepts to provide a diagnostic assessment of student understanding for the upcoming chapter.

- **Speed Tests** appear in lessons to test computational fluency.

- **Mastery Checkpoints** provide assessments for skills that should be mastered at particular points in the program. The Mastery Checkpoint Chart provides a class view of student progress toward mastery of particular skills.

- **Oral Assessment** in the middle of the chapter is an opportunity for teachers to interact individually with students to assess their growth in proficiency. An Individual Oral Assessment recording sheet is available in **Assessment** for each Oral Assessment for teacher convenience.

- **Daily Quizzes** are available to provide a quick review and assessment of student understanding of lesson concepts and skills.

- **Chapter Tests** offer a way to assess student understanding of chapter content and skills.

 Assess

The **eAssess** program offers a powerful way to record and track student progress. Teachers can enter data on a daily or weekly basis. The more data a teacher inputs—including records of Formal and Informal Assessments, completion of student pages, completion of projects, and additional activities—the more comprehensive and reliable the reports that can be generated will be.

Using **eAssess,** teachers can generate reports that show student performance in reference to the entire class, to the individual, and to state and/or national standards. These reports provide a comprehensive view of individual student and class performance that can provide valuable feedback for your instruction and for student and parent conferences.

More information, including masters of recording sheets and tests, can be found in **Assessment.**

Handwriting Models

Starting point, straight down

Starting point, around right, slanting left, and straight across right

Starting point, around right, in at the middle, and around right

Starting point, straight down, and straight across right. Starting point, straight down, and crossing line
(Avoid confusion with 9.)

Straight down, curve around right and up. Starting point, straight across right
(Avoid confusion with S.)

Starting point, slanting left, around the bottom curving up around left and into the curve

Starting point, straight across right, and slanting down left

Starting point, curving left, curving down and around right, slanting up right to starting point

Starting point, curving around left all the way, and straight down

Starting point, straight down. Starting point, curving left all the way around to starting point

*Students follow natural developmental progressions in learning, developing mathematical ideas in their own ways. Curriculum research has revealed sequences of activities that are effective in guiding students through these levels of thinking. These developmental paths can be described as learning trajectories. Each learning trajectory has levels of understanding, each more sophisticated than the last, and with tasks that promote growth from one level to the next. The **Building Blocks** Learning Trajectories give simple labels, descriptions, and examples of each level. Complete learning trajectories describe the goals of learning, the thinking and learning processes of students at various levels, and the learning activities in which they might engage.*

Learning Trajectories for Primary Grades Mathematics

Developmental Levels

The following provides the developmental levels from the first signs of development in different strands of mathematics through approximately age 8. Research shows that when teachers understand how students develop mathematics understanding, they are more effective in questioning, analyzing, and providing activities that further students' development than teachers who are unaware of the development process. Consequently, students have a much richer and more successful math experience in the primary grades.

Frequently Asked Questions (FAQ)

1. **When are students "at" a level?** Students are at a certain level when most of their behaviors reflect the thinking— ideas and skills—of that level. Often, they show a few behaviors from the next (and previous) levels as they learn.

2. **Can students work at more than one level at the same time?** Yes, although most students work mainly at one level or in transition between two levels (naturally, if they are tired or distracted, they may operate at a much lower level). Levels are not "absolute." They are "benchmarks" of complex growth that represent distinct ways of thinking. So, another way to think of them is as a sequence of different patterns of thinking. Students are continually learning within levels and moving between them.

3. **Can students jump ahead?** Yes, especially if there are separate "subtopics." For example, we have combined many counting competencies into one "Counting" sequence with subtopics, such as verbal counting skills. Some students learn to count to 100 at age six after

learning to count objects to 10 or more; some may learn that verbal skill earlier. The subtopic of verbal counting skills would still be followed.

4. **How do these developmental levels support teaching and learning?** The levels help teachers, as well as curriculum developers, to assess, teach, and sequence activities. *Teachers who understand learning trajectories and the developmental levels that are at their foundation are more effective and efficient.* Through planned teaching and also by encouraging informal, incidental mathematics, teachers help students learn *at an appropriate and deep level.*

5. **Should I plan to help students develop just the levels that correspond to my students' ages?** No! The ages in the table are typical ages when students develop these ideas. *But these are rough guides only—students differ widely.* Furthermore, the ages below are lower bounds on what students achieve without instruction. So, these are "starting levels," not goals. We have found that students who are provided high-quality mathematics experiences are capable of developing to levels one or more years beyond their peers.

Each column in the table, such as "Counting," represents a main developmental progression that underlies the learning trajectory for that topic.

Clements, D. H., Sarama, J., & DiBiase, A.M. *Engaging Young Students in Mathematics: Standards for Early Childhood Mathematics Education.* Mahwah, NJ: Lawrence Erlbaum Associates.

Clements, D. H., & Sarama, J. "Early Childhood Mathematics Learning." In F. K. Lester, Jr. (Ed.), *Second Handbook of Research on Mathematics Teaching and Learning.* New York: Information Age Publishing.

Learning Trajectories

Developmental Levels for Counting

The ability to count with confidence develops over the course of several years. Beginning in infancy, students show signs of understanding numbers. With instruction and number experience, most students can count fluently by age eight, with much progress in counting occurring in kindergarten and first grade. Most students follow a natural developmental progression in learning to count with recognizable stages or levels. This developmental path can be described as part of a learning trajectory.

Age Range	Level Name	Level	Description
1–2	Precounter	1	A student at the earliest level of counting may name some numbers meaninglessly. The student may skip numbers and have no sense of sequence.
1–2	Chanter	2	At this level, a student may sing-song numbers, but without meaning.
2	Reciter	3	At this level, the student may verbally count with separate words, but not necessarily in the correct order.
3	Reciter (10)	4	A student at this level may verbally count to 10 with some correspondence with objects. He or she may point to objects to count a few items, but then lose track.
3	Corresponder	5	At this level, a student may keep one-to-one correspondence between counting words and objects—at least for small groups of objects laid in a line. A corresponder may answer "how many" by recounting the objects starting over with one each time.
4	Counter (Small Numbers)	6	At around 4 years of age, students may begin to count meaningfully. They may accurately count objects to 5 and answer the "how many" question with the last number counted. These students may count verbally to 10 and may write or draw to represent 1–5.
4	Producer— Counter to (Small Numbers)	7	The next level after counting small numbers is to produce a group of four objects. When asked to show four of something, for example, this student may give four objects.
4	Counter (10)	8	This student may count structured arrangements of objects to 10. He or she may be able to write or draw to represent 10 and may accurately count a line of nine blocks and say there are 9. A student at this level may find the number just after or just before another number, but only by counting up from 1.
5	Counter and Producer— Counter to (10+)	10	Around 5 years of age, students may begin to count out objects accurately to 10 and then beyond to 30. They may keep track of objects that have and have not been counted, even in different arrangements. They may write or draw to represent 1 to 10 and then 20 and 30, and may give the next number to 20 or 30. They also begin to recognize errors in others' counting and are able to eliminate most errors in their own counting.

Age Range	Level Name	Level	Description
5	Counter Backward from 10	10	Another milestone at about age 5 is being able to count backward from 10.
6	Counter from N (N+1, N−1)	11	Around 6 years of age, students may begin to count on, counting verbally and with objects from numbers other than 1. Another noticeable accomplishment is that students may determine the number immediately before or after another number without having to start back at 1.
6	Skip Counting by 10s to 100	12	A student at this level may count by 10s to 100. They may count through decades knowing that 40 comes after 39, for example.
6	Counter to 100	13	A student at this level may count by 1s through 100, including the decade transitions from 39 to 40, 49 to 50, and so on.
6	Counter On Using Patterns	14	At this level, a student may keep track of counting acts by using numerical patterns, such as tapping as he or she counts.
6	Skip Counter	15	At this level, students can count by 5s and 2s with understanding.
6	Counter of Imagined Items	16	At this level, a student may count mental images of hidden objects.
6	Counter On Keeping Track	17	A student at this level may keep track of counting acts numerically with the ability to count up one to four more from a given number.
6	Counter of Quantitative Units	18	At this level, a student can count unusual units, such as "wholes" when shown combinations of wholes and parts. For example, when shown three whole plastic eggs and four halves, a student at this level will say there are five whole eggs.
6	Counter to 200	19	At this level, a student may count accurately to 200 and beyond, recognizing the patterns of ones, tens, and hundreds.
7	Number Conserver	20	A major milestone around age 7 is the ability to conserve number. A student who conserves number understands that a number is unchanged even if a group of objects is rearranged. For example, if there is a row of ten buttons, the student understands there are still ten without recounting, even if they are rearranged in a long row or a circle.
7	Counter Forward and Back	21	A student at this level may count in either direction and recognize that sequence of decades mirrors single-digit sequence.

Developmental Levels for Comparing and Ordering Numbers

Comparing and ordering sets is a critical skill for students as they determine whether one set is larger than another in order to make sure sets are equal and "fair." Prekindergartners can learn to use matching to compare collections or to create equivalent collections. Finding out how many more or fewer in one collection is more demanding than simply comparing two collections. The ability to compare and order sets with fluency develops over the course of several years. With instruction and number experience, most students develop foundational understanding of number relationships and place value at ages four and five. Most students follow a natural developmental progression in learning to compare and order numbers with recognizable stages or levels. This developmental path can be described as part of a learning trajectory.

Age Range	Level Name	Level	Description
2	Object Corresponder	1	At this early level, a student puts objects into one-to-one correspondence, but with only intuitive understanding of resulting equivalence. For example, a student may know that each carton has a straw, but does not necessarily know there are the same numbers of straws and cartons.
2	Perceptual Comparer	2	At this level, a student can compare collections that are quite different in size (for example, one is at least twice the other) and know that one has more than the other. If the collections are similar, the student can compare very small collections.
3	First-Second Ordinal Counter	3	At this level the student can identify the "first" and often "second" object in a sequence.
3	Nonverbal Comparer of Similar Items	4	At this level, a student can identify that different organizations of the same number of small groups are equal and different from other sets (1–4 items). For example, a student can identify ••• and •‎•• as equal and different from •• or •‎•.
3	Nonverbal Comparer of Dissimilar Items	5	At this level, a student can match small, equal collections of dissimilar items, such as shells and dots, and show that they are the same number.
6	Nonverbal Comparer of Dissimilar Items	6	A student at this level can match small, equal collections of shells and dots, thus showing they are the same number.
4	Matching Comparer	7	As students progress, they begin to compare groups of 1–6 by matching. For example, a student gives one toy bone to every dog and says there are the same number of dogs and bones.
4	Knows-to-Count Comparer	8	A significant step occurs when the student begins to count collections to compare. At the early levels, students are not always accurate when a larger collection's objects are smaller in size than the objects in the smaller collection. For example, a student at this level may accurately count two equal collections, but when asked, says the collection of larger blocks has more.
4	Counting Comparer (Same Size)	9	At this level, students make accurate comparisons via counting, but only when objects are about the same size and groups are small (about 1–5 items).
5	Counting Comparer (5)	10	As students develop their ability to compare sets, they compare accurately by counting, even when a larger collection's objects are smaller. A student at this level can figure out how many more or less.

Age Range	Level Name	Level	Description
5	Ordinal Counter	11	At this level, a student identifies and uses ordinal numbers from "first" to "tenth." For example, the student can identify who is "third in line."
6	Counting Comparer (10)	12	This level can be observed when the student compares sets by counting, even when a larger collection's objects are smaller, up to 10. A student at this level can accurately count two collections of 9 items each, and says they have the same number, even if one collection has larger blocks.
6	Mental Number Line to 10	13	As students move into this level, they begin to use mental rather than physical images and knowledge of number relationships to determine relative size and position. For example, a student at this level can answer which number is closer to 6, 4, or 9 without counting physical objects.
6	Serial Orderer to 6+	14	The student demonstrates development in comparing when they begin to order lengths marked into units (1–6, then beyond). For example, given towers of cubes, this student can put them in order, 1 to 6. Later the student begins to order collections. For example, given cards with one to six dots on them, the student can put them in order.
7	Place Value Comparer	15	Further development is made when a student begins to compare numbers with place value understanding. For example, a student at this level can explain that "63 is more than 59 because six tens is more than five tens, even if there are more than three ones."
7	Mental Number Line to 100	16	Students demonstrate the next level in comparing and ordering when they can use mental images and knowledge of number relationships, including ones embedded in tens, to determine relative size and position. For example, when asked, "Which is closer to 45, 30 or 50?" a student at this level may say "45 is right next to 50, but 30 isn't."
8+	Mental Number Line to 1,000s	17	At about age 8, students may begin to use mental images of numbers up to 1,000 and knowledge of number relationships, including place value, to determine relative size and position. For example, when asked, "Which is closer to 3,500—2,000 or 7,000?" a student at this level may say "70 is double 35, but 20 is only fifteen from 35, so twenty hundreds, 2,000, is closer."

Learning Trajectories

Developmental Levels for Recognizing Number and Subitizing (Instantly Recognizing)

The ability to recognize number values develops over the course of several years and is a foundational part of number sense. Beginning at about age two, students begin to name groups of objects. The ability to instantly know how many are in a group, called *subitizing,* begins at about age three. By age eight, with instruction and number experience, most students can identify groups of items and use place values and multiplication skills to count them. Most students follow a natural developmental progression in learning to count with recognizable stages or levels. This developmental path can be described as part of a learning trajectory.

Age Range	Level Name	Level	Description
2	Small Collection Namer	1	The first sign occurs when the student can name groups of 1 to 2, sometimes 3. For example, when shown a pair of shoes, this young student says, "two shoes."
3	Nonverbal Subitizer	2	This level occurs when, shown a small collection (1 to 4), the student can put out a matching group nonverbally, but cannot necessarily give the number telling how many. For example, when 4 objects are shown, the student makes a set of 4 objects to "match."
3	Maker of Small Collections	3	At this level, a student can nonverbally make a small collection (no more than 5, usually 1 to 3) with the same number as another collection. For example, when shown a collection of 3, the student makes another collection of 3.
4	Perceptual Subitizer to 4	4	Progress is made when a student instantly recognizes collections up to 4 and verbally names the number of items. For example, when shown 4 objects briefly, the student says "4."
5	Perceptual Subitizer to 5	5	This level is the ability to instantly recognize collections up to 5 and verbally name the number of items. For example, when shown 5 objects, the student says "5."

Age Range	Level Name	Level	Description
5	Conceptual Subitizer to 5	6	At this level, the student can verbally label all arrangements to 5, using groups. For example, a student at this level might say, "I saw 2 and 2, and so I saw 4."
5	Conceptual Subitizer to 10	7	This step is when the student can verbally label most arrangements to 6, then up to 10, using groups. For example, a student at this level might say, "In my mind, I made 2 groups of 3 and 1 more, so 7."
6	Conceptual Subitizer to 20	8	Next, a student can verbally label structured arrangements up to 20, using groups. For example, the student may say, "I saw 3 fives, so 5, 10, 15."
7	Conceptual Subitizer with Place Value and Skip Counting	9	At this level, a student is able to use skip counting and place value to verbally label structured arrangements. For example, the student may say, "I saw groups of tens and twos, so 10, 20, 30, 40, 42, 44, 46...46!"
8+	Conceptual Subitizer with Place Value and Multiplication	10	As students develop their ability to subitize, they use groups, multiplication, and place value to verbally label structured arrangements. At this level, a student may say, "I saw groups of tens and threes, so I thought, 5 tens is 50 and 4 threes is 12, so 62 in all."

Developmental Levels for Composing (Knowing Combinations of Numbers)

Composing and decomposing are combining and separating operations that allow students to build concepts of "parts" and "wholes." Most prekindergartners can "see" that two items and one item make three items. Later, students learn to separate a group into parts in various ways and then to count to produce all of the number "partners" of a given number. Eventually students think of a number and know the different addition facts that make that number. Most students follow a natural developmental progression in learning to compose and decompose numbers with recognizable stages or levels. This developmental path can be described as part of a learning trajectory.

Age Range	Level Name	Level	Description
4	Pre-Part-Whole Recognizer	1	At the earliest levels of composing, a student only nonverbally recognizes parts and wholes. For example, when shown 4 red blocks and 2 blue blocks, a young student may intuitively appreciate that "all the blocks" includes the red and blue blocks, but when asked how many there are in all, the student may name a small number, such as 1.
5	Inexact Part-Whole Recognizer	2	A sign of development is that the student knows a whole is bigger than parts, but does not accurately quantify. For example, when shown 4 red blocks and 2 blue blocks and asked how many there are in all, the student may name a "large number," such as 5 or 10.
5	Composer to 4, then 5	3	At this level, a student begins to know number combinations. A student at this level quickly names parts of any whole, or the whole given the parts. For example, when shown 4, then 1 is secretly hidden, and then shown the 3 remaining, the student may quickly say "1" is hidden.

Age Range	Level Name	Level	Description
6	Composer to 7	4	The next sign of development is when a student knows number combinations to totals of 7. A student at this level quickly names parts of any whole, or the whole when given parts, and can double numbers to 10. For example, when shown 6, then 4 are secretly hidden, and then shown the 2 remaining, the student may quickly say "4" are hidden.
6	Composer to 10	5	This level is when a student knows number combinations to totals of 10. A student at this level may quickly name parts of any whole, or the whole when given parts, and can double numbers to 20. For example, this student would be able to say "9 and 9 is 18."
7	Composer with Tens and Ones	6	At this level, the student understands two-digit numbers as tens and ones, can count with dimes and pennies, and can perform two-digit addition with regrouping. For example, a student at this level may explain, "17 and 36 is like 17 and 3, which is 20, and 33, which is 53."

Learning Trajectories

Developmental Levels for Adding and Subtracting

Single-digit addition and subtraction are generally characterized as "math facts." It is assumed students must memorize these facts, yet research has shown that addition and subtraction have their roots in counting, counting on, number sense, the ability to compose and decompose numbers, and place value. Research has also shown that learning methods for addition and subtraction with understanding is much more effective than rote memorization of seemingly isolated facts. Most students follow an observable developmental progression in learning to add and subtract numbers with recognizable stages or levels. This developmental path can be described as part of a learning trajectory.

Age Range	Level Name	Level	Description
1	Pre +/−	1	At the earliest level, a student shows no sign of being able to add or subtract.
3	Nonverbal +/−	2	The first sign is when a student can add and subtract very small collections nonverbally. For example, when shown 2 objects, then 1 object being hidden under a napkin, the student identifies or makes a set of 3 objects to "match."
4	Small Number +/−	3	This level is when a student can find sums for joining problems up to 3 + 2 by counting with objects. For example, when asked, "You have 2 balls and get 1 more. How many in all?" the student may count out 2, then count out 1 more, then count all 3: "1, 2, 3, 3!"
5	Find Result +/−	4	**Addition** Evidence of this level in addition is when a student can find sums for joining (you had 3 apples and get 3 more; how many do you have in all?) and part-part-whole (there are 6 girls and 5 boys on the playground; how many students were there in all?) problems by direct modeling, counting all, with objects. For example, when asked, "You have 2 red balls and 3 blue balls. How many in all?" the student may count out 2 red, then count out 3 blue, then count all 5. **Subtraction** In subtraction, a student can also solve take-away problems by separating with objects. For example, when asked, "You have 5 balls and give 2 to Tom. How many do you have left?" the student may count out 5 balls, then take away 2, and then count the remaining 3.
5	Find Change +/−	5	**Addition** At this level, a student can find the missing addend (5 + _ = 7) by adding on objects. For example, when asked, "You have 5 balls and then get some more. Now you have 7 in all. How many did you get?" The student may count out 5, then count those 5 again starting at 1, then add more, counting "6, 7," then count the balls added to find the answer, 2. **Subtraction** A student can compare by matching in simple situations. For example, when asked, "Here are 6 dogs and 4 balls. If we give a ball to each dog, how many dogs will not get a ball?" a student at this level may count out 6 dogs, match 4 balls to 4 of them, then count the 2 dogs that have no ball.
5	Make It	6	A significant advancement occurs when a student is able to count on. This student can add on objects to make one number into another without counting from 1. For example, when told, "This puppet has 4 balls, but she should have 6. Make it 6," the student may put up 4 fingers on one hand, immediately count up from 4 while putting up 2 fingers on the other hand, saying, "5, 6," and then count or recognize the 2 fingers.

Age Range	Level Name	Level	Description
6	Counting Strategies +/−	7	This level occurs when a student can find sums for joining (you had 8 apples and get 3 more…) and part-part-whole (6 girls and 5 boys…) problems with finger patterns or by adding on objects or counting on. For example, when asked "How much is 4 and 3 more?" the student may answer "4…5, 6, 7. 7!" Students at this level can also solve missing addend (3 + _ = 7) or compare problems by counting on. When asked, for example, "You have 6 balls. How many more would you need to have 8?" the student may say, "6, 7 [puts up first finger], 8 [puts up second finger]. 2!"
6	Part-Whole +/−	8	Further development has occurred when the student has part-whole understanding. This student can solve problems using flexible strategies and some derived facts (for example, "5 + 5 is 10, so 5 + 6 is 11"), can sometimes do start-unknown problems (_ + 6 = 11), but only by trial and error. When asked, "You had some balls. Then you get 6 more. Now you have 11 balls. How many did you start with?" this student may lay out 6, then 3, count, and get 9. The student may put 1 more, say 10, then put 1 more. The student may count up from 6 to 11, then recount the group added, and say, "5!"
6	Numbers-in-Numbers +/−	9	Evidence of this level is when a student recognizes that a number is part of a whole and can solve problems when the start is unknown (_ + 4 = 9) with counting strategies. For example, when asked, "You have some balls, then you get 4 more balls, now you have 9. How many did you have to start with?" this student may count, putting up fingers, "5, 6, 7, 8, 9." The student may look at his or her fingers and say, "5!"
7	Deriver +/−	10	At this level, a student can use flexible strategies and derived combinations (for example, "7 + 7 is 14, so 7 + 8 is 15") to solve all types of problems. For example, when asked, "What's 7 plus 8?" this student thinks: 7 + 8 = 7 + [7 + 1] = [7 + 7] + 1 = 14 + 1 = 15. The student can also solve multidigit problems by incrementing or combining 10s and 1s. For example, when asked "What's 28 + 35?" this student may think: 20 + 30 = 50; + 8 = 58; 2 more is 60, and 3 more is 63. Combining 10s and 1s: 20 + 30 = 50. 8 + 5 is like 8 plus 2 and 3 more, so it is 13–50 and 13 is 63.
8+	Problem Solver +/−	11	As students develop their addition and subtraction abilities, they can solve by using flexible strategies and many known combinations. For example, when asked, "If I have 13 and you have 9, how could we have the same number?" this student may say, "9 and 1 is 10, then 3 more makes 13. 1 and 3 is 4. I need 4 more!"
8+	Multidigit +/−	12	Further development is shown when students can use composition of 10s and all previous strategies to solve multidigit +/− problems. For example, when asked, "What's 37 − 18?" this student may say, "Take 1 ten off the 3 tens; that's 2 tens. Take 7 off the 7. That's 2 tens and 0…20. I have one more to take off. That's 19." Or, when asked, "What's 28 + 35?" this child may think, 30 + 35 would be 65. But it's 28, so it's 2 less…63.

Developmental Levels for Multiplying and Dividing

Multiplication and division builds on addition and subtraction understanding and is dependent upon counting and place-value concepts. As students begin to learn to multiply, they make equal groups and count them all. They then learn skip counting and derive related products from products they know. Finding and using patterns aids in learning multiplication and division facts with understanding. Students typically follow an observable developmental progression in learning to multiply and divide numbers with recognizable stages or levels. This developmental path can be described as part of a learning trajectory.

Age Range	Level Name	Level	Description
2	Non-quantitative Sharer "Dumper"	1	Multiplication and division concepts begin very early with the problem of sharing. Early evidence of these concepts can be observed when a student dumps out blocks and gives some (not an equal number) to each person.
3	Beginning Grouper and Distributive Sharer	2	Progression to this level can be observed when a student is able to make small groups (fewer than 5). This student can share by "dealing out," but often only between 2 people, although he or she may not appreciate the numerical result. For example, to share 4 blocks, this student may give each person a block, check that each person has one, and repeat this.
4	Grouper and Distributive Sharer	3	The next level occurs when a student makes small equal groups (fewer than 6). This student can deal out equally between 2 or more recipients, but may not understand that equal quantities are produced. For example, the student may share 6 blocks by dealing out blocks to herself and a friend one at a time.
5	Concrete Modeler ×/÷	4	As students develop, they are able to solve small-number multiplying problems by grouping—making each group and counting all. At this level, a student can solve division/sharing problems with informal strategies, using concrete objects—up to 20 objects and 2 to 5 people—although the student may not understand equivalence of groups. For example, the student may distribute 20 objects by dealing out 2 blocks to each of 5 people, then 1 to each, until the blocks are gone.
6	Parts and Wholes ×/÷	5	A new level is evidenced when the student understands the inverse relation between divisor and quotient. For example, this student may understand "If you share with more people, each person gets fewer."

Age Range	Level Name	Level	Description
7	Skip Counter ×/÷	6	As students develop understanding in multiplication and division, they begin to use skip counting for multiplication and for measurement division (finding out how many groups). For example, given 20 blocks, 4 to each person, and asked how many people, the student may skip count by 4, holding up 1 finger for each count of 4. A student at this level may also use trial and error for partitive division (finding out how many in each group). For example, given 20 blocks, 5 people, and asked how many each should get, this student may give 3 to each, then 1 more, then 1 more.
8+	Deriver ×/÷	7	At this level, students use strategies and derived combinations and solve multidigit problems by operating on tens and ones separately. For example, a student at this level may explain "7 × 6, five 7s is 35, so 7 more is 42."
8+	Array Quantifier	8	Further development can be observed when a student begins to work with arrays. For example, given 7 × 4 with most of 5 × 4 covered, a student at this level may say, "There are 8 in these 2 rows, and 5 rows of 4 is 20, so 28 in all."
8+	Partitive Divisor	9	This level can be observed when a student is able to figure out how many are in each group. For example, given 20 blocks, 5 people, and asked how many each should get, a student at this level may say, "4, because 5 groups of 4 is 20."
8+	Multidigit ×/÷	10	As students progress, they begin to use multiple strategies for multiplication and division, from compensating to paper-and-pencil procedures. For example, a student becoming fluent in multiplication might explain that "19 times 5 is 95, because 20 fives is 100, and 1 less five is 95."

Learning Trajectories

Developmental Levels for Measuring

Measurement is one of the main real-world applications of mathematics. Counting is a type of measurement which determines how many items are in a collection. Measurement also involves assigning a number to attributes of length, area, and weight. Prekindergarten students know that mass, weight, and length exist, but they do not know how to reason about these or to accurately measure them. As students develop their understanding of measurement, they begin to use tools to measure and understand the need for standard units of measure. Students typically follow an observable developmental progression in learning to measure with recognizable stages or levels. This developmental path can be described as part of a learning trajectory.

Age Range	Level Name	Level	Description
3	Length Quantity Recognizer	1	At the earliest level, students can identify length as an attribute. For example, they might say, "I'm tall, see?"
4	Length Direct Comparer	2	In this level, students can physically align 2 objects to determine which is longer or if they are the same length. For example, they can stand 2 sticks up next to each other on a table and say, "This one's bigger."
5	Indirect Length Comparer	3	A sign of further development is when a student can compare the length of 2 objects by representing them with a third object. For example, a student might compare the length of 2 objects with a piece of string. Additional evidence of this level is that when asked to measure, the student may assign a length by guessing or moving along a length while counting (without equal-length units). The student may also move a finger along a line segment, saying 10, 20, 30, 31, 32.
6	Serial Orderer to 6+	4	At this level, a student can order lengths, marked in 1 to 6 units. For example, given towers of cubes, a student at this level may put them in order, 1 to 6.
6	End-to-End Length Measurer	5	At this level, the student can lay units end-to-end, although he or she may not see the need for equal-length units. For example, a student might lay 9-inch cubes in a line beside a book to measure how long it is.

Age Range	Level Name	Level	Description
7	Length Unit Iterater	6	A significant change occurs when a student can use a ruler and see the need for identical units.
7	Length Unit Relater	7	At this level, a student can relate size and number of units. For example, the student may explain, "If you measure with centimeters instead of inches, you'll need more of them because each one is smaller."
8	Length Measurer	8	As students develop measurement ability, they begin to measure, knowing the need for identical units, the relationships between different units, partitions of unit, and the zero point on rulers. At this level, the student also begins to estimate. The student may explain, "I used a meterstick 3 times, then there was a little left over. So, I lined it up from 0 and found 14 centimeters. So, it's 3 meters, 14 centimeters in all."
8	Conceptual Ruler Measurer	9	Further development in measurement is evidenced when a student possesses an "internal" measurement tool. At this level, the student mentally moves along an object, segmenting it, and counting the segments. This student also uses arithmetic to measure and estimates with accuracy. For example, a student at this level may explain, "I imagine one meterstick after another along the edge of the room. That's how I estimated the room's length to be 9 meters."

Developmental Levels for Recognizing Geometric Shapes

Geometric shapes can be used to represent and understand objects. Analyzing, comparing, and classifying shapes helps create new knowledge of shapes and their relationships. Shapes can be decomposed or composed into other shapes. Through their everyday activities, students build both intuitive and explicit knowledge of geometric figures. Most students can recognize and name basic two-dimensional shapes at four years of age. However, young students can learn richer concepts about shape if they have varied examples and nonexamples of shape, discussions about shapes and their characteristics, a wide variety of shape classes, and interesting tasks. Students typically follow an observable developmental progression in learning about shapes with recognizable stages or levels. This developmental path can be described as part of a learning trajectory.

Age Range	Level Name	Level	Description
2	Shape Matcher—Identical	1	The earliest sign of understanding shape is when a student can match basic shapes (circle, square, typical triangle) with the same size and orientation.
2	Sizes	2	A sign of development is when a student can match basic shapes with different sizes.
2	Orientations	3	This level of development is when a student can match basic shapes with different orientations.
3	Shape Recognizer—Typical	4	A sign of development is when a student can recognize and name a prototypical circle, square, and, less often, a typical triangle. For example, the student names this a square. ☐ Some students may name different sizes, shapes, and orientations of rectangles, but also accept some shapes that look rectangular but are not rectangles. Students name these shapes "rectangles" (including the nonrectangular parallelogram).
3	Shape Matcher—More Shapes	5	As students develop understanding of shape, they can match a wider variety of shapes with the same size and orientation.
4	Shape Recognizer—Circles, Squares, and Triangles	6	This sign of development is when a student can recognize some nonprototypical squares and triangles and may recognize some rectangles, but usually not rhombi (diamonds). Often, the student does not differentiate sides/corners. The student at this level may name these as triangles.
4	Constructor of Shapes from Parts Looks Like	7	A significant sign of development is when a student represents a shape by making a shape "look like" a goal shape. For example, when asked to make a triangle with sticks, the student may create the following: ☐ .

Age Range	Level Name	Level	Description
5	Shape Recognizer—All Rectangles	8	As students develop understanding of shape, they recognize more rectangle sizes, shapes, and orientations of rectangles. For example, a student at this level may correctly name these shapes "rectangles."
5	Side Recognizer	9	A sign of development is when a student recognizes parts of shapes and identifies sides as distinct geometric objects. For example, when asked what this shape is, the student may say it is a quadrilateral (or has 4 sides) after counting and running a finger along the length of each side.
5	Angle Recognizer	10	At this level, a student can recognize angles as separate geometric objects. For example, when asked, "Why is this a triangle," the student may say, "It has three angles" and count them, pointing clearly to each vertex (point at the corner).
5	Shape Recognizer—More Shapes	11	As students develop, they are able to recognize most basic shapes and prototypical examples of other shapes, such as hexagon, rhombus (diamond), and trapezoid. For example, a student can correctly identify and name all the following shapes:
6	Shape Identifier	12	At this level, the student can name most common shapes, including rhombi, "ellipses-is-not-circle." A student at this level implicitly recognizes right angles, so distinguishes between a rectangle and a parallelogram without right angles. A student may correctly name all the following shapes:
6	Angle Matcher	13	A sign of development is when the student can match angles concretely. For example, given several triangles, the student may find two with the same angles by laying the angles on top of one another.

Learning Trajectories

Age Range	Level Name	Level	Description
7	Parts of Shapes Identifier	14	At this level, the student can identify shapes in terms of their components. For example, the student may say, "No matter how skinny it looks, that's a triangle because it has 3 sides and 3 angles."
7	Constructor of Shapes from Parts—Exact	15	A significant step is when the student can represent a shape with completely correct construction, based on knowledge of components and relationships. For example, when asked to make a triangle with sticks, the student may create the following:
8	Shape Class Identifier	16	As students develop, they begin to use class membership (for example, to sort) not explicitly based on properties. For example, a student at this level may say, "I put the triangles over here, and the quadrilaterals, including squares, rectangles, rhombi, and trapezoids, over there."
8	Shape Property Identifier	17	At this level, a student can use properties explicitly. For example, a student may say, "I put the shapes with opposite sides that are parallel over here, and those with 4 sides but not both pairs of sides parallel over there."

Age Range	Level Name	Level	Description
8	Angle Size Comparer	18	The next sign of development is when a student can separate and compare angle sizes. For example, the student may say, "I put all the shapes that have right angles here, and all the ones that have bigger or smaller angles over there."
8	Angle Measurer	19	A significant step in development is when a student can use a protractor to measure angles.
8	Property Class Identifier	20	The next sign of development is when a student can use class membership for shapes (for example, to sort or consider shapes "similar") explicitly based on properties, including angle measure. For example, the student may say, "I put the equilateral triangles over here, and the right triangles over here."
8	Angle Synthesizer	21	As students develop understanding of shape, they can combine various meanings of angle (turn, corner, slant). For example, a student at this level could explain, "This ramp is at a 45° angle to the ground."

Developmental Levels for Composing Geometric Shapes

Students move through levels in the composition and decomposition of two-dimensional figures. Very young students cannot compose shapes but then gain ability to combine shapes into pictures, synthesize combinations of shapes into new shapes, and eventually substitute and build different kinds of shapes. Students typically follow an observable developmental progression in learning to compose shapes with recognizable stages or levels. This developmental path can be described as part of a learning trajectory.

Age Range	Level Name	Level	Description
2	Pre-Composer	1	The earliest sign of development is when a student can manipulate shapes as individuals, but is unable to combine them to compose a larger shape.
3	Pre-Decomposer	2	At this level, a student can decompose shapes, but only by trial and error.
4	Piece Assembler	3	Around age 4, a student can begin to make pictures in which each shape represents a unique role (for example, one shape for each body part) and shapes touch. A student at this level can fill simple outline puzzles using trial and error.
5	Picture Maker	4	As students develop, they are able to put several shapes together to make one part of a picture (for example, 2 shapes for 1 arm). A student at this level uses trial and error and does not anticipate creation of the new geometric shape. The student can choose shapes using "general shape" or side length, and fill "easy" outline puzzles that suggest the placement of each shape (but note that the student is trying to put a square in the puzzle where its right angles will not fit).
5	Simple Decomposer	5	A significant step occurs when the student is able to decompose ("take apart" into smaller shapes) simple shapes that have obvious clues as to their decomposition.
5	Shape Composer	6	A sign of development is when a student composes shapes with anticipation ("I know what will fit!"). A student at this level chooses shapes using angles as well as side lengths. Rotation and flipping are used intentionally to select and place shapes.

Age Range	Level Name	Level	Description
6	Substitution Composer	7	A sign of development is when a student is able to make new shapes out of smaller shapes and uses trial and error to substitute groups of shapes for other shapes in order to create new shapes in different ways. For example, the student can substitute shapes to fill outline puzzles in different ways.
6	Shape Decomposer (with Help)	8	As students develop, they can decompose shapes by using imagery that is suggested and supported by the task or environment.
7	Shape Composite Repeater	9	This level is demonstrated when the student can construct and duplicate units of units (shapes made from other shapes) intentionally, and understands each as being both multiple, small shapes and one larger shape. For example, the student may continue a pattern of shapes that leads to tiling.
7	Shape Decomposer with Imagery	10	A significant sign of development is when a student is able to decompose shapes flexibly by using independently generated imagery.
8	Shape Composer— Units of Units	11	Students demonstrate further understanding when they are able to build and apply units of units (shapes made from other shapes). For example, in constructing spatial patterns, the student can extend patterning activity to create a tiling with a new unit shape—a unit of unit shapes that he or she recognizes and consciously constructs. For example, the student may build Ts out of 4 squares, use 4 Ts to build squares, and use squares to tile a rectangle.
8	Shape Decomposer — Units of Units	12	As students develop understanding of shape, they can decompose shapes flexibly by using independently generated imagery and planned decompositions of shapes that themselves are decompositions.

Learning Trajectories

Developmental Levels for Comparing Geometric Shapes

As early as four years of age, students can create and use strategies, such as moving shapes to compare their parts or to place one on top of the other for judging whether two figures are the same shape. From PreK to Grade 2, they can develop sophisticated and accurate mathematical procedures for comparing geometric shapes. Students typically follow an observable developmental progression in learning about how shapes are the same and different with recognizable stages or levels. This developmental path can be described as part of a learning trajectory.

Age Range	Level Name	Level	Description
3	"Same Thing" Comparer	1	The first sign of understanding is when the student can compare real-world objects. For example, the student may say two pictures of houses are the same or different.
4	"Similar" Comparer	2	Thist sign of development occurs when the student judges two shapes to be the same if they are more visually similar than different. For example, the student may say, "These are the same. They are pointy at the top."
4	Part Comparer	3	At this level, a student can say that two shapes are the same after matching one side on each. For example, a student may say, "These are the same" (matching the two sides).
4	Some Attributes Comparer	4	As students develop, they look for differences in attributes, but may examine only part of a shape. For example, a student at this level may say, "These are the same" (indicating the top halves of the shapes are similar by laying them on top of each other).
5	Most Attributes Comparer	5	At this level, the student looks for differences in attributes, examining full shapes, but may ignore some spatial relationships. For example, a student may say, "These are the same."
7	Congruence Determiner	6	A sign of development is when a student determines congruence by comparing all attributes and all spatial relationships. For example, a student at this level may say that two shapes are the same shape and the same size after comparing every one of their sides and angles.
7	Congruence Superposer	7	As students develop understanding, they can move and place objects on top of each other to determine congruence. For example, a student at this level may say that two shapes are the same shape and the same size after laying them on top of each other.
8	Congruence Representer	8	Continued development is evidenced as students refer to geometric properties and explain transformations. For example, a student at this level may say, "These must be congruent because they have equal sides, all square corners, and I can move them on top of each other exactly."

Developmental Levels for Spatial Sense and Motions

Infants and toddlers spend a great deal of time learning about the properties and relations of objects in space. Very young students know and use the shape of their environment in navigation activities. With guidance they can learn to "mathematize" this knowledge. They can learn about direction, perspective, distance, symbolization, location, and coordinates. Students typically follow an observable developmental progression in developing spatial sense with recognizable stages or levels. This developmental path can be described as part of a learning trajectory.

Age Range	Level Name	Level	Description
4	Simple Turner	1	An early sign of spatial sense is when a student mentally turns an object to perform easy tasks. For example, given a shape with the top marked with color, the student may correctly identify which of three shapes it would look like if it were turned "like this" (90 degree turn demonstrated), before physically moving the shape.
5	Beginning Slider, Flipper, Turner	2	This sign of development occurs when a student can use the correct motions, but is not always accurate in direction and amount. For example, a student at this level may know a shape has to be flipped to match another shape, but flips it in the wrong direction.
6	Slider, Flipper, Turner	3	As students develop spatial sense, they can perform slides and flips, often only horizontal and vertical, by using manipulatives. For example, a student at this level may perform turns of 45, 90, and 180 degrees and know a shape must be turned 90 degrees to the right to fit into a puzzle.
7	Diagonal Mover	4	A sign of development is when a student can perform diagonal slides and flips. For example, a student at this level may know a shape must be turned or flipped over an oblique line (45 degree orientation) to fit into a puzzle.
8	Mental Mover	5	Further signs of development occur when a student can predict results of moving shapes using mental images. A student at this level may say, "If you turned this 120 degrees, it would be just like this one."

Developmental Levels for Patterning and Early Algebra

Algebra begins with a search for patterns. Identifying patterns helps bring order, cohesion, and predictability to seemingly unorganized situations and allows one to make generalizations beyond the information directly available. The recognition and analysis of patterns are important components of the young student's intellectual development because they provide a foundation for the development of algebraic thinking. Although prekindergarten students engage in pattern-related activities and recognize patterns in their everyday environment, research has revealed that an abstract understanding of patterns develops gradually during the early childhood years. Students typically follow an observable developmental progression in learning about patterns with recognizable stages or levels. This developmental path can be described as part of a learning trajectory.

Age Range	Level Name	Level	Description
2	Pre-Patterner	1	A student at the earliest level does not recognize patterns. For example, a student may name a striped shirt with no repeating unit a "pattern."
3	Pattern Recognizer	2	At this level, the student can recognize a simple pattern. For example, a student at this level may say, "I'm wearing a pattern" about a shirt with black and white stripes.
4	Pattern Fixer	3	At this level the student fills in missing elements of a pattern.
4	Pattern Duplicator AB	4	A sign of development is when the student can duplicate an ABABAB pattern, although the student may have to work alongside the model pattern. For example, given objects in a row, ABABAB, the student may make his or her own ABABAB row in a different location.
4	Pattern Duplicator	5	At this level, the student is able to duplicate simple patterns (not just alongside the model pattern). For example, given objects in a row, ABBABBABB, the student may make his or her own ABBABBABB row in a different location.

Age Range	Level Name	Level	Description
5	Pattern Extender	6	A sign of development is when the student can extend simple patterns. For example, given objects in a row, ABBABBABB, he or she may add ABBABB to the end of the row.
6	Pattern Maker from *n*	7	As a student develops patterning, he or she is able to fill in a missing element of a pattern. For example, given objects in a row with one missing, ABBAB_ABB, he or she may identify and fill in the missing element.
7	Pattern Unit Recognizer	8	At this level, a student can identify the smallest unit of a pattern. For example, given objects in a row with one missing, ABBAB_ABB, he or she may identify and fill in the missing element.

Glossary

A

absolute value The distance of a number from 0. For example, the absolute value of 7, written as |7|, is 7. The absolute value of −4, written as |−4|, is 4.

acute angle An angle with a measure greater than 0 degrees and less than 90 degrees.

addend One of the numbers being added in an addition sentence. In the sentence 41 + 27 = 68, the numbers 41 and 27 are addends.

addition A mathematical operation used for "putting things together." Numbers being added are called *addends*. The result of addition is called a *sum*. In the number sentence 15 + 63 = 78, the numbers 15 and 63 are addends.

additive inverses Two numbers whose sum is 0. For example, 9 + −9 = 0. The additive inverse of 9 is −9, and the additive inverse of −9 is 9.

adjacent angles Two angles with a common side that do not otherwise overlap. In the diagram, angles 1 and 2 are adjacent angles. So are angles 2 and 3, angles 3 and 4, and angles 4 and 1.

algorithm A step-by-step procedure for carrying out a computation or solving a problem.

angle Two rays with a common endpoint. The common endpoint is called the vertex of the angle.

area A measure of the surface inside a closed boundary. The formula for the area of a rectangle or parallelogram is $A = b \times h$, where A represents the area, b represents the length of the base, and h the height of the figure.

array A rectangular arrangement of objects in rows and columns in which each row has the same number of elements and each column has the same number of elements.

attribute A feature such as size, shape, or color.

average See **mean.** The **median** and **mode** are also sometimes called the average.

axis (plural **axes**) A number line used in a coordinate grid.

B

bar graph A graph in which the lengths of horizontal or vertical bars represent the magnitude of the data represented.

base See **exponential notation.**

base (of a parallelogram) One of the sides of a parallelogram; also, the length of this side. The length of a perpendicular line segment between the base and the side opposite the base is the height of the parallelogram.

base (of a polyhedron) The "bottom" face of a polyhedron; the face whose shape determines the type of prism or pyramid.

base (of a rectangle) One of the sides of a rectangle; also, the length of this side. The length of the side perpendicular to the base is the height of the rectangle.

base (of a triangle) One of the sides of a triangle; also, the length of this side. The shortest distance between the base and the vertex opposite the base is the height of the triangle.

base ten The commonly used numeration system, in which the ten digits 0, 1, 2,..., 9 have values that depend on the place in which they appear in a numeral (ones, tens, hundreds, and so on, to the left of the decimal point; tenths, hundredths, and so on, to the right of the decimal point).

benchmark A number or measure used as a standard of comparison for other numbers or measures.

bisect To divide a segment, angle, or figure into two parts of equal measure.

C

capacity A measure of how much liquid or substance a container can hold. See also **volume.**

centi- A prefix for units in the metric system meaning one hundredth.

centimeter (cm) In the metric system, a unit of length defined as $\frac{1}{100}$ of a meter; equal to 10 millimeters or $\frac{1}{10}$ of a decimeter.

circle The set of all points in a plane that are a given distance (the radius) from a given point (the center of the circle).

circle graph A graph in which a circular region is divided into sectors to represent the categories in a set of data. The circle represents the whole set of data.

circumference The distance around a circle or sphere.

clipped range In a set of numbers, the range calculated without the greatest and least value, or with the two or three greatest and least values removed.

closed figure A figure that divides the plane into two regions, inside and outside the figure. A closed space figure divides space into two regions in the same way.

common denominator Any nonzero number that is a multiple of the denominators of two or more fractions.

common factor Any number that is a factor of two or more numbers.

complementary angles Two angles whose measures total 90 degrees.

composite function A function with two or more operations. For example, this function multiplies the input number by 5 then adds 3.

composite number A whole number that has more than two whole number factors. For example, 14 is a composite number because it has more than two whole number factors.

concave (nonconvex) **polygon** A polygon in which a line segment between two of the points on the boundary lies outside the polygon.

cone A space figure having a circular base, curved surface, and one vertex.

congruent Having identical sizes and shapes. Congruent figures are said to be congruent to each other.

convex polygon A polygon in which line segments between any two points on the boundary lie inside or on the polygon.

coordinate One or more numbers used to fix the position of a point (on a line, in a plane, in space, and so on).

coordinate grid A device for locating points in a plane by means of ordered pairs or coordinates. A coordinate grid is formed by two number lines that intersect at their 0-points.

corresponding angles Two angles in the same relative position in two figures, or in similar locations in relation to a transversal intersecting two lines. In the diagram below, angles 1 and 5, 3 and 7, 2 and 6, and 4 and 8 are corresponding angles. If the lines are parallel, then the corresponding angles are congruent.

corresponding sides Two sides in the same relative position in two figures. In the diagram, AB and A'B', BC and B'C', and AC and A'C' are corresponding sides.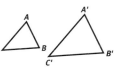

cube A space figure whose six faces are congruent squares that meet at right angles.

cubic centimeter (cm³) A metric unit of volume; the volume of a cube 1 centimeter on an edge. 1 cubic centimeter is equal to 1 milliliter.

cubic unit A unit used in a volume and capacity measurement.

customary system of measurement The measuring system used most often in the United States. Units for linear measure (length, distance) include inch, foot, yard, and mile; units for weight include ounce and pound; units for capacity (amount of liquid or other substance a container can hold) include fluid ounce, cup, pint, quart, and gallon.

cylinder A space figure having a curved surface and parallel circular or elliptical bases that are congruent.

D

decimal A number written in standard notation, usually one containing a decimal point, as in 3.78.

decimal approximation A decimal that is close to the value of a rational number. By extending the decimal approximation to additional digits, it is possible to come as close as desired to the value of the rational number. For example, decimal approximations of $\frac{1}{12}$ are 0.083, 0.0833, 0.08333, and so on.

decimal equivalent A decimal that names the same number as a fraction. For example, the decimal equivalent of $\frac{3}{4}$ is 0.75. The only rational numbers with decimal equivalents are those that can be written as fractions whose denominators have prime factors only of 2 and 5. For example, $\frac{1}{2}$, $\frac{1}{4}$, and $\frac{1}{20}$ have decimal equivalents, but $\frac{1}{6}$, $\frac{1}{7}$, and $\frac{1}{9}$ have only decimal approximations.

degree (°) A unit of measure for angles; based on dividing a circle into 360 equal parts. Also, a unit of measure for temperature.

degree Celsius (°C) In the metric system, the unit for measuring temperature. Water freezes at 0°C and boils at 100°C.

degree Fahrenheit (°F) In the U.S. customary system, the unit for measuring temperature. Water freezes at 32°F and boils at 212°F.

deltahedron A polyhedron whose faces are congruent equilateral triangles.

denominator The number of equal parts into which a whole is divided. In the fraction $\frac{a}{b}$, b is the denominator. See also **numerator.**

diameter A line segment, going through the center of a circle, that starts at one point on the circle and ends at the opposite point on the circle; also, the length of such a line segment. The diameter of a circle is twice its radius. AB is a diameter of this circle. See also **circle.**

difference The result of subtraction. In the subtraction sentence 40 − 10 = 30, the difference is 30.

digit In the base-ten numeration system, one of the symbols 0, 1, 2, 3, 4, 5, 6, 7, 8, 9. Digits can be used to write a numeral for any whole number in the base-ten numbering system. For example, the numeral 145 is made up of the digits 1, 4, and 5.

distributive law A law that relates two operations on numbers, usually multiplication and addition, or multiplication and subtraction. Distributive law of multiplication over addition: $a \times (b + c) = (a \times b) + (a \times c)$

dividend See **division.**

divisibility rule A rule that indicates whether a whole number is divisible by another whole number. For example, to tell whether a number is divisible by 3, check whether the sum of its digits is divisible by 3. The number 48 is divisible by 3 since 4 + 8 = 12, and 12 is divisible by 3.

divisible by One whole number is divisible by another whole number if the result of the division is a whole number (with a remainder of 0). For example, 35 is divisible by 5, because 35 divided by 5 is 7 with a remainder of 0. If a number n is divisible by a number x, then x is a factor of n. See also **factor of a whole number n.**

division A mathematical operation used for "equal sharing" or "separating into equal parts." Division is the inverse operation of multiplication. The *dividend* is the total before sharing. The *divisor* is the number of equal parts or the number in each equal part. The *quotient* is the result of division. For example, in 35 ÷ 5 = 7, 35 is the dividend, 5 is the divisor, and 7 is the quotient. If 35 objects are separated into 5 equal parts, there are 7 objects in each part. If 35 objects are separated into parts with 5 in each part, there are 7 equal parts. The number left over when a set of objects is shared equally or separated into equal groups is called the *remainder*. For 35 ÷ 5, the quotient is 7 and the remainder is 0. For 36 ÷ 5, the quotient is 7 and the remainder is 1.

divisor See **division.**

dodecahedron A space figure with twelve faces. In a regular dodecahedron, each face is formed by a pentagon.

E

edge The line segment where two faces of a polyhedron meet.

endpoint The point at either end of a line segment; also, the point at the end of a ray. Line segments are named after their endpoints; a line segment between and including points A and B is usually called segment AB or segment BA.

equation A mathematical sentence that states the equality of two expressions. For example, $3 + 7 = 10$, $y = x + 7$, and $4 + 7 = 8 + 3$ are equations.

equilateral polygon A polygon in which all sides are the same length.

equivalent Equal in value, but in a different form. For example, $\frac{1}{2}$, $\frac{2}{4}$, 0.5, and 50% are equivalent forms of the same number.

equivalent fractions Fractions that have different numerators and denominators but name the same number. For example, $\frac{2}{3}$ and $\frac{6}{9}$ are equivalent fractions.

estimate A judgment of a time, measurement, number, or other quantity that may not be exactly right.

evaluate an algebraic expression To replace each variable in an algebraic expression with a particular number and then calculate the value of the expression.

evaluate a numerical expression To carry out the operations in a numerical expression to find the value of the expression.

even number A whole number such as 0, 2, 4, 6, and so on, that can be divided by 2 with no remainder. See also **odd number.**

event A happening or occurrence. The tossing of a coin is an event.

exponent See **exponential notation.**

exponential notation A shorthand way of representing repeated multiplication of the same factor. For example, 4^3 is exponential notation for $4 \times 4 \times 4$. The small raised 3, called the *exponent*, indicates how many times the number 4, called the *base*, is used as a factor.

expression A group of mathematical symbols (numbers, operation signs, variables, grouping symbols) that represents a number (or can represent a number if values are assigned to any variables it contains).

F

face A flat surface on a space figure.

fact family A group of addition or multiplication facts grouped together with the related subtraction or division facts. For example, 4 + 8 = 12, 8 + 4 = 12, 12 − 4 = 8, and 12 − 8 = 4 form an addition fact family. The facts 4 × 3 = 12, 3 × 4 = 12, 12 ÷ 3 = 4, and 12 ÷ 4 = 3 form a multiplication fact family.

Glossary

factor (noun) One of the numbers that is multiplied in a multiplication expression. For example, in $4 \times 1.5 = 6$, the factors are 4 and 1.5. See also **multiplication.**

factor (verb) To represent a quantity as a product of factors. For example, 20 factors to 4×5, 2×10, or $2 \times 2 \times 5$.

factor of a whole number n A whole number, which, when multiplied by another whole number, results in the number n. The whole number n is divisible by its factors. For example, 3 and 5 are factors of 15 because $3 \times 5 = 15$, and 15 is divisible by 3 and 5.

factor tree A method used to obtain the prime factorization of a number. The original number is represented as a product of factors, and each of those factors is represented as a product of factors, and so on, until the factor string consists of prime numbers.

fair A coin, spinner, number cube, and so on is said to be fair if, over a large number of tosses, the results are consistent with the predictions of probability. On a fair coin, heads and tails should come up about equally often; the six sides of a fair number cube should come up about equally often.

fair game A game in which each player has the same chance of winning. If any player has an advantage or disadvantage (for example, by playing first), then the game is not fair.

finger sets An organized way taught in *Real Math* of showing numbers using fingers.

formula A general rule for finding the value of something. A formula is usually written as an equation with variables representing unknown quantities. For example, a formula for distance traveled at a constant rate of speed is $d = r \times t$, where d stands for distance, r for rate, and t for time.

fraction A number in the form $\frac{a}{b}$, where a and b are integers and b is greater than 0. Fractions are used to name part of a whole object or part of a whole collection of objects, or to compare two quantities. A fraction can represent division; for example, $\frac{2}{5}$ can be thought of as 2 divided by 5.

frequency The number of times an event or value occurs in a set of data.

function machine An imaginary machine that processes numbers according to a certain rule. A number (input) is put into the machine and is transformed into a second number (output) by application of the rule.

G

greatest common factor The largest factor that two or more numbers have in common. For example, the common factors of 24 and 30 are 1, 2, 3, and 6. The greatest common factor of 24 and 30 is 6.

H

height (of a polygon) The length of the line segment perpendicular to the base of the polygon (or an extension of the base) from the opposite side or vertex.

height (of a polyhedron) The perpendicular distance between the bases of the polyhedron or between a base and the opposite vertex.

heptagon A polygon with seven sides.

hexagon A polygon with six sides.

histogram A bar graph in which the labels for the bars are numerical intervals.

hypotenuse In a right triangle, the side opposite the right angle.

I

icosahedron A space figure with twenty triangular faces.

improper fraction A fraction that names a number greater than or equal to 1; a fraction whose numerator is equal to or greater than its denominator. Examples of improper fractions are $\frac{4}{3}$, $\frac{10}{8}$, and $\frac{4}{4}$.

inch (in.) In the U. S. customary system, a unit of length equal to $\frac{1}{12}$ of a foot.

independent events Events A and B for which knowing that event A has occurred does not influence the probability that event B will occur.

indirect measurement Methods for determining heights, distances, and other quantities that cannot be measured or are not measured directly.

inequality A number sentence stating that two quantities are not equal. Relation symbols for inequalities include < (is less than), > (is greater than), and ≠ (is not equal to).

integers The set of integers is {..., -4, -3, -2, -1, 0, 1, 2, 3, 4, ...}. The set of integers consists of whole numbers and their opposites.

intersect To meet (at a point, a line, and so on), sharing a common point or points.

interior The set of all points in a plane "inside" a closed plane figure, such as a polygon or circle. Also, the set of all points in space "inside" a closed space figure, such as a polyhedron or sphere.

K

kilo- A prefix for units in the metric system meaning one thousand.

L

least common denominator The least common multiple of the denominators of every fraction in a given set of fractions. For example, 12 is the least common denominator of $\frac{2}{3}$, $\frac{1}{4}$, and $\frac{5}{6}$. See also **least common multiple.**

least common multiple The smallest number that is a multiple of two or more numbers. For example, some common multiples of 6 and 8 are 24, 48, and 72. 24 is the least common multiple of 6 and 8.

leg of a right triangle A side of a right triangle that is not the hypotenuse.

line A straight path that extends infinitely in opposite directions.

line graph (broken-line graph) A graph in which points are connected by line segments to represent data.

line of symmetry A line that separates a figure into halves. The figure can be folded along this line into two parts which exactly fit on top of each other.

line segment A straight path joining two points, called *endpoints* of the line segment. A straight path can be described as the shortest distance between two points.

line symmetry A figure has line symmetry (also called *bilateral symmetry*) if a line of symmetry can be drawn through the figure.

liter (L) A metric unit of capacity, equal to the volume of a cube 10 centimeters on an edge. $1 \text{ L} = 1{,}000 \text{ mL} = 1{,}000 \text{ cm}^3$. A liter is slightly larger than a quart. See also **milliliter (mL).**

M

map scale A ratio that compares the distance between two locations shown on a map with the actual distance between them.

mean A typical or central value that may be used to describe a set of numbers. It can be found by adding the numbers in the set and dividing the sum by the number of numbers. The mean is often referred to as the *average*.

median The middle value in a set of data when the data are listed in order from least to greatest (or greatest to least). If the number of values in the set is even (so that there is no "middle" value), the median is the mean of the two middle values.

isosceles Having two sides of the same length; commonly used to refer to triangles and trapezoids.

meter (m) The basic unit of length in the metric system, equal to 10 decimeters, 100 centimeters, and 1,000 millimeters.

metric system of measurement A measurement system based on the base-ten numeration system and used in most countries in the world. Units for linear measure (length, distance) include millimeter, centimeter, meter, kilometer; units for mass (weight) include gram and kilogram; units for capacity (amount of liquid or other substance a container can hold) include milliliter and liter.

midpoint A point halfway between two points.

milli- A prefix for units in the metric system meaning one thousandth.

milliliter (mL) A metric unit of capacity, equal to 1/1,000 of a liter and 1 cubic centimeter.

millimeter (mm) In the metric system, a unit of length equal to 1/10 of a centimeter and 1/1,000 of a meter.

minuend See **subtraction.**

mixed number A number greater than 1, written as a whole number and a fraction less than 1. For example, $5\frac{1}{2}$ is equal to $5 + \frac{1}{2}$.

mode The value or values that occur most often in a set of data.

multiple of a number _n_ The product of a whole number and the number _n_. For example, the numbers 0, 4, 8, 12, and 16 are all multiples of 4 because $4 \times 0 = 0$, $4 \times 1 = 4$, $4 \times 2 = 8$, $4 \times 3 = 12$, and $4 \times 4 = 16$.

multiplication A mathematical operation used to find the total number of things in several equal groups, or to find a quantity that is a certain number of times as much or as many as another number. Numbers being multiplied are called _factors_. The result of multiplication is called the _product_. In $8 \times 12 = 96$, 8 and 12 are the factors and 96 is the product.

multiplicative inverses Two numbers whose product is 1. For example, the multiplicative inverse of $\frac{2}{5}$ is $\frac{5}{2}$, and the multiplicative inverse of 8 is $\frac{1}{8}$. Multiplicative inverses are also called _reciprocals_ of each other.

N

negative number A number less than 0; a number to the left of 0 on a horizontal number line.

number line A line on which equidistant points correspond to integers in order.

number sentence A sentence that is made up of numerals and a relation symbol ($<$, $>$, or $=$). Most number sentences also contain at least one operation symbol. Number sentences may also have grouping symbols, such as parentheses.

numeral The written name of a number.

numerator In a whole divided into a number of equal parts, the number of equal parts being considered. In the fraction $\frac{a}{b}$, _a_ is the numerator.

O

obtuse angle An angle with a measure greater than 90 degrees and less than 180 degrees.

octagon An eight-sided polygon.

octahedron A space figure with eight faces.

odd number A whole number that is not divisible by 2, such as 1, 3, 5, and so on. When an odd number is divided by 2, the remainder is 1. A whole number is either an odd number or an even number.

opposite of a number A number that is the same distance from 0 on the number line as the given number, but on the opposite side of 0. If _a_ is a negative number, the opposite of _a_ will be a positive number. For example, if $a = -5$, then $-a$ is 5. See also **additive inverses.**

ordered pair Two numbers or objects for which order is important. Often, two numbers in a specific order used to locate a point on a coordinate grid. They are usually written inside parentheses; for example, (2, 3). See also **coordinate.**

ordinal number A number used to express position or order in a series, such as first, third, tenth. People generally use ordinal numbers to name dates; for example, "May fifth" rather than "May five."

origin The point where the _x_- and _y_-axes intersect on a coordinate grid. The coordinates of the origin are (0, 0).

outcome The result of an event. Heads and tails are the two outcomes of the event of tossing a coin.

P

parallel lines (segments, rays) Lines (segments, rays) going in the same direction that are the same distance apart and never meet.

parallelogram A quadrilateral that has two pairs of parallel sides. Pairs of opposite sides and opposite angles of a parallelogram are congruent.

parentheses A pair of symbols, (and), used to show in which order operations should be done. For example, the expression $(3 \times 5) + 7$ says to multiply 5 by 3 then add 7. The expression $3 \times (5 + 7)$ says to add 5 and 7 and then multiply by 3.

pattern A model, plan, or rule that uses words or variables to describe a set of shapes or numbers that repeat in a predictable way.

pentagon A polygon with five sides.

percent A rational number that can be written as a fraction with a denominator of 100. The symbol % is used to represent percent. 1% means 1/100 or 0.01. For example, "53% of the students in the school are girls" means that out of every 100 students in the school, 53 are girls.

perimeter The distance along a path around a plane figure. A formula for the perimeter of a rectangle is $P = 2 \times (B + H)$, where _B_ represents the base and _H_ is the height of the rectangle. Perimeter may also refer to the path itself.

perpendicular Two rays, lines, line segments, or other figures that form right angles are said to be perpendicular to each other.

pi The ratio of the circumference of a circle to its diameter. Pi is the same for every circle, approximately 3.14 or $\frac{22}{7}$. Also written as the Greek letter π.

pictograph A graph constructed with pictures or icons, in which each picture stands for a certain number. Pictographs make it easier to visually compare quantities.

place value A way of determining the value of a digit in a numeral, written in standard notation, according to its position, or place, in the numeral. In base-ten numbers, each place has a value ten times that of the place to its right and one-tenth the value of the place to its left.

plane A flat surface that extends forever.

plane figure A figure that can be contained in a plane (that is, having length and width but no height).

point A basic concept of geometry; usually thought of as a location in space, without size.

polygon A closed plane figure consisting of line segments (sides) connected endpoint to endpoint. The interior of a polygon consists of all the points of the plane "inside" the polygon. An _n_-gon is a polygon with _n_ sides; for example, an 8-gon has 8 sides.

polyhedron A closed space figure, all of whose surfaces (faces) are flat. Each face consists of a polygon and the interior of the polygon.

Glossary

power A product of factors that are all the same. For example, $6 \times 6 \times 6$ (or 216) is called 6 to the third power, or the third power of 6, because 6 is a factor three times. The expression $6 \times 6 \times 6$ can also be written as 6^3.

power of 10 A whole number that can be written as a product using only 10 as a factor. For example, 100 is equal to 10×10 or 10^2, so 100 is called 10 squared, the second power of 10, or 10 to the second power. Other powers of 10 include 10^1, or 10, and 10^3, or 1,000.

precision (of a count or measurement) An indicator of how close a count or measure is believed to be to the actual count or measure. The precision of a measurement may be improved by using measuring instruments with smaller units.

prime factorization A whole number expressed as a product of prime factors. For example, the prime factorization of 18 is $2 \times 3 \times 3$. A number has only one prime factorization (except for the order in which the factors are written).

prime number A whole number greater than 1 that has exactly two whole number factors, 1 and itself. For example, 13 is a prime number because its only factors are 1 and 13. A prime number is divisible only by 1 and itself. The first five prime numbers are 2, 3, 5, 7, and 11. See also **composite number.**

prism A polyhedron with two parallel faces (bases) that are the same size and shape. Prisms are classified according to the shape of the two parallel bases. The bases of a prism are connected by parallelograms that are often rectangular.

probability A number between 0 and 1 that indicates the likelihood that something (an event) will happen. The closer a probability is to 1, the more likely it is that an event will happen.

product See **multiplication.**

protractor A tool for measuring or drawing angles. When measuring an angle, the vertex of the angle should be at the center of the protractor and one side should be aligned with the 0 mark.

pyramid A polyhedron in which one face (the base) is a polygon and the other faces are formed by triangles with a common vertex (the apex). A pyramid is classified according to the shape of its base, as a triangular pyramid, square pyramid, pentagonal pyramid, and so on.

Pythagorean Theorem A mathematical theorem, proven by the Greek mathematician Pythagoras and known to many others before and since, that states that if the legs of a right triangle have lengths a and b, and the hypotenuse has length c, then $a^2 + b^2 = c^2$.

Q

quadrilateral A polygon with four sides.

quotient See **division.**

R

radius A line segment that goes from the center of a circle to any point on the circle; also, the length of such a line segment.

random sample A sample taken from a population in a way that gives all members of the population the same chance of being selected.

range The difference between the maximum and minimum values in a set of data.

rate A ratio comparing two quantities with unlike units. For example, a measure such as 23 miles per gallon of gas compares mileage with gas usage.

ratio A comparison of two quantities using division. Ratios can be expressed with fractions, decimals, percents, or words. For example, if a team wins 4 games out of 5 games played, the ratio of wins to total games is $\frac{4}{5}$, 0.8, or 80%.

rational number Any number that can be represented in the form $a \div b$ or $\frac{a}{b}$, where a and b are integers and b is positive. Some, but not all, rational numbers have exact decimal equivalents.

ray A straight path that extends infinitely in one direction from a point, which is called its *endpoint*.

reciprocal See **multiplicative inverses.**

rectangle A parallelogram with four right angles.

reduced form A fraction in which the numerator and denominator have no common factors except 1.

reflection A transformation in which a figure "flips" so that its image is the reverse of the original.

regular polygon A convex polygon in which all the sides are the same length and all the angles have the same measure.

regular polyhedron (plural **polyhedra**) A polyhedron with faces that are all congruent regular polygons with their interiors. The same number of faces meet at each vertex. There are five regular polyhedra:

tetrahedron four faces, each formed by an equilateral triangle

cube six faces, each formed by a square

octahedron eight faces, each formed by an equilateral triangle

dodecahedron twelve faces, each formed by a regular pentagon

icosahedron twenty faces, each formed by an equilateral triangle

relation symbol A symbol used to express the relationship between two numbers or expressions. Among the symbols used in number sentences are = for "is equal to," < for "is less than," > for "is greater than," and ≠ for "is not equal to."

remainder See **division.**

rhombus A parallelogram whose sides are all the same length.

right angle An angle with a measure of 90 degrees, representing a quarter of a full turn.

right triangle A triangle that has a right angle.

rotation A transformation in which a figure "turns" around a center point or axis.

rotational symmetry Property of a figure that can be rotated around a point (less than a full, 360-degree turn) in such a way that the resulting figure exactly matches the original figure. If a figure has rotational symmetry, its order of rotational symmetry is the number of different ways it can be rotated to match itself exactly. "No rotation" is counted as one of the ways.

rounding Changing a number to another number that is easier to work with and is close enough for the purpose. For example, 12,924 rounded to the nearest thousand is 13,000 and rounded to the nearest hundred is 12,900.

S

sample A subset of a group used to represent the whole group.

scale The ratio of the distance on a map or drawing to the actual distance.

scalene triangle A triangle in which all three sides have different lengths.

scale drawing An accurate picture of an object in which all parts are drawn to the same scale. If an actual object measures 32 by 48 meters, a scale drawing of it might measure 32 by 48 millimeters.

scale model A model that represents an object or display in proportions based on a determined scale.

scientific notation A method of expressing a number as the product of two factors, one of which is a number greater than or equal to 1 but less than 10, and the other of which is a power of 10. The notation is used to describe very great (or very small) numbers. For example, 4,000,000 in scientific notation is 4×10^6.

similar figures Figures that are exactly the same shape but not necessarily the same size.

space figure A figure which cannot be contained in a plane. Common space figures include the rectangular prism, square pyramid, cylinder, cone, and sphere.

sphere The set of all points in space that are a given distance (the radius) from a given point (the center). A ball is shaped like a sphere.

square number A number that is the product of a whole number and itself. The number 36 is a square number, because $36 = 6 \times 6$.

square of a number The product of a number multiplied by itself. For example, 2.5 squared is $(2.5)^2$.

square root The square root of a number n is a number which, when multiplied by itself, results in the number n. For example, 8 is a square root of 64, because $8 \times 8 = 64$.

square unit A unit used to measure area—usually a square that is 1 inch, 1 centimeter, 1 yard, or other standard unit of length on each side.

standard notation The most familiar way of representing whole numbers, integers, and decimals by writing digits in specified places; the way numbers are usually written in everyday situations.

statistics The science of collecting, classifying, and interpreting numerical data as it is related to a particular subject.

stem-and-leaf plot A display of data in which digits with larger place values are named as stems, and digits with smaller place values are named as leaves.

straight angle An angle of 180 degrees; a line with one point identified as the vertex of the angle.

subtraction A mathematical operation used for "taking away" or comparing ("How much more?"). Subtraction is the inverse operation of addition. The number being subtracted is called the *subtrahend*; the number it is subtracted from is called the *minuend*; the result of subtraction is called the *difference*. In the number sentence $63 - 45 = 18$, 63 is the minuend, 45 is the subtrahend, and 18 is the difference.

subtrahend See **subtraction.**

supplementary angles Two angles whose measures total 180 degrees.

surface area The sum of the areas of the faces or surfaces of a space figure.

symmetrical Having the same size and shape across a dividing line or around a point.

T

tessellation An arrangement of closed shapes that covers a surface completely without overlaps or gaps.

tetrahedron A space figure with four faces, each formed by an equilateral triangle.

theorem A mathematical statement that can be proved to be true (or, sometimes, a statement that is proposed and needs to be proved). For example, the Pythagorean Theorem states that if the legs of a right triangle have lengths a and b, and the hypotenuse has length c, then $a^2 + b^2 = c^2$.

transformation An operation that moves or changes a geometric figure in a specified way. Rotations, reflections, and translations are types of transformations.

translation A transformation in which a figure "slides" along a line.

transversal A line which intersects two or more other lines.

trapezoid A quadrilateral with exactly one pair of parallel sides.

tree diagram A tool used to solve probability problems in which there is a series of events. This tree diagram represents a situation where the first event has three possible outcomes and the second event has two possible outcomes.

triangle A polygon with three sides. An *equilateral* triangle has three sides of the same length. An *isosceles* triangle has two sides of the same length. A *scalene* triangle has no sides of the same length.

U

unit (of measure) An agreed-upon standard with which measurements are compared.

unit fraction A fraction whose numerator is 1. For example, $\frac{1}{2}, \frac{1}{3}$, and $\frac{1}{10}$ are unit fractions.

unit cost The cost of one item or one specified amount of an item. If 20 pencils cost 60¢, then the unit cost is 3¢ per pencil.

unlike denominators Unequal denominators, as in $\frac{3}{4}$ and $\frac{5}{6}$.

V

variable A letter or other symbol that represents a number, one specific number, or many different values.

Venn diagram A picture that uses circles to show relationships between sets. Elements that belong to more than one set are placed in the overlap between the circles.

vertex The point at which the rays of an angle, two sides of a polygon, or the edges of a polyhedron meet.

vertical angles Two intersecting lines form four adjacent angles. In the diagram, angles 2 and 4 are vertical angles. They have no sides in common. Their measures are equal. Similarly, angles 1 and 3 are vertical angles.

volume A measure of the amount of space occupied by a space figure.

W

whole number Any of the numbers 0, 1, 2, 3, 4, and so on. Whole numbers are the numbers used for counting and zero.

Addition (Whole Numbers)

	PreK	K	1	2	3	4	5	6
Meaning of addition	•	•	•	•				
Basic facts			•	•	•	•	•	•
Missing addend problems			•	•	•	•	•	•
Three or more addends			•	•	•	•	•	•
Two-digit numbers			•	•	•	•	•	•
Three-digit numbers				•	•	•	•	•
Greater numbers					•	•	•	•
Adding money			•	•	•	•	•	•
Estimating sums			•	•	•	•	•	•

Algebra

	PreK	K	1	2	3	4	5	6
Properties of whole numbers				•	•	•	•	•
Integers (negative numbers)					•	•	•	•
Operations with integers						•	•	•
Missing-term problems	•			•	•	•	•	•
Making and solving number sentences and equations				•	•	•	•	•
Variables					•	•	•	•
Parentheses and order of operations						•	•	•
Inverse operations			•	•	•	•	•	•
Function machines/tables		•	•	•	•	•	•	•
Function rules		•	•	•	•	•	•	•
Inverse functions			•	•	•	•	•	•
Composite functions				•	•	•	•	•
Coordinate graphing								
One quadrant				•	•	•	•	•
Four quadrants						•	•	•
Graphing linear functions					•	•	•	•
Graphing nonlinear functions						•	•	•
Using formulas						•	•	•
Square numbers					•	•	•	•
Square roots						•	•	•

Decimals and Money

	PreK	K	1	2	3	4	5	6
Place value				•	•	•	•	•
Comparing and ordering				•	•	•	•	•
Rounding						•	•	•
Relating decimals and fractions				•	•	•	•	•
Relating decimals and percents						•	•	•
Adding				•	•	•	•	•
Estimating sums					•	•	•	•
Subtracting				•	•	•	•	•
Estimating differences				•	•	•	•	•
Multiplying by powers of 10						•	•	•
Multiplying by a whole number						•	•	•
Multiplying by a decimal							•	•
Estimating products						•	•	•
Dividing by powers of 10						•	•	•
Dividing by a whole number					•	•	•	•
Dividing by a decimal								•
Estimating quotients							•	•

	PreK	K	1	2	3	4	5	6
Identifying and counting currency		•	•	•	•	•		
Exchanging money		•	•	•	•			
Making change			•	•	•			
Computing with money		•	•	•	•	•	•	•

Division (Whole Numbers)

	PreK	K	1	2	3	4	5	6
Meaning of division	•	•	•	•	•	•		
Basic facts				•	•	•	•	•
Remainders					•	•	•	•
Missing-term problems				•	•	•	•	•
One-digit divisors					•	•	•	•
Two-digit divisors						•	•	•
Greater divisors							•	•
Dividing by multiples of 10							•	•
Dividing money							•	•
Estimating quotients					•	•	•	•

Fractions

	PreK	K	1	2	3	4	5	6
Fractions of a whole		•	•	•	•	•	•	•
Fractions of a set			•	•	•	•	•	•
Fractions of a number			•	•	•	•	•	•
Comparing/ordering			•	•	•	•	•	•
Equivalent fractions			•	•	•	•	•	•
Reduced form						•	•	•
Mixed numbers and improper fractions					•	•	•	•
Adding—like denominators					•	•	•	•
Adding—unlike denominators						•	•	•
Adding mixed numbers						•	•	•
Subtracting—like denominators					•	•	•	•
Subtracting—unlike denominators						•	•	•
Subtracting mixed numbers						•	•	•
Multiplying by a whole number						•	•	•
Multiplying by a fraction or mixed number						•	•	•
Reciprocals							•	•
Dividing a fraction by a whole number							•	•
Dividing by a fraction or mixed number							•	•

Geometry

	PreK	K	1	2	3	4	5	6
Identifying/drawing figures	•	•	•	•	•	•	•	•
Classifying figures	•	•	•	•	•	•	•	•
Classifying triangles			•	•	•	•	•	•
Classifying quadrilaterals			•	•	•	•	•	•
Solid figures		•	•	•	•	•	•	•
Congruence	•	•	•	•	•	•	•	•
Similarity						•	•	•
Line symmetry		•	•	•	•	•	•	•
Rotational symmetry						•	•	•
Translation/reflection/rotation	•			•	•	•	•	•
Measuring and classifying angles				•	•	•	•	•
Parallel and perpendicular lines				•	•	•	•	•
Relationships with parallel lines				•	•	•	•	•
Perimeter			•	•	•	•	•	•

	PreK	K	1	2	3	4	5	6
Radius and diameter					•	•	•	•
Circumference					•	•	•	•
Areas of triangles					•	•	•	•
Areas of quadrilaterals				•	•	•	•	•
Surface area					•	•	•	•
Volume				•	•	•	•	•
Pythagorean Theorem						•	•	•
Points, lines, and planes (new category)						•	•	•
Open and closed figures (new category)			•					
Spatial visualization	•						•	•

Manipulatives

	PreK	K	1	2	3	4	5	6
Used in concept development	•	•	•	•	•	•	•	•
Used in reteaching and individualized instruction	•	•	•	•	•	•	•	•

Measurement

	PreK	K	1	2	3	4	5	6
Converting within customary system					•	•	•	•
Converting within metric system					•	•	•	•
Length								
Estimate	•	•	•	•	•	•	•	•
Compare	•	•	•	•	•			•
Use nonstandard units	•	•	•	•	•			
Use customary units				•	•	•	•	•
Use metric units				•	•	•	•	•
Mass/Weight								
Estimate	•	•	•	•	•			
Compare	•	•	•	•				
Use nonstandard units		•	•	•				
Use customary units					•	•	•	•
Use metric units					•	•	•	•
Capacity								
Estimate	•	•	•	•				
Compare	•	•	•	•				
Use nonstandard units		•	•	•				
Use customary units				•	•	•	•	•
Use metric units				•	•	•	•	•
Temperature								
Estimate		•						•
Use degrees Fahrenheit				•	•	•	•	•
Use degrees Celsius				•	•	•	•	•
Telling time								
To the hour		•	•	•	•			
To the half hour		•	•	•	•			
To the quarter hour				•	•			
To the minute				•	•			
Adding and subtracting time				•	•	•	•	
A.M. and P.M.				•	•			
Estimating time		•	•					
Calculating elapsed time				•	•	•	•	
Reading a calendar		•	•	•	•		•	
Reading maps		•	•	•	•	•	•	•

Mental Arithmetic

	PreK	K	1	2	3	4	5	6
Basic fact strategies—addition and subtraction								
Use patterns			•	•				
Count on			•	•				
Count on or back	•	•	•	•				
Use doubles			•	•				
Use doubles plus 1			•	•				
Multiples of 10/Base-ten		•	•	•	•	•		
Use properties			•	•	•			
Use related facts			•	•				
Basic fact strategies—multiplication and division								
Use patterns				•	•	•		
Use skip counting				•	•			
Use properties					•	•		
Use related facts					•	•		
Chain calculations				•	•	•	•	•
Multidigit addition and subtraction				•	•	•	•	•
Multidigit multiplication and division					•	•	•	•
Multiples and powers of 10				•	•	•	•	•
Using computational patterns				•	•	•	•	•
Approximation				•	•	•	•	•
Find a fraction of a number					•	•	•	•
Find a percent of a number						•	•	•
Use divisibility rules						•	•	•
Find equivalent fractions, decimals, and percents						•	•	•

Multiplication (Whole Numbers)

	PreK	K	1	2	3	4	5	6
Meaning of multiplication			•	•	•	•	•	•
Basic facts				•	•	•	•	•
Missing-factor problems				•	•	•	•	•
One-digit multipliers				•	•	•	•	•
Two-digit multipliers						•	•	•
Greater multipliers						•	•	•
Multiplying by multiples of 10					•	•	•	•
Multiplying money					•	•	•	•
Estimating products					•	•	•	•

Number and Numeration

	PreK	K	1	2	3	4	5	6
Reading and writing numbers	•	•	•	•	•	•	•	•
Number lines	•	•	•	•	•	•	•	•
Counting	•	•	•	•	•	•		
Skip counting			•	•	•	•		
Ordinal numbers	•	•	•	•				
Place value				•	•	•	•	•
Comparing and ordering numbers	•		•	•	•	•	•	•
Rounding				•	•	•	•	•
Estimation/Approximation			•	•	•	•	•	•
Integers (negative numbers)					•	•	•	•
Even/odd numbers			•	•	•	•		
Prime and composite numbers						•	•	•
Factors and prime factorization						•	•	•

	PreK	K	1	2	3	4	5	6
Common factors						•	•	•
Common multiples						•	•	•
Checking divisibility						•	•	•
Exponents						•	•	•
Exponential notation and scientific notation							•	•
Square roots						•		•

Patterns, Relations, and Functions

	PreK	K	1	2	3	4	5	6
Classifying objects	•	•	•	•				
Number patterns	•	•	•	•	•	•	•	•
Picture patterns	•	•	•	•				
Geometric patterns	•	•	•	•				•
Ordered pairs					•	•	•	•
Graphing ordered pairs					•	•	•	•
Inequalities			•	•	•	•	•	•
Function machines/tables		•	•	•	•	•	•	•
Function rules		•	•	•	•	•	•	•
Graphing functions					•	•	•	•

Probability

	PreK	K	1	2	3	4	5	6
Determining possible outcomes		•	•	•	•	•	•	•
Predicting outcomes		•	•	•	•	•	•	•
Conducting experiments		•	•	•	•	•	•	•
Experimental probability		•	•	•	•	•	•	
Theoretical probability						•	•	•
Using probability to plan strategies			•	•	•	•	•	•

Problem Solving

	PreK	K	1	2	3	4	5	6
Multistep problems			•	•	•	•	•	•
Multiple solutions			•	•	•	•	•	•
No solutions			•	•	•	•	•	•
Interpreting data		•	•	•	•	•	•	•
Checking reasonableness		•	•	•	•	•	•	•
Solving problems with too much information						•	•	•
Interpreting the quotient and remainder						•	•	•
Choosing the appropriate operation		•	•	•	•	•	•	•
Using estimation		•	•	•	•	•	•	•
Using guess, check, and adjust		•	•	•	•	•	•	•
Solving a simpler problem					•	•	•	•
Eliminating possibilities						•	•	•
Acting it out	•	•	•	•	•	•	•	•
Using/finding a pattern		•	•	•	•	•	•	•
Using/making a table			•	•	•	•	•	•
Using/drawing a picture or diagram	•	•	•	•	•	•	•	•
Using manipulatives	•	•	•	•	•	•	•	•

Ratio and Proportion

	PreK	K	1	2	3	4	5	6
Meaning/use of ratio and proportion						•	•	•
Rates						•	•	•
Similar figures						•	•	•
Map scales						•	•	•
Meaning of percent						•	•	•
Percent of a number						•	•	•

	PreK	K	1	2	3	4	5	6
Percent discounts							•	•
Sales tax							•	•
Simple/compound interest							•	•

Statistics and Graphing

	PreK	K	1	2	3	4	5	6
Surveying			•	•	•	•	•	•
Tallying			•	•	•	•	•	•
Making tables with data			•	•	•	•	•	•
Real and picture graphs		•	•	•	•	•		
Bar graphs		•	•	•	•	•	•	•
Line graphs				•	•	•	•	•
Circle graphs				•	•	•	•	•
Analyzing graphs		•	•	•	•	•	•	•
Finding the mean						•	•	•
Finding the median						•	•	•
Finding the mode						•	•	•

Subtraction (Whole Numbers)

	PreK	K	1	2	3	4	5	6
Meaning of subtraction	•	•	•	•				
Basic facts			•	•	•	•	•	•
Missing-term problems			•	•	•	•	•	•
Two-digit numbers			•	•	•	•	•	•
Three-digit numbers				•	•	•	•	•
Greater numbers					•	•	•	•
Subtracting money			•		•	•	•	•
Estimating differences				•	•	•	•	•

Technology

Calculators

	PreK	K	1	2	3	4	5	6
Computation with whole numbers						•	•	•
Computation with decimals						•	•	•
Computation with fractions							•	•
Computation with integers (negative numbers)							•	•
Using function rules						•	•	•
Order of operations							•	•
Function keys							•	•

Computers

	PreK	K	1	2	3	4	5	6
Spreadsheets					•	•	•	•
Functions		•	•	•	•	•	•	•
Graphs			•	•	•	•	•	•
Geometry	•	•	•	•	•		•	•
Charts and tables				•	•	•	•	•

Game Directory

Game	Principle Skills	Begin Using* Student Edition	Begin Using* Teacher's Edition
Roll a Number	Using place value and intuitive notions of probability		Lesson 1.1
Roll a 15 🖳Games	Adding two, three, or four numbers (0-10); using intuitive notions of probability	Page 7	Lesson 1.2
Frog Pond Game	Adding with two addends of 10 or less		Lesson 1.2
Addition Crossing Game	Practicing basic facts; using addends up to 10; using mathematical reasoning		Lesson 1.3
Rummage Sale Game	Changing money ($1, $10, and $100 bills for those of larger denominations); regrouping in preparation for multidigit addition		Lesson 2.1
Roll a Problem Game	Adding and subtracting multidigit numbers; place value; using intuitive notions of probability	Page 47	Lesson 2.2
Checkbook Game	Adding and subtracting two-digit and three-digit numbers; maintaining a record of money transactions		Lesson 2.8
Make 1,000 🖳Games	Approximating answers to multidigit addition and subtraction problems; solving multidigit addition and subtraction problems		Lesson 2.9
Minutes Game	Telling time to five-minute intervals		Lesson 3.1
Time Game	Telling time to the hour and half hour		Lesson 3.1
Find the Distance 1 Game	Estimating straight distances to the nearest centimeter; comparing line lengths		Lesson 3.4
Find the Distance 2 Game	Estimating straight distances to the nearest centimeter; comparing line lengths		Lesson 3.4
Multiplication Table Game 🖳Games	Using a multiplication table; multiplying with two factors of 5 or less		Lesson 4.4
Harder Multiplication Table Game	Using a multiplication table; multiplying with two factors of 10 or less		Lesson 4.4
Squares to 200	Multiplication facts	Page 183	Lesson 5.4
Mul-Tack-Toe	Multiplying two numbers from 0–10	Page 191	Lesson 5.5
Multigo 1 Game 🖳Games	Solving missing-factor problems related to the multiplication facts; using mathematical reasoning		Lesson 5.8

Game	Principle Skills	Begin Using*	
		Student Edition	Teacher's Edition
Multigo 2 Game	Solving missing-factor problems related to the multiplication facts; using mathematical reasoning		Lesson 5.9
Shopping Game	Multiplying with factors up to 9; forming amounts of money; making change		Lesson 6.1
Cube 100 ⓔGames	Adding; multiplying one- and two-digit numbers by one-digit numbers; using mathematical reasoning	Page 269	Lesson 7.6
Fraction Game ⓔGames	Recognizing fractional areas of a circle; recognizing which fractional areas when combined are more than half the area of a circle		Lesson 8.3
Metric Unit Game	Determining which metric units of weight and length make sense with given numbers to describe given objects		Lesson 9.7
Decimal Roll a Problem Game	Computation with decimal numbers, place value, and mathematical reasoning	Page 393	Lesson 10.5
Store Game	Forming amounts of money (multiples of $0.25); making change		Lesson 10.9

* These games and their variations should be used many times throughout the year. Feel free to use them again anytime after they are introduced.
** Games in red are from the Game Mat Kit.
ⓔGames These games are available as *eGames.*

ADDITION CROSSING

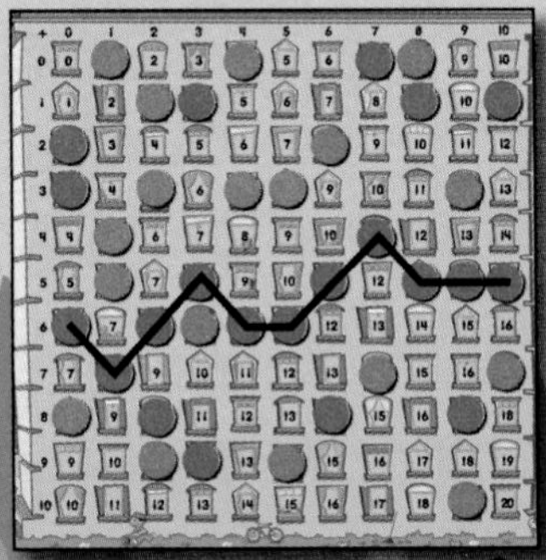

+	0	1	2	3	4	5	6	7	8	9	10
0	0	1	2	3	4	5	6	7	8	9	10
1	1	2	3	4	5	6	7	8	9	10	11
2	2	3	4	5	6	7	8	9	10	11	12
3	3	4	5	6	7	8	9	10	11	12	13
4	4	5	6	7	8	9	10	11	12	13	14
5	5	6	7	8	9	10	11	12	13	14	15
6	6	7	8	9	10	11	12	13	14	15	16
7	7	8	9	10	11	12	13	14	15	16	17
8	8	9	10	11	12	13	14	15	16	17	18
9	9	10	11	12	13	14	15	16	17	18	19
10	10	11	12	13	14	15	16	17	18	19	20

Math Focus:
- Practicing basic facts – using addends up to 10
- Using an addition table

Object of the Game: To be the first to complete a continuous path across the board

Players: Two

MATERIALS

Two cubes   Two cubes

25 counters of the same color for each player

SET UP

▲ Choose a direction. One of you will move horizontally (left to right) and the other will move vertically (up and down).

▲ Players roll the 0–5 **Number Cube.** The person who rolls the greater number chooses his or her counters and is followed by the second player.

HOW TO PLAY

1. Take turns rolling any two cubes. Put a counter on any square that shows the sum of the addition fact you rolled. (For example, if you roll 3 and 8, you can put a counter on 3 + 8 or 8 + 3.)

2. The first player to make a continuous path from one side to the opposite side is the winner. Your path can go up, down, forward, backward, or diagonally, as long as all the squares are touching each other.

Sunday	Monday	Tuesday	Wednesday	Thursday	Friday	Saturday
Start Your Balance is $1000	**1** Supermarket — Pay $35	**2** Dentist Bill — Pay $50	**3** Electric Bill — Pay $26	**4** STOCK DIVIDEND — Earn $50	**5** Insurance Bill — Pay $38	**6** THEATER TICKETS — Pay $20
7 Eat in Restaurant — Pay $20	**8** WORK OVERTIME — Earn $23	**9** Supermarket — Pay $51	**10** United Fund — Pay $100	**11** Go Back 7 Spaces	**12** Income TAX — Pay $212	**13** Go to Movies — Pay $5
14 Visit Museum — FREE	**15** RENT — Pay $150	**16** Holiday! — No bills today	**17** Supermarket — Pay $47	**18** BUY BOOKS — Pay $14	**19** Telephone Bill — Pay $17	**20** Receive Rebate Check — Earn $15
21 VISIT ZOO — FREE	**22** Supermarket — Pay $35	**23** Go Back 7 Spaces	**24** Parking Ticket — Pay $5	**25** Go Ahead 2 Spaces	**26** Automobile Repairs — Pay $285	**27** WORK OVERTIME — Earn $48
28 Eat in Restaurant — Pay $22	**29** NEW SHOES — Pay $15	**30** Supermarket — Pay $51	**31** Go Back 7 Spaces	**Finish** Wait until all players finish		

CHECKBOOK GAME

Math Focus:
- Adding and subtracting two-digit and three-digit numbers
- Maintaining a record of money transactions

Object of the Game: To have the largest balance at the end of the month

Players: Two or three

MATERIALS

Place markers   Cube   One balance sheet per player

SET UP

▶ Photocopies of the sample balance sheet can be handed out to students.

▶ Players prepare their balance sheets by writing "Start" on the first line under DATE and "$1000" on the first line under BALANCE.

▶ Players put their place markers on START.

▶ Players roll the 0–5 *Number Cube.* The person who rolls the highest number goes first.

HOW TO PLAY

1. Players take turns rolling the cube and moving their markers the number of spaces indicated.

2. Players follow the directions on the spaces where they land, entering the date and all payments or earnings on their balance sheets and recalculating their balances.

3. Play continues until all the players have either reached FINISH or run out of money.

4. The player with the largest balance at the end of the game is declared the winner. The other players then check the addition and subtraction in the winner's balance sheet. If the balance does not check, the player with the highest correct balance becomes the winner.

SAMPLE BALANCE SHEET

Date	Earn	Pay	Balance

CHECKBOOK GAME

Sunday	Monday	Tuesday	Wednesday	Thursday	Friday	Saturday
Start Your Balance is $1000.00	**1** Supermarket — Pay $35.22	**2** Dentist Bill — Pay $50.00	**3** Electric Bill — Pay $26.14	**4** STOCK DIVIDEND — Earn $50.00	**5** Insurance Bill — Pay $38.17	**6** THEATER TICKETS — Pay $20.00
7 Eat in Restaurant — Pay $20.82	**8** WORK OVERTIME — Earn $23.50	**9** Supermarket — Pay $51.62	**10** United Fund — Pay $100.00	**11** Go Back 7 Spaces	**12** Income TAX — Pay $212.00	**13** Go to Movies — Pay $5.00
14 Visit Museum — FREE	**15** RENT — Pay $150.00	**16** Holiday! — No bills today	**17** Supermarket — Pay $47.94	**18** BUY BOOKS — Pay $14.50	**19** Telephone Bill — Pay $17.36	**20** WORK OVERTIME — Earn $43.71
21 VISIT ZOO — FREE	**22** Supermarket — Pay $35.61	**23** Go Back 7 Spaces	**24** Parking Ticket — Pay $5.00	**25** Go Ahead 2 Spaces	**26** Automobile Repairs — Pay $285.00	**27** JOB BONUS — Earn $250.00
28 Eat in Restaurant — Pay $22.16	**29** NEW SHOES — Pay $15.45	**30** Supermarket — Pay $51.62	**31** Go Back 7 Spaces	**Finish** Wait until all players finish		

HARDER CHECKBOOK GAME

Math Focus:
- Adding and subtracting two-digit, three-digit, and four-digit numbers
- Maintaining a record of money transactions

Object of the Game: To have the largest balance at the end of the month

Players: Two or three

MATERIALS

Place markers

Cube

One balance sheet per player

SET UP

▶ Photocopies of the balance sheet for the **Harder Checkbook Game** can be handed out to students.

▶ Players prepare their balance sheets by writing "Start" on the first line under DATE and "$1000" on the first line under BALANCE.

▶ Players put their place markers on START.

▶ Players roll the 0–5 **Number Cube.** The person who rolls the highest number goes first.

HOW TO PLAY

1 Players take turns rolling the cube and moving their markers the number of spaces indicated.

2 Players follow the directions on the spaces where they land, entering the date and all payments or earnings on their balance sheets and recalculating their balances.

3 Play continues until all the players have either reached FINISH or run out of money.

4 The player with the largest balance at the end of the game is declared the winner. The other players then check the addition and subtraction in the winner's balance sheet. If the balance does not check, the player with the highest correct balance becomes the winner.

SAMPLE BALANCE SHEET

Date	Earn	Pay	Balance

HARDER CHECKBOOK GAME

CUSTOMARY UNIT GAME

INCHES FEET YARDS
OUNCES POUNDS TONS

TONS YARDS POUNDS
INCHES FEET OUNCES

AIRPLANE
Weight About 2 — ounces
Length About 2 — feet
Weight About 400 — tons
Length About 75 — yards

NECKTIE

PENALTY
Cover a circle

TELESCOPE
Weight About 40 — pounds
Length About 100 — inches

Length About 6 — inches

HOT DOG
Weight About 2 — ounces

LADDER
Weight About 30 — pounds
Length About 6 — feet

BLUE WHALE
Length About 100 — feet
Weight About 220 — tons

DICTIONARY
Weight About 3 — pounds
Length About 10 — inches

MOTORCYCLE
Weight About 600 — pounds
Length About 6 — feet

ROLL OF 50 PENNIES
Length About 4 — inches
Weight About 5 — ounces

BROOM
Length About 54 — inches
Weight About 36 — ounces

DOG
Weight About 40 — pounds
Length About 3 — feet

START

PIANO
Length About 2 — yards
Weight About 650 — pounds

HOW TO PLAY

1. Players take turns rolling the cube and moving their place markers the number of spaces indicated.

2. After landing on a space, players must state *either* the appropriate customary unit of length or weight for the object pictured there.

3. Players check their answers by looking under the counter. If correct, the player keeps the counter; if incorrect, the player replaces it. A player can win only one counter per turn.

4. Once the counter on a circle has been won, the circle remains empty. Players who land on a space with two empty circles cannot win a counter and must wait until the next turn to roll again.

5. A player who rolls a 0 cannot win a counter.

6. Players who land on the space marked PENALTY must, if possible, place one of their own counters on any empty circle on the mat.

7. A player who lands on the space marked START collects one counter from every other player.

8. The player with the most counters at the end of the game wins.

Math Focus: Choosing appropriate customary units of weight and length for various objects

Object of the Game: To have the most counters at the end of the game

Players: Two, three, or four

MATERIALS

Place markers

Cube

24 counters or pennies

SET UP

▲ Every circle on the mat must be covered with a counter.

▲ Players put their place markers on the space marked START.

▲ Players roll the 0–5 *Number Cube.* The person who rolls the greatest number goes first.

▲ Inform players that all lengths are given in inches, feet, or yards, and all weights are given in ounces, pounds, or tons.

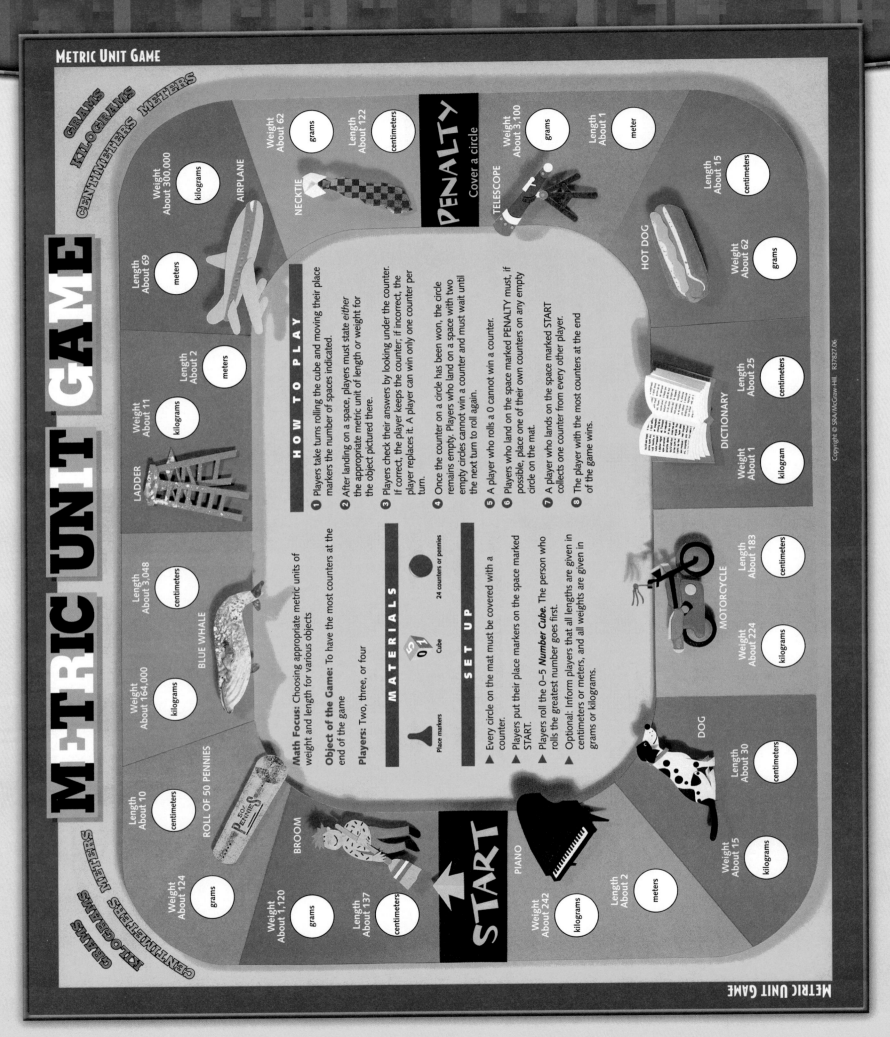

METRIC UNIT GAME

GRAMS KILOGRAMS CENTIMETERS METERS

GRAMS KILOGRAMS CENTIMETERS METERS

HOW TO PLAY

1. Players take turns rolling the cube and moving their place markers the number of spaces indicated.

2. After landing on a space, players must state *either* the appropriate metric unit of length or weight for the object pictured there.

3. Players check their answers by looking under the counter. If correct, the player keeps the counter; if incorrect, the player replaces it. A player can win only one counter per turn.

4. Once the counter on a circle has been won, the circle remains empty. Players who land on a space with two empty circles cannot win a counter and must wait until the next turn to roll again.

5. A player who rolls a 0 cannot win a counter.

6. Players who land on the space marked PENALTY must, if possible, place one of their own counters on any empty circle on the mat.

7. A player who lands on the space marked START collects one counter from every other player.

8. The player with the most counters at the end of the game wins.

Math Focus: Choosing appropriate metric units of weight and length for various objects

Object of the Game: To have the most counters at the end of the game

Players: Two, three, or four

MATERIALS

Place markers

Cube

24 counters or pennies

SET UP

▲ Every circle on the mat must be covered with a counter.

▲ Players put their place markers on the space marked START.

▲ Players roll the 0–5 *Number Cube.* The person who rolls the greatest number goes first.

▲ Optional: Inform players that all lengths are given in centimeters or meters, and all weights are given in grams or kilograms.

AIRPLANE — Weight About 300,000 kilograms — Length About 69 meters

NECKTIE — Weight About 62 grams — Length About 122 centimeters

PENALTY — Cover a circle

TELESCOPE — Weight About 3,100 grams — Length About 1 meter

HOT DOG — Length About 15 centimeters — Weight About 62 grams

LADDER — Weight About 11 kilograms — Length About 2 meters

BLUE WHALE — Length About 3,048 centimeters

DICTIONARY — Length About 25 centimeters — Weight About 1 kilogram

MOTORCYCLE — Length About 183 centimeters — Weight About 224 kilograms

ROLL OF 50 PENNIES — Weight About 164,000 kilograms

BROOM — Weight About 124 grams

DOG — Length About 30 centimeters — Weight About 15 kilograms

START

PIANO — Weight About 242 kilograms — Length About 2 meters

Weight About 1,120 grams — Length About 137 centimeters

Length About 10 centimeters

Copyright © SRA/McGraw-Hill R37827.06

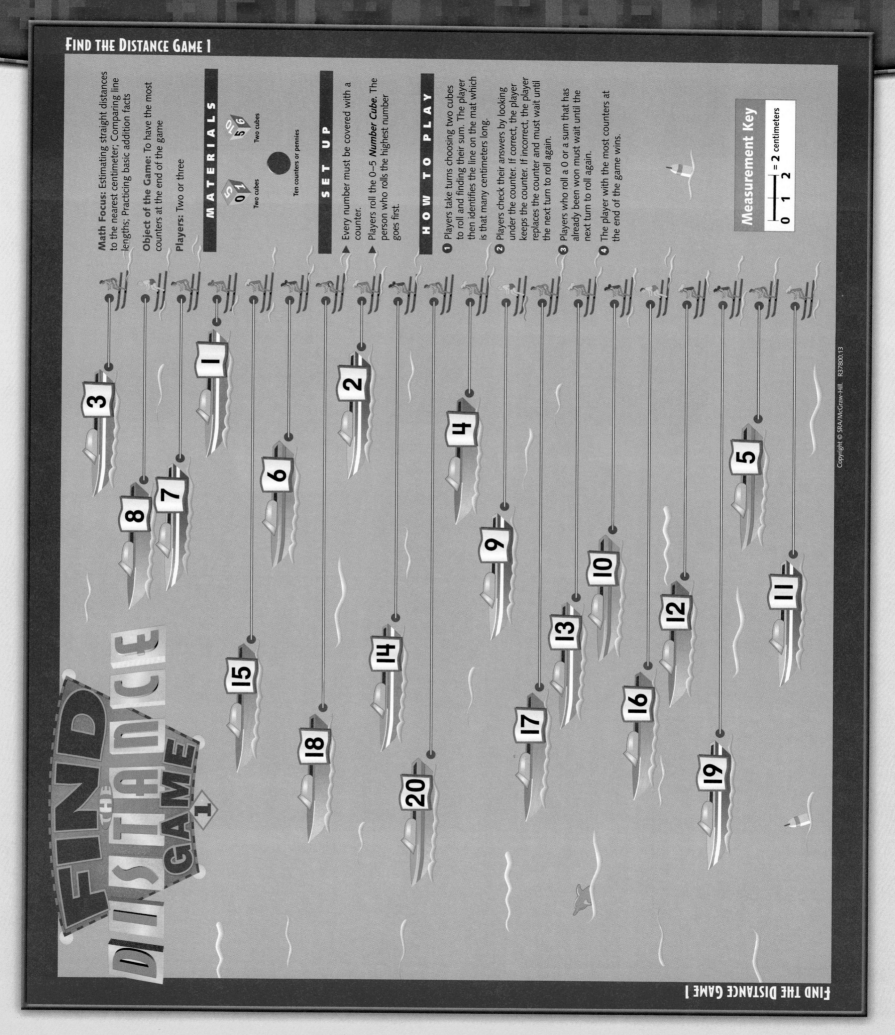

FIND THE DISTANCE GAME 1

Math Focus: Estimating straight distances to the nearest centimeter; Comparing line lengths; Practicing basic addition facts

Object of the Game: To have the most counters at the end of the game

Players: Two or three

MATERIALS

Two cubes

Two cubes

Ten counters or pennies

SET UP

▶ Every number must be covered with a counter.

▶ Players roll the 0–5 *Number Cube.* The person who rolls the highest number goes first.

HOW TO PLAY

1. Players take turns choosing two cubes to roll and finding their sum. The player then identifies the line on the mat which is that many centimeters long.

2. Players check their answers by looking under the counter. If correct, the player keeps the counter. If incorrect, the player replaces the counter and must wait until the next turn to roll again.

3. Players who roll a 0 or a sum that has already been won must wait until the next turn to roll again.

4. The player with the most counters at the end of the game wins.

Measurement Key

= 2 centimeters

0 1 2

Copyright © SRA/McGraw-Hill. R37800.13

FIND THE DISTANCE GAME 1

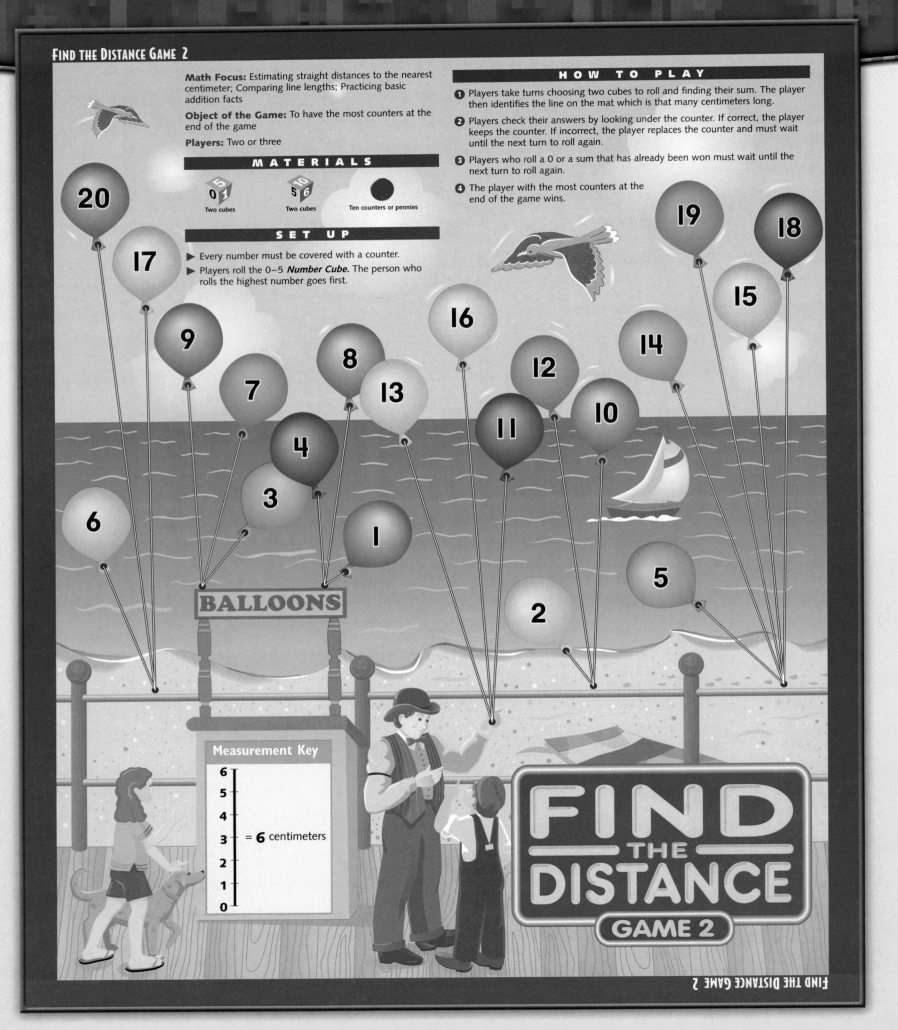

FIND THE DISTANCE GAME 2

Math Focus: Estimating straight distances to the nearest centimeter; Comparing line lengths; Practicing basic addition facts

Object of the Game: To have the most counters at the end of the game

Players: Two or three

MATERIALS

Two cubes   Two cubes   Ten counters or pennies

SET UP

► Every number must be covered with a counter.

► Players roll the 0–5 *Number Cube.* The person who rolls the highest number goes first.

HOW TO PLAY

1. Players take turns choosing two cubes to roll and finding their sum. The player then identifies the line on the mat which is that many centimeters long.

2. Players check their answers by looking under the counter. If correct, the player keeps the counter. If incorrect, the player replaces the counter and must wait until the next turn to roll again.

3. Players who roll a 0 or a sum that has already been won must wait until the next turn to roll again.

4. The player with the most counters at the end of the game wins.

BALLOONS

Measurement Key

= **6** centimeters

FIND THE DISTANCE GAME 2

FRACTION GAME

$\frac{1}{1}$

$\frac{1}{2}$ $\frac{1}{2}$

$\frac{1}{2}$ $\frac{1}{2}$

$\frac{1}{3}$ $\frac{1}{3}$ $\frac{1}{3}$

$\frac{1}{2}$ $\frac{1}{2}$

$\frac{1}{3}$ $\frac{1}{3}$ $\frac{1}{3}$

$\frac{1}{3}$ $\frac{1}{3}$ $\frac{1}{3}$

$\frac{1}{4}$ $\frac{1}{4}$ $\frac{1}{4}$ $\frac{1}{4}$

$\frac{1}{4}$ $\frac{1}{4}$ $\frac{1}{4}$ $\frac{1}{4}$ $\frac{1}{4}$ $\frac{1}{4}$

$\frac{1}{5}$ $\frac{1}{5}$ $\frac{1}{5}$ $\frac{1}{5}$ $\frac{1}{5}$

$\frac{1}{3}$ $\frac{1}{3}$ $\frac{1}{3}$

$\frac{1}{4}$ $\frac{1}{4}$ $\frac{1}{4}$ $\frac{1}{4}$

$\frac{1}{5}$ $\frac{1}{5}$ $\frac{1}{5}$ $\frac{1}{5}$ $\frac{1}{5}$

$\frac{1}{5}$ $\frac{1}{5}$ $\frac{1}{5}$ $\frac{1}{5}$ $\frac{1}{5}$

$\frac{1}{4}$ $\frac{1}{4}$ $\frac{1}{4}$ $\frac{1}{4}$

$\frac{1}{5}$ $\frac{1}{5}$ $\frac{1}{5}$ $\frac{1}{5}$ $\frac{1}{5}$

Math Focus:
- Recognizing fractional areas of a circle up to fifths
- Recognizing which common fractions sum to more than one half when added together

Object of the Game: To own more circles at the end of the game

Players: Two

MATERIALS

0 1 5

Two cubes

25 counters of the same color for each player, or 25 pennies and 25 nickels

SET UP

▶ Players roll the 0–5 *Number Cube.* The person who rolls the higher number goes first.

▶ The first player chooses his or her counters. The second player uses the remaining pieces.

HOW TO PLAY

1 Players take turns rolling the cubes and making fractions equal to or less than 1.

2 Players may divide their roll between more than one circle. For example, a player who rolls a 4 and a 5 may cover 1/5 of one circle and 3/5 of another.

3 Players who roll one 0 cannot place a counter. Players who roll double 0s may roll both cubes again.

4 A circle is awarded to a player who has covered more than half of it. That player puts a counter in the center of the circle and returns any of the opponent's counters. If half of a circle is covered by one player and half by the other player, neither player may own the circle.

5 Play continues until all the circles are either owned or completely covered. The player with more circles is the winner.

FROG POND GAME

Math Focus: Practicing basic math—using two addends of 10 or less

Object of the Game: To have the most counters at the end of the game

Players: Two or three

MATERIALS

Place markers

Cube

20 counters or pennies per player

SET UP

▲ Every circle on the mat must be covered with a counter.

▲ Extra counters are placed on the space marked BANK.

▲ Players put their place markers on GO.

▲ Players roll the 0–5 **Number Cube.** The person who rolls the highest number goes first.

HOW TO PLAY

1. Players take turns rolling the cube and moving their markers the number of spaces indicated.

2. After landing on a space, a player may win the counter there by correctly completing the addition sentence.

3. Players check their answers by lifting the counters. If correct, the player keeps the counter. If incorrect, the player replaces the counter and remains on that space.

4. A player cannot win a counter if there is none in a space. A player who gives an incorrect answer and rolls a 0 on the next turn can try again to win the counter.

5. Players collect two counters from the bank each time they pass or land on GO.

6. The player with the most counters at the end of the game wins.

Go →

$0 + 9 = 9$

$4 + 4 = 8$

$9 + 3 = 12$

$10 + 10 = 20$

$5 + 6 = 11$

$8 + 8 = 16$

$1 + 8 = 9$

$8 + 7 = 15$

$3 + 2 = 5$

bank

$5 + 1 = 6$

$7 + 6 = 13$

$2 + 9 = 11$

$3 + 6 = 9$

$6 + 9 = 15$

$7 + 2 = 9$

$10 + 4 = 14$

Copyright © SRA/McGraw-Hill. R00006008

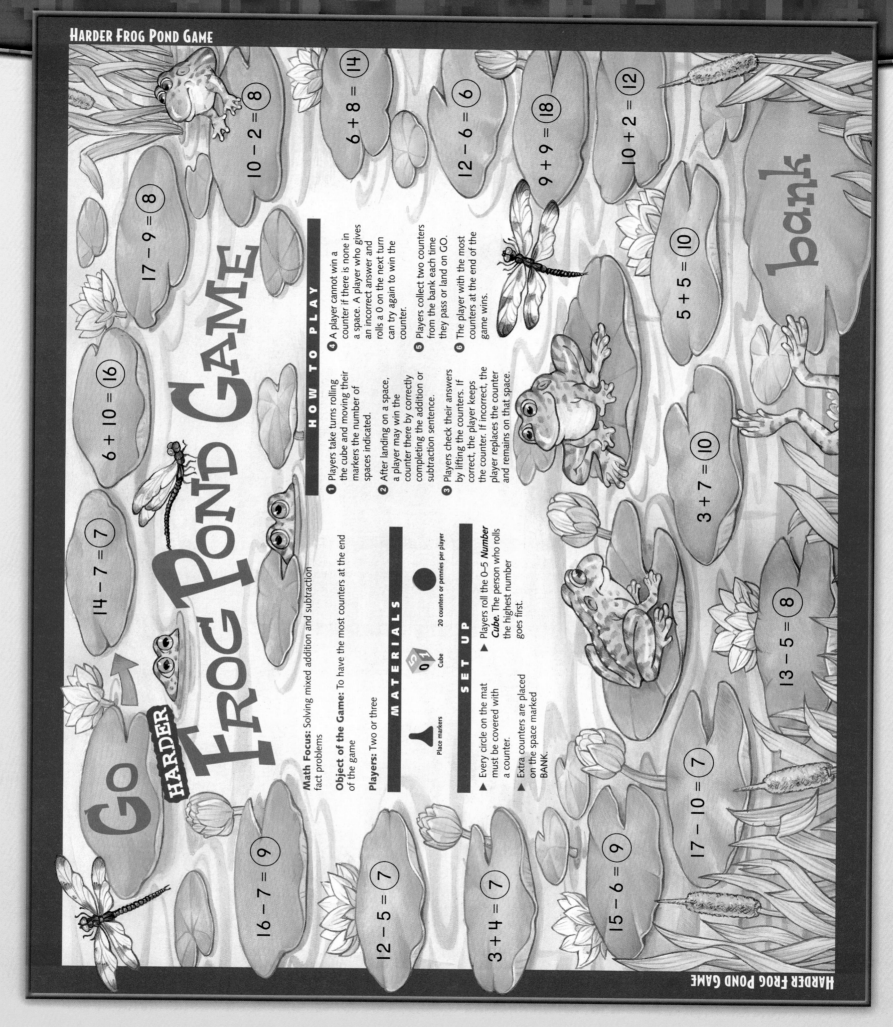

Go

HARDER

Frog Pond Game

Math Focus: Solving mixed addition and subtraction fact problems

Object of the Game: To have the most counters at the end of the game

Players: Two or three

MATERIALS

Place markers

Cube

20 counters or pennies per player

SET UP

▲ Every circle on the mat must be covered with a counter.

▲ Extra counters are placed on the space marked BANK.

▲ Players roll the 0–5 *Number Cube.* The person who rolls the highest number goes first.

HOW TO PLAY

1. Players take turns rolling the cube and moving their markers the number of spaces indicated.

2. After landing on a space, a player may win the counter there by correctly completing the addition or subtraction sentence.

3. Players check their answers by lifting the counters. If correct, the player keeps the counter. If incorrect, the player replaces the counter and remains on that space.

4. A player cannot win a counter if there is none in a space. A player who gives an incorrect answer and rolls a 0 on the next turn can try again to win the counter.

5. Players collect two counters from the bank each time they pass or land on GO.

6. The player with the most counters at the end of the game wins.

bank

Board spaces:

$10 - 2 = 8$

$6 + 8 = 14$

$12 - 6 = 6$

$9 + 9 = 18$

$10 + 2 = 12$

$17 - 9 = 8$

$6 + 10 = 16$

$14 - 7 = 7$

$16 - 7 = 9$

$12 - 5 = 7$

$3 + 4 = 7$

$15 - 6 = 9$

$17 - 10 = 7$

$13 - 5 = 8$

$3 + 7 = 10$

$5 + 5 = 10$

Go →

9:15

2:40

8:40

12:10

Minutes

3:35

1:25

2:05

11:05

9:25

12:50

Math Focus: Telling time to five-minute intervals

Object of the Game: To have the most counters at the end of the game

Players: Two or three

M A T E R I A L S

Place markers   Cube   16 counters or pennies

S E T   U P

▶ The red answer circles in each space must be covered by a counter.

▶ Players put their place markers on the space marked GO.

▶ Players roll the 0–5 **Number Cube.** The person who rolls the highest number goes first.

H O W   T O   P L A Y

❶ Players take turns rolling the cube and moving their place markers the number of spaces indicated. Players must correctly state the time indicated on the clock in each space where they land.

❷ Players check their answers by looking under the counter. If correct, the player keeps the counter; if incorrect, the player replaces the counter.

❸ A player who gives an incorrect answer and then rolls a 0 on the next turn may try again to win the counter.

❹ Players who land on empty circles cannot win a counter and must wait until the next turn to roll again.

❺ Players who land on the space marked PENALTY must, if possible, place one of their own counters on an empty circle.

❻ The player with the most counters at the end of the game wins.

6:50

4:45

4:10

5:55

10:20

7:05

Penalty
COVER AN ANSWER

Go →

11:32

4:07

10:23

2:02

HARDER Minutes

3:18

8:56

1:51

6:49

3:09

11:05

9:32

12:26

Math Focus: Telling time to the minute

Object of the Game: To have the most counters at the end of the game

Players: Two or three

MATERIALS

Place markers

Cube

16 counters or pennies

SET UP

► The red answer circles in each space must be covered by a counter.

► Players put their place markers on the space marked GO.

► Players roll the 0–5 *Number Cube.* The person who rolls the highest number goes first.

HOW TO PLAY

1. Players take turns rolling the cube and moving their place markers the number of spaces indicated. Players must correctly state the time indicated on the clock in each space where they land.

2. Players check their answers by looking under the counter. If correct, the player keeps the counter; if incorrect, the player replaces the counter.

3. A player who gives an incorrect answer and then rolls a 0 on the next turn may try again to win the counter.

4. Players who land on empty circles cannot win a counter and must wait until the next turn to roll again.

5. Players who land on the space marked PENALTY must, if possible, place one of their own counters on an empty circle.

6. The player with the most counters at the end of the game wins.

7:19

5:14

6:11

1:53

Penalty

COVER AN ANSWER

HARDER MINUTES

MULTIGO 1

Math Focus: Solving missing-factor problems related to the multiplication facts

Object of the Game: To capture five squares in a straight line

Players: Two

MATERIALS

Cube

Cube

15 counters or pennies per player

SET UP

▲ Players roll the 0–5 *Number Cube.* The person who rolls the greater number goes first.

▲ The first player chooses either Card 1 or Card 2 on the game mat. The second player uses the other card.

HOW TO PLAY

1. Players take turns rolling either cube and multiplying the number rolled by any other number between 0 and 10 to equal one of the products on their game card.

2. Players say the correct multiplication sentence. For example, a player who rolls a 7 and wants to capture the 42 square on his or her card would say "7 times 6 equals 42." If the sentence is correct, the player puts a counter on the appropriate square. If incorrect, the player cannot put down a counter.

3. The first player to capture five squares in a straight line (vertically, horizontally, or diagonally) is the winner.

2

27	24	21	18	15
36	32	28	24	20
45	40	35	30	25
54	48	42	36	30
63	56	49	42	35

1

45	40	35	30	25
54	48	42	36	30
63	56	49	42	35
72	64	56	48	40
81	72	63	54	45

Math Focus: Solving missing-factor problems related to the multiplication facts

Object of the Game: To capture five squares in a straight line

Players: Two

MATERIALS

Cube (0 1 5)

Cube (5 6 10)

15 counters or pennies per player

SET UP

- Players roll the 0–5 *Number Cube.* The person who rolls the greater number goes first.
- The first player chooses Card 1, 2, or 3 on the game mat, and then the second player chooses a card.

HOW TO PLAY

1. Players take turns rolling either cube and multiplying the number rolled by any other number between 0 and 10 to equal one of the products on their game card.
2. Players say the correct multiplication sentence. For example, a player who rolls a 7 and wants to capture the 42 square on his or her card would say "7 times 6 equals 42." If the sentence is correct, the player puts a counter on the appropriate square. If incorrect, the player cannot put down a counter.
3. The first player to capture five squares in a straight line (vertically, horizontally, or diagonally) is the winner.

Card 3

80	48	18	27	32
30	100	64	49	10
14	45	0	35	24
63	50	36	72	54
42	81	56	20	40

Card 2

81	28	12	54	70
10	35	42	64	27
63	15	0	36	45
40	49	56	16	30
90	72	32	48	24

Card 1

40	56	42	18	72
64	25	36	60	32
28	30	0	54	27
35	49	24	81	70
63	20	45	48	21

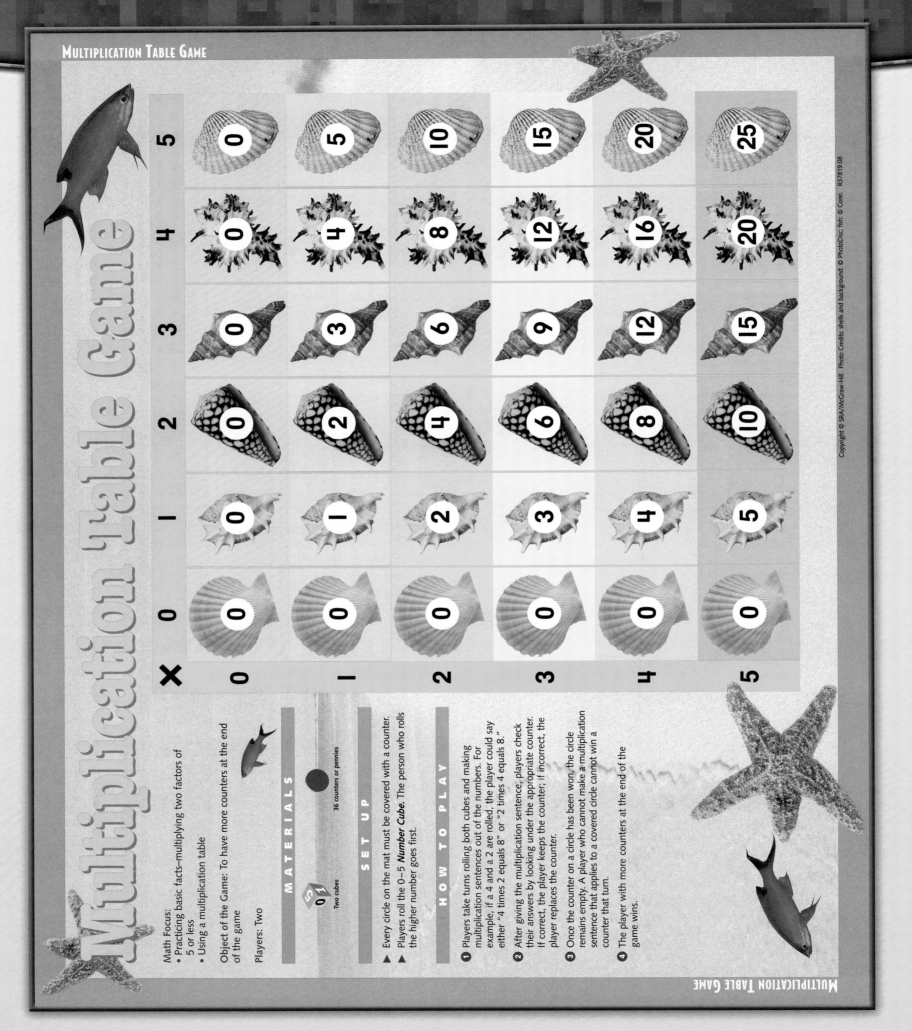

Multiplication Table Game

Math Focus:
- Practicing basic facts—multiplying two factors of 5 or less
- Using a multiplication table

Object of the Game: To have more counters at the end of the game

Players: Two

MATERIALS

Two cubes

36 counters or pennies

SET UP

▲ Every circle on the mat must be covered with a counter.

▲ Players roll the 0–5 *Number Cube.* The person who rolls the higher number goes first.

HOW TO PLAY

1. Players take turns rolling both cubes and making multiplication sentences out of the numbers. For example, if a 4 and a 2 are rolled, the player could say either "4 times 2 equals 8" or "2 times 4 equals 8."

2. After giving the multiplication sentence, players check their answers by looking under the appropriate counter. If correct, the player keeps the counter; if incorrect, the player replaces the counter.

3. Once the counter on a circle has been won, the circle remains empty. A player who cannot make a multiplication sentence that applies to a covered circle cannot win a counter that turn.

4. The player with more counters at the end of the game wins.

✕	0	1	2	3	4	5
0	0	0	0	0	0	0
1	0	1	2	3	4	5
2	0	2	4	6	8	10
3	0	3	6	9	12	15
4	0	4	8	12	16	20
5	0	5	10	15	20	25

MULTIPLICATION TABLE GAME

HARDER
Multiplication Table Game

Math Focus:
- Practicing basic facts—multiplying two factors of 10 or less
- Using a multiplication table

Object of the Game: To have more counters at the end of the game

Players: Two

MATERIALS

Cube
Two cubes

36 counters or pennies

SET UP

▲ Every circle on the mat must be covered with a counter.

▲ Players roll the 0–5 *Number Cube.* The person who rolls the higher number goes first.

HOW TO PLAY

1. There are actually two harder versions of this game. One game is played rolling one 0–5 and one 5–10 *Number Cube.* The second game is played with two 5–10 *Number Cubes.* Players take turns rolling both cubes and making multiplication sentences out of the numbers. For example, if a 4 and a 9 are rolled, the player could say either "4 times 9 equals 36" or "9 times 4 equals 36."

2. After giving the multiplication sentence, players check their answers by looking under the appropriate counter.

3. If correct, the player keeps the counter; if incorrect, the player replaces the counter.

4. Once the counter on a circle has been won, the circle remains empty. A player who cannot make a multiplication sentence that applies to a covered circle cannot win a counter that turn.

5. The player with more counters at the end of the game wins.

Table 1 (× 5–10)

×	5	6	7	8	9	10
5	25	30	35	40	45	50
6	30	36	42	48	54	60
7	35	42	49	56	63	70
8	40	48	56	64	72	80
9	45	54	63	72	81	90
10	50	60	70	80	90	100

Table 2 (× 0–5)

×	0	1	2	3	4	5
5	0	5	10	15	20	25
6	0	6	12	18	24	30
7	0	7	14	21	28	35
8	0	8	16	24	32	40
9	0	9	18	27	36	45
10	0	10	20	30	40	50

HARDER MULTIPLICATION TABLE GAME

RUMMAGE SALE GAME

GO!

$100

$22

$10

$23

$201

$110

$47

$101

$63

$114

$3

$35

$14

$81

$5

$25

SET UP

► Players sort the money into piles next to the game mat.

► Players put their place markers on GO.

► Players roll the 0–5 *Number Cube.* The person who rolls the highest number goes first.

HOW TO PLAY

1. Players take turns rolling the cube and moving their place markers the number of spaces indicated.

2. After landing on a space, the player says the price of the object pictured there and collects that amount from the money next to the game mat. Players must count the bills aloud.

3. Players do not collect money for passing or landing on GO.

4. Players should keep their $1, $10, and $100 bills in separate piles. They must trade up whenever possible: ones for tens, tens for hundreds, and hundreds for a thousand. The first player to collect a $1,000 bill wins the game.

Math Focus:
• Changing money ($1, $10, $100)
• Practicing regrouping in preparation for multidigit addition

Object of the Game: To be the first player to collect a $1,000 bill

Players: Two or three

MATERIALS

Place markers

Cube

Per player:
ten $1 bills
ten $10 bills
ten $100 bills
one $1,000 bill

Copyright © SRA/McGraw-Hill. All photos: © PhotoDisc   R37819.09

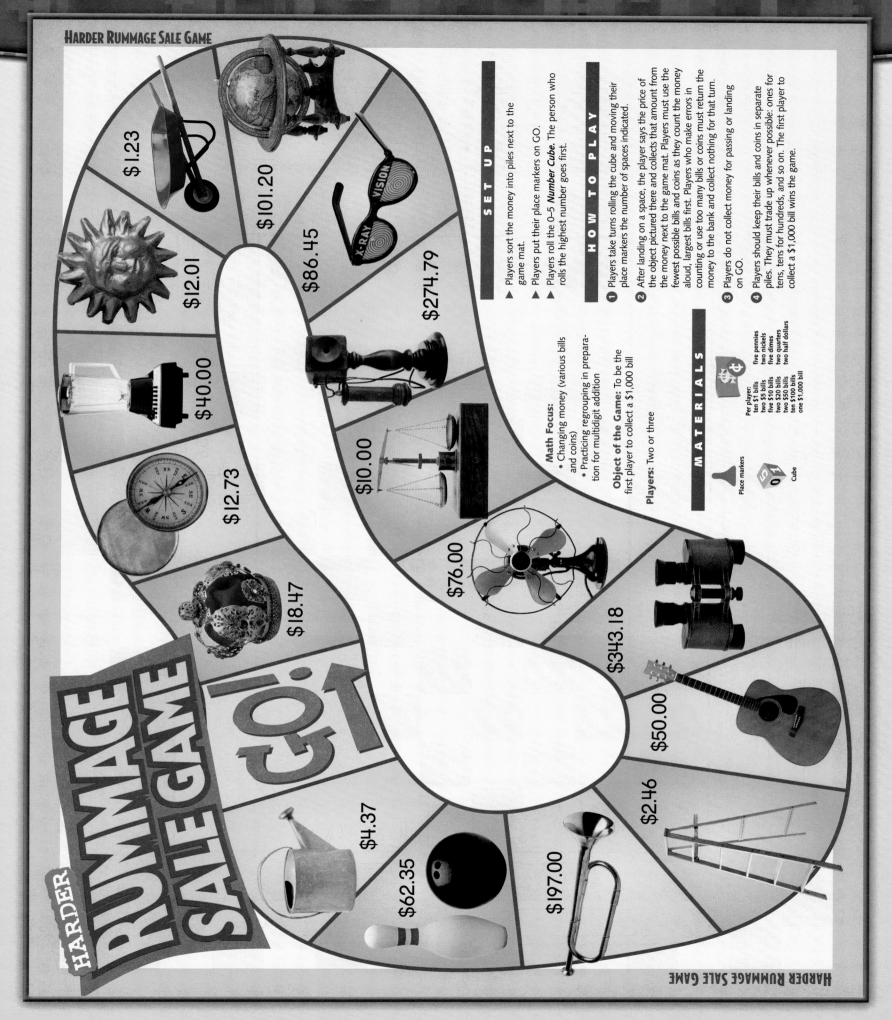

HARDER RUMMAGE SALE GAME

$1.23

$101.20

$12.01

$86.45

$274.79

$40.00

$10.00

$12.73

$76.00

$18.47

$343.18

$50.00

$4.37

$62.35

$197.00

$2.46

HARDER

RUMMAGE SALE GAME

GO!

SET UP

▲ Players sort the money into piles next to the game mat.

▲ Players put their place markers on GO.

▲ Players roll the 0–5 *Number Cube*. The person who rolls the highest number goes first.

HOW TO PLAY

1. Players take turns rolling the cube and moving their place markers the number of spaces indicated.

2. After landing on a space, the player says the price of the object pictured there and collects that amount from the money next to the game mat. Players must use the fewest possible bills and coins as they count the money aloud, largest bills first. Players who make errors in counting or use too many bills or coins must return the money to the bank and collect nothing for that turn.

3. Players do not collect money for passing or landing on GO.

4. Players should keep their bills and coins in separate piles. They must trade up whenever possible: ones for tens, tens for hundreds, and so on. The first player to collect a $1,000 bill wins the game.

Math Focus:
• Changing money (various bills and coins)
• Practicing regrouping in preparation for multidigit addition

Object of the Game: To be the first player to collect a $1,000 bill

Players: Two or three

MATERIALS

Place markers

Cube

five pennies
two nickels
five dimes
two quarters
two half dollars

Per player:
ten $1 bills
two $5 bills
five $10 bills
two $20 bills
two $50 bills
ten $100 bills
one $1,000 bill

HARDER RUMMAGE SALE GAME

SPORTING GOODS

$8 $1 $7

START

Shopping Game

Math Focus:
- Practicing basic facts—multiplying with factors up to 9
- Forming amounts of money and making change

Object of the Game: To be the first to have $250

Players: Two, three, or four

MATERIALS

Place markers

Cube

Per player:
one $50 bill
two $20 bills
three $10 bills
five $5 bills
five $1 bills

SET UP

▶ Players select stores to own. If two are playing, each player chooses two stores; if three are playing, one store will not be owned by anyone.

▶ Players put their place markers on the space marked START.

▶ Players roll the 0–5 *Number Cube.* The person who rolls the highest number goes first.

HOW TO PLAY

❶ Players take turns rolling the cube and moving their place markers the number of spaces indicated.

❷ After landing on a space, players roll the cube to see how many of the items pictured they must buy, and then they pay the store owner. For example, a player who lands on an item that costs $8 and then rolls a 3 must pay the owner $24 for three of the items.

❸ Even if a player has already bought an item, the player must buy it again if he or she lands on that space again.

❹ Players who roll a 0, land in their own stores, or land on stores that nobody owns buy nothing.

❺ A player who lands on the space marked START collects $5 from every player.

❻ The first player to have $250 wins.

TOY STORE

$2 $6 $8

REST

SCHOOL SUPPLIES

$8 $2 $7

FASHION SHOP

$3 $5 $6

SHOPPING GAME

Copyright © SRA/McGraw-Hill. R378 27 09

SPORTING GOODS

START

$23 $13 $42

HARDER Shopping Game

Math Focus:
• Practicing basic facts—multiplying with factors up to 9
• Forming amounts of money and making change

Object of the Game: To be the first to have $450

Players: Two, three, or four

MATERIALS

Place markers

Cube

Per player:
one $100 bill   three $10 bills
two $50 bills   five $5 bills
five $20 bills   five $1 bills

SET UP

▶ Players select stores to own. If two are playing, each player chooses two stores; if three are playing, one store will not be owned by anyone.

▶ Players put their place markers on the space marked START.

▶ Players roll the 0–5 *Number Cube*. The person who rolls the highest number goes first.

HOW TO PLAY

❶ Players take turns rolling the cube and moving their place markers the number of spaces indicated.

❷ After landing on a space, players roll the cube to see how many of the items pictured they must buy, and then they pay the store owner. For example, a player who lands on an item that costs $29 and then rolls a 4 must pay the owner $116 for four of the items.

❸ Even if a player has already bought an item, the player must buy it again if he or she lands on that space again.

❹ Players who roll a 0, land in their own stores, or land on stores that nobody owns buy nothing.

❺ A player who lands on the space marked START collects $5 from every player.

❻ The first player to have $450 wins.

TOY STORE

$32

$28

$19

REST

$34

$18

$29

$17 $47 $16

SCHOOL SUPPLIES

FASHION SHOP

HARDER SHOPPING GAME

SHOES

$96.50

$65.75

$3.75

BIG SALE

BUY NOW!

START

BAKERY

$85.75

$6.50

$73.75

STORE GAME

Math Focus:
• Forming amounts of money (multiples of 25¢)
• Making change

Object of the Game: To be the first to have $500

Players: Two, three, or four

MATERIALS

Place markers

Cube

0 1

Per player:
one $100 bill
one $50 bill
two $20 bills
three $10 bills

four $5 bills
eight $1 bills
two half dollars
four quarters

SET UP

▲ Players select departments in the store to manage. If two are playing, each can choose two departments; if three are playing, one department will not be managed by anyone.

▲ Players sort their money into piles in front of them.

▲ Players put their place markers on the space marked START.

▲ Players roll the 0–5 *Number Cube.* The person who rolls the highest number goes first.

HOW TO PLAY

① Players take turns rolling the cube and moving their place markers the number of spaces indicated.

② After landing on a space, the player says the price of the object pictured there and pays the amount shown to the player who manages the department. Players must count out the money as they pay, largest bills first.

③ Even if a player has already bought an item, the player must buy it again if she or he lands on that space again.

④ If a player lands in a department that he or she manages, or that nobody manages, no payment is made.

⑤ Players who land on the space marked START collect $10 from every other player.

⑥ A player who rolls a 0 does not move that turn but also does not have to buy the item again on that turn.

⑦ The first player to have $500 wins.

HARDWARE

$8.75

$85.75

$71.50

BUY NOW!

$8.25

$89.50

$68.75

BIG SALE

TRAVEL

REST

SHOES

$3.96

$1.51

$0.78

BIG SALE

BUY NOW!

START

$0.69

HARDWARE

$3.51

BAKERY

$3.33

$1.79

HARDER STORE GAME

$0.95

$1.93

REST

SET UP

▲ Players select departments in the store to manage. If two are playing, each can choose two departments; if three are playing, one department will not be managed by anyone.

▲ Players sort their money into piles in front of them.

▲ Players put their place markers on the space marked START.

▲ Players roll the 0–5 *Number Cube*. The person who rolls the highest number goes first.

HOW TO PLAY

① Players take turns rolling the cube and moving their place markers the number of spaces indicated.

② After landing on a space, the player says the price of the object pictured there and pays the amount shown to the player who manages the department. Players must count out the money as they pay, largest bills or coins first.

③ Even if a player has already bought an item, the player must buy it again if she or he lands on that space again.

④ If a player lands in a department that he or she manages, or that nobody manages, no payment is made.

⑤ Players who land on the space marked START collect $1 from every other player.

⑥ A player who rolls a 0 does not move that turn but also does not have to buy the item again on that turn.

⑦ The first player to have $20 wins.

Math Focus:
• Forming amounts of money
• Making change

Object of the Game: To be the first to have $20

Players: Two, three, or four

MATERIALS

0 1

Cube

Place markers

Per player:
one $5 bill
seven $1 bills
two half dollars

four quarters
six dimes
six nickels
ten pennies

$1.98

BUY NOW!

$3.45

$0.82

BIG SALE

TRAVEL

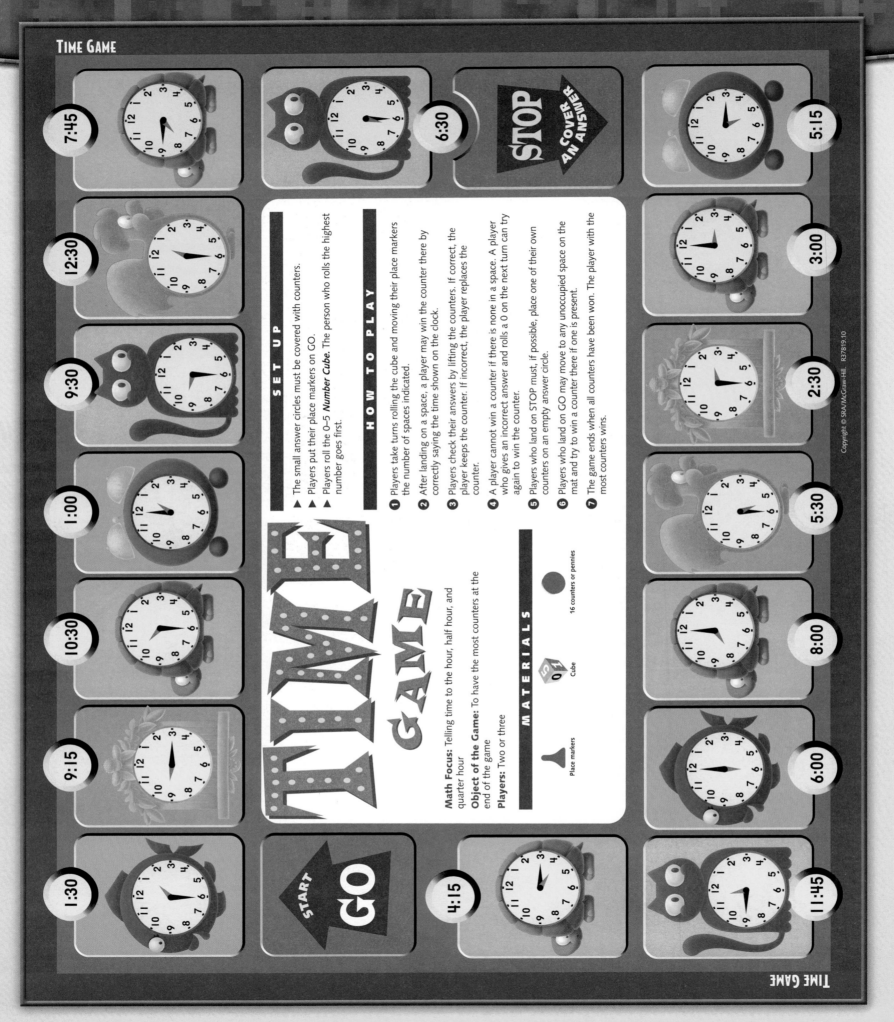

TIME GAME

Math Focus: Telling time to the hour, half hour, and quarter hour

Object of the Game: To have the most counters at the end of the game

Players: Two or three

MATERIALS

Place markers

Cube

16 counters or pennies

SET UP

▲ The small answer circles must be covered with counters.

▲ Players put their place markers on GO.

▲ Players roll the 0–5 *Number Cube.* The person who rolls the highest number goes first.

HOW TO PLAY

1 Players take turns rolling the cube and moving their place markers the number of spaces indicated.

2 After landing on a space, a player may win the counter there by correctly saying the time shown on the clock.

3 Players check their answers by lifting the counters. If correct, the player keeps the counter. If incorrect, the player replaces the counter.

4 A player cannot win a counter if there is none in a space. A player who gives an incorrect answer and rolls a 0 on the next turn can try again to win the counter.

5 Players who land on STOP must, if possible, place one of their own counters on an empty answer circle.

6 Players who land on GO may move to any unoccupied space on the mat and try to win a counter there if one is present.

7 The game ends when all counters have been won. The player with the most counters wins.

Copyright © SRA/McGraw-Hill. R37819.10

7:45
6:30
STOP
COVER AN ANSWER
5:15

12:30
3:00

9:30
2:30

1:00
5:30

10:30
8:00

9:15
6:00

1:30
GO START
4:15
11:45

Go

Time Game

9:15

2:40

8:40

12:10

1:25

3:35

2:05

11:05

9:25

6:50

12:50

4:45

Math Focus: Telling time to five-minute intervals

Object of the Game: To have the most counters at the end of the game

Players: Two or three

MATERIALS

Place markers

Cube

16 counters or pennies

SET UP

▶ The red answer circles in each space must be covered by a counter.

▶ Players put their place markers on the space marked GO.

▶ Players roll the 0–5 *Number Cube.* The person who rolls the highest number goes first.

HOW TO PLAY

❶ Players take turns rolling the cube and moving their place markers the number of spaces indicated. Players must correctly state the time indicated on the clock in each space where they land.

❷ Players check their answers by looking under the counter. If correct, the player keeps the counter; if incorrect, the player replaces the counter.

❸ A player who gives an incorrect answer and then rolls a 0 on the next turn may try again to win the counter.

❹ Players who land on empty circles cannot win a counter and must wait until the next turn to roll again.

❺ Players who land on the space marked PENALTY must, if possible, place one of their own counters on an empty circle.

❻ The player with the most counters at the end of the game wins.

4:10

5:55

10:20

7:05

Penalty
COVER AN ANSWER

HARDER TIME GAME

Index

Index

Index

Index

Index

Index

Index